A History of Engineering and Science in the Bell System

A History of Engineering and Science in the Bell System

Physical Sciences
(1925-1980)

Prepared by Members of the Technical Staff,
AT&T Bell Laboratories.

S. Millman, Editor.

AT&T Bell Laboratories

Credits for figures taken from
other than Bell System sources
appear on page 641.

First Printing, 1983

International Standard Book Number: 0-932764-03-7

Library of Congress Catalog Card Number: 83-62738

Printed in the United States of America

Contents

Part I. Research in Physics

I. The Physics of Magnetic Solids, 19. Ferromagnetic Metals and Alloys, 20. Ferromagnetic Domains, 22. Magnetic Oxides— Ferrimagnetic Garnets, 26. Magnetic Moments and Interatomic Magnetic Interactions, 31. II. Magnetic Resonance and Solid State Spectroscopy—The Gyrator and Paramagnetic Amplifier, 35. Nuclear Magnetic Resonance, 36. Electron Paramagnetic Resonance, 39. Ferromagnetic Resonance, 46. Electron Orbital Resonance, 50. Resonance Experiments in the Far-Infrared, 52. III. Mössbauer Spectroscopy, 53. Hyperfine Structure Studies in Magnetic Materials, 53. Layer-Structure Compounds, 57. Amorphous Materials, 58. Studies of Electroplating, 58. References, 60.

I. Semiconductor Research up to 1948—The Point-Contact Transistor, 72. II. The Junction Transistor and Other Semiconductor Amplifiers, 74. The p-n Junction, 74. p-n Junction Transistors, 74. Field Effect Transistors, 76. The Read Diode, 78. Acoustic-Wave Amplifiers, 79. III. The Bell Solar Photovoltaic Cell, 79. IV. Transport Properties, 80. Phonon Drag and Thermal Transport, 81. V. Semiconductor Spectroscopy, 83. Band Structure in Semiconductors, 83. Pair Spectra, 87. Light Emitting Diodes, 89. Thin Layers, 90. Deep Levels, 91. Electron-Hole Liquids, 92. VI. Molecular Beam Epitaxy, 93. VII. Semiconductor Research Supplement—The Story of the "Genesis of the Transistor," 96. "The Genesis of the Transistor," 97. J. B. Fisk's Letter to Ralph Bown, 101. Walter H. Brattain's Personal Reminiscences, Recorded by Brattain in 1975, 101. References, 102.

Surface Studies, 330. **IV. Neutron Scattering, 331.** Phase Transition in
Magnetic Systems, 333. Electronic Structure of Magnetic Systems, 334.
References, 335.

Part II. Research in Materials

Foreword

The Bell System had its origins in scientific research. Alexander Graham Bell was engaged in research on speech and hearing and on aids to the deaf when he became intrigued with the possibility of transmitting musical sounds by telegraphic instruments. This led him to the conception of the telephone and to the discovery of a workable arrangement for its realization.

Bell's inventive nature and interest in exploring the unknown was well expressed in his words: "Leave the beaten track occasionally and dive into the woods. You will be certain to find something that you have never seen before."

Even in those early days of what is now the Bell System a central theme was recognized, one that has dominated the science and technology of communications ever since—progress results from bringing together knowledge and ideas of many kinds. James Clerk Maxwell, who laid the theoretical basis for a fundamental understanding of electromagnetism, and who was a contemporary of Bell's, said, "I shall consider the telephone as a material symbol of the widely separated departments of human knowledge, the cultivation of which has led by as many converging paths to the invention of this instrument by Professor Graham Bell." In a very real sense, the early research in telephony was a forerunner of what later came to be known as industrial research.

In the years after Bell's discovery, research continued to play an essential role and contributed importantly to the company's growth. It brought together theory and experiment, need and opportunity, science and application—exemplified in the achievements of such early giants as G. A. Campbell, in his work on loading theory and on filters, and H. D. Arnold, in the development of the vacuum-tube amplifier invented by L. deForest, as noted in Chapter 10, "The Spirit of Research," in the first volume of this series, *The Early Years (1875-1925)*.

Those early events not only served to establish and build the Bell System as a science and technology based business enterprise, but also firmly implanted a research tradition and role that has continued to this day. Especially in the second half-century of its history—the period in which Bell Laboratories has existed, and which is covered in this volume—the Bell System has been the source of an extraordinary flow of research that has transformed telecommunications in the

United States and worldwide. From C. J. Davisson's and L. H. Germer's 1927 experiment demonstrating the wave nature of the electron, which earned for Davisson the 1937 Nobel Prize in physics, to the discovery of the background radiation in outer space by A. A. Penzias and R. W. Wilson, for which they were awarded the 1978 Nobel Prize in physics, there has been a stunning record of invention and discovery. Among the outstanding were H. S. Black and negative feedback, G. C. Southworth and the waveguide, K. Jansky and radio astronomy, J. B. Johnson and thermal noise, H. Nyquist, S. Darlington, S. O. Rice, and H. W. Bode for network theory, G. R. Stibitz and the electrical digital computer, W. H. Shewhart and quality control theory, C. E. Shannon and information theory, J. Bardeen, W. A. Brattain, and W. Shockley and the transistor, W. G. Pfann and zone refining, A. Schawlow and C. H. Townes and the concept of the laser, C. J. Frosch and L. Derick and oxide masking, and P. W. Anderson and localized electronic states in solids. These, and many other accomplishments, are described in the chapters of this volume, dealing with the physical sciences, and in the volume that is to follow, recording the accomplishments in the communications sciences.

What caused the flourishing of research that produced such extraordinary discoveries and successes as these?

The ideas behind all of this may be understood in the light of Bell Laboratories' responsibilities within the Bell System. The mission is clear—to provide new telecommunications technology. This technology includes not only equipment designs but also the engineering and planning of the telecommunications network and the technology for its operation and maintenance. It is the function of research in Bell Laboratories to support this mission through ideas and knowledge that initiate or reinforce the development of the new telecommunications technology for the Bell System. The basic notion underlying this research function is simple—science is *useful*. The Bell System's technology is rooted in science, and new technological opportunities arise from it and are supported by it.

The Bell System and a few other companies recognized this usefulness of science at an early stage, and the success of the research laboratories they founded inspired the research activities that followed in many other industrial organizations. Research in the Bell System preceded the creation of Bell Telephone Laboratories in 1925, but the founding of a separate unit to conduct research and development work recognized the importance of an organizational environment that fostered the creative activities and inspiration of its scientists and engineers and permitted them to combine these most effectively to advance telephony. Under the leadership of Frank B. Jewett throughout its early years, the research organization took form and flourished. The first director of research, H. D. Arnold, expressed the philosophy behind the research in these words:[*]

> Research is the effort of the mind to comprehend relationships which no one has previously known, and in its finest exemplifications it is practical as well as theoretical; trending always toward worthwhile relationships, demanding common sense as well as uncommon ability.

The worth of this guiding philosophy is amply illustrated by the events recorded in this volume, but what is remarkable is that the importance of research at Bell Laboratories was so clearly understood in its essential elements from the very beginning; the support and understanding provided initially have never wavered. This continuity has been of utmost importance in providing the environment needed for the maximum encouragement of creative people.

As Arnold so clearly stated, research is an exploration of the unknown. It deals constantly with uncertainty, except that there is ever present the *certainty* that important new things remain to be discovered. Research operates in a different time frame than development. Development is concerned with the application of technology for the relatively near term, seeking new and useful ways to apply scientific knowledge. Research is concerned with invention and discovery, and with the creation of new knowledge. These lead to technological development over the longer term, perhaps ten, twenty, or even more years. Over this longer term, it is clear that new technology will depend upon new science; in the short term, perhaps five years, technology must depend largely upon existing science.

Thus, there are challenges for research. It must assure the flow of invention and new science that will enable future technologies to be developed. And it must see the ways this invention and new science can be exploited by the Bell System.

The flow of invention and useful new science for the Bell System is only partly a result of internal basic research programs. This history of telecommunications technology offers many examples of successes of Bell Laboratories research. But Bell Laboratories' discoveries and its generation of new science, impressive as these may be, cannot possibly be the source of more than a small part of all that relate to communications. Accordingly, Bell Laboratories research is structured to provide a coupling to the rest of the scientific world, so that scientific discovery elsewhere becomes more readily accessible and exploitable. Thus, the Bell System can

---

[*] Inscribed in the foyer of the Bell Laboratories, Murray Hill, New Jersey, auditorium, to serve as a reminder to later generations of scientists and engineers; quoted also in Chapter 10 of the first volume of this series, *The Early Years (1875-1925)*.

effectively use *all* the world's new science in the development of new technology and systems. The strategy has been to strive for excellence in all fields judged to be important to the interests of the Bell System and to encourage a close coupling of research to the most advanced work elsewhere, in the secure knowledge that this would bring to Bell Laboratories the benefits of advances in scientific knowledge, wherever they might occur.

We see a striking example of this strategy in the field of solid state physics. Prior to World War II it was a recognized but not a dominant subfield of physics. Only the beginnings of a basic theoretical understanding of the electronic properties of solids had been attempted, experiments often produced puzzling and unexplained results, and applications were few. Immediately after the war a research group at Bell Labs began to investigate the properties of semiconductors, which had played an important role as signal detectors in military electronics but were still understood at only a rudimentary level. The group had as its objectives both an improvement in this understanding and its application in telecommunications technology. As we see it now, the group set out to invent a transistor, and it did, not much more than two years later. This invention triggered an explosion in solid state physics—mainly in semiconductors, but also in other classes of solids, and set in motion the revolution in electronics that not only transformed communications but also led to whole new industries, such as consumer electronics and computers.

Bell Laboratories played a prominent part in this rise in solid state physics. Its research in basic physics and in the related materials sciences paced research throughout the world and helped spawn a series of important inventions and technological advances. Equally importantly, this research served to put Bell Labs scientists and engineers into close contact with forefront work elsewhere, in a field that was attracting leading scientists all over the world, and which rapidly proved to be of crucial importance to the Bell System. The information flow, together with the research findings, played an essential part in the building of a knowledge base for semiconductors, and then for other classes of solids. This knowledge was closely coupled to application, so that invention and application within Bell Labs occurred at an almost breathtaking pace. That history is described in the pages that follow.

One task of research is to provide a window on the entire world of science and to see opportunities that arise from science, wherever it may be done. Thus, the first solid-state, continuous-wave microwave maser was demonstrated within three months of the time that the first knowledge was available of theoretical work at Harvard University that gave a clue as to how such a device could be constructed. This maser, which allowed construction of an extremely low-noise amplifier, was a key to the operation of the first active communications satellite, Telstar, launched by the American Telephone and Telegraph Company in collaboration with the National Aeronautics and Space Administration.

Research at Bell Laboratories has created whole fields of science, such as radio astronomy, or has been the stimulant to a vast expansion of others, such as solid state physics. This research also has had an enormous impact on other industrial sectors. The discovery of the transistor led to the solid state electronics that not only provides the basis for modern telecommunications, but, equally, the basis for all consumer products depending upon electronics, such as radio, television, hand calculators, and digital watches, for computers, and for the electronics used in a thousand industrial, military, medical, scientific, and other applications. The statistical principles of quality control have assured the reliability of Bell System equipment for five decades, and they guide the manufacturing processes of the world's industries. New materials discovered at Bell Laboratories are used throughout industry.

Asking *why* research should be done leads to the complementary question, *how* should it be done? Many industrial organizations have thought they perceived potential values in research but have stumbled when it came to implementation. In large part the reason for this was that they failed to see the subtleties in institutional attitudes and practices that are conducive to productive research, and mistook largely superficial aspects for those that are fundamental. Some understanding of the reasons research has flourished at Bell Laboratories for so many years can be gained from the characteristics of the environment in which it operates, and the manner in which it is organized and managed.

Central to the success of an industrial research organization is a clear sense of purpose and an understanding of mission. At Bell Laboratories it has always been clear that our mission is new communications technology, to allow the Bell System to provide better and cheaper communications services. This definition of mission has made it equally clear that the responsibility of research is to provide basic knowledge and new opportunities for the longer term, in support of the mission. Thus the research organization at Bell Laboratories has an unmistakable statement of purpose, against which its programs can be measured.

Based upon this mission, it can be seen why research at Bell Laboratories is conducted in some areas of science but not in others. These areas are not chosen at random or as the result of some whim, but are carefully selected because of their promise for discoveries and knowledge of value to the Bell System. This selectivity still allows a great latitude for choice, but not so great that it extends to all of science, in contrast to what might be appropriate to a large research-oriented university. The size of the research effort in a particular broad area reflects the likelihood that discoveries in that area will bring values to the Bell System. Thus, there is a clear rationale for research choices and priorities, but it in no way restricts the very necessary freedom for talented and creative individuals, because the breadth of science pertaining to communications is very large and offers enormous scope to the individual.

Freedom of choice is of utmost importance to the research scientist, because research is an exploration of the unknown and there are no road maps to tell what course to take. Each discovery affects the future course of research and no one can predict or schedule discovery. Thus Bell Laboratories research managers have provided the maximum possible freedom to the research staff, consistent with the institutional purpose. Research people have been chosen for their creative abilities and are encouraged to exercise these to the fullest. Indeed, they are the source of the ideas and of the research programs, and are not at all the implementers of directives handed down by some authority. Nor are they constrained to subjects chosen to meet some immediate needs of development organizations or the operating telephone companies. An individual research program is, therefore, the result of an idea on the part of the individual, who often cannot see exactly where the idea will lead but has the creative instincts to see the promise that lies in that particular direction. Only by giving such creative instincts freedom is it possible to maintain inquiry and invention at a high level throughout the research organization. In the words of W. O. Baker, former president of Bell Laboratories and vice president of research, "Research must 'look away' from everyday pressures of the ongoing development and engineering enterprise toward the vistas opened by new knowledge and technique."

Another aspect of the freedom for Bell Laboratories research people is that they are free to do research and are not expected to become developers or "firefighters," unless they choose to do so. Thus, they are asked to do what they do best, not something else. A corollary is that the institution must have a capable development organization, which can take from research its best ideas for new technology and develop them, while research goes on to other pursuits. A close relationship between research and development has always characterized Bell Laboratories. This association has kept the research organization from living in an ivory tower, and by the same token has provided it full protection and freedom to do *research* because the development responsibility has been assigned to a close and capable partner. Equally important, the development people have been a constant source of stimulation to the research staff by feeding back to them a stream of questions, proposals, and needs; this process often has led to new ideas and focus for research, even though it has never been taken to constitute the research agenda.

In order to fulfill their highest potential, research people must publish their results, as it is only through publication that they can reach the worldwide community of their peers, from whom they also receive new knowledge. Publication gives Bell Laboratories research people access to leading laboratories everywhere, and brings leading researchers from those laboratories to Bell Laboratories.

For research to flourish, it must have outstanding people. Seven recipients of the Nobel Prize in physics attest to the devotion of Bell Laboratories to the principle of excellence in research over all the years of its existence. The research people have widely varying interests, appropriate to the broad mission, but they constantly experience the benefits of mutual stimulation and frequently join together in collaborative research endeavors. A great advantage of the industrial research environment is the ease with which interdisciplinary research partnerships among professionals are formed, when such partnerships offer benefits. A mathematician and a chemist, a theoretician and an experimentalist, a physicist and a materials scientist, find reason to collaborate in research of mutual interest. Always, this is based upon mutual recognition of the advantages to both in having as a temporary partner someone who is equally proficient in research and who brings to the partnership a different but needed expertise and point of view.

Not surprisingly, much of the research at Bell Laboratories has been in fields now easily identified with communications technology, although some were not so obviously so when the research began. J. B. Fisk, a former president and vice president of research at Bell Laboratories, and other technical leaders have, from time to time, pointed to certain enduring themes that run through much of its research history, such as research on the transmission of electrical signals and, in the last half-century, research on the electronic properties of solids. But the research has struck out in completely new directions when an opportunity was perceived. Thus research in the behavioral sciences was instituted to allow exploration of those aspects of human behavior most relevant to the business—such as the interaction of man with machines, the fundamental bases for learning, and perception. Research in economics was added when it was seen that Bell Laboratories could add needed basic understanding—beyond that coming from research in the universities—in regulatory and financial economic theory. The criterion for appropriateness has not been one that constrained research to a too narrow view of itself, and there has been a constant searching for and evaluation of new research areas.

Stability and continuity in Bell Laboratories support for research have been essential to its health. Sufficient resources have been placed at its disposal to allow it to do what was needed to stay at the forefront of knowledge. And understanding of the peculiar nature of the research environment and needs of research people has characterized the institution. Part of the reason for the success of Bell Laboratories research is that the research managers understand these things; they themselves have all risen from the research ranks, but only after they have demonstrated a superior ability to do research themselves. People of this kind are most able to maintain the respect of and successfully guide an outstanding research staff. To do this, the managers must be completely current in their science, and many research managers assure this by remaining active in their own research. Managers play an essential role in establishing connections—intellectual and otherwise—between research and development, and in seeing new opportunities for research. The results of research must be communicated to be of use to others. The role of these managers in guiding the work of outstanding research people is a subtle one, and they must create an environment that provides maximum encouragement for creativity and productivity.

More easily discerned than described is the quality of the environment for research. Bell Laboratories has consistently generated an atmosphere of excitement, with great things expected of the individual and the appreciation of peers as perhaps the most satisfying reward for accomplishment. And it has enjoyed the constant support of the leaders of its parent company, who have consistently taken a long-term view of the Bell System's future; thus, a former president and chairman of the board of the American Telephone and Telegraph Company, F. R. Kappel, said, "If it were not for basic research, none of these things [I have shown] would exist. So we in the Bell System are deeply committed to basic research."

As we have noted, research in Bell Laboratories has been carried out in all fields of knowledge judged to be important to the Bell System. These fields can be broadly grouped into the physical sciences (physics, chemistry, and materials science), and the mathematical and communications sciences (mathematics, computer science, systems research), and the behavioral and social sciences. For convenience, the history of research in Bell Laboratories is to be recorded in two volumes reflecting these general groupings. In this first volume, the half-century of research in the physical sciences since the formation of Bell Laboratories in 1925 is recorded.* The companion volume will cover the history of the communications sciences in the same time period.

This record of the history of Bell Laboratories research not only reminds us of the great people and events that made the institution the premiere industrial research laboratory of the world, but it also allows us to reflect on the institutional and individual purposes and incentives that underlay these achievements. It thus illustrates the process of innovation and technological change and reflects a successful strategy for enhancing this process. In times when there is a reexamination of this process in broad national terms in order to relate it to the national capability for productivity improvement, economic growth, and the greater use of technology for social gains, this history may serve a useful purpose by describing a successful institution, one with both a history and a future. Bell Laboratories research people are proud of their past, but they are looking to the future in the expectation that their research in the next fifty years will be as significant as it was in the past fifty years.

N. B. Hannay
Vice President for Research
Bell Laboratories
November, 1981

---

* The research history prior to 1925 is described mainly in three chapters of the first volume of this series, titled, "The Early Years (1875-1925)." These chapters are: Chapter 4, "Telephone Transmission—The Wire Plant," Chapter 8, "Materials and Components," and Chapter 10, "The Spirit of Research."

Acknowledgments

The Physical Sciences volume is the first of two volumes scheduled to be published on Research at Bell Laboratories, as part of the series entitled *A History of Engineering and Science in the Bell System*. The manuscript was prepared from written material contributed by about 75 authors. The vast majority of the contributors have themselves carried out research and published in the fields of physics or material science that they wrote about. We have indicated at the bottom of the first page of each of 20 chapters, in alphabetical order, the principal contributors, i.e., those who took the responsibility of preparing a relatively important segment of the chapter. In addition, a fairly large number of scientists made smaller contributions, either by providing a manuscript on a single topic covering their respective research or by providing critical and constructive comments on drafts of chapters in the various stages of preparation. The comments played a vital role in shaping the character of this book, contributing greatly to the accuracy and readability of these chronicles, and providing some semblance of balance to the vast number of research contributions covered in this volume. These contributors are listed below:

S. J. Allen, P. W. Anderson, A. Ashkin, G. A. Baraff, R. J. Birgeneau, F. K. Bovey, W. S. Boyle, W. H. Brattain, W. F. Brinkman, W. L. Brown, S. J. Buchsbaum, T. M. Buck, R. M. Burns, M. Campagna, M. J. Cardillo, R. P. H. Chang, G. Y. Chin, A. M. Clogston, R. C. Dynes, J. Eisinger, L. C. Feldman, P. A. Fleury, R. R. Freeman, I. Freund, T. A. Fulton, J. K. Galt, A. G. Ganz, C. G. B. Garrett, T. H. Geballe, S. Geschwind, H. M. Gibbs, E. I. Gordon, A. C. Gossard, C. C. Grimes, H. J. Guggenheim, D. R. Hamann, N. B. Hannay, J. J. Hauser, E. Helfand, A. Heller, C. H. Henry, G. S. Indig, K. B. Jefferts, D. W. Johnson, D. Kahng, E. O. Kane, H. D. Keith, A. C. Keller, H. E. Kern, L. C. Kimerling, B. M. Kincaid, H. Kogelnik, J. E. Kunzler, D. V. Lang, R. A. Laudise, M. Lax, M. Leventhal, M. E. Lines, G. Q. Lumsden, S. Matsuoka, B. T. Matthias, K. B. McAfee, D. W. McCall, E. G. McRae, W. B. Mims, L. F. Mollenauer, G. E. Moore, S. O. Morgan, D. E. Murnick, C. A. Murray, S. R. Nagel, V. Narayanamurti, D. F. Nelson, H. M. Obryan, P. B. O'Connor, D. D. Osheroff, M. B. Panish, C. K. N. Patel, J. R. Patel, A. A. Penzias, W. G. Pfann, J. C. Phillips, T. G. Phillips, J. M. Poate, R. S. Raghavan, W. A. Reed, J. P. Remeika, M. Robbins, D. L. Rosseau, A. L. Schawlow, T. D. Schlabach, P. H. Schmidt, M. R.

Schroeder, N. Schwartz, R. W. Sears, C. V. Shank, R. C. Sherwood, W. P. Slichter, R. A. Stern, R. H. Stolen, K. H. Storks, H. Suhl, N. H. Tolk, A. J. Torsiglieri, J. A. Tyson, L. G. Van Uitert, C. M. Varma, L. R. Walker, W. W. Warren, Jr., J. H. Wernick, G. K. Wertheim, R. H. Willens, J. C. Williams, F. H. Winslow, E. A. Wood.

As in previous volumes of this series, the research recorded here is primarily that of Bell Labs scientists, but in each field efforts were made to identify pioneering contributions by scientists in other institutions. The period covered is roughly from 1925, the year when Bell Telephone Laboratories was formed and where Volume I of this series left off, to approximately 1980.

Special recognition is due to A. C. Johnson and her coworkers in the History and Archive Services Department, who were responsible for preparing this volume and seeing it through the press. The preparation of the various drafts for each of the chapters was greatly facilitated by the use of the UNIX* operating system. The individual contributions of E. Edelman, V. A. Gordon, V. M. King, and C. D. Martin are gratefully acknowledged. The checking and completion of the vast number of references were in the capable hands of R. L. Stumm and L. S. Goller.

S. Millman
Editor

---

* UNIX is a trademark of Bell Laboratories.

Part I

Research in Physics

Overview —

Research in Physics

The first part of this volume of *A History of Science and Engineering in the Bell System* deals with the history of physics research at Bell Laboratories during the period 1925-1980. In this interval of fifty-five years, physics research at Bell Labs grew several times in size, keeping pace with the rapidly growing dependence of the Bell System on technology derived from physics, especially the physics of the solid state of matter. This growth in size was accompanied by far-reaching changes in subject matter and outlook as solid state physics came under the pervasive influence of concepts of quantum mechanics and recognition grew of the extraordinary importance of solid state electronics for communications technology. A third force for change was the movement of communications technology upward in the electromagnetic spectrum through microwave into optical frequencies.

In the earliest years of the period, physics research concentrated on magnetism, noise in electrical conductors, electromechanics, and the surface physics of thermoelectric emission. At that time C. J. Davisson and L. H. Germer carried out their famous experiments on the diffraction of electrons from nickel crystals which demonstrated the wave nature of matter, and K. Jansky conducted his studies of galactic sources of radio noise, thereby laying the foundations of radio astronomy. Jansky's tradition was continued by A. A. Penzias and R. W. Wilson in their search for noise from galactic space. Toward the end of the period, research was concentrating on the physics of semiconductors and their applications to electronics and photonics, on optical and X-ray physics, on plasma physics, low temperature physics, nonclassical conductivity in one- and two-dimensional conductors, and on greatly expanded research on the surfaces and interfaces of solids. These changes grew out of and gave rise to radical new instruments and methods of research, including the introduction of magnetic resonance spectroscopy, the discovery of intense and tunable sources of laser radiation, the extension of cryogenic techniques to a few millidegrees Kelvin, the introduction of powerful sources of ultraviolet and X-ray radiation, and the development of vacuum technology making pressures as low as 10^{-10} Torr routinely available. By the end of the period W. Shockley, J. Bardeen, and W. H. Brattain had won

1

the Nobel Prize in physics for their discovery of the transistor, P. W. Anderson had won the Prize for fundamental theoretical discoveries about the nature of electrical conduction and magnetism in disordered solids, and Penzias and Wilson had won the Prize for discovery of the cosmic microwave background radiation. This period was also marked by the invention of the laser by A. L. Schawlow and C. H. Townes.

From the beginning, physics research at Bell Laboratories has included both the search for fundamental new knowledge and for fundamental innovations in technology. This approach to research has been so successful in advancing the science and art of communications that it has become a matter of course that science and invention should be organizationally coupled. This has proved to be not only an effective way to bring science to bear on the invention of technology needed by the Bell System, but also to stimulate research in new and productive directions. Furthermore, the search for fundamental innovations carried out by the research divisions has proved to be an effective way to bridge the gap between research and development and to couple new science into Bell Labs engineering work.

Such a background of experience has led to an enduring conviction at Bell Labs that fundamental research is important to the future of Bell System technology, and has created the climate needed for sustained strong support of research in fundamental physics and physics-based technology. The two presumptions behind such support are that research in physics should be of the highest quality and carried out in fields *with impact* on Bell System technology.

This philosophy of research derives ultimately from the overall mission of Bell Labs to supply the technology the Bell System needs to do its job in the long term as well as in the short term, and translates into two missions for physics research. The first is to pursue research aimed at discovering new knowledge in areas of physics expected to be important to future Bell System technology, thereby keeping Bell Labs in close contact with advanced physical science in these areas, and assuring that Bell Labs originates or participates in any significant advance in physics that may be important to communications. The second is to pursue research to discover new technology in order to exploit recently developed physical science in areas of importance to Bell Labs' operations.

The extent to which these missions have succeeded is described in the chapters that follow. The purpose of this introduction is to give an overview of physics research between 1925 and 1980. At the end of the introduction is a list of some of the major contributions to communications science and technology that have grown out of physics research at Bell Labs in these years, as a way of summarizing the achievements of a remarkable concentration of scientific talent during this time.

Part I of this volume records the history of physics research at Bell Laboratories since 1925. It concentrates on research for the most part carried on after the end of World War II in 1945. There are two reasons for this. First, the five-year span of the second World War interrupted the continuity of research at Bell Laboratories as physicists turned their attention away from telephone work to problems of national defense, particularly microwave radar. After the war many of these people went on to other tasks unrelated to their former research. Second, after the war, physics research at Bell Laboratories was restructured, resulting in the formation of new groups explicitly focused on physical electronics and solid state physics. The first steps in this direction had been taken as early as 1936 by M. J. Kelly, director of research, and later to become president of Bell Laboratories, based on his perception that a solid state amplifier would be necessary for the further expansion of the telephone system, and that the best hope for this lay in fundamental research in solid state physics. Although considerable momentum in this direction had been developed by 1940, it was dissipated by the war and a fresh start was necessary in 1945.

The year 1945 represented a new beginning. There appears, in retrospect, to have been a deliberate plan by the research managers at Bell Laboratories that was directed on the one hand toward the discovery of a solid state amplifier and on the other toward the need for a better understanding of gas discharges for possible devices to replace relays as switching cross points.

There were at least three events that took place during the war that opened up new directions for research in physics. These were the development of processes for making relatively pure silicon and germanium, the discovery of insulating ferromagnets in Holland, and the development of tunable, continuous-wave sources of microwave radiation along with the accessory microwave circuitry.

The extraordinarily prompt discovery in 1947 of transistor action in germanium sparked a rapid growth of solid state physics research at Bell Labs and in many other laboratories throughout the United States and Europe. In early 1945, there were about 50 people at Bell Labs carrying on basic and applied research in physics, excluding work in acoustics. By 1950 there were 80, in 1960 there were 180, in 1965 there were 230, and in 1980 there were about 300. Thus, although there was a strong physics research effort before the war, it tends to be somewhat overshadowed by the very much larger effort after 1945.

Although this volume concentrates on the years after 1945, certain events of special significance in the earlier period stand out. Chief among these was the demonstration by Davisson and Germer of the wave nature of the electron with their famous experiment in which they scattered a beam of electrons off a single crystal of nickel and observed an unexpected pattern of diffraction similar to the diffraction of X-rays. This story is told in Chapter 3 with an interesting addendum which indicates that Davisson and Germer narrowly missed observing the electron spin postulated by G. E. Uhlenbeck and S. A. Goudsmit to explain the doublet structure of spectral lines in the alkali metals. In addition to its very fundamental implications, this early work by Davisson and Germer laid the foundation for study of the surface crystallography of single crystals using the technique of low energy electron diffraction. This was later developed by Germer and his colleagues into a universally applied tool for understanding surface structures of metals, semiconductors, and adsorbed atoms.

A second major event was the discovery by J. B. Johnson that the electrical resistance of any material is a generator of white noise with a spectral frequency density proportional to its resistance and absolute temperature. The reason for this was explained by H. Nyquist and is discussed briefly in Chapter 10 as a striking example of the impetus which has been given to physics research throughout this whole period of fifty-five years by the close interaction of theory and experiment.

Also in this early period beginning in the 1930s, a strong research effort in magnetism was established by R. M. Bozorth, building on earlier work by G. W. Elmen, which had led to discovery of the well-known alloys Permalloy, Permendur, and other magnetic alloys having high initial permeability or high coercive force.

As mentioned above, these early directions of physics research were augmented in 1936 by the assembly of a new group working in solid state physics. By that time research was already being carried out on semiconductors, magnetism, surfaces, dielectrics, phase transitions, and secondary emission, among many other topics. These were the beginnings of threads of research that have been pursued with increasing intensity since 1945. Interwoven with them are many new threads not imaginable at that time.

As might be expected from the nearly six-fold increase in size since 1945, physics research at Bell Labs had by 1980 become the largest organized industrial physics research effort in the United States, and it has made a correspondingly large contribution to the areas of science in which it concentrates. The first ten chapters in this volume will describe many fundamental contributions to science, particularly in condensed-matter physics, surface physics, quantum electronics, and solid state electronics, that have been crucial to the growth of important areas of research and technology. The work described is, of course, inextricably intertwined with the related research of physicists in other research institutions. Every effort has been made to make these mutual dependencies clear in the text and references. This close interface with worldwide science has always been viewed as one of the strengths of physics research at Bell Laboratories. Physicists at Bell Laboratories have benefited enormously from the interaction and acknowledge their debt to colleagues in other institutions.

Although the research recorded over the last 35 years has included a much wider range of specialties than before World War II, it has continued to emphasize such traditional areas as magnetism, semiconductors, and surfaces. Mentioning first the field of magnetism, fundamental work has been done on the structure and motion of domain walls, including the earliest observations of bubble domains, on ferromagnetic resonance and the propagation of electromagnetic waves in gyromagnetic media, including invention of the first nonreciprocal gyromagnetic devices, and on the origin of spin interactions in magnetic insulators through the superexchange mechanism discovered by P. W. Anderson. A particularly important discovery was the ferrimagnetic garnet structure, typified by $Y_3Fe_5O_{12}$, known as yttrium iron garnet, or YIG for short. The magnetic garnets have played an important role in the science and application of ferromagnetic resonance and in the development of practical bubble memories. A new chapter in the science of magnetism was opened up in 1958 with the discovery that atoms such as iron possessed a local magnetic moment when dissolved in very dilute amounts in certain metal host crystals but not in others. Elucidation of this effect had an important influence on the general understanding of ferromagnetism in metals and on the effect of impurities on superconductivity. It formed an important part of the body of work for which Anderson received the Nobel Prize in 1977. The possibility of a fundamental antagonism between magnetism and superconductivity has been an enduring theme of research and culminated in the discovery of competition between the superconductive and magnetic phases of a class of ternary rare earth boron compounds.

The early history of semiconductor research is dominated by the discovery of hole injection leading to the point contact transistor in 1947. In retrospect that can be seen as the beginning of expanded research on the Group IV semiconductors, silicon and germanium, that led in a relatively short time to the invention of the junction transistor, silicon solar cells, various *pnpn* devices, the field effect transistor, and the Read diode. Later work included fundamental experimental and theoretical research on the transport properties of germanium and silicon, while their band structure was studied by means of extensive cyclotron resonance measurements and theoretical calculations. Beginning around 1963, research began on the Group III-V semiconductors, particularly GaP and GaAs, and included research on the physics of recombination centers that led to the earliest efficient light emitting diodes and to the earliest practical heterostructure semiconductor lasers.

Semiconductor research has been strongly influenced by development of the technique of deep level transient spectroscopy. This technique has led to a much improved understanding of deep traps in semiconductors that are unavailable to optical excitation, has stimulated a successful new attack on the theory of point defects, especially the silicon vacancy, and has led to a new understanding of the mobility of defects under irradiation by photons of energy higher than the band gap. It has also been important in gaining a fundamental understanding of the energy level structure of amorphous semiconductors.

Another strong influence on semiconductor research has been the development and application of molecular beam epitaxy (MBE) of GaAs and related semiconductors. This sophisticated crystal-growing technique has led to experimental fabrication of very high quality double-heterostructure lasers, the invention of modulation doping which greatly increases the mobility of carriers in GaAs, the creation of quantum wells with important applications to research and technology, and to the invention of a series of graded band gap devices which show great promise for the efficient generation and detection of lightwaves. The successful development of MBE of silicon and metal silicides has opened up many new possibilities for silicon devices adaptable to submicron dimensions.

Surfaces have been a matter of continuing concern for physics research ever since Davisson's pioneering work on electron diffraction from nickel. This work itself led directly many years later to the development by Germer of low energy electron diffraction as a practical method of surface crystallography, and remains today one of the most important diagnostic tools used in surface science and technology. Much of the early research on surfaces was concerned with thermionic and secondary electron emission because of the crucial role of the vacuum tube in communications technology until the early 1950s, at which time it reached its peak in the close spaced triode and the traveling wave tube. Continuing work on secondary emission led to Auger spectroscopy for the chemical analysis of surfaces and adsorbates as a second important tool for the diagnosis of surfaces.

Waning interest in the vacuum tube after the 1950s implied no corresponding loss of interest in surfaces, since the need for fundamental understanding of interfaces in all kinds of semiconductor devices made the matter even more urgent. This concern was already evident in early attempts by Bardeen to understand the role surface states played in preventing external modulation of the surface resistance of semiconductors. The opportunity to carry out fundamental research on well-characterized surfaces arrived in the early 1960s with the concept of the controlled surface in ultrahigh vacuum developed by H. D. Hagstrum. Since that time, but particularly since 1970, research on clean surfaces and clean surfaces covered with monolayers of known adsorbates has moved rapidly ahead with the introduction of multiple probes including ion neutralization spectroscopy, ultraviolet photoelectron spectroscopy, X-ray photoelectron spectroscopy, electron loss spectroscopy, and Rutherford backscattering. Each of these tools measures a particular aspect of the atomic and electronic structure of surfaces and taken together have provided fundamentally new understanding of the nature of surfaces. This has included the structure of surfaces with thin overlays of metals leading for the first time to basic understanding of Schottky barriers.

A new era in surface physics began about 1973 with the advent of synchrotron radiation as a powerful source of ultraviolet radiation and X-rays. These sources greatly improved the ease and accuracy of surface research have also led to the introduction of some entirely new techniques. These include surface X-ray absorption fine structure, which provides information about the immediate surroundings of surface atoms; the X-ray standing wave technique, which measures the position of adsorbate atoms with high precision relative to the surface; and X-ray reflection-refraction, which allows surface crystallography to be done without the multiple scattering problems encountered in low energy electron diffraction. Another new technique recently introduced is the diffraction of monochromatic beams of helium atoms from surfaces, which has the advantage of looking only at the outermost layers of atoms. This technique also has the advantage that the atom beams can carry energy to or remove energy from the surface, thereby providing information about surface excitations.

An altogether new aspect of surface physics emerged in the early 1970s in the recognition that some planar systems are rigorously two-dimensional in behavior because the quantization of energy levels in the normal direction confines the effective degrees of freedom to the plane. Examples are the depletion layer in metal-oxide-semiconductor structures, electrons moving on the surface of liquid helium, thin films of superconductors, intercalated atoms in layered compounds such as graphite and $NbSe_2$, and monolayer films of liquid crystals. Practical applications of such effects are being made in quantum well devices produced by depositing very thin layers of semiconductors with molecular beam epitaxy. In 1980, an observation of considerable scientific importance was the quantized two-dimensional Hall effect in high-mobility layers of GaAs produced by MBE.

Radar research during World War II left a legacy of a fully developed technology in the electromagnetic spectrum from 1 to 30 gigahertz. This technology, which included strong and stable oscillators, sensitive detectors, and a sophisticated array of coaxial and waveguide circuit elements at S-band (3 GHz), X-band (10 GHz), and K-band (24 GHz), strongly affected the directions of physics research after the war by opening up the field of resonance physics at microwave frequencies. At Bell Laboratories pioneering work began on the microwave absorption spectroscopy of gases at K-band, particularly of linear molecules like carbonyl. In semiconductors, X- and K-band research began on electron spin resonance of substitutional impurities leading to a greatly improved understanding of the band-structure of silicon and the energy level structure of donor impurities like phosphorous. Studies of the hyperfine structure of these resonances eventually led to development of the important technique of electron nuclear double resonance, or ENDOR. In the area of electron paramagnetic resonance, work on the energy level structure of rare earth compounds led to experimental realization of the first solid state maser along lines suggested by N. Bloembergen of Harvard University.

As mentioned above, research begun in the early 1950s at the K- and X- bands on ferromagnetic resonance in ferrites led to invention of the ferromagnetic gyrator and isolator that played an important role in the development of advanced radars. This research also led to fundamental understanding of the loss mechanisms and high power instabilities encountered in ferromagnetic resonance. In turn, the work on resonance instabilities led to invention of the ferromagnetic parametric amplifier, and a reawakening of general interest in parametric amplification.

Stimulated by this general climate of interest in resonance physics, the field of nuclear magnetic resonance (NMR) also became an active area of research in the late 1950s, centering principally on the hyperfine interaction between nuclear spins and the magnetic fields arising from electron spin and orbital motions. There were two main branches to this. The first involved NMR in magnetic metals and compounds, in the course of which the first observations were made of nuclear resonance in a magnetically ordered compound. The second involved NMR in transition metals and intermetallic compounds with high orbital and spin susceptibility where important contributions were made to the understanding of negative as well as temperature dependent frequency shifts of the resonance frequency. The nuclear magnetic resonance work also included the earliest observations of transferred hyperfine, or so-called superhyperfine, interactions on the spin resonance of magnetic ions in dilute solutions. These results threw considerable light on the covalent charge and spin transfer or superexchange that result in spin ordering of magnetic compounds.

A different aspect of the hyperfine interaction was involved in the so-called Mössbauer effect which takes advantage of the hyperfine splitting of the gamma ray emission lines of certain nuclei such as ^{57}Fe. Work began on the Mössbauer effect at Bell Laboratories around 1960, soon after its discovery in Germany, and led to many important contributions to the understanding of magnetic ordering in solids.

Beginning about 1959 the more ready availability of strong magnetic fields and low temperatures, as well as improved calculational methods, gave rise to renewed interest in the energy band structure of metals, particularly the band structure at the energy of the highest occupied levels, the so-called Fermi surface. At Bell Labs and elsewhere many different tools were brought to bear on the problem—including cyclotron resonance in the Azbel'-Kaner geometry (magnetic field parallel to the surface), magnetoresistance, DeHaas-van-Alphen effect, the magneto-thermal effect, and the magneto-acoustic effect. Experimental research at Bell Laboratories concentrated on the transition metals and transition metal compounds, and important contributions were made to understanding their band structure. Accurate band structure calculations were also begun at Bell Labs during this period using the augumented plane-wave method, including in particular a calculation of the complicated band structure of V_3Si, one of the highest transition temperature superconducting compounds.

The invention of the laser at Bell Laboratories in 1958 by Schawlow and Townes firmly established the new field of quantum electronics which had its beginning with the invention of the maser by Townes and his students at Columbia University in 1954. Although the idea of population inversion between optical energy levels was a natural extension of work at microwaves, the recognition that a Fabry-Perot interferometer could be used at optical frequencies as a low loss multimode resonant cavity was a major conceptual advance. After 1958 laser research at Bell Labs grew very rapidly, the first major advance being A. Javan's invention of the He-Ne gas laser in 1959, which in 1960 produced light in the visible region 1000 times more nearly monochromatic than any other source then available. The carbon dioxide laser not only opened up the longer, infrared portion of the electromagnetic spectrum, but also produced unprecedented coherent power. Bell Labs' contributions to the development of color-center lasers and a variety of dye lasers helped to make these sources valuable tools in scientific research. Important advances were also made in the understanding of noise and coherence, the natural electromagnetic modes of oscillation, and the invention of Brewster angle windows which allowed the use of external mirrors for the resonant cavity.

Although the laser phenomenon itself became a major research interest at Bell Labs, the high intensity, nearly monochromatic light produced by the laser led to a revolution in optics research at Bell Labs and other laboratories in the fields of high resolution spectroscopy, two photon spectroscopy, Raman scattering, coherent optical effects, nonlinear optics, and optical parametric amplification.

By far the biggest impact of the laser on Bell Laboratories, however, has been in opening up the field of optical communications. In 1968, I. Hayashi and M. B. Panish succeeded in making a double-heterostructure GaAs laser that operated continuously at room temperature with a reasonable life expectancy. This advance, along with advances in optical fiber technology, have made possible practical lightwave systems that will clearly play a very important part in the communications networks of the future. This initial work on heterostructure lasers has been followed at Bell Labs by the invention of many novel laser structures with greatly improved oscillation characteristics, and intensive work on the physics of degradation processes and unwanted phenomena such as self-pulsing. By 1980, excellent lasers were made for the first time using molecular beam epitaxy, a process that may eventually provide a new level of manufacturing control over the fabrication of communications lasers and make accessible new materials systems for longer wavelength lasers. By 1980, the physics, materials science, and technology of semiconductor lasers had become a major theme of physics research at Bell Labs.

Although the principal emphasis of physics research at Bell Labs since 1945 has been on the physics of the solid state, smaller but substantial research efforts have also been carried on in the closely allied fields of atomic and molecular physics and in plasma physics. To a considerable extent this research has been stimulated by and benefited from the intense monochromatic light available from lasers. One notable achievement in atomic and molecular physics has been the measurement of the Lamb shift in the heavy hydrogenic ions C^{5+}, O^{7+}, F^{8+}, and Cl^{16+}, which have confirmed the predictions of quantum electrodynamics for high nuclear charge within the accuracy of current calculations and indeed made possible a choice between alternative theoretical calculations in the case of Cl^{16+}. A second experimental tour de force was the measurement of the hyperfine structure of the H_2^+ ion, which confirmed the quantum mechanical calculations of this simplest three-body problem. A third achievement in atomic and molecular physics has been the development of opto-acoustic spectroscopy based on the spin-flip Raman laser. This has been applied to the measurement of pollutant gases such as NO and HCN from automobile exhausts and, most importantly, to the measurement of NO concentrations in the stratosphere where this molecule acts as a catalyst to destroy ozone.

Plasma physics research had an early history at Bell Labs because of the interest in gas discharges as possible talking-path switches. Serious work on gas discharges began as early as 1939 on glow discharges from cold cathodes and was continued after the war when investigations were begun into fundamental physical processes involved in gas discharges. Emphasis on this aspect of plasma physics continued up through 1962 when it was decided that mechanical relays offered superior reliability.

Plasmas exist in metals, semimetals, semiconductors, gases, and electron beams, and research has been conducted at Bell Laboratories since 1945 in all these areas with special emphasis on the collective modes of oscillation exhibited by both neutral and charged plasmas. In the case of electron beams, research began as early as 1934 on space charge fluctuations in vacuum tubes, but was intensified after the war following the introduction of the traveling wave tube which depended for its operation on the interaction between an external traveling electromagnetic wave and a collective mode propagating along an electron beam. Extensions of this work to the case of interactions between two electron beams or between an electron beam and an ion beam led to some of the earliest understanding of instabilities in plasmas.

In the case of gases and solids, research has most often concentrated on plasmas immersed in a strong magnetic field and has been directed toward understanding the collective plasma oscillations that exist under these circumstances, reflecting the orbital cyclotron motion of the electrons. In metals and semimetals these modes are called helicons and Alfvén waves, respectively, and basic contributions were made at Bell Labs to both fields between 1959 and 1965. In semiconductors the ability to generate dense plasmas by illumination with an intense laser beam has led to fundamental new work on electron-hole droplets which behave like metallic condensates, and to strip line devices that can switch electrical signals at picosecond rates, thereby opening up a new picosecond measurement technology.

About 1960, basic studies of the hybrid plasma cyclotron resonances known as Bernstein modes started at Bell Labs. Although gas plasma physics has never become a major research emphasis, this work has continued and by 1980 a substantial effort was being devoted to such subjects as turbulence in plasmas, nonlinear interaction between plasma waves, and the interaction of charged beams with plasma waves. Scattering of CO_2 laser radiation has been successfully applied to the study of collective waves and turbulence in prototype fusion reactors.

The developments in molecular biology during the 1950s stirred the imagination of several Bell Labs physicists, who initiated a research effort in molecular biophysics in the early 1960s. The functional macromolecules and aggregates found in biological systems are complex materials that carry out processes such as energy transduction, information storage and processing, signaling, and process control. Other Bell Labs scientists had been engaged in fundamental studies of a large variety of organic nonbiological macromolecules and aggregates using spectroscopic methods, predominantly magnetic resonance spectroscopy (NMR and EPR) and luminescence spectroscopy in the visible and ultraviolet ranges. The biophysics effort started out by applying magnetic resonance and luminescence techniques to the study of alterations to DNA caused by ultraviolet light. In the late 1960s, magnetic resonance was directed toward structure/function studies in a variety of macromolecules. In the mid-1970s, NMR was used to study metabolism and bioenergetics in intact living cells and organelles. Luminescence techniques extending into the X-ray region were applied to photobiological studies of more complex systems.

The physics research techniques used in biological studies made a significant impact on biophysical research. One such technique, front-face fluorometry of whole blood, has been developed into a rapid test for lead intoxication and an assay for risk of brain damage in jaundiced newborn infants.

An enduring theme of physics research at Bell Labs has been astrophysics. The interest in this field has grown largely out of concern for sources of noise that interfere with long distance transmission of radio signals. In 1932 Jansky, searching for the source of interference at 20 MHz on transatlantic radio circuits, founded the science of radio astronomy by discovering that the galactic center was a strong noise source. Thirty-three years later Penzias and Wilson explained a small but persistent noise at 4 GHz in satellite transmission circuits when they discovered the cosmic microwave background radiation that is one of the strongest pieces of evidence that our universe began with a single explosive event some 18 billion years ago. Other astrophysics research has grown out of unique electronic instrumentation available at Bell Labs, and has served to stimulate the development of radiation detectors of extreme sensitivity or at extremely high frequencies. Examples are a gravity wave detector which for several years was the most sensitive in existence, a balloon-lofted gamma-ray telescope that has established the center of the galaxy as an intense source of electron-positron recombination radiation, and extremely sensitive millimeter wave detectors that have detected a variety of molecules in space and effectively founded the field of space chemistry.

A new area of research opened up at Bell Labs when it was decided to enter the field of nuclear physics in 1958. This decision was based on the recognition that nuclear physics was a rapidly developing field of science that might have an unknown but important impact on communications science and technology. This expectation has been fulfilled through the application of accelerated ion beams to the study and modification of surfaces and solids, particularly semiconductors, and through the development of new instrumentation such as particle counters essential to a wide range of modern scattering experiments. Nuclear physics research was first pursued in collaboration with Brookhaven National Laboratory using their high-flux neutron facility. Starting in 1965, it was continued through an arrangement with Rutgers University for collaborative use of a 16 MeV tandem Van de Graaff accelerator, and by the installation of several lower energy ion accelerators at Bell Labs, Murray Hill.

Although the resources devoted to nuclear physics have never been large, the research has resulted in important discoveries in nuclear structure, nuclear spectroscopy, and nuclear excited state lifetimes. The investment has also paid off in unexpected directions. As a result of experience with particle detectors invented at Bell Labs between 1949 and 1959, it was possible to make important measurements of radiation intensities in the Van Allen belts in 1961 during the flight of the first communications satellite, Telstar. Moreover, work with transistorized circuits in the high neutron flux environment at Brookhaven made possible the diagnosis and correction of failures of some critical transistor circuits in the satellite resulting from high energy electrons in the inner Van Allen belt probably injected by a high-altitude nuclear explosion.

The most important outgrowth of the nuclear physics program at Bell Labs has been the use of ion beams as a means of studying the structure and composition of thin films and surfaces and of modifying the near-surface regions of solids. In the mid-1960s, research on ion channeling through thin crystals was applied not only to the measurement of ultrashort lifetimes of excited nuclei, but also to the location of impurity sites in crystals. This work then led directly to the use of ion implantation as a means of doping semiconductors, and some of the earliest ion-implanted semiconductor devices were made at Bell Labs. More recently, implantation of ions is being used to modify the surface layers of insulators and metals. New studies of sputtering using ion beams has revealed interesting information about the equilibrium surface compositions of alloys and revealed that molecular solids such as thin films of ice exhibit an anomalously fast sputtering rate compared to metals and semiconductors. This result has considerable significance in understanding the surface erosion of the icy moons of Saturn and Jupiter under bombardment by the solar wind.

Ion beams have been developed into a powerful tool for studying the composition and structure of thin films important for research and Bell System technology. In a process known as Rutherford backscattering, the light ions H^+ and He^+ accelerated in the Bell Labs 3.75 MeV Van de Graaff accelerator are scattered off atoms in a solid to yield precise information about the mass and location of the scattering ion. Carried out under ultrahigh vacuum conditions compatible with other methods of surface analysis, this method has been used for the precise determination of the composition profile of thin films, the structure of interfaces such as that between silicon and SiO_2, and for the study of the relaxed free surfaces of metals.

An additional outgrowth of the nuclear physics program related to the measurements of the radiation belts has been a study of the structure of the magnetosphere using ground based magnetometers in Antarctica and Canada. This natural laboratory for studying magnetically confined plasmas has led to a basic understanding of magnetohydrodynamic waves in the magnetosphere, and has helped in understanding the origin of terrestrial magnetic storms which can have a serious effect on long-distance telephony.

Until the early 1970s, experimental solid state physics as a field of research was characterized by small-scale experiments carried out by individual or small groups of scientists on apparatus that could be accommodated in modest-sized laboratories. The major exceptions to this were magnetic structure experiments at the high neutron flux reactors at Brookhaven and Oak Ridge National Laboratories, and high magnetic field experiments carried out at the M.I.T. National Magnet Laboratory. Even this latter case was largely obviated by the advent of high-field superconducting magnets. Thus entry into nuclear physics and the use of Van de Graaff accelerators for ion-solid interaction experiments was the first real venture into "big machine" physics for research at Bell Labs, and introduced a new pattern of research that was not characteristic of solid state physics at that time. Beginning about 1970, however, there have been new involvements with big machines, which represent a new trend in solid state physics, resulting from a convergence of methods of condensed-matter physics and nuclear or high-energy physics. The convergence has to do with the use of directed beams of particles or photons scattered from a target (crystal, nucleus, or nucleon, as the case may be) to determine energy levels, momentum, distribution, and structure.

Since the mid-1950s, physicists at Bell Labs have been using directed beams of neutrons from the high flux reactor at Brookhaven

National Laboratory to determine magnetic structures. In the late 1960s, the emphasis turned to the measurement of phonon spectra of crystals, and to experiments on the spin dynamics of magnetically ordered systems. This included phase transitions in one- and two-dimensional systems that led to fundamental new understanding of the nature of second-order magnetic phase transitions. Most recently attention has turned to the study of structural phase transitions and the phase transitions that give rise to charge density waves in layered transition metal compounds.

Inelastic X-ray scattering experiments began at Bell Labs around 1968 using a high-intensity rotating anode X-ray source for measurements of the momentum distribution of electrons in a variety of low atomic number materials such as atomic helium, molecular hydrogen, oxygen, nitrogen, and metallic lithium and sodium. Since 1970 this has also become an area of big machine physics with the availability of very large X-ray and ultraviolet photon fluxes from the synchrotron radiation sources at Stanford University, the University of Wisconsin, and Cornell University, providing intensities up to one million times greater than those available from conventional sources. There has been a very large expansion in research on solids and surfaces using X-ray and ultraviolet photons available from these sources, and many new kinds of experiments have become practically possible. Notable among these are extended X-ray absorption fine structure measurements which allow determinations of local atomic structure to the unprecedented accuracy of 0.01Å, X-ray standing wave experiments that allow accurate determination of the positions of adsorbed atoms on the surface of near-perfect crystals, and X-ray and ultraviolet photoelectron measurements of energy levels of electrons in solids including core electrons, valence electrons, conduction electrons, and electrons associated with adsorbed atoms on surfaces.

The fact that electrons in some solids can move freely over macroscopic distances is such a familiar observation that it no longer evokes much wonder. Although metallic conduction in metals such as copper, and semiconduction in semiconductors such as silicon, are the fundamental bases of communications technology, the mobility of electrons in such materials is a quantum-mechanical phenomenon that is not at all obvious from the properties of free atoms. Conductivity, nevertheless, is essentially a matter of single-particle (electron) excitations in solids, and although complicated wave mechanical calculations are often necessary for its complete explanation, in principle it is easy to understand. Solids, however, also exhibit collective movements of their atoms and electrons that lead to ordered phases that are often much more difficult to conceptualize. Such ordered phases are described by an order parameter that can vary in time and space and can therefore support collective modes of excitation. These modes have been characterized by Anderson as exhibiting broken symmetry and present one of the most scientifically compelling areas of modern condensed-matter research. Ordered phases, and the transitions between ordered phases, consequently have become a major area of physics research at Bell Laboratories in recent years.

In one sense the field of ordered states an old and familiar field of physics research since the crystalline state is an ordered state of matter, and crystal structures have been studied at Bell Labs for at least 50 years, going back to the electron diffraction experiments of Davisson and Germer and early studies of magnetism in metals and alloys. More recent work on the crystalline state has concentrated on structural phase transitions and crystallization phenomena in two-dimensional systems such as layered transitional metal compounds and graphite, electron crystals on the surface of liquid helium, and thin liquid crystals.

Superconductivity is a less familiar ordered state in which conductors below a critical temperature, T_c, lose all resistance and exhibit nearly perfect diamagnetism. Experimental research in superconductivity began at Bell Labs in the early 1950s and resulted in many important discoveries including the high transition temperature intermetallic compounds Nb_3Sn and Nb_3Ge, the high current carrying capability of some superconductors, the absence of an isotope effect in ruthenium, the measurements of the phonon density of states by superconductive tunneling, and the first experimental observations of tunneling of superconducting currents through thin insulating layers. Important contributions were also made to the theory of superconductivity discovered by Bardeen, Cooper, and Schrieffer at the University of Illinois. These included an explanation for the lack of gauge invariance of the theory, strong coupling theory, the theory of dirty superconductors, and discovery of an upper field limit to the magnetic field sustainable by a Type II superconductor.

Superfluidity is another ordered state of matter found only (to date) in liquid ^{4}He and liquid ^{3}He. The lack of resistance to hydrodynamic flow found in these two liquids is closely related to the lack of electrical resistance in superconductors and both are explained by similar theories. Liquid ^{3}He is an especially interesting case because it orders into a strange type of magnetic liquid at very low temperatures. In the 1970s fundamental theoretical and experimental contributions have been made at Bell Labs to the understanding of the complex properties of this magnetic superfluid.

Magnetism, superconductivity, and superfluidity are all examples of the general class of second-order or continuous-phase transitions that show universal behavior of their thermodynamic and fluctuation phenomena near the transition temperature T_c. The thermodynamic quantities such as specific heat, susceptibility, and bulk modulus, as well as the dynamic quantities such as density and spin fluctuations and thermal conductivity, all show critical behavior near T_c that map from system to system according to a theory of dynamic scaling and which can be calculated by the method of renormalization group theory. Beginning in the mid-1960s, many fundamental experimental and theoretical contributions were made by physicists at Bell Labs to the understanding of second-order phase transitions. These included extension of the scaling theories and renormalization group theories to dynamic phenomena, and a series of measurements on the superfluid transition in liquid ^{4}He that set a new standard of precision in the field and made possible accurate verification of the scaling theories.

The physics research described in the following chapters and summarized in this overview has resulted in many important contributions to Bell System communications science and technology, especially over the last 35 years. These contributions are listed in Table I divided into the five-year periods in which they occurred. Although the achievements listed are commonly closely associated with Bell Laboratories, it should be remembered that parallel research was done at other laboratories in the United States and abroad. The list therefore represents innovations in communications science and technology growing out of physics research at Bell Labs which in turn was closely coupled to worldwide science through the exchange of ideas and people. The list offers a unique example of the power of research carried out in an environment that puts a high value both on research directed toward new conceptual levels of scientific understanding and research directed toward the creative innovation of new technology.

A. M. Clogston
Executive Director—Research,
Physics, and Academic
Affairs Division
Bell Laboratories
November, 1981

Table I. Contributions to Communications Science and Technology
Growing out of Physics Research at Bell Laboratories

1945-50	Point Contact Transistor Invention of Junction Transistor	Semiconductor Particle Detectors
1951-55	Ferrite Gyrator Silicon Solar Cells *pnpn* Devices	Invention of Field Effect Transistor High-Temperature Superconductivity Garnets and Magnetic Bubbles
1956-60	Invention of the Laser He-Ne Gas Laser Oxide Masking Localization Theory	Rediscovery of the Parametric Amplifier Experimental Demonstration of the 3-Level Maser Low Energy Electron Diffraction
1961-65	Experimental Discovery of Superconductive Tunneling Cosmic Background Noise Carbon Dioxide Laser	High Field Strength Superconducting Magnets Optical Parametric Oscillator
1966-70	Red Light Emitting Diodes Green Light Emitting Diodes Ion Implantation	Double-Heterostructure Laser Molecular Beam Epitaxy (MBE) Spin-Flip Raman Laser
1971-75	Ion Backscattering and Channeling Deep Level Transient Spectroscopy	Picosecond Switching Bistable Optical Devices
1976-80	Current Switched Josephson Junction Integrated Circuits MBE Lasers and Field Effect Transistors Modulation Doping Graded Barrier Rectifier	Low Noise Millimeter-Wave Diodes Silicon Molecular Beam Epitaxy Bistable Liquid Crystal Devices Epitaxial Silicide Conductors Ion Beam Lithography Laser Annealing

Chapter 1

Magnetism
and Magnetic Resonance

The Bell System's interest in magnetic materials dates back to the very beginning of the telephone. It was recognized early that understanding the physics of magnetism would be crucial to progress in the technology using magnetic materials—whether for finding magnetic metals or alloys having high permeability or low ac loss for transformers and loading coils, or for designing permanent magnets with large remanent magnetization. The research activities on ferromagnetic metals and alloys, on the physics of magnetic domains, and on magnetic oxides—ferrites and garnets—extended the application of magnetic devices to the higher frequencies needed for larger carrier capacity.

The techniques of magnetic resonance were introduced in solid state physics in the mid-1940s. They probe the internal fields of magnetic materials on the atomic level and deepen our understanding of the fundamentals of magnetism—the interaction between elemental atomic magnets and the much weaker nuclear magnetic moments. The techniques of Mössbauer spectroscopy make use of the very narrow gamma rays emitted by the nuclei of certain magnetic materials and provide complementary information on fundamental magnetic interactions.

Magnetic fields are involved in many physics experiments discussed in other chapters of this volume—in magnetoresistance (Chapter 4), plasma physics (Chapter 6), superfluidity in ^3He (Chapter 9), and magnetospheric physics (Chapter 7).

I. THE PHYSICS OF MAGNETIC SOLIDS

G. W. Elmen's discovery of Permalloy, Perminvar, and other materials has already been described in Chapter 8, section 2, of the first volume of this series, *The Early Years (1875-1925)*. L. W. McKeehan

---

Principal authors: R. L. Cohen, J. F. Dillon, S. Geschwind, L. R. Walker, and W. M. Walsh

and R. M. Bozorth introduced the technique of using X-ray diffraction to study the effect of heat treatment of ferromagnetic materials in the presence of a magnetic field on the magnetic properties relevant to communications technology. Their accomplishments reinforced the confidence of Western Electric management in the role that basic research could play in solving the long-term needs of the evolving communication systems, particularly when carrier frequencies were rapidly increasing into the microwave region of the electromagnetic spectrum.

Thus, right after World War II the atmosphere was conducive to the initiation of scientific investigations of the fundamental atomic processes that give rise to magnetism. There was ample encouragement to use and to contribute to the most up-to-date quantum mechanical theories and related experimental techniques. X-ray diffraction techniques were extended to many single crystals and to detailed analyses of crystal structures. These techniques led to the explanation of the magnetic properties of materials and to the discovery of interesting new materials. It was found to be very fruitful to couple these investigations with crystal chemistry research and the application of physics research tools such as nuclear magnetic resonance and ferromagnetic resonance. Consequently, a program was initiated to study the role of ferromagnetic domains and domain-wall motion in determining basic magnetic properties such as permeability, ac losses, and coercive force. Studies were conducted on the effect of atomic exchange and superchange forces on ferromagnetism, on localized magnetic moments, on the role of conduction electrons in ferromagnetic metals, on spin waves, and on the propagation of electromagnetic waves in media containing ferromagnetic material. Other aspects of magnetism received attention in superconductivity research and in magnetosphere studies.

1.1 Ferromagnetic Metals and Alloys

Soon after joining Western Electric in 1906, Elmen started looking for a magnetic material that would have high permeability at low magnetic flux density with very low hysteresis losses. (For more on Elmen's work see Chapter 10 of the first volume of this series.) In the mid-1920s McKeehan introduced the techniques of X-ray diffraction to the study of crystal structure in iron-nickel (Fe-Ni) alloys. He studied the effect of anisotropy and magnetostriction on the magnetic properties of ferromagnetic materials such as Permalloy.[1] McKeehan's studies led him to suggest that the electrons in deeper levels, rather than the valence electrons, are involved in determining the magnetic properties of alloys.

Bozorth [Fig. 1-1] joined Western Electric in 1923 and, with E. A. Kelsall and J. F. Dillinger, started a series of measurements of the magnetic properties of nickel-cobalt-iron (Ni-Co-Fe) alloys subjected to annealing in the presence of a magnetic field.[2] Using these techniques, Bozorth found the conditions needed to obtain a nearly square hysteresis loop in the Ni-Co-Fe alloy Perminvar with 65 to 70 percent nickel. He also conducted a number of studies of ferromagnetic anisotropy and magnetostriction in single crystals and polycrystalline materials.[3] One technological outcome of these studies was his explanation that the improvement in the magnetic properties of silicon steel was caused by the orientation of crystals aligned by the rolling process.[4] Bozorth is probably best known for his classic book *Ferromagnetism*, a comprehensive compilation of the properties of ferromagnetic metals and alloys published in 1951. It is a widely used

Fig. 1-1. R. M. Bozorth pioneered in fundamental investigations of the magnetic properties of ferromagnetic metals and alloys.

reference source of worldwide research in ferromagnetic materials published prior to 1950, as well as an exposition of the phenomenological and theoretical basis giving rise to important magnetic properties of ferromagnetic materials.

In the early 1950s research in ferromagnetism shifted to a new group of materials, the rare earths—elements of the Periodic Table with atomic numbers ranging from 58 to 70. The rare earth atoms have strong paramagnetic moments arising from an incomplete 4f subshell of the fourth electron shell in the usually trivalent ions. These materials became more available after World War II because of their presence in uranium and thorium ores. Wide scientific and technological interest developed in the properties of these elements, their alloys, and compounds. At Bell Laboratories E. A. Nesbitt and J. H. Wernick initiated a study of the magnetic properties of rare earth alloys and intermetallic compounds, including such compounds as $SmCo_5$ and $PrCo_5$,[5] which were found to have hexagonal crystal structures, large ferromagnetic moments, and the largest magnetic anisotropies known.[6] These studies are discussed in Chapter 12 of this volume.

1.2 Ferromagnetic Domains

The concept of a ferromagnetic domain, or a region where all the elementary atomic magnets point in the same direction, has played a central role in the understanding of the magnetic properties of ferromagnetic materials. This, in turn, has led to the development of improved magnetic materials for inductors with high permeability and low hysteresis loss, and of permanent magnets having high residual magnetization and large coercive force. As early as 1907, P. Weiss, at the University of Strasbourg, proposed that a ferromagnetic material is composed of many regions, each magnetized to saturation in some direction.[7] In the unmagnetized state, which generally prevails in the absence of an externally applied magnetic field, the directions along which the domain are situated are either randomly distributed or are perhaps distributed along preferred ("easy") directions of magnetization, so that the resultant magnetization of the specimen as a whole is zero.

The first observation of effects caused by domains was made in 1919 by H. Barkhausen of the Technische Hochschule of Dresden.[8] He detected noise or clicks in earphones connected to a coil wound around an iron specimen that was demagnetized continuously. This could be interpreted as caused by the fact that the actual demagnetization of the specimen proceeded in jumps, even though the demagnetizing current was increased continuously, arising from the discontinuous change in magnetization direction of the whole domain. At

Bell Labs Bozorth and Dillinger repeated the Barkhausen experiment in 1930 and by refined measurements, were able to deduce the average volume of a domain associated with Barkhausen discontinuities.[9] However, direct observation of such domains was to take another 15 years.

1.2.1 Domains in Single Crystals

Shortly after the end of World War II, W. Shockley and H. J. Williams initiated a study designed to develop more direct techniques for identifying a single ferromagnetic domain and for following its movement when the strength of an externally applied field is varied slowly. This work was undertaken with the expectation of providing a sound physical understanding of the magnetic properties of ferromagnetic materials in terms of the domain picture. In 1947, using the technique involving colloidal particles of Fe_3O_4 that had been developed after 1931 by F. Bitter and others,[10] Williams observed a domain pattern in an electrolytically polished strain-free surface of single-crystal iron having about 4 percent silicon.[11] This was followed by a more detailed study of the domain pattern on strain-free, single-crystal surfaces and a comparison with theory, published in 1949 by Williams, Bozorth, and Shockley.[12] Later that year Williams and Shockley published the results of measurements on a beautifully designed hollow rectangular sample cut from a single crystal of silicon-iron with edges and surfaces all cut along easy directions of magnetization.[13] Each leg of this "picture-frame" single crystal was about 1.5 by 0.1 by 0.1 centimeters in size. [Fig. 1-2]

Williams and Shockley observed the position of the wall boundary between the domains with magnetization in opposite directions at the same time that they measured the magnetization of the specimen with an appropriate flux meter. Their study established a direct correlation of magnetization with domain boundary motion and demonstrated that changes in magnetization in such an experimental arrangement occur by the growth of one domain at the expense of its neighboring domain.

In the late 1940s the study of magnetic domains continued to flourish at Bell Labs. Williams and his coworkers adapted and perfected the technique of using a colloidal suspension of magnetic on electropolished surfaces of metallic magnets to observe the domain structure of hundreds of samples. Williams produced several moving pictures concerning domains and the response of magnetic domain structure to applied fields. These movies were of great educational importance.[14] They gave a whole generation of students and research workers a feeling for this fundamental view of magnetic properties.

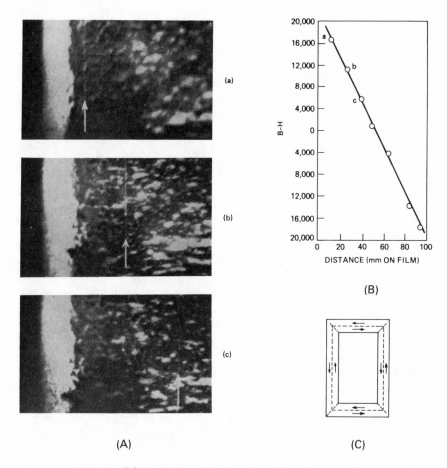

Fig. 1-2. (A) A photograph showing magnetic domain walls (at arrows). (B) Magnetization curve. Circles labeled (a), (b), and (c) correspond to domain walls (a), (b), and (c) in (A). (C) The shape of the single-crystal silicon-iron sample. [Williams and Shockley, *Phys. Rev.* **75** (1949): 179,181].

1.2.2 Domain Structure Theory

Complementing the experimental work on magnetic domains, C. Kittel carried out theoretical calculations on a variety of domain problems. He explained the domain structure in thin films and fine particles, and the magnetic losses exhibited by magnetic materials with domain structure. In a review article published in 1949, and a subsequent paper published with J. K. Galt in 1956, Kittel presented a complete account of the physical phenomena involved in ferromagnetic domains.[15,16] Most of the volume of a ferromagnetic specimen is contained in one domain or another. Between two domains there is a thin transition region, the domain wall, in which the magnetization direction gradually changes from that of one domain to that of a neighboring domain. [Fig. 1-3] These fundamental magnetic domain concepts have served to explain the magnetic behavior of the soft metals and alloys used in transformers and have provided a theoretical foundation for the design of high coercive-force permanent magnets.

1.2.3 Application to Permanent Magnet Design

The snagging of a domain wall by an imperfection was one of the phenomena seen vividly in the domain observation experiments, and the understanding of the effect has had clear technological impact. A void or a nonmagnetic inclusion was observed to anchor a domain wall and to restrain its motion. A coercive field could be measured as the field necessary to break the wall free from a particular imperfection. In 1961, Nesbitt and E. M. Gyorgy deliberately introduced imperfections into the magnetically very soft alloy known as 79 Permalloy.[17] They added gold to the components, and by careful heat treatments were able to bring about the precipitation of a gold-rich phase that interfered with the motion of domain walls. Variations of the alloy and its heat treatment enabled them to control the coercive force of the material and its switching behavior to achieve highly

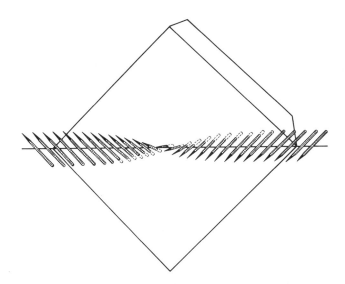

Fig. 1-3. The Bloch wall, showing the gradual change in direction of magnetization in a domain wall. [Kittel and Galt, *Sol. State Phys.* **3** (1956): 474].

desirable properties. The same approach was subsequently applied to several other systems. One example was the study of cobalt-iron-gold by Nesbitt, G. Y. Chin, and D. Jaffe.[18] The alloy, 84%Co-12%Fe-4%Au, when annealed gave a very square hysteresis loop and a coercive force of about 12 oersteds. This alloy found extensive application in a memory device known as the piggyback twistor. Piggyback twistors were used as the basic storage elements in the early versions of the Traffic Service Position System and the Electronic Translator System, used respectively in long distance dialing and long distance call routing.

The domain point of view also helped to improve the understanding of the properties of permanent magnet materials. The theory shows that a domain wall has a finite width, in many cases about 1000Å [angstrom unit (Å) = 10^{-10} meters], and that magnetic particles smaller than that width simply cannot support a domain wall.[19] The magnetization of such particles reverses only by the rotation of the whole domain, a process that might require much higher magnetic fields than those needed for the domain wall motion process that proceeds by the growth of one domain at the expense of its neighbor. In 1950, Kittel, Nesbitt, and Shockley suggested that the properties of the permanent magnet alloy Alnico 5 could be explained in terms of the shape anisotropy of plate-like precipitates that could be produced by the heat treatment of the material in a magnetic field.[20] [Fig. 1-4]

Shortly thereafter, Nesbitt and R. D. Heidenreich demonstrated that the precipitates could be observed by electron microscopy.[21] They were able to correlate precipitate morphology with magnetic properties. In materials with the optimum properties, the precipitate particles were about 75Å to 100Å across by about 400Å long, with spacings between the rows of about 200Å.

1.3 Magnetic Oxides — Ferrimagnetic Garnets

1.3.1 Ferrites

Because of their high resistivity, the non-metallic magnetic materials have been of particular interest for the reduction of eddy-current losses in transformers and other related applications. Research on metallic oxides at Bell Labs and elsewhere increased rapidly after World War II. Initially, the most prominent of such magnetic materials were the ferrites or ferrimagnetic spinels. The chemical formula for ferrites may be written as MFe_2O_4, where M could be any of the divalent ions of magnesium, zinc, copper, nickel, iron, cobalt, or manganese, or a mixture of these ions. Except for compounds containing the divalent iron ions, these ferrites may be made with resistivities in the range of 10^2 to 10^6 ohm-cm. This is contrasted with a resistivity

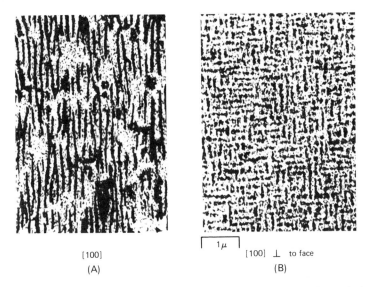

[100]   1 μ   [100] ⊥ to face

(A)   (B)

Fig. 1-4. Electron micrographs of oxide replicas taken from a single crystal of Alnico 5 cooled at 2° per second from 1300°C with a magnetic field along [100] and then aged 2 hours at 800°C to grow the precipitate. Note the long rods of precipitate in (A). Photograph (B), taken on a surface normal to the heat treatment field, shows that the rods aggregate to form rough plates. [Nesbitt, *Encyclopedia of Chem. Tech.* **12** (1967): 737].

of about 10^{-5} ohm-cm for the ferromagnetic metals. These high resistivities make it possible to use ferrites in devices operating at radio frequencies up to tens of thousands of megahertz. Though there had been significant earlier work, interest in the ferrites was greatly stimulated by the publication in 1947 of reports of work done at the Philips Research Laboratories in the Netherlands during the war.[22] The materials effort on ferrites and the application of ferrites to inductors, transformers, and filters are discussed in Chapter 12 of this volume.

The work of the French Nobel laureate, Louis Neél of the University of Grenoble, provided a basic understanding of the ferrites.[23] These oxides belong to a class of magnetic materials known as ferrimagnets. The metal ions in these mixed oxides may be at either of two types of sites. At the *A*, or tetrahedral sites, the metal ions are surrounded by four oxygen ions at the corners of a tetrahedron. At the *B*, or the octahedral sites, the metal ions are surrounded by six oxygen ions at the corners of an octahedron. The magnetization of the crystal is determined by three interactions: between metal ions within the lattice of tetrahedral sites; between ions within the lattice of octahedral sites; and between ions on an *A* site and ions on a *B* site. The dominant interaction is the antiferromagnetic *A-B* coupling, so that in most cases of interest the moments of A-site ions are parallel to each other and antiparallel to those of B-site ions.

Because the sum of the A-site moments generally differs from the sum of the B-site moments, the crystal has a net magnetization, giving rise to ferromagnetic-like properties. The term ferrimagnetic is used to designate an arrangement of magnetic moments in two sublattices, with the magnetic moments in one sublattice all pointing in one direction and the magnetic moments in the second sublattice all pointing in the opposite direction.

The technological interest in the ferrites and similar magnetic oxides arises from two fundamental properties: the high resistivity, and the relatively high magnetization. Therefore, the magnetic oxides are very useful for high-frequency inductors and are particularly important for microwave communications. When properly inserted in a waveguide with an externally applied magnetic field, the material possesses a strong Faraday rotation of the plane of polarization of a propagating electromagnetic field. This forms the basis for the microwave gyrator and the related circulators and one-way isolators.

In order to understand the loss mechanism in ferrites, in 1952 Galt studied the motion of single magnetic domain walls in crystals of nickel—iron ferrites. J. F. Dillon used more perfect single crystals of a different ferrite, $Mn_{1.4}Fe_{1.6}O_4$, to perform experiments in which the characteristic behavior of a simple wall system was much more evident.[26] He also observed that there was a steep rise in the losses experienced by the domain wall as temperature was lowered. In both the nickel and manganese ferrites comparisons were made with the losses observed in microwave ferromagnetic resonance experiments on the same compositions. Based on these observations, Galt[27] and A. M. Clogston[28] were able to apply relaxation theories to explain the observed losses.

1.3.2 The Magnetic Garnets

In the mid-1950s, a considerable expansion in the research at Bell Laboratories on new magnetic materials resulted from the collaborative work of S. Geller, M. A. Gilleo, and J. P. Remeika. This began as a study of the crystallographic properties of the rare earth orthoferrites having perovskite-like structures. These orthoferrites belong to a class of materials called "canted antiferromagnets" in which the elementary magnetic moments of the ions are arranged very nearly antiferromagnetically; that is, the sum of the moments in each of the two sublattices are equal but are not lined up in precisely opposite directions. [Fig. 1-5]   These rare earth orthoferrites provided a fruitful

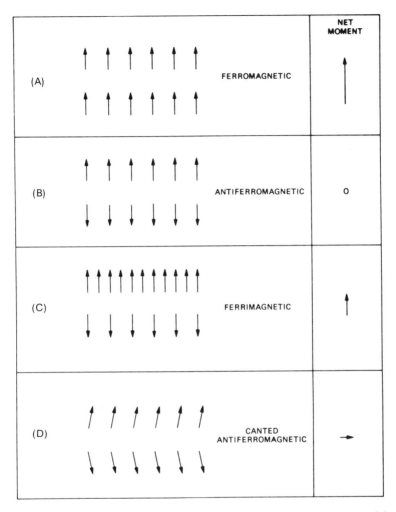

Fig. 1-5. Diagrams of magnetic moment ordering. (A) Ferromagnetic. (B) Antiferromagnetic. (C) Ferrimagnetic. (D) Canted antiferromagnetic. The resulting net magnetization is shown at the right for each case.

field for the study of magnetic interactions and magnetic domain behavior. These studies led to the discovery of the ferrimagnetic garnets, of which $Y_3Fe_5O_{12}$, yttrium iron garnet (YIG), is a prototype.[29-31] The orthoferrites were first used at Bell Labs for an experimental verification of the ideas involved in the invention of magnetic bubbles. For a discussion of the materials effort on magnetic garnets, see Chapter 12, section III.

These garnets became the favored experimental system for a great variety of fundamental experiments in magnetism. In particular, many advances in the study of microwave losses in magnetic materials were made possible by the availability of garnet crystals with few imperfections or impurities.

An important technological advantage of the magnetic garnets compared with the ferrites is that the metallic ions in the garnets are ordinarily all trivalent and there is no loss mechanism corresponding to the hopping of electrons from the divalent to the trivalent iron ions in the ferrites.

Ferrimagnetic garnets were independently discovered in France by F. Bertaut and F. Forrat.[32] Soon after their discovery and the initial publications of Geller and Gilleo, many academic, government, and industrial laboratories throughout the world became active in studies of this important class of magnetic materials.

1.3.3 Observation of Domains in Garnets—Magnetic Bubbles

Shortly after single crystals of the magnetic garnets became available, Dillon discovered that thin sections (about 0.01 cm thick) of such crystals are transparent to visible light.[33] Furthermore, in passing through the crystal, the light interacts with the magnetization and undergoes a magneto-optical rotation; that is, if linearly polarized light enters the crystal, its direction of polarization is found to be rotated upon leaving the crystal. The amount of the rotation depends on the direction of the magnetization relative to the path of the light beam. Thus, Dillon was able to see the magnetic domain structure with a polarizing microscope. [Fig. 1-6]   Soon after Dillon's discovery, Williams, R. C. Sherwood, and Remeika found that a number of the orthoferrites and other magnetic oxides were transparent in the same way.[34] They also found that many of these crystals were transparent in the near infrared region, and that by using a polarizing microscope with an infrared converter, domains could be seen in quite thick specimens. Viewing domain structure in transmitted light has many advantages over the magnetic-powder colloid technique used by Williams (see section 1.2.1 above). It becomes possible to see structure inside the crystal rather than just on the surface, and with flash or strobe lighting it makes possible the observation of rapidly moving domain systems. Most important, it is peculiarly applicable to the nonmetallic magnetic materials that became of such great interest in the late 1960s.

The fundamental studies of the physics of magnetism, involving ferrimagnetism, domain behavior, single crystals, and optical properties, formed the basis for the investigation of magnetic bubble devices, as described in Chapter 12, section 3.1. A 1972 report of the National Academy of Sciences (known as the Bromley Report) is a

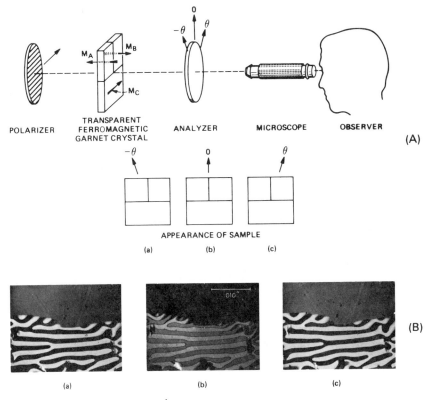

Fig. 1-6. (A) Schematic drawing illustrating the visibility of magnetic domains in the ferrimagnetic garnet. (B) Magnetic domains seen in a gadolinium iron garnet single crystal with an optical polariscope, as shown in (A). Parts (a), (b), and (c) correspond to the three cases shown in (A). The light and dark regions in the lower half of (a) and (c) are domains with magnetization parallel and antiparallel to the line of sight. The upper half of the field is occupied by domains with magnetization in the plane. [Dillon, Jr. and Earl, *Am. J. Phys.* **27** (1959): 203,204].

case study in the relationship between fundamental research programs and the evolution of new technology.[36]

1.4 Magnetic Moments and Interatomic Magnetic Interactions

The research in magnetism described in the preceding sections of this chapter dealt principally with the behavior of magnetic materials. There has also been extensive activity, both theoretical and experimental, concerned with the more fundamental aspects of magnetism and its microscopic foundations. There are a few very basic problems in magnetism. For example: What is the origin of the magnetism in a given material? How do the magnetic sources interact with one another? What are the collective properties of a system of interacting magnets?

Naturally, these questions overlap and what each means depends upon whether it is asked about an insulator or a metal. Crudely, the answer to the first two questions is that the electrons are themselves magnetic, that is, that there is a magnetic moment associated with the electron spin, and that their interaction is principally of electrostatic origin. It appears as a magnetic interaction because the exclusion principle forces the wave function of two parallel spins to be different from that of two antiparallel spins, thus changing the electrostatic energies in the two cases. This is the exchange interaction between electrons. To go from this simple example of two lonely spins to a real material consisting of electrons bound to nuclei to form ions which, in turn, are bound to form crystals, is an exceedingly complicated problem. Major contributions have been made in this area by C. Herring and by P. W. Anderson, as described below.

Herring was mainly concerned with magnetism in pure metals and alloys. In the transition metals, where ferromagnetism occurs, there is a broad band of itinerant s electrons whose energies overlap those of the d electrons. A difficult problem, to which experiment gives no simple answer, is to decide whether the d electrons are localized or itinerant, or whether these terms are perhaps inapplicable. Another problem is to decide to what extent the clearly itinerant s electrons are polarized and in what way they mediate the exchange coupling. Earlier, it was also important to understand how such concepts as the domain wall and spin waves could be treated in the itinerant models. Herring discussed these latter problems in 1951-1952 and maintained a continuous, critical interest in this field for many years.[37] His analyses[38] of the state of the theory culminated in a monumental review article published in 1966, "Exchange Interaction Among Itinerant Electrons."[39]

One way of clarifying the problem of the occurrence of magnetism in metals is to study the magnetic properties of dissolved magnetic-impurity atoms in nonmagnetic metals, including superconductors. In 1959, B. T. Matthias and coworkers studied the effect of transition metal impurities in titanium, zirconium, vanadium, and niobium on the superconducting transition temperature, T_c.[40] It had already been established that impurities will always alter T_c, up or down, because they change the electron concentration in the metal. However, if the impurities have a magnetic moment, this would interfere with the spin pairing effect and always *lower* T_c. Matthias found no evidence for such a magnetic contribution in his experiments. Similarly, small amounts of iron dissolved in titanium, vanadium, or niobium gave no additional magnetic susceptibility. It was apparent that iron atoms dissolved in certain hosts carried no moment. However, in 1960, Matthias and coworkers found that iron added to the superconducting alloy $Mo_{0.8}Re_{0.2}$ strongly depressed T_c and contributed to the susceptibility, showing that in this host the iron carried a moment.[41] By dissolving small amounts of iron in a series of Nb-Mo alloys they found a threshold molybdenum concentration for moment formation at 40 percent, above which the iron moment increases. In a definitive series of experiments, in which 1 percent of iron was dissolved in an extensive series of $4d$ transition hosts covering a continuous range of electron concentrations, Clogston and coworkers showed that iron first acquires a value-of-moment between niobium and molybdenum. The moment rises to a maximum value of 2.8 Bohr magnetons, then falls to zero at rhenium. It reappears between ruthenium and rhodium, and rises to the huge value of 12.7 Bohr magnetons near palladium before decreasing sharply again.[42]

A qualitative explanation of these remarkable results was given by P. A. Wolff et al.[43] and by Clogston,[44] based on approximate band structures of the $4d$ transition metals and on studies of localized states and moments. [Fig. 1-7]   An alternative interpretation of certain features of these results was given by V. Jaccarino and L. R. Walker, which suggested that moment formation may depend statistically on the particular local environment of each iron ion.[45] The key paper in this area, which attacks the basic question "Why does a moment form at all?", was published earlier by Anderson.[46] Anderson showed that

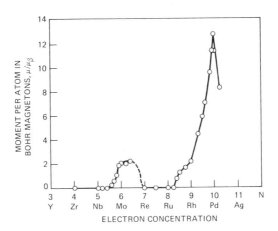

Fig. 1-7. Magnetic moment in Bohr magnetons of an iron atom dissolved in various second-row transition metals and alloys as a function of electron concentration.

a very simple model, stripped of specific local features, contains the essential physics. This model includes a single, localized d orbital on an isolated ion, a band of itinerant electrons interacting with the d orbital, and, most significantly, a term that describes the Coulomb repulsion which appears if one attempts to put two electrons of opposite spin into the d orbital. He then found that a localized moment may or may not appear, the result depending upon the parameters of the problem. The energies involved here are such that in any real material the existence or nonexistence of the moment will be essentially indifferent to the temperature; an iron ion, for example, either has a moment or it does not. Its environment is the determining factor.

For insulators, the magnetic moment is a specific property of a particular ion, and its origin is usually well understood. So here the question is: How do the ions interact magnetically? The answer comes down to calculating the change in wave function (and thus of electrostatic interactions that yield the exchange forces) when one ion of a pair changes its spin orientation. It had been clear that the nonmagnetic ions separating the magnetic ones in an insulator transmit this rearrangement of wave function in a process referred to as superexchange. In 1959, Anderson made a major advance in theory by showing that if a clear separation was made between the bonding problem of the nonmagnetic to magnetic ions and the magnetic problem, the latter can be reasonably discussed as a perturbation.[47] This "renormalization" of the problem led to an immediate simplification of thinking about exchange interactions in real crystals and to a number of qualitative working rules to predict behavior. Important calculations carried out in 1963 by R. G. Shulman and S. Sugano on the problem of covalent bonding have close connections with Anderson's work.[48] By an extensive study of simple magnetic systems, consisting of isolated clusters of transition metal ions and coupling anions embedded in organic matrices, A. P. Ginsberg and M. E. Lines were able to verify many predictions of the superexchange theory in considerable detail.[49]

Another area to which Anderson contributed significantly in the 1950s was the understanding of antiferromagnetic and ferrimagnetic insulators.[50] Here well-defined, localized moments interact in a known manner and the problems are concerned with the collective behavior of such a system. Questions may be asked about the ground state (no longer intuitively obvious as for ferromagnets because of quantum mechanical effects), about the low-energy excitations, or the low-temperature thermodynamics. Anderson gave a very penetrating discussion of these topics and introduced a useful semiclassical treatment of the spin wave oscillations, providing a clear physical insight into such systems.

II. MAGNETIC RESONANCE AND SOLID STATE SPECTROSCOPY – THE GYRATOR AND PARAMAGNETIC AMPLIFIER

Starting with the first observation of nuclear magnetic resonance (NMR) in a beam of molecules by I. I. Rabi and coworkers at Columbia University in 1938, the technique of magnetic resonance has proved to be a powerful research tool in physics.[51] It is based on the simple and fundamental relation that holds for the frequency of precession of an elementary magnet when placed in a magnetic field, namely,

$$f \propto gH$$

where f is the frequency of precession, g is the ratio of the magnetic moment to the angular momentum of the precessing magnet, and H is the magnitude of magnetic field. An external oscillating magnetic field is applied and its frequency varied until it is in resonance with the precession frequency. Since the oscillating frequency of an electrical circuit can be measured with great precision, it is necessary merely to arrange experimental conditions so that resonance can be detected. In the case of a molecular beam, resonance condition is established by noting the change of intensity in the detected beam as the frequency of the applied oscillating field is varied. In other cases, changes in the resistance or reactance in the circuit arranged to produce the applied oscillating field may be observed, as was discovered in 1946 by E. M. Purcell, H. C. Torrey, and R. V. Pound,[52] and independently by F. Bloch, W. W. Hansen, and M. Packard.[53]

In solid state physics research the interest in magnetic resonance arises from the fact that the total magnetic field at a nucleus having a magnetic moment or at a spinning electron in a paramagnetic atom— to cite two examples—is the sum of the externally applied (and easily measured) magnetic field and the internal magnetic field arising from various interactions. It is the sorting out of the origin of such interactions that is of interest to the researcher.

A similar observation can be made for the case of the motion of an elementary charged particle in a magnetic field. The frequency of the circular transverse motion (the cyclotron frequency) for a free, electrically charged particle is proportional to the charge-to-mass ratio and the magnetic field. For the motion of such a charged particle in a crystal under isotropic conditions, the cyclotron resonance can be used to determine the effective mass of the charge carrier. For solids with more complex electronic structure, cyclotron resonance experiments can serve as additional tests of the validity of theoretical calculations describing the motion of the charged carriers in the solid.

2.1 Nuclear Magnetic Resonance

2.1.1 Nuclear Magnetic Resonance in Metals

One of the early applications of the techniques of NMR was to the study of the Knight shift, first observed by W. D. Knight at the University of California at Berkeley.[54] (The Knight shift shows the fractional increase in the NMR frequency of an atomic nucleus in a metal relative to that in an insulator for the same value of H.) C. H. Townes, Herring, and Knight showed that the Knight shift of a few percent observed in the NMR frequency of nuclei in metals (such as lithium and sodium) was due to the hyperfine field at the nucleus produced by the interaction of the conduction electrons and the innermost (s) electrons.[55]

Several years later W. E. Blumberg and coworkers at Bell Labs found negative Knight shifts (that is, of a sign opposite to that observed in simple metals) in silicon, antimony, gallium, and platinum of the intermetallic compounds V_3Si, V_3Sb, V_3Ga, and V_3Pt.[56] [Fig. 1-8] This led to an important generalization by Clogston and Jaccarino of the origins of Knight shifts in metals and made it necessary to include two terms in addition to the contact hyperfine interaction term at the nucleus caused by conduction s electrons.[57] The first is caused by electrons in the unfilled d band, which normally have a vanishing density at the nucleus. However, the exchange interaction between these electrons with the paired core s electrons alters the radial distribution of inner-shell electrons with spin up relative to those with spin down. This results in an unpaired s electron spin density at the nucleus from the different atomic shells of such a sign as to give rise to a negative Knight shift. Still another source of hyperfine field at the nuclei of metals is the orbital paramagnetism induced by the applied field acting on unfilled, orbitally degenerate bands.[58]

Thus, a comprehensive picture of Knight shifts in metals emerged which involved these different contributions, the analysis of which was facilitated by introduction of the Knight shift versus susceptibility plot.[59] This analysis of the different contributions to the Knight shift became an important tool in the understanding of the electronic structure of many intermetallic compounds and important transition metals such as platinum, palladium, and rhodium.[60] Additional information on the electronic structure of metals was provided by the study of nuclear spin relaxation arising from the fluctuating parts of

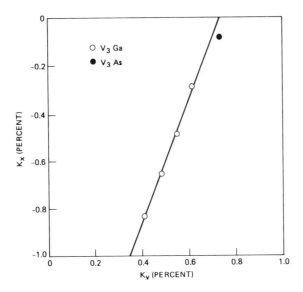

Fig. 1-8. Knight shift K_V vs. Knight shift K_X in two V_3X compounds: V_3Ga and V_3As. The different points for a given compound correspond to measurements made at different temperatures. [Clogston and Jaccarino, *Phys. Rev.* **121** (1961): 1361].

the different hyperfine fields mentioned above.[61] These fundamental ideas on the origin of Knight shifts and relaxation formed the basis of the interpretation of NMR results in the metal-insulator transitions in the vanadium oxides and studies of local moments in metals.[62] Quite apart from the general studies previously discussed, a particularly noteworthy result in NMR research at Bell Labs was the first microscopic observation of diamagnetic domains in silver by J. H. Condon and R. E. Walstedt.[63] They observed the NMR shifts caused by the demagnetizing fields of these domains.

2.1.2 *Nuclear Magnetic Resonance in Electroconducting Liquids*

NMR has been extensively exploited by W. W. Warren to study the metal-nonmetal transition and attendant localization processes in a series of liquid metals.[64] When there are sufficient mobile electrons present the NMR relaxation rate remains insensitive to disorder, but it increases abruptly when localization takes place. U. El-Hanany and Warren have also used Knight shift measurements as a probe of electron density changes in liquid mercury subjected to very large volume changes as the metal is being heated toward the liquid-gas critical point.[65]

2.1.3 Nuclear Magnetic Resonance in Magnetic Insulators

In 1956, Shulman and Jaccarino discovered large paramagnetic shifts in the NMR frequency of ^{19}F nuclei in single crystals of MnF_2 above the temperature at which the ionic spins are ordered, the Néel temperature.[66] These shifts were caused by the unpairing of the $2s$ electrons on the fluorine atoms by interaction with the d electron spin of the Mn^{2+} ion, and the associated hyperfine field of the fractionally unpaired fluorine $2s$ electron.[66] From the size of the shift in the paramagnetic state Shulman and Jaccarino were able to predict and observe the hyperfine field and NMR frequency of the fluorine nucleus when the Mn^{2+} ions were fully aligned in the antiferromagnetic state at low temperature. Because, in the absence of an external magnetic field, the NMR frequency of the fluorine nucleus in the ordered state is proportional to the manganese sublattice magnetization, the measurement of the NMR frequency as a function of temperature became the most accurate and powerful way of studying sublattice magnetization. The studies confirmed the behavior predicted by spin wave theory.[67]

Similar studies of the sublattice magnetization were subsequently carried out in many other magnetic compounds.[68] Among these were studies of $CrBr_3$ by A. C. Gossard, Jaccarino, and Remeika, where the predictions of spin wave theory were accurately verified for the first time in a ferromagnetic insulator.[69]

This NMR technique of measuring sublattice magnetization was extended to compounds such as K_2MnF_4 and K_2NiF_4 with antiferromagnetic interactions exclusively within a plane.[70] Theory had predicted that even at the lowest temperature, zero-point fluctuations exist in an antiferromagnet so that the average value of the manganese sublattice magnetization would not correspond to aligned spins with $S = 5/2$, although it would in a ferromagnet. The deviation in MnF_2 is less than 2 percent and so is obscured by other effects of similar size. However, in the planar antiferromagnets, this effect was more than 8 percent for Mn^{2+} and almost 20 percent for Ni^{2+}, and was, therefore, more easily measured. These studies led to a detailed understanding of the spin-wave and thermodynamic behavior of these two-dimensional magnetic systems.[71] In 1958-1959, H. Suhl[72] and, independently, T. Nakamura[73] showed that there is an interaction between nuclei in magnetic systems arising from the virtual emission and absorption of spin waves. This interaction gives rise to observable line shifts and line broadening effects in NMR.

2.2 Electron Paramagnetic Resonance

2.2.1 *Electron Paramagnetic Resonance in Insulators*

The resonance frequency at which a paramagnetic ion placed in an external magnetic field will absorb microwaves depends upon the magnitude of the total magnetic field at the ion, which is the sum of the external field and that arising from the electronic structure of the ion. Since the magnetic field produced by the electronic configuration depends on the particulars of the crystalline environment in which the ion exists, electron paramagnetic resonance (EPR) is a fundamental probe for investigating the electronic structure of magnetic ions in crystals. Moreover, the electrostatic and magnetic interactions between the electrons of the magnetic ion and its nucleus give rise to additional absorption frequencies. An analysis of the complete spectrum can also yield information on important nuclear properties such as spin, magnetic moment, and electric quadrupole moments.

Shortly after E. Zavoisky's discovery of EPR in a copper salt,[74] the observation by R. L. Cummerow and D. Halliday of the EPR of a manganese salt,[75] and the initiation of a program in microwave EPR at the Clarendon Laboratory in Oxford, England,[76] A. N. Holden and coworkers at Bell Labs reported their observation of EPR in organic free radicals.[77] They noted that the observed linewidth was more than an order of magnitude narrower than what was expected from the dipolar interaction between the electron magnetic moments. They indicated that this was due to the effective reduction of the dipole interaction by the rapid flipping of the electrons caused by exchange, as proposed theoretically by Van Vleck of Harvard University. This exchange narrowing became an important interpretive tool in EPR as well as in NMR in magnetic materials.

2.2.2 *Electron Paramagnetic Resonance in Semiconductors—Electron-Nuclear Double Resonance*

In 1954, R. C. Fletcher and coworkers reported the observation of the first EPR of shallow donors in semiconductors.[78] [Fig. 1-9]   A well-resolved hyperfine structure (hfs) arising from the field produced by the nuclear moments at the electron or from the electron spin density at the nucleus was observed for arsenic and phosphorus donors in silicon. A comparison of the magnitude of the observed

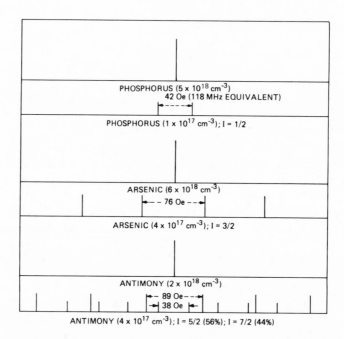

Fig. 1-9. Hyperfine splitting in spin resonance of Group V donors in silicon, electron spin of 1/2. For phosphorus, nuclear spin (I) is 1/2; the two vertical lines correspond to the two values of m_I, +1/2 and −1/2, the projections of I along the direction of the magnetic field. For arsenic, I = 3/2; the four vertical lines correspond to m_I values of +3/2, +1/2, −1/2, and −3/2. For antimony (14 vertical lines), six lines pertain to isotope Sb^{121} (I = 5/2), and eight lines pertain to isotope Sb^{123} (I = 7/2). In each case, if the impurity concentration is greater than 10^{18} per cm^3, only single lines appear. [Fletcher et al., *Phys. Rev.* **95** (1954): 844].

hfs with the corresponding values found for the free arsenic and phosphorus atoms played a central role in the development of the theory of shallow donors by W. Kohn and J. M. Luttinger.[79] The unpaired s electron of the donor in the silicon lattice moves around the donor nucleus in a hydrogenic-like orbit of very large radius (30Å) caused by the dielectric shielding and reduced effective mass of the electron in the solid. This results in a reduced electron spin density at the nucleus and a smaller hfs, as compared with the corresponding values for the free atom. G. Feher extended the work on the properties of shallow donors in silicon, studying their spin-lattice relaxation and developing techniques for polarizing the donor nuclei.[80] This work led to one of the landmark developments in EPR—the discovery by Feher of electron-nuclear double resonance (ENDOR).[81] [Figs. 1-10 and 1-11] The ENDOR technique allows NMR transitions to be studied at the nucleus of a paramagnetic ion or in

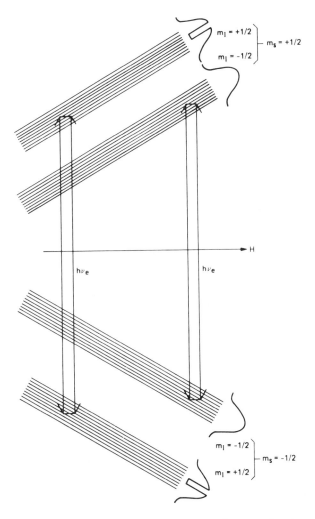

Fig. 1-10. Schematic representation of the energy-level diagram of a donor electron in phosphorus-doped silicon as a function of an externally applied magnetic field. Each of the two electronic states corresponding to the electron spin (S) of phosphorus, $m_S = \pm 1/2$, is split by hyperfine interaction with the phosphorus nuclear spin (I) of 1/2 and designated by $m_I = \pm 1/2$. The allowed transitions between $m_S = 1/2$ and $m_S = -1/2$, which take place at microwave frequencies (about 10 MHz), are between the same m_I's, resulting in the two absorption lines separated by about 118 MHz shown in Fig. 1-9. Each of the m_S, m_I levels is split further by interaction with Si^{29} nuclei (the much more abundant Si^{28} not having a nuclear moment), but these splittings—which are in the MHz range—are too small to be resolved in the electron-spin resonance spectrum. However, if a strong microwave field is applied to saturate the electronic transition and superimposes an auxiliary radio frequency in the MHz range corresponding to the separation between nuclear sublevels, the microwave signal corresponding to the sublevel transition is unsaturated. This results in an intensity change that is far easier to detect (because of a greater population difference affected) than the direct absorption of radio frequency by the nuclear spins. [Feher, *Phys. Rev.* **114** (1959): 1219].

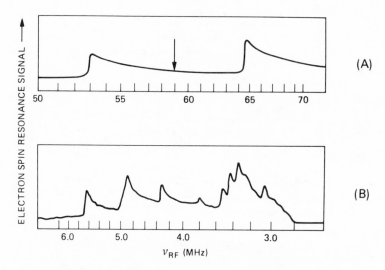

Fig. 1-11. (A) Microwave absorption representing the interaction of the phosphorus electron spin with the phosphorus nuclear spin (see Fig. 1-10). The center of the two lines, indicated by the arrow, is the measurement of the hyperfine interaction. The difference of the two lines is the measurement of the nuclear moment. (B) Microwave absorption representing the interaction of the phosphorus electron spin with neighboring Si^{29} nuclear spins. [Feher, *Phys. Rev.* **114** (1959): 1223].

surrounding nuclei by monitoring a change in EPR intensity, rather than by observing direct radio frequency absorption corresponding to transitions induced in the nuclei. The significance of this was two-fold: it enabled the study of small hfs that was unresolved in the EPR spectrum; and the increased sensitivity provided by EPR versus NMR detection enabled the determination of nuclear moments in small concentration. The ENDOR technique was applied by Feher to plot the donor wavefunction in silicon by studying the ENDOR of silicon nuclei at different lattice sites moving out from the *P* donor.[82] This study was the prototype of many studies in other systems, such as the *F* center in alkali halides.[83]

Feher's activity in EPR led to his collaboration with H. E. D. Scovil and H. Seidel in 1956 to build the first continuous-wave (cw) solid-state maser (microwave amplification by stimulated emission of radiation) using the Gd^{3+} ion in lanthanum ethylsulfate. It is interesting to note that building this maser provided the first demonstration of EPR cross relaxation. A small amount of cerium was used to cross relax certain gadolinium levels to prevent population buildup, which would be undesirable from the point of view of maser action, in a particular gadolinium level.

W. B. Mims was the first to apply the electron-spin echo technique to measure cross relaxation in paramagnetic systems. He developed even more sensitive ways of using ENDOR and measuring electric field shifts in paramagnetic ions by echo techniques.[84] Electron-spin echo signals were observed to decay in a periodic manner and not monotonically as would be expected for a normal relaxation mechanism; the echo-decay envelope being effectively modulated by the superhyperfine or ENDOR frequencies characteristic of the material.

This nuclear modulation effect in electron spin echoes was discovered in 1961 by Mims, K. Nassau, and J. D. McGee at Bell Labs[85] and independently by J. A. Cowen and D. E. Kaplan at the Lockheed Research Laboratories[86] in the course of experiments that were aimed at understanding the physical principles underlying the maser. The nuclear modulation effect provides one of the quickest and most convenient methods for investigating electron nuclear coupling in glasses and in many biological materials. At Bell Labs it has been also used to study coupling with nitrogen nuclei in hemoglobin and in a number of other metalloproteins.

2.2.3 *Electron Paramagnetic Resonance and Optical Fluorescence*

The activity in the study of solid state masers and lasers in the late 1950s stimulated an interest in the structure of excited states of paramagnetic ions in crystals that were separated from the ground state by an energy corresponding to an optical frequency. Direct detection of EPR in these excited states was generally not feasible because of the small number of ions that could be maintained in the excited levels by optical pumping. However, instead of observing the microwave absorption directly, S. Geschwind and coworkers monitored the change in the optical fluorescence from an excited state of ruby when microwave EPR transitions were induced among its magnetic sublevels.[87] In effect, the absorption of a microwave photon was converted to a change in fluorescence corresponding to one optical photon, which is far easier to detect. This first experiment on optical detection of EPR of excited states in solids was followed by detailed analysis of hfs and relaxation of a number of excited states of transition metal ions and rare earth ions in solids.[88] [Fig. 1-12]   Connected with these experiments was the demonstration by G. F. Imbusch and Geschwind that an optically pumped excited state in solids retains memory of the ground state magnetization even after having gone through complicated vibrational decays in the excited state.[89] This technique of optical detection of EPR was later applied to the study of relaxed excited states of color centers in solids[90] and became widely used for the study of excited triplet states in organic molecules.[91]

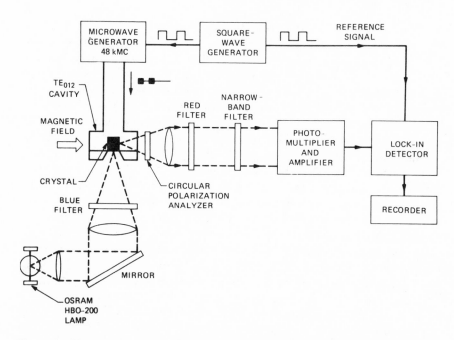

Fig. 1-12. Block diagram of the system used for optical detection of electron paramagnetic resonance in the $E(^2E)$ state of Al_2O_3:Mn^{4+}. [Imbusch and Geschwind, *Phys. Lett.* **18** (August 15, 1965): 109].

In 1959, W. J. Brya, Geschwind, and G. E. Devlin utilized the technique of Brillouin light scattering to demonstrate conclusively that in EPR, paramagnetic ions relaxing to equilibrium may heat the lattice vibrations in a narrow frequency range around the microwave frequency.[92] This microwave phonon bottleneck, as it was called, had been a long outstanding problem in EPR. Prior to this work the evidence for its existence was only indirect, since it could only be inferred from the behavior of the EPR signal itself.

2.2.4 Electron Paramagnetic Resonance in Metals

In contrast to insulators, EPR in metals is dominated by the physics of the translational motion of the conduction electrons. This is true whether it is the EPR of the conduction electrons or of the localized moments interacting with conduction electrons that is being investigated. Greater experimental difficulties are encountered in the measurement of EPR in metals as compared with corresponding measurements in insulators primarily because the microwaves penetrate the metal sample only to the extent of the microwave skin depth (10^{-4} to 10^{-5} cm). Difficulties may also occur because the relaxation times of the electronic moments in metals are generally shorter. However, along with the development of more sophisticated techniques specific to metals and the general high sensitivity of EPR, it has been possible to use EPR to make significant progress in a number of areas of metal physics.

The first EPR in metals at Bell Laboratories was reported by M. Peter and Matthias, who observed a g-value in europium metal characteristic of Eu^{2+}.[93] This confirmed that europium was divalent, in agreement with earlier susceptibility measurements of Bozorth and Van Vleck. Peter and coworkers also studied the g-shift of the Gd^{3+} local moment in a variety of intermetallic compounds and in alloys of elements of the second transition series.[94] These measurements indicated the presence of a negative electronic Knight shift caused by an exchange interaction between the conduction electrons and the Gd^{3+} local moment. The sign of this exchange, as determined by the sign of the g-shift, was in accord with NMR Knight shift measurements in these compounds made by Jaccarino and coworkers.[95] These resonance experiments were important adjuncts to susceptibility and specific heat measurements as well as to the intensive theoretical work on local moments in metals that was carried on at Bell Labs in the early 1960s.

The relaxation time, or linewidth, of a local moment in a metal is another source of information regarding its interaction with conduction electrons. This relaxation corresponds to the flow of energy when the local moment is resonated with microwaves, from the local moment magnetization to the conduction electron magnetization, and subsequent equilibration of the conduction electron spins to the lattice temperature. Gossard, A. J. Heeger, and J. H. Wernick showed that at a high-enough concentration of local moment (only a few percent manganese in copper), the flow of energy is bottlenecked by the relatively low heat capacity of the conduction electron spins.[96] This bottleneck was predicted theoretically by H. Hasegawa and must be taken into account in order to properly interpret local moment relaxation behavior in metals.[97]

Another area of EPR in metals in which Bell Labs was very active in the mid-1960s was the EPR measurement of conduction electrons in alkali metals by W. M. Walsh, L. W. Rupp, and P. H. Schmidt.[98] This program was aided by the success in preparing ultra-pure alkali metals. The most significant aspect of these results was the indication that core-polarization contribution to electronic g-shifts plays an important role in the heavier alkalies such as cesium and rubidium.

A key contribution was the theoretical work of P. M. Platzman and P. A. Wolff on spin waves in nonferromagnetic metals.[99] Using the Landau theory, they calculated the wave-number-dependent radio frequency susceptibility of an interacting system of conduction elec-

trons and showed that sidebands on the EPR line in sodium and
potassium seen by S. Shultz and G. Dunnifer[100] were caused by these
spin waves.

2.3 Ferromagnetic Resonance

Ferromagnetic resonance (FMR) was discovered in England in 1946
by J. H. E. Griffiths in iron, nickel, and cobalt.[101] However, the
observed FMR frequencies were puzzling as they were far from
agreement with predictions based on the measured gyromagnetic
ratios determined from torque experiments. It remained for Kittel,
who was at M.I.T. at that time, to account for these results by pointing out the importance of the large demagnetizing fields in determining the FMR frequency.[102] He also derived expressions for the complex microwave permeability. W. A. Yager and Bozorth at Bell Labs
carefully checked the quantitative predictions of Kittel by doing FMR
on thin sheets of Supermalloy, which was particularly suitable for
that purpose because of its low anisotropy.[103] Shortly thereafter, Kittel generalized his result to obtain the resonance frequency of uniform precession for an arbitrary spheroid. These expressions were
experimentally verified at Bell Labs by Kittel, Yager, and Merritt.[104]

2.3.1 The Gyrator

The development of relatively low-loss magnetic insulators, with
properties determined by an applied dc magnetic field, led to a
wealth of technological applications and a new industry. These were
initiated by the invention and exploitation of a practical gyrator by
C. L. Hogan in 1951.[105] [Fig. 1-13]   The idea (and the name) of the
gyrator—an ideal, passive, four-terminal device with nonreciprocal
transmission properties, shifting the phase by 180° in one direction
and by 0° in the other—had been advanced by B. D. H. Tellegen at
the Philips Research Laboratories in the Netherlands.[106] Hogan realized that ferrite placed in a magnetic field close to that required for
FMR is a medium capable of possessing nonreciprocal properties to a
utilizable extent. He also observed that the nonreciprocity would be
acceptably broad-band. He proceeded to construct a gyrator and a
series of successful microwave isolators and circulators in the 9 GHz
range using ferrite slugs placed suitably in waveguide.

2.3.2 Resonance Linewidth and Losses in Ferrites and Garnets

Research aimed at understanding the origin of losses in FMR, or
equivalently, the FMR linewidth, was central to the improvement of
microwave ferrite devices. Galt and coworkers[107] and Clogston[108]

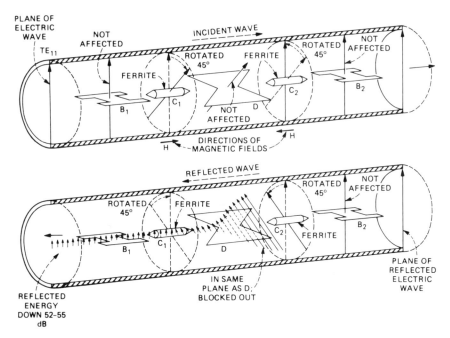

Fig. 1-13. Simplified drawings showing the rotation of the plane of polarization produced in ferrite rods in a gyrator used as a microwave isolator. The upper part shows the polarization conditions inside the cylindrical guide for a wave propagating from left to right; the lower part shows the polarization conditions for a wave propagating from right to left. The resistance sheets are good radio frequency absorbers for waves polarized parallel to the surface but very poor absorbers for waves polarized normal to the surface. For the incident wave, the rotation of the plane of polarization produced by the Faraday effect in ferrite specimen C_1 is clockwise as viewed in the direction of propagation; in C_2 it is counterclockwise, because the direction of the applied field is reversed. Similar rotation takes place for the reflected wave, as indicated, leading to the absorption of the wave in resistance sheet D.

formulated a valence exchange theory of loss applicable to certain ferrites such as $NiFe_2O_4$, in which Fe^{2+} and Fe^{3+} exist on physically equivalent sites. Because of spin-orbit coupling the "extra" electron on the Fe^{2+} may find it more energetically favorable to be on one site or on the other when the magnetization moves. This extra electron requires a certain relaxation time to return to thermal equilibrium when the magnetization moves, introducing a lagging torque and a consequent loss mechanism. However, such a valence exchange mechanism is essentially absent in yttrium iron garnet (YIG), because all of the metal ions are trivalent.

With the elimination of the major source of microwave losses, other loss mechanisms came to the fore. In 1956, Anderson and Suhl pointed out that as a result of the dipole-dipole interaction between spins in a ferromagnet, the resonance arising from the uniform precession mode of FMR is degenerate with a portion of the spin-wave spectrum.[109] This degeneracy was shown to be the basis of a loss mechanism for FMR by Clogston and coworkers.[110] They pointed out that disorder, such as impurities or irregularities in the crystal, provided a coupling mechanism for drawing energy from the uniform precession mode to the degenerate manifold of spin waves. Extensive experiments on YIG, many of which were done at Bell Labs by R. C. LeCraw, E. G. Spencer, and C. S. Porter from 1958 to 1963, showed that pits left on the surface of the sample by the polishing process provided the irregularity necessary for coupling the uniform precession.[111] Increased surface smoothness resulted in lower linewidths. However, even at the highest surface polish a peak in the FMR linewidth as a function of temperature was still observed, as first reported by Dillon.[112] This peak was shown by Dillon and J. W. Nielsen to be caused by traces of other fast-relaxing, rare earth impurities.[113] Several theories of this rare earth relaxation appropriate to different magnitudes of relaxation of rare earth ions have been given.[114] T. Kasuya and LeCraw used ultrapure YIG prepared by Remeika to obtain an extremely narrow linewidth of 0.05 Gauss, limited by fundamental spin wave-phonon interactions in the crystal.[115] The surface pit scattering and rare earth impurity linewidth mechanisms are an outstanding example of interplay between theory and experiment culminating in the practical realization of the ultimate linewidth in so important a technological material as YIG.

2.3.3 Parametric Ferromagnetic Amplifier

There were many other significant advances in FMR at Bell Laboratories. Suhl discussed and explained the fundamental behavior of FMR at high powers, the related saturation and instability effects, and showed how a parametric ferromagnetic amplifier could be built.[116] He proposed that a ferrite sample, under an applied dc magnetic field, be placed in a cavity that is simultaneously resonant to two signal frequencies, f_1 and f_2.[117] When a high-power "pumping" field of frequency $f_1 + f_2$ is applied to the sample, amplification or oscillation should be observed at the signal frequencies f_1 and f_2. The frequency condition for the pumping field, $f = f_1 + f_2$, was predicted earlier by J. M. Manley and H. E. Rowe.[118] Shortly thereafter, M. T. Weiss demonstrated such a ferrite microwave amplifier and oscillator operating at 4.5 GHz.[119] P. K. Tien invented a traveling-wave parametric amplifier that included, in addition to the frequency condition mentioned earlier, a phase-matching condition, $\beta(\text{pump}) = \beta_1(\text{signal}) + \beta_2(\text{idler})$, which is also known as the Tien Beta relation.[120] This phase-matching condition became widely used in non-linear optics and in quantum electronics.

The wave-type parametric amplifiers, including the forward-wave-type and the backward-wave-type amplifiers proposed by Tien, were quickly demonstrated in the form of diode amplifiers by M. E. Hines,[121] and by M. Uenohara and W. M. Sharpless,[122] and in the form of cyclotron-wave electron-beam amplifiers by R. Adler and G. Hrbek,[123] and by T. J. Bridges and A. Ashkin.[124] What made the parametric amplifiers important is that signals are amplified by an electron beam or by semiconductor diodes in the form of a variable reactance that does not contribute noise.[125] A diode parametric amplifier at 6 GHz with a noise figure as low as 0.3 decibel has been built at Bell Laboratories.[126] (This noise figure should be compared with a noise figure of 6 to 10 decibels in typical traveling wave tubes built in the late 1950s.)

2.3.4 Ferromagnetic Resonance in Rare Earth Ferrimagnetic Materials

In 1956, Dillon[127] observed simultaneously with R. L. White, J. H. Solt, and J. E. Mercereau,[128] a large number of subsidiary ferromagnetic resonance absorptions. These are called magnetostatic modes because they correspond to the natural oscillations of a system of coupled dipoles. A complete theory was given for general spheroidal samples by L. R. Walker in 1957.[129] Geschwind and Clogston pointed out theoretically and showed experimentally how an inhomogeneous broadening in FMR is narrowed by the dipolar forces.[130] This latter phenomenon is important for linewidth analysis in polycrystalline materials.

Some of the most interesting work in FMR was done on systems in which a magnetic rare earth ion was substituted for yttrium in YIG.[131] These are ferrimagnetic structures, with the rare earth ions, the iron ions on octahedral sites, and the iron ions on tetrahedral sites each forming a magnetic sublattice. The fact that the rare earth ions have widely different magnetic properties gives rise to a rich variety of behavior in the substituted garnets. The rare earth ions have a complicated level structure, heavily dependent upon their crystal environment, in many cases with low-lying levels. One consequence in such a case is that the field for ferromagnetic resonance may be highly anisotropic, varying by as much as several kilooersteds with crystal direction. A prototypical system is YIG doped with terbium, where dramatic effects were observed. Dillon and Walker developed an extension of the usual FMR theory to include ions with complex level structure that gave a satisfactory explanation of these results.[132]

2.4 Electron Orbital Resonance

A charged particle in the presence of a uniform magnetic field moves in a spiral path around the flux lines. The frequency of the circular transverse motion is called the cyclotron frequency and is proportional to both the charge-to-mass ratio of the particle and the strength of the magnetic field. If a radio frequency (rf) electric field is also applied transverse to the fixed magnetic field and its polarization is made to rotate at a frequency equal to that of the particle's cyclotron motion, a resonant transfer of energy will occur. This will lead to an increase (or a decrease, depending on the relative phase) in the transverse component of the particle's velocity and a loss of energy from the driving circuit. The phenomenon is known as cyclotron resonance since it requires equality of the excitation and cyclotron frequencies. It has been widely exploited in particle accelerators, mass spectrometers, in an early version of the magnetron (a high-power microwave oscillator), and, in the mid-1970s, in a new millimeter wave generator, the Gyrotron.[133]

In fusion research the cyclotron resonances of various charged particles in a plasma or dense gas discharge offer a means of plasma heating. Cyclotron resonance has also proved to be a powerful spectroscopic tool in solid state physics. It has contributed greatly to the understanding of the motion of electrons and holes in semiconductors, semimetals, and metals. In addition, it has led to a much more general understanding of the collective dielectric behavior of these conducting solids, an area of research known as solid state plasma physics (see Chapter 6, section 2.2.3).

2.4.1 Orbital Resonance in Semiconductors

In order to measure the charge-to-mass ratios of mobile charged particles with some accuracy using cyclotron resonance methods, the motion of those particles should be well defined. This means that the particles should complete several orbital cycles around the magnetic flux lines without disturbance. While this condition is easily achieved for free particles in a good vacuum, it is most difficult to obtain in solids because of the scattering by the thermal vibrations of the crystal lattice, and static imperfections such as vacancies, dislocations and, above all, charged impurities. Thus, despite prior theoretical suggestions that cyclotron resonance in solids would be very interesting, it was not until 1953 that Shockley could point out that improvements made in the purity and crystalline perfection of the elemental semiconductors germanium and silicon (motivated by the nascent transistor technology) should increase the mean-free path sufficiently to permit observation of cyclotron resonance in these semiconductors.[134] Following this suggestion, scientists at the University of California at Berkeley,[135] and at the Lincoln Laboratory of M.I.T.[136] investigated a variety of cyclotron resonance absorption lines in both germanium and silicon arising from electrons moving in multiple and highly anisotropic conduction-band valleys. Less well-resolved cyclotron absorption caused by holes at the valence-band edges were also seen. At Bell Laboratories, Fletcher, Yager, and Merritt discovered that the hole resonances were much more complex than had first been expected, exhibiting a fine structure caused by the quantum nature of the motions of the particles.[137]

The full elucidation of the quantum structure has required considerable effort on the part of both experimenters and theorists over many years. Using cyclotron resonance as a monitor of free carriers, J. C. Hensel, T. G. Phillips, and T. M. Rice determined the work function of a novel metallic condensate, the electron-hole droplet formed by high densities of carriers in germanium at low temperatures.[138] (For more on this topic see section 5.6 of Chapter 2.)

Cyclotron resonance in semiconductors has also been used to study the two-dimensional space-charge region formed at the Si-SiO$_2$ interface in metal-oxide semiconductor (MOS) devices.[139] Since scattering times are short in the disturbed potential at the interface the experiments require very high frequencies and, correspondingly, very strong magnetic fields. Variations of effective-mass ratios and scattering times have been observed as functions of the space-charge density and temperature. Whether some of these variations are manifestations of many-body interactions is a question of continuing interest.

The phenomenon of cyclotron resonance may also be probed by light scattering rather than by direct resonance absorption. This was clearly demonstrated by R. E. Slusher, C. K. N. Patel, and P. A. Fleury in InSb using CO$_2$ laser radiation that was inelastically scattered because of excitation of both cyclotron and spin-flip transitions.[140] The latter scattering provides the basis for the magnetically tunable spin-flip laser. (For more on this topic see section 7.3 of Chapter 5.)

2.4.2 Orbital Resonance in the Semimetals Bismuth and Graphite

Shortly after the first observations of cyclotron resonance in semiconductors, Galt initiated similar experiments in a different class of conducting solids—the semimetals whose archetype is the element bismuth.[141] A semimetal differs from a semiconductor in that the conduction and valence bands overlap and, therefore, equal numbers of mobile electrons and holes are present even at the lowest attainable temperatures. This high conductivity restricts penetration of the rapidly time-varying electrical excitation to a thin surface layer, the skin depth, and severely complicates the resonance phenomenon.

Galt found that the clearest results could be obtained if the uniform magnetic field was directed perpendicular to a carefully polished flat surface of the semimetal. His study showed that the cyclotron resonances then took the form of absorption steps or edges rather than simple absorption lines. The data analysis was greatly aided by a calculation of Anderson that explained the step-like character of the resonance under skin-effect conditions.[142] Galt's paper later proved to be the precursor of plasma aspects of orbital resonance phenomena. Despite the inherent complexities, Galt and his coworkers were able to unravel the spectra of elemental bismuth and some dilute alloys and, thus, to confirm theoretical calculations of the electronic band structure of these materials.[143] Their use of circularly polarized microwave excitation to distinguish between electron and hole resonances was particularly noteworthy. A similar investigation of graphite was also performed by Galt and his coworkers[144] and later interpreted by P. Noziéres.[145] The concept of magnetospectroscopy of semimetals was extended from the microwave to the infrared region by W. S. Boyle, A. D. Brailsford, and Galt,[146] and later by J. C. Burgiel and L. C. Hebel.[147]

2.5 Resonance Experiments in the Far-Infrared

Many of the collective excitations in solids, such as spin waves, lattice waves, and charge density waves, occur in the far infrared region of the electromagnetic spectrum. Important solid state spectroscopic data in this region remained relatively untapped until the late 1950s because of a lack of strong broadband sources and sensitive detectors.

Since the days of A. A. Michelson's work with an optical interferometer,[148] spectral data could be obtained by using interferometers as well as by using dispersion spectrometers. However, to extract the spectral information from the data obtained with the interferometer required laborious and tedious calculations. With the availability of fast computers, these calculations were no longer prohibitive and Fourier transform spectroscopy came into its own. After the initial developments of far infrared interferometers by H. A. Gebbie and G. A. Vanasse,[149] and by J. Strong at Johns Hopkins University,[150] the techniques were successfully applied to problems in solid state physics by P. L. Richards and S. J. Allen at Bell Labs as well as by workers in other laboratories.

A wide variety of problems have been attacked with this spectroscopic tool. The influence of impurities on the superconducting energy gap was shown by Richards to agree with Anderson's predictions. Antiferromagnetic spin waves were studied by Richards and others in a number of magnetic insulators.[151] Of particular interest was the effect of orbital degeneracy on the magnetism of such molecules as UO_2.[152] Rotation of molecules trapped in β-quenol clathrate inclusion compounds were graphically expressed by their far infrared absorption.[153] The crystal field environment of iron in hemoglobin was deduced from its far infrared electron spin resonance. The diffusion rate of mobile cations in solid electrolytes like Naβ-alumina, used in a sodium sulfur battery, contains as a factor the vibration frequencies of the cations in their potential wells, and these frequencies lie in the far-infrared.[154] Perhaps one of the most productive areas of far-infrared spectroscopy concerns electron states in semiconductors. Plasma waves, cyclotron resonance, and donor state spectroscopy are revealed in the far infrared. In 1978, D. C. Tsui and coworkers were able to probe the electron states confined to the inversion layer of a silicon metal-oxide semiconductor field-effect transistor (MOSFET).[155]

III. MÖSSBAUER SPECTROSCOPY

The Mössbauer effect was discovered by R. L. Mössbauer in 1957 at Heidelberg, Germany.[156] He found that when radioactive atoms that emit gamma rays are bound in a solid, the solid absorbs the recoil of the emission and the emitted gamma ray has the full energy of the nuclear transition. These gamma rays can be resonantly absorbed by another nucleus of the same type. [Fig. 1-14] The comparison of source emission energies and absorber energies leads to a new form of spectroscopy—Mössbauer spectroscopy. The primary importance of this technique is that it allows accurate measurements of the very small changes produced in nuclear energy levels by the electrons of an ion and its neighbors in the solid. Thus, Mössbauer spectroscopy can serve as a probe to study chemical bonding, structure, and magnetism, as seen by individual nuclei.

3.1 Hyperfine Structure Studies in Magnetic Materials

The use of Mössbauer spectroscopy was begun at Bell Laboratories in 1959 by G. K. Wertheim. Wertheim's initial approach was to try to relate the hyperfine interactions known to be observable via the Mössbauer effect—the magnetic hyperfine splitting and the quadrupole splitting—to the electronic structure of solids by studying the Mössbauer spectra of relatively well understood materials.[157] In this process, he discovered a new interaction, the isomer shift, which arises from the electrostatic interaction of the nucleus with the electronic charge density. With Walker and Jaccarino, Wertheim demonstrated that ionic wave functions previously calculated could be used to explain the observed isomer shift values for Fe^{57}, the most commonly used Mössbauer nucleus.[158] They also determined the size of

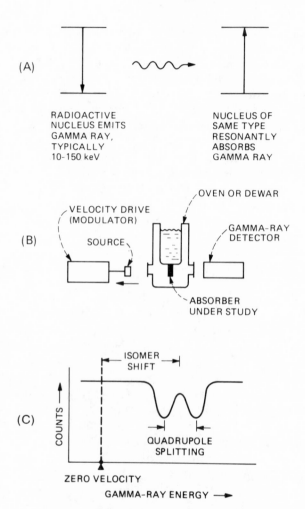

Fig. 1-14. (A) Diagram showing that the Mössbauer effect is based on the resonant absorption of gamma rays emitted in the decay of a radioactive nucleus, which can be resonantly absorbed by a nucleus of the same kind in the ground state. (B) "Standard" configuration of a simple Mössbauer experiment. The source is moved with precisely controlled velocity to modulate the gamma-ray energy by means of the Doppler effect. When the gamma rays have proper energy to be resonantly absorbed by nuclei in the absorber, fewer of them pass through to the detector, and the counting rate decreases. (C) The result normally is plotted as shown, in terms of the transmission, or counting rate, versus the Doppler velocity applied to the source. The idealized spectrum shown would be obtained for a quadrupole-split doublet. [*Science* **178** (November 1972): 829].

the nuclear radius change between excited and ground states. This approach established a systematic relationship between the parameters observed by Mössbauer spectroscopy and known magnetic and chemical structure. Using this information, it was subsequently possible to learn about new materials from their Mössbauer spectra.

This technique was immediately useful in studying complex new magnetic materials. There were three important advantages:[159]

1. Measurements of magnetization could be made without a field applied to the sample, so that good data could be obtained even on materials that were hard to saturate magnetically.

2. In complex materials with magnetically inequivalent sites, the magnetism of the different ions could be directly determined from the Mössbauer spectrum.

3. Powder samples could be studied; single crystals were not required.

The experimental results on Mössbauer spectra, together with information from nuclear magnetic resonance, turned the attention of physicists to the problem of understanding the various contributions to the hyperfine field at the nucleus in magnetic materials. An early series of experiments on alloys of iron diluted with other elements showed that the effects of this alloying on the hyperfine spectrum could be very simply explained.[160] For each substitution of a non-iron neighbor in the near-neighbor shells of the iron probe atom, both the isomer shift and hyperfine field were altered by fixed amounts. These results showed that simple additive behavior could be expected for many alloys, and enormously simplified the interpretation of data on more complex systems. Subsequently, the model was also shown to be valid for alloys of gold with transition metals.[161]

3.1.1 Hyperfine Fields in Rare Earths

Several rare-earth isotopes can be used for Mössbauer spectroscopy. Hyperfine structure measurements allow the magnetism and ionic structure of metals, intermetallic compounds, and insulators to be related. This approach was used to study the magnetism of rare earth iron garnets, in which europium was used as a Mössbauer probe.[162–169] The hyperfine field observed in the Mössbauer spectrum is proportional to the exchange field on the europium. The sources of the exchange could be ascertained by substituting nonmagnetic ions for the iron in the garnet. [Fig. 1-15] The results of the experiments showed that the two tetrahedrally coordinated iron nearest neighbors to the europium ions provided almost all of the exchange field, in contradiction with a previously accepted model. This infor-

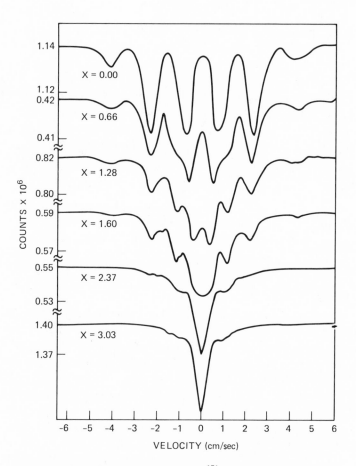

Fig. 1-15. Mössbauer spectra of Eu^{151} in gallium-doped europium iron garnet, $Eu_3 Fe_{5-x} Ga_x O_{12}$, for various values of x. The origins of the magnetic interactions in garnets can be determined from these spectra. [Nowik and Ofer, *Phys. Rev.* **153** (1967): 413].

mation on the origins of garnet magnetism proved useful in the design of complex mixed garnets for bubble-domain memory devices.

3.1.2 Microstructure of Magnetic Alloys

In 1978, M. Eibschutz and coworkers used the Mössbauer spectroscopy of iron alloys to study the microscopic structure of the Chromindur cold-formable, high-energy-product permanent magnet materials. These alloys are generated by means of spinodal decomposition of a Co-Cr-Fe alloy, which produces precipitates of only a few hundred angstroms. It was shown that this complex material contains two ferromagnetic phases at room temperature, with the coercive force arising from the domain-wall-particle interaction of the two magnetic phases, making it a good permanent magnet.[170]

3.1.3 *Hyperfine Measurements and Electron Spin Relaxation*

Initially, Mössbauer spectra were considered to arise from static hyperfine fields. However, as measurements were extended to additional systems, it became apparent that many of the observed spectral features were arising from dynamic phenomena. This meant that the hyperfine fields seen by a nucleus were changing during the characteristic time of the Mössbauer absorption (typically 10^{-9} to 10^{-7} seconds).

An early experiment by Wertheim and J. P. Remeika studying the hyperfine spectrum of Fe^{3+} as a dilute impurity in corundum $(\alpha-Al_2O_3)$ established the idealized extremum of the "slow relaxation limit."[171] By making the iron dilute enough to remove the iron-iron relaxation mechanism, and cooling to eliminate thermally excited relaxation mechanisms, the spectra of the individual paramagnetic states of isolated ions could be determined. The spectra of these states were shown to correspond to those expected for the known iron-ion wave functions in this host. These experiments laid the groundwork for a theoretical model that showed how to obtain the hyperfine spectrum for the case of moderately fast relaxation by considering rapid stochastic transitions among the paramagnetic basis states of the ion in the magnetic field.[172] This theory was quite successful in explaining the spectra of materials where the iron-iron distances were large, such as the dithiocarbamates, and in rare earth materials such as dysprosium ethyl sulphate[173] and erbium orthochromite.[174]

3.2 Layer-Structure Compounds

The discovery by Bell Labs scientists in 1974 that layer-structure compounds such as TaS_2 and $TaSe_2$ could have charge density waves, that is, a coupled periodic distortion of the conduction electron density and of the lattice, led to a whole new range of experiments in which the Mössbauer effect was used to study the physics of these interesting new materials. Although none of the species in these compounds could be studied easily by Mössbauer spectroscopy, the compounds could be doped with small amounts of Fe^{57} and the added isotope used as a probe. The Mössbauer isomer shift was used by Eibschutz and F. J. DiSalvo as an indicator of the electron density of the host. It provided a direct determination of the physical variable of interest, namely the variation in electron density from point to point inside the crystal, and the temperature dependence of that density.[175]

3.3 Amorphous Materials

Mössbauer spectroscopy has also been used to study glasses and amorphous materials and crystals containing many defects. In these systems, the relatively low resolution, and the sensitivity of the Mössbauer hyperfine structure parameters only to nearby ions, can be an advantage. Well-resolved spectra can be obtained for materials where only short-range order is present, materials for which many other techniques are not applicable. An early study by C. R. Kurkjian of iron in glasses took advantage of this.[176] Direct evidence was provided that Fe^{3+} was four-fold coordinated in silicate glasses, but six-fold coordinated in phosphate glasses. It was also possible to observe directly the precipitation of Fe_2O_3 during the annealing of glasses in which the Fe^{3+} was insoluble.

Mössbauer studies using Fe^{57} have also been extremely effective in studying the thermal decomposition of europium ferricyanide, ferrous sulphate, and mixed Fe-Ni oxalates.[177] The reactions and intermediate stages involved in these decompositions are of commercial importance because the same processes are used to manufacture magnetic oxides and complex mixed ferrites for magnetic tape, transformer cores, and computer memory devices. Since the Mössbauer spectroscopy technique is sensitive to the surroundings of individual atoms, it is capable of much more detailed elucidation of the decomposition processes than, for example, X-ray diffraction, which requires decomposition products to be at least a few hundred angstroms in size to be identifiable.

3.4 Studies of Electroplating

Mössbauer spectroscopy of Sn^{119} was very successfully applied by R. L. Cohen and K. W. West to the study of the materials and processes used in preparing plastic surfaces for metallization by electrodeless plating. These processes, despite their wide use in the automotive and electronics industries, had never been extensively studied. The chemistry was extremely complex and poorly controlled, and the mechanisms were not well understood. Most of these processes used tin in various forms. It was possible to follow the main reaction chains by using Mössbauer spectroscopy to monitor the chemical state of the tin. First, the chemistry of processes used to prepare commercial catalyst solutions was determined.[178] [Fig. 1-16] These processes were shown to depend on the formation of a complex between divalent tin and divalent palladium, and the subsequent decomposi-

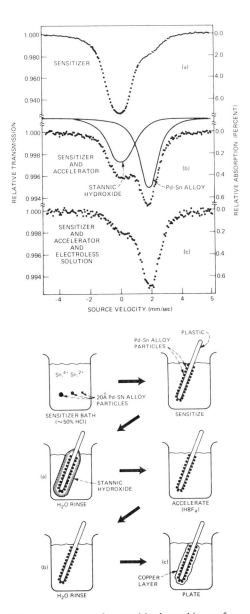

Fig. 1-16. (Top) Mössbauer spectra of a sensitized graphite surface at various processing stages, (bottom) labeled (a), (b), and (c). After sensitization and rinsing, the deposit consists of a large amount of stannic hydroxide (resonance minimum at zero velocity) and a relatively weak resonance minimum corresponding to the Pd-Sn alloy (line near 2 mm/second). After acceleration (center left, note change of vertical scale), about 95 percent of the stannic hydroxide and about half of the Pd-Sn alloy have been removed. The curves shown for comparison with the data are actual Mössbauer spectra of bulk samples of stannic hydroxide and the $Pd_{0.86}Sn_{0.14}$ alloy. Plating in the electroless solution further decreases the amount of stannic hydroxide but leaves the amount of Pd-Sn alloy essentially unaffected. [Cohen, *Advances in Chemistry Series* (1981)].

tion of this complex to form an extremely fine colloid of metallic tin-palladium alloy, with coagulation prevented by an adsorbed stabilizing layer of Sn^{2+}. It was then established that these colloidal particles were adsorbed on the plastic surface to be plated, and formed the catalytic layer required for the subsequent electroless plating.[179] Undesirable side reactions were also defined,[180] and improved processing techniques to avoid them were developed.[181]

The chemistry and metallurgy of "hard gold," an electrodeposited alloy of gold with small amounts of cobalt, widely used for connectors and contacts, has also been studied by Mössbauer spectroscopy. Both the gold host[182] and the cobalt alloying ingredient[183] were studied to determine how the impurities (especially carbon, nitrogen, hydrogen, and oxygen) were combined with the metallic species in the deposit. It was also possible to observe the effects of accelerated aging on the decomposition of the deposit, and the composition of the high-resistance surface layer formed by extended exposure of the deposit to air.

REFERENCES

1. L. W. McKeehan, "The Significance of Magnetostriction in Permalloy," *Phys. Rev.* **28** (July 1926), pp. 158-166.

2. R. M. Bozorth, J. F. Dillinger, and G. A. Kelsall, "Magnetic Material of High Permeability Attained by Heat Treatment in a Magnetic Field," *Phys. Rev.* **45** (May 1934), p. 742; R. M. Bozorth and J. F. Dillinger, "Heat Treatment of Magnetic Materials in a Magnetic Field," *Physics* **6** (September 1935), pp. 285-291.

3. R. M. Bozorth, "Determination of Ferromagnetic Anisotropy in Single Crystals and in Polycrystalline Sheets," *Phys. Rev.* **50** (December 1936), pp. 1076-1081.

4. R. M. Bozorth, "The Orientation of Crystals in Silicon Iron," *Trans. Am. Soc. Metals* **23** (December 1935), pp. 1107-1111.

5. E. A. Nesbitt, J. H. Wernick, and G. Corenzwit, "Magnetic Moments of Alloys and Compounds of Iron and Cobalt with Rare Earth Metal Additions," *J. Appl. Phys.* **30** (March 1959), pp. 365-369.

6. J. H. Wernick, "Recent Developments in Magnetic Materials," *Ann. Rev. Mat. Sci.* **2** (1972), pp. 607-640.

7. P. Weiss, "L'Hypothese du Champ Moleculaire et la Propriete Ferromagnetique," *J. de Physique*, **Ser. 4,6** (1907), pp. 661-690.

8. H. Barkhausen, "Zwei mit Hilfe der neuen Verstarker entdeckte Erscheinungen," *Physik. Zeitschr.* **XX** (September 1919), pp. 401-403.

9. R. M. Bozorth and J. F. Dillinger, "Barkhausen Effect. II. Determination of the Average Size of the Discontinuities in Magnetization," *Phys. Rev.* **35** (April 1930), pp. 733-752.

10. F. Bitter, "On Inhomogeneities in the Magnetization of Ferromagnetic Surface Magnetization in Ferromagnetic Crystals," Letters to the Editor, *Phys. Rev.* **38** (November 15, 1931), pp. 1903-1905; L. W. McKeehan and W. C. Elmore, "Surface Magnetization in Ferromagnetic Crystals," Letters to the Editor, *Phys. Rev.* **46** (August 1, 1934), pp. 226-228.

11. H. J. Williams, "Direction of Domain Magnetization in Powder Patterns," Letters to the Editor, *Phys. Rev.* **71** (May 1, 1947), pp. 646-647.

12. H. J. Williams, R. M. Bozorth, and W. Shockley, "Magnetic Domain Patterns on Single Crystals of Silicon Iron," *Phys. Rev.* **75** (January 1949), pp. 155-178.
13. H. J. Williams and W. Shockley, "A Simple Domain Structure in an Iron Crystal Showing a Direct Correlation with the Magnetization," *Phys. Rev.* **75** (January 1949), pp. 178-183.
14. Two of these 16mm films as well as a later one by E. A. Nesbitt are available from Bell Laboratories: "Formation of Ferromagnetic Domains," by J. K. Galt, C. Kittel, and H. J. Williams, and "Ferromagnetic Domains," by E. A. Nesbitt. Information about borrowing these films may be obtained from the Film Library, Bell Laboratories, Murray Hill, New Jersey 07974.
15. C. Kittel, "Physical Theory of Ferromagnetic Domains," *Rev. Mod. Phys.* **21** (October 1949), pp. 541-583.
16. C. Kittel and J. K. Galt, "Ferromagnetic Domain Theory," *Solid State Physics, Advances in Research and App.* **3**, ed. F. Seitz and D. Turnbull (New York: Academic Press, 1956), pp. 437-564.
17. E. A. Nesbitt and E. M. Gyorgy, "Two-Phase Permalloy for High-Speed Switching," *J. Appl. Phys.* **32** (July 1961), p. 1305.
18. E. A. Nesbitt, G. Y. Chin, and D. Jaffe, "New Low-Magnetostrictive Permanent-Magnet Alloys," *J. Appl. Phys.* **39** (February 1968), pp. 1268-1269.
19. C. Kittel, "Theory of the Structure of Ferromagnetic Domains in Films and Small Particles," *Phys. Rev.* **12** (December 1946), p. 965.
20. C. Kittel, E. A. Nesbitt, and W. Shockley, "Theory of Magnetic Properties and Nucleation in Alnico V," Letters to the Editor, *Phys. Rev.* **77** (March 15, 1950), pp. 839-840.
21. R. D. Heidenreich and E. A. Nesbitt, "Physical Structure and Magnetic Anistropy of Alnico 5. Part I," *J. Appl. Phys.* **23** (March 1952), pp. 352-365.
22. J. L. Snoek, *New Developments in Ferromagnetic Materials* (New York: Elsevier, 1947).
23. L. Neél, "Proprietes Magnetiques des Ferrites; Ferrimagnetisme et Antiferromagnetisme," *Ann. Phys.* **3** (1948), pp. 137-198.
24. J. K. Galt, "Motion of a Ferromagnetic Domain Wall in Fe^{304}," *Phys. Rev.* **84** (February 1952), pp. 664-669.
25. J. K. Galt, "Motion of Individual Domain Walls in a Nickel-Iron Ferrite," *Bell System Tech. J.* **33** (September 1954), pp. 1023-1054.
26. J. F. Dillon, Jr., and H. E. Earl, Jr., "Domain Wall Motion and Ferrimagnetic Resonance in a Manganese Ferrite," *J. Appl. Phys.* **30** (February 1959), pp. 202-213.
27. See reference 25.
28. A. M. Clogston, "Relaxation Phenomena in Ferrites," *Bell System Tech. J.* **34** (July 1955), pp. 739-760.
29. S. Geller and M. A. Gilleo, "Structure and Ferrimagnetism of Yttrium and Rare-Earth-Iron Garnets," *Acta Cryst.* **10** (March 1957), p. 239.
30. M. A. Gilleo and S. Geller, "Magnetic and Crystallographic Properties of Substituted Yttrium-Iron Garnet, $3Y_2O_3.xM_2O_3.(5-x)Fe_2O_3$," *Phys. Rev.* **110** (April 1958), pp. 73-78.
31. S. Geller, H. J. Williams, G. P. Espinosa, and R. C. Sherwood, "Importance of Intrasublattice Magnetic Interactions and of Substitutional Ion Type in the Behavior of Substituted Yttrium Iron Garnets," *Bell System Tech. J.* **43** (March 1964), pp. 565-623.
32. F. Bertaut and F. Forrat, "Radiocristallographie," *C. R. Academie des Sciences,* Paris **242** (1956), pp. 382-384.
33. J. F. Dillon, Jr., "Optical Properties of Several Ferrimagnetic Garnets," *J. Appl. Phys.* **29** (March 1958), pp. 539-541.
34. H. J. Williams, R. C. Sherwood, and J. P. Remeika, "Magnetic Domains in

   $-Fe_2O_3$," Letters to the Editor, *J. Appl. Phys.* **29** (December 1958), p. 1772.

35. A. H. Bobeck and H. E. D. Scovil, "Magnetic Bubbles," *Scientific American* **224** (June 1971), pp. 278-290.

36. *Physics in Perspective* Vol. II, Part A, Physics Survey Committee, National Research Council, National Academy of Sciences, Washington, D. C. (1972), pp. 475-481.

37. C. Herring and C. Kittel, "On the Theory of Spin Waves in Ferromagnetic Media," *Phys. Rev.* **81** (March 1951), pp. 869-880; C. Herring, "Energy of a Bloch Wall on the Band Picture. I. Spiral Approach," *Phys. Rev.* **85** (March 1952), pp. 1003-1011; C. Herring, "Energy of a Bloch Wall on the Band Picture. II. Perturbation Approach," *Phys. Rev.* **87** (July 1952), pp. 60-70.

38. C. Herring, "State of d Electrons in Transition Metals," *J. Appl. Phys.* **31** (1960), p. 3S.

39. C. Herring, in *Magnetism: A Treatise on Modern Theory and Materials*, ed. G. T. Rado and H. Suhl (New York: Academic Press, 1966).

40. B. T. Matthias, V. B. Compton, H. Suhl, and E. Corenzwit, "Ferromagnetic Solutes in Superconductors," *Phys. Rev.* **115** (September 1959), pp. 1597-1598.

41. B. T. Matthias, M. Peter, H. J. Williams, A. M. Clogston, E. Corenzwit, and R. C. Sherwood, "Magnetic Moment of Transition Metal Atoms in Dilute Solutions and Their Effect on Superconducting Transition Temperature," *Phys. Rev. Lett.* **5** (December 15, 1960), pp. 542-544.

42. A. M. Clogston, B. T. Matthias, M. Peter, H. J. Williams, E. Corenzwit, and R. C. Sherwood, "Local Magnetic Moment Associated with an Iron Atom Dissolved in Various Transition Metal Alloys," *Phys. Rev.* **125** (January 1962), pp. 541-552.

43. P. A. Wolff, P. W. Anderson, A. M. Clogston, B. T. Matthias, M. Peter, and H. J. Williams, "Magnetization of Localized States in Metals," *J. Appl. Phys.* **33** (March 1962), pp. 1173-1177.

44. A. M. Clogston, "Impurity States in Transition Metals," *Phys. Rev.* **136** (November 1964), pp. 1417-1427; idem, "Localized Magnetic Moments," *J. Metals* **17** (January 1965), pp. 728-734.

45. V. Jaccarino and L. R. Walker, "Discontinuous Occurrence of Localized Moments in Metals," *Phys. Rev. Lett.* **15** (August 9, 1965), pp. 258-259.

46. P. W. Anderson, "Localized Magnetic States in Metals," *Phys. Rev.* **124** (October 1961), pp. 41-53.

47. P. W. Anderson, "New Approach to the Theory of Superexchange Interactions," *Phys. Rev.* **115** (July 1959), pp. 2-13.

48. R. G. Shulman and S. Sugano, "Covalency Effects in $KNiF_3$. I. Nuclear Magnetic Resonance Studies," *Phys. Rev.* **130** (April 1963), pp. 506-511; S. Sugano and R. G. Shulman, "Covalency Effects in $KNiF_3$. III. Theoretical Studies," *Phys. Rev.* **130** (April 1963), pp. 517-530.

49. A. P. Ginsberg and M. E. Lines, "Magnetic Exchange in Transition Metal Complexes. VI. Aspects of Exchange Coupling in Magnetic Cluster Complexes," *Inorganica Chimica Acta, Review* **5** (1971), pp. 45-68; M. E. Lines, A. P. Ginsberg, and R. L. Martin, "Evidence for Large Antisymmetric Superexchange in Tetrameric Copper Complexes," *Phys. Rev.* **28** (March 1972), pp. 684-687.

50. P. W. Anderson, "Limits on the Energy of the Antiferromagnetic Ground State," Letters to the Editor, *Phys. Rev.* **83** (September 15, 1951), p. 1260; idem, "An Approximate Quantum Theory of the Antiferromagnetic Ground State," *Phys. Rev.* **86** (June 1952), pp. 694-701.

51. I. I. Rabi, J. R. Zacharias, S. Millman, and P. Kusch, "A New Method of Measuring Nuclear Magnetic Moment," Letters to the Editor, *Phys. Rev.* **53** (February 15, 1938), p. 318.

52. E. M. Purcell, H. C. Torrey, and R. V. Pound, "Resonance Absorption by Nuclear Magnetic Moments in a Solid," Letters to the Editor, *Phys. Rev.* **69** (January 1946), p. 37.

53. F. Bloch, W. W. Hansen, and M. Packard, "Nuclear Induction," Letters to the Editor, *Phys. Rev.* **69** (February 1946), p. 127.

54. W. D. Knight, "Nuclear Magnetic Resonance Shift in Metals," *Phys. Rev.* **76** (October 1949), pp. 1259-1260.

55. C. H. Townes, C. Herring, and W. D. Knight, "The Effect of Electronic Paramagnetism on Nuclear Magnetic Resonance Frequencies in Metals," Letters to the Editor, *Phys. Rev.* **77** (March 15, 1950), pp. 852-853.

56. W. E. Blumberg, J. Eisinger, V. Jaccarino, and B. Matthias, "Correlations Between Superconductivity and Nuclear Magnetic Resonance Properties," *Phys. Rev. Lett.* **5** (August 15, 1960), pp. 149-152.

57. A. M. Clogston and V. Jaccarino, "Susceptibilities and Negative Knight Shifts of Intermetallic Compounds," *Phys. Rev.* **121** (March 1961), pp. 1357-1362.

58. A. M. Clogston, A. C. Gossard, V. Jaccarino, and Y. Yafet, "Orbital Paramagnetism and the Knight Shift of D-Band Superconductors," *Phys. Rev. Lett.* **9** (September 15, 1962), pp. 262-266.

59. A. M. Clogston, V. Jaccarino, and Y. Yafet, "Interpretation of Knight Shifts and Susceptibilities of Transition Metals: Platinum," *Phys. Rev.* **134** (May 1964), pp. A650-A661.

60. See reference 59; also, J. A. Seitchik, A. C. Gossard, and V. Jaccarino, "Knight Shifts and Susceptibilities of Transition Metals: Palladium," *Phys. Rev.* **136** (November 1964), pp. A1119-A1125; J. A. Seitchik, V. Jaccarino, and J. Wernick, "Knight Shift Studies of Transition Metals: Rhodium and Rhodium Intermetallic Compounds," *Phys. Rev.* **138** (April 1965), pp. A148-A152.

61. Y. Yafet and V. Jaccarino, "Nuclear Spin Relaxation in Transition Metals: Core Polarization," *Phys. Rev.* **133** (March 1964), pp. A1630-A1637.

62. A. C. Gossard, A. Menth, W. W. Warren, Jr., and J. P. Remeika, "Metal-Insulator Transitions of V_2O_3: Magnetic Susceptibility and Nuclear-Magnetic-Resonance Studies," *Phys. Rev.* **B3** (June 1971), pp. 3993-4002; A. Narath, "Magnetic Hyperfine Interaction Studies of Magnetic Impurities in Metals," *CRC Critical Reviews in Solid State Sciences* **3** (March 1972), pp. 1-37.

63. J. H. Condon and R. E. Walstedt, "Direct Evidence for Magnetic Domains in Silver," *Phys. Rev. Lett.* **21** (August 26, 1968), pp. 612-614.

64. W. W. Warren, Jr., "Evidence for the Existence of a Pseudogap in a Semiconducting Liquid: Temperature Dependent In^{115} Knight Shift in In_2Te_3," *J. Non-Crystalline Solids* **4** (April 1970), pp. 168-177; idem, "Observation of Localized Electronic States in a Liquid Semiconductor: NMR in Liquid Ga_2Te_3," *Solid State Communications* **8** (August 15, 1970), pp. 1269-1273; idem, "Nuclear Magnetic Resonance and Relaxation in the Liquid Semiconductors, In_2Te_3, Ga_2Te_3, and Sb_2Te," *Phys. Rev.* **B3** (June 1971), pp. 3708-3724; W. W. Warren, Jr. and R. Dupree, "Structural and Electronic Transformations of Liquid Selenium at High Temperature and Pressure: A ^{77}Se NMR Study," *Phys. Rev.* **B22** (September 1980), pp. 2257-2275.

65. U. El-Hanany and W. W. Warren, Jr., "Knight Shift in Expanded Liquid Mercury," *Phys. Rev. Lett.* **34** (May 19, 1975), pp. 1276-1279.

66. R. G. Shulman and V. Jaccarino, "Effects of Superexchange on the Nuclear Magnetic Resonance of MnF_2," Letters to Editor, *Phys. Rev.* **103** (August 15, 1956), pp. 1126-1127; idem, "Nuclear Magnetic Resonance in Paramagnetic MnF_2," *Phys. Rev.* **108** (December 1957), pp. 1219-1231.

67. V. Jaccarino and L. R. Walker, "NMR in Antiferromagnetic $Mn^{19}F_2$," *Le Journal de Physique et Le Radium* **20** (February-March 1959), p. 341.

68. V. Jaccarino, "Nuclear Resonance in Antiferromagnetics," *Magnetism IIA*, ed. G. T. Rado and H. Suhl (New York: Academic Press, 1965), pp. 307-355.

69. A. C. Gossard, V. Jaccarino, and J. P. Remeika, "Experimental Test of the Spin-Wave Theory of a Ferromagnet," *Phys. Rev. Lett.* **7** (September 15, 1961), pp. 122-124.

70. H. W. de Wijn, R. E. Walstedt, L. R. Walker, and J. J. Guggenheim, "Sublattice Magnetization of Quadratic Layer Antiferromagnets," *Phys. Rev. Lett.* **24,** (April 13, 1970), pp. 832-835; R. E. Walstedt, H. W. de Wijn, and H. J. Guggenheim, "Observation of Zero-Point Spin Reduction in Quadratic Layer Antiferromagnets," *Phys. Rev. Lett.* **25** (October 19, 1970), pp. 1119-1122.

71. H. W. de Wijn, L. R. Walker, and R. E. Walstedt, "Spin-Wave Analysis of the Quadratic-Layer Antiferromagnets K_2NiF_4, K_2MnF_4, and Rb_2MnF_4," *Phys. Rev.* **B8** (July 1973), pp. 285-299.

72. H. Suhl, "Effective Nuclear Spin Interactions in Ferromagnets," Letters to the Editor, *Phys. Rev.* **109** (January 15, 1958), p. 606.

73. T. Nakamura, "Indirect Coupling of Nuclear Spins in Antiferromagnet with Particular Reference to MnF2 at Very Low Temperatures," *Prog. Theor. Phys.* **20** (1958), pp. 542-552.

74. E. Zavoisky, "Paramagnetic Relaxation of Liquid Solutions for Perpendicular Fields," *J. Physics* (USSR) **9** (1945), pp. 211-216; idem, "Spin-Magnetic Resonance in Paramagnetics," *J. Physics* (USSR) **9** (1945), p. 245.

75. R. L. Cummerow and D. Halliday, "Paramagnetic Losses in Two Manganous Salts," Letters to the Editor, *Phys. Rev.* **70** (September 1946), p. 433.

76. A. Abragam and B. Bleaney, *Electron Paramagnetic Resonance of Transition Ions* (Clarendon Press, 1970).

77. A. N. Holden, C. Kittel, F. R. Merritt, and W. A. Yager, "Microwave Resonance Absorption in a Paramagnetic Organic Compound," Letters to the Editor, *Phys. Rev.* **75** (May 1949), p. 1614; idem, "Determination of g-Values in Paramagnetic Organic Compounds by Microwave Resonance," Letters to the Editor, *Phys. Rev.* **77** (January 1, 1950), p. 147.

78. R. C. Fletcher, W. A. Yager, G. L. Pearson, and F. R. Merritt, "Hyperfine Splitting in Spin Resonance of Group V Donors in Silicon," Letters to the Editor, *Phys. Rev.* **95** (August 1, 1954), p. 844; R. C. Fletcher, W. A. Yager, G. L. Pearson, A. N. Holden, W. T. Read, and F. R. Merritt, "Spin Resonance of Donors in Silicon," Letters to the Editor, *Phys. Rev.* **94** (June 1, 1954), p. 1392.

79. W. Kohn and J. M. Luttinger, "Theory of Donor States in Silicon," *Phys. Rev.* **98** (May 1955), pp. 915-922.

80. G. Feher and E. A. Gere, "Polarization of Phosphorus Nuclei in Silicon," Letters to the Editor, *Phys. Rev.* **103** (July 15, 1956), pp. 501-503.

81. G. Feher, "Method of Polarizing Nuclei in Paramagnetic Substances," Letters to the Editor, *Phys. Rev.* **103** (July 15, 1956), pp. 500-501.

82. G. Feher, "Electron Spin Resonance Experiments on Donors in Silicon. I. Electronic Structure of Donors by the Electron Nuclear Double Resonance Technique," *Phys. Rev.* **114** (June 1959), pp. 1219-1244.

83. G. Feher, "Electronic Structure of F Centers in KCl by the Electron Spin Double-Resonance Technique," Letters to the Editor, *Phys. Rev.* **105** (February 1, 1957), pp. 1122-1123; W. C. Holton, H. Blum, and W. P. Slichter, "Hyperfine Structure of the F Center in LiF," *Phys. Rev. Lett.* **5** (September 1, 1960), pp. 197-200.

84. W. B. Mims, "Electric Field Effects in Spin Echoes," *Phys. Rev.* **133** (February 3, 1964), pp. A835-A840; idem, "Electron Spin Echoes," *Electron Paramagnetic Resonance*, ed. S. Geschwind (New York: Plenum Press, 1972), pp. 263-351.

85. W. B. Mims, K. Nassau, and J. D. McGee, "Spectral Diffusion in Electron Resonance Lines," *Phys. Rev.* **123** (September 1961), pp. 2059-2069.

86. J. A. Cowen and D. E. Kaplan, "Spin-Echo Measurement of the Spin-Lattice and Spin-Spin Relaxation in Ce^{3+} in Lanthanum Magnesium Nitrate," *Phys. Rev.* **124** (November 1961), pp. 1098-1101.

87. S. Geschwind, R. J. Collins, and A. L. Schawlow, "Optical Detection of Paramagnetic Resonance in an Excited State of Cr^{3+} in Al_2O_3," *Phys. Rev. Lett.* **3**

(December 15, 1959), pp. 545-548; S. Geschwind, G. E. Devlin, R. L. Cohen, and S. R. Chinn, "Orbach Relaxation and Hyperfine Structure in the Excited E(^{2}E) State of Cr^{3+} in Al$_2$O$_3$," *Phys. Rev.* **137** (February 1965), pp. A1087-A1100.

88. G. F. Imbusch, S. R. Chinn, and S. Geschwind, "Optical Detection of Spin-Lattice Relaxation and hfs in the Excited E(^{2}E) State of V^{2+} and Mn^{4+} in A1203," *Phys. Rev.* **161** (September 1967), pp. 295-309; L. L. Chase, "Microwave-Optical Dougle Resonance of the Metastable 4f^{6}5d Level of Eu^{2+} in the Flourite Lattices," *Phys. Rev.* **B2** (October 1970), pp. 2308-2318.

89. G. F. Imbusch and S. Geschwind, "Ground-State Spin Memory in the E(^{2}E) Level of Ruby in Optical Pumping via the Bands," *Phys. Rev. Lett.* **17** (August 1, 1966), pp. 238-240.

90. L. F. Mollenauer, S. Pan, and S. Y. Yngvesson, "Electron-Spin Memory in the Optical-Pumping Cycle of F Centers in Alkali Halides and Electron-Spin Resonance of the Relaxed Excited State," *Phys. Rev. Lett.* **23** (September 29, 1969), pp. 683-686; L. F. Mollenauer and S. Pan, "Dynamics of the Optical-Pumping Cycle of F Centers in Alkali Halides-Theory and Application to Detection of Electron-Spin and Electron-Nuclear-Double-Spin Resonance in the Relaxed-Excited State," *Phys. Rev.* **B6** (August 1972), pp. 772-787; P. Edel, C. Hennies, Y. Merle D'Aubigne, R. Romestain, and Y. Twarowski, "Optical Detection of Paramagnetic Resonance in the Excited State of F Centers in CaO," *Phys. Rev. Lett.* **28** (May 8, 1972), pp. 1268-1270.

91. A. L. Kwiram, "Optical Detection of Magnetic Resonance in Molecular Triplet States," *MTP International Review of Science, Physical Chemistry, Series One, Volume 4: Magnetic Resonance*, ed. C. A. McDowell (London: Butterworths, 1972).

92. W. J. Brya, S. Geschwind, and G. E. Devlin, "Direct Observation of a Phonon Bottleneck Using Brillouin Light Scattering," *Phys. Rev. Lett.* **21** (December 30, 1968), pp. 1800-1802; idem, "Brillouin Scattering from a Microwave-Phonon Bottleneck in MgO:Ni^{2+}," *Phys. Rev.* **B6** (September 1972), pp. 1924-1950.

93. M. Peter and B. T. Matthias, "Paramagnetic Resonance in Metallic Europium and Intermetallic Compounds," *Phys. Rev. Lett.* **4** (May 1, 1960), pp. 449-450.

94. M. Peter, D. Shaltiel, J. H. Wernick, H. J. Williams, J. B. Mock, and R. C. Sherwood, "Paramagnetic Resonance of S-State Ions in Metals," *Phys. Rev.* **126** (May 1962), pp. 1395-1402.

95. V. Jaccarino, B. T. Matthias, M. Peter, H. Suhl, and J. H. Wernick, "Magnitude and Sign of the Conduction Electron Polarization in Rare-Earth Metals," *Phys. Rev. Lett.* **5** (September 15, 1960), pp. 251-253.

96. A. C. Gossard, A. J. Heeger, and J. H. Wernick, "Paramagnetic Relaxation of Manganese in Copper Metal," *J. Appl. Phys.* **38** (March 1, 1967), pp. 1251-1253.

97. H. Hasegawa, "Dynamical Properties of s-d Interaction," *Prog. Theoret. Phys.* (Kyoto) **21** (April 1959), pp. 483-500.

98. W. M. Walsh, Jr., L. W. Rupp, Jr., and P. H. Schmidt, "g Values of Rubidium and Cesium Conduction Electrons," *Phys. Rev. Lett.* **16** (January 31, 1966), pp. 181-183.

99. P. M. Platzman and P. A. Wolff, "Spin-Wave Excitation in Nonferromagnetic Metals," *Phys. Rev. Lett.* **18** (February 20, 1967), pp. 280-285.

100. S. Schultz and G. Dunnifer, "Observation of Spin Waves in Sodium and Potassium," *Phys. Rev. Lett.* **18** (February 20, 1967), pp. 283-287.

101. J. H. E. Griffiths, "Anomalous High-Frequency Resistance of Ferromagnetic Metals," *Nature* **158** (November 9, 1946), pp. 670-671.

102. C. Kittel, "Interpretation of Anomalous Larmor Frequencies in Ferromagnetic Resonance Experiment," Letters to the Editor, *Phys. Rev.* **71** (February 1947), pp. 270-271.

103. W. A. Yager and R. M. Bozorth, "Ferromagnetic Resonance at Microwave Frequencies," Letters to the Editor, *Phys. Rev.* **72** (July 1, 1947), p. 80.

104. C. Kittel, W. A. Yager, and F. R. Merritt, "On the Gorter Normal Field Ferromagnetic Resonance Experiment," *Physica* **XV** (April 1949), pp. 256-257.

105. C. L. Hogan, "The Ferromagnetic Faraday Effect at Microwave Frequencies and its Applications. The Microwave Gyrator,"*Bell System Tech. J.* **31** (January 1952), pp.1-31.

106. B. D. H. Tellegen, "The Gyrator, a New Electric Network Element," *Philips Res. Reports* **3** (1948), pp. 81-101.

107. J. K. Galt, W. A. Yager, and F. R. Merritt, "Temperature Dependence of Ferromagnetic Resonance LineWidth in a Nickel Iron Ferrite: A New Loss Mechanism," Letters to the Editor, *Phys. Rev.* **93** (March 1, 1954), pp. 1119-1120; idem, "Ferromagnetic Resonance in Two Nickel-Iron Ferrites," *Phys. Rev.* **99** (August 1955), pp. 1203-1210.

108. See reference 28.

109. P. W. Anderson and H. Suhl, "Instability in the Motion of Ferromagnets at High Microwave Power Levels," Letters to the Editor, *Phys. Rev.* **100** (December 15, 1955), p. 1788.

110. A. M. Clogston, H. Suhl, L. R. Walker, and P. W. Anderson, "Possible Source of Line Width in Ferromagnetic Resonance," Letters to the Editor, *Phys. Rev.* **101** (January 15, 1956), pp. 903-905; idem, "Ferromagnetic Resonance Line Width in Insulating Materials," *J. Phys. Chem. Solids* **1** (November 1956), pp. 129-136.

111. R. C. LeCraw, E. G. Spencer, and C. S. Porter, "Ferromagnetic Resonance Line Width in Yttrium Iron Garnet Single Crystals," *Phys. Rev.* **110** (June 1958), pp. 1311-1313.

112. J. F. Dillon, Jr., "Ferrimagnetic Resonance in Yttrium Iron Garnet," Letters to the Editor, *Phys. Rev.* **105** (January 15, 1957), pp. 759-760.

113. J. F. Dillon, Jr., and J. W. Neilsen, "Effects of Rare Earth Impurities on Ferrimagnetic Resonance in Yttrium Iron Garnet," *Phys. Rev. Lett.* **3** (July 1, 1959), pp. 30-31; J. F. Dillon, Jr., "Ferrimagnetic Resonance Line Width in Rare Earth Doped Yttrium Iron Garnet," *J. Physical Society of Japan* **17, Suppl. B-I** (1962), pp. 376-379.

114. P. G. De Gennes, C. Kittel, and A. M. Portis, "Theory of Ferromagnetic Resonance in Rare Earth Garnets. II. Line Widths," *Phys. Rev.* **166** (October 1959), pp. 323-330; J. H. Van Vleck and R. Orbach, "Ferrimagnetic Resonance of Dilute Rare-Earth Doped Iron Garnets," *Phys. Rev. Lett.* **11** (July 15, 1963), pp. 65-67.

115. T. Kasuya and R. C. LeCraw, "Relaxation Mechanisms in Ferromagnetic Resonance," *Phys. Rev. Lett.* **6** (March 1, 1961), pp. 223-225.

116. H. Suhl, "Theory of Ferromagnetic Resonance at High Signal Powers," *J. Phys. Chem. Solids* **1** (April 1957), pp. 209-227.

117. H. Suhl, "Proposal for a Ferromagnetic Amplifier in the Microwave Range," Letters to the Editor, *Phys. Rev.* **106** (April 15, 1957), pp. 384-385; idem, "Origin and Use of Instabilities in Ferromagnetic Resonance," *J. Appl. Phys.* **29** (March 1958), pp. 416-421.

118. J. M. Manley and H. E. Rowe, "Some General Properties of Nonlinear Elements," *Proc. IRE* **44** (1956), p. 904.

119. M. T. Weiss, "A Solid-State Microwave Amplifier and Oscillator Using Ferrites," Letters to the Editor, *Phys. Rev.* **107** (July 1, 1957), p. 317.

120. P. K. Tien, "Parametric Amplification and Frequency Mixing in Propagating Circuits," *J. Appl. Phys.* **29** (September 1958), pp. 1347-1357.

121. M. E. Hines, "Amplification with Nonlinear Modulators," Electron Tube Research Conference 1957 (unpublished).

122. M. Uenohara and W. M. Sharpless, "An Extremely Low-Noise 6 kmc Parametric Amplifier Using Gallium Arsenide Point-Contact Diodes," *Proc. IRE* **47** (December 1959), pp. 2114-2115.

123. R. Adler and G. Hrbek, "A Low-Noise Electron-Beam Parametric Amplifier," *Proc. IRE* **46** (October 1958), pp. 1756-1757.

124. T. J. Bridges and A. Ashkin, "A Microwave Adler Tube," *Proc. IRE* **48** (March 1960), pp. 361-363.

125. P. K. Tien, "Noise in Parametric Amplifiers," *Acta Electronica* **4** (July 1960), pp. 424-446.

126. See reference 122.

127. J. F. Dillon, Jr., "Ferromagnetic Resonance in Thin Disks of Manganese Ferrite," *Bulletin of the APS,* **Series 2,1** (March 15, 1956), p. 125.

128. R. L. White, J. H. Solt, and J. E. Mercereau, "Multiple Ferromagnetic Resonance Absorption in Manganese and Manganese-Zinc Ferrite," *Bulletin of the APS,* **Series 2,1** (March 15, 1956), p. 12.

129. L. R. Walker, "Magnetostatic Modes in Ferromagnetic Resonance," *Phys. Rev.* **105** (January 1957), pp. 390-399.

130. S. Geschwind and A. M. Clogston, "Narrowing Effect of Dipole Forces on Inhomogeneously Broadened Lines," *Phys. Rev.* **108** (October 1957), pp. 49-53.

131. J. F. Dillon, Jr., and J. W. Nielsen, "Ferrimagnetic Resonance in Rare-Earth Doped Yttrium Iron Garnet. I. Field for Resonance," *Phys. Rev.* **120** (October 1960), pp. 105-113.

132. J. F. Dillon, Jr., and L. R. Walker, "Ferrimagnetic Resonance in Rare-Earth Doped Yttrium Iron Garnet. II. Terbium Substitution," *Phys. Rev.* **124** (December 1961), pp. 1401-1413.

133. V. A. Flayson, A. V. Gaponov, M. I. Petelin, and V. K. Yulpatov, "The Gyrotron," *IEEE Trans.* **MTT-25** (1977), pp. 514-521.

134. W. Shockley, "Cyclotron Resonances, Magnetoresistance, and Brillouin Zones in Semiconductors," Letters to the Editor, *Phys. Rev.* **90** (May 1, 1953), p. 491.

135. G. Dresselhaus, A. F. Kip, and C. Kittel, "Observation of Cyclotron Resonance in Germanium Crystals," Letters to the Editor, *Phys. Rev.* **92** (November 1, 1953), p. 827; idem, "Spin-Orbit Interaction and the Effective Masses of Holes in Germanium," Letters to the Editor, *Phys. Rev.* **95** (July 15, 1954), pp. 568-569.

136. B. Lax, H. J. Zeiger, R. Dexter, and E. S. Rosenblum, "Directional Properties of the Cyclotron Resonance in Germanium," Letters to the Editor, *Phys. Rev.* **93** (March 15, 1954), pp. 1418-1420; R. N. Dexter, H. J. Zeiger, and B. Lax, "Anistropy of Cyclotron Resonance of Holes in Germanium," Letters to the Editor, *Phys. Rev.* **95** (July 15, 1954), p. 557.

137. R. C. Fletcher, W. A. Yager, and F. R. Merritt, "Observation of Quantum Effects in Cyclotron Resonance," *Phys. Rev.* **100** (October 1955), pp. 747-748.

138. J. C. Hensel, T. G. Phillips, and T. M. Rice, "Evaporation of Metallic Exciton Droplets in Optically Pumped Germanium," *Phys. Rev. Lett.* **30** (February 5, 1973), pp. 227-230.

139. S. J. Allen, Jr., D. C. Tsui, and J. V. Dalton, "Far Infrared Cyclotron Resonance in the Inversion Layer of Silicon," *Phys. Rev. Lett.* **32** (January 21, 1974), pp. 107-110.

140. R. E. Slusher, C. K. N. Patel, and P. A. Fleury, "Inelastic Light Scattering from Landau-Level Electrons in Semiconductors," *Phys. Rev. Lett.* **18** (January 16, 1967), pp. 77-80.

141. J. K. Galt, W. A. Yager, F. R. Merritt, B. B. Cetlin, and H. W. Dail, Jr., "Cyclotron Resonance in Metals: Bismuth," Letters to the Editor, *Phys. Rev.* **100** (October 15, 1955), pp. 748-749.

142. P. W. Anderson, "Electromagnetic Theory of Cyclotron Resonance in Metals," Letters to the Editor, *Phys. Rev.* **100** (October 15, 1955), pp. 749-750.

143. J. K. Galt, W. A. Yager, F. R. Merritt, B. B. Cetlin, and A. D. Brailsford, "Cyclotron Absorption in Metallic Bismuth and Its Alloys," *Phys. Rev.* **114** (June 1959), pp. 1396-1413.

144. J. K. Galt, W. A. Yager, and H. W. Dail, Jr., "Cyclotron Resonance Effects in Graphite," *Phys. Rev.* **103** (September 1956), pp. 1586-1587.

145. P. Noziéres, "Cyclotron Resonance in Graphite," *Phys. Rev.* **109** (March 1958), pp. 1510-1521.

146. W. S. Boyle, A. D. Brailsford, and J. K. Galt, "Dielectric Anomalies and Cyclotron Absorption in the Infrared: Observations on Bismuth," Letters to the Editor, *Phys. Rev.* **109** (February 15, 1958), pp. 1396-1398.

147. J. C. Burgiel and L. C. Hebel, "Far-Infrared Spin and Combination Resonance in Bismuth," *Phys. Rev.* **140** (November 1965), pp. A925-A929.

148. A. A. Michelson, "Visibility of Interference-Fringes in the Focus of a Telescope," *Phil. Mag.*, **Series 5,31** (1891), pp. 256-259.

149. H. A. Gebbie and G. A. Vanasse, "Interferometric Spectroscopy in the Far Infrared," *Nature* **178** (August 25, 1956), p. 432.

150. J. Strong and G. A. Vanasse, "Interferometric Spectroscopy in the Far Infrared," *J. Opt. Soc. Am.* **49** (September 1959), pp. 844-850.

151. P. L. Richards, "Anisotropy of the Superconducting Energy Gap in Pure and Impure Tin," *Phys. Rev. Lett.* **7** (December 1, 1961), pp. 412-413; idem, "Antiferromagnetic Resonance in CoF_2, NiF_2, and $MnCO_3$, *J. Appl. Phys.* **35** (March 1964), pp. 850-851; idem, "Far-Infrared Magnetic Resonance in CoF_2, NiF_2, $KNiF_3$, and YbIG," *J. Appl. Phys.* **34** (April 1963), pp. 1237-1238.

152. S. J. Allen, Jr., R. Loudon, and P. L. Richards, "Two-Magnon Absorption in Antiferromagnetic MnF_2," *Phys. Rev. Lett.* **16** (March 14, 1966), pp. 463-466; S. J. Allen, Jr., "Spin-Lattice Interaction in UO_2. I. Ground State and Spin-Wave Excitations," *Phys. Rev.* **166** (February 1968), pp. 530-539; idem, "Spin-Lattice Interaction in UO_2. II. Theory of the First-Order Phase Transition," *Phys. Rev.* **167** (March 10, 1968), pp. 492-496.

153. J. C. Burgiel, H. Meyer, and P. L. Richards, "Far-Infrared Spectra of Gas Molecules Trapped in β-Quinol Clathrates," *J. Chem. Phys.* **43** (December 15, 1965), pp. 4291-4299; S. J. Allen, "Far-Infrared Spectra of HCl Trapped in the β-Quinol Clathrate," *J. Chem. Phys.* **44** (January 1, 1966), pp. 394-404.

154. S. J. Allen, Jr. and J. P. Remeika, "Direct Measurement of the Attempt Frequency for Ion Diffusion in Ag and Na β-Alumina," *Phys. Rev. Lett.* **33** (December 16, 1974), pp. 1478-1481.

155. P. C. Tsui, S. J. Allen, Jr., R. A. Logan, A. Kamger, and S. M. Coppersmith, "High Frequency Conductivity in Silicon Inversion Layers: Drude Relaxation, 2D Plasmons and Minigaps in a Surface Superlattice," *Surface Science* **73** (1978), pp. 419-433.

156. R. L. Mössbauer, "Kernresonanzabsorption von Gammastrahlung in Ir," *Naturweissenschaften* **45** (1958), pp. 538-539; idem, "Kernresonanzfloureszenz von Gammastrahlung in Ir," *Z. Fur Physik* **151** (1958), pp. 124-143.

157. G. K. Wertheim, *Mössbauer Effect: Principles and Applications* (New York: Academic Press, 1964).

158. L. R. Walker, G. K. Wertheim, and V. Jaccarino, "Interpretation of the Fe^{57} Isomer Shift," *Phys. Rev. Lett.* **6** (February 1, 1961), pp. 99-101.

159. R. L. Cohen, ed., *Applications of Mössbauer Spectroscopy*, Vol I (New York: Academic Press, 1976).

160. G. K. Wertheim, V. Jaccarino, J. H. Wernick, and D. N. E. Buchanan, "Range of the Exchange Interaction in Iron Alloys," *Phys. Rev. Lett.* **12** (January 6, 1964), pp. 24-27.

161. R. L. Cohen and K. W. West, "Magnetic Structure of Disordered Au-Mn Alloys," *J. Phys.* **32** (February/March 1971), pp. 781-782.

162. I. Nowik and S. Ofer, "Rare-Earth-Iron Exchange Interactions in Europium Iron Garnet," *Phys. Rev.* **153** (January 1967), pp. 409-415.

163. S. Ofer, I. Nowik, and S. G. Cohen, "The Mössbauer Effect in Rare Earths and Their Compounds," *Chemical Applications of Mössbauer Spectroscopy*, ed. V. I. Goldanskii and R. H. Herbert (New York: Academic Press, 1968), pp. 427-503.

164. M. Eibschutz, R. L. Cohen, and J. H. Wernick, "Solid State and Nuclear Results in ^{149}Sm Mössbauer Measurements," *Hyperfine Interactions in Excited Nuclei*, ed. B. Goldring and R. Kalish (New York: Gordon and Breach Science Publishers, 1971), pp. 720-722.

165. M. Eibschutz, R. L. Cohen, and K. W. West, "Mössbauer Effect of Er^{166} in Erbium Orthochromite," *Phys. Rev.* **178** (February 1969), pp. 572-575.

166. R. L. Cohen, S. Hufner, and K. W. West, "First-Order Phase Transition in Europium Metal," *Phys. Rev.* **184** (August 1969), pp. 263-270.

167. R. L. Cohen, "Mössbauer Effect in Dy^{160}," *Phys. Rev.* **137** (March 1965), pp. A1809-A1813.

168. R. L. Cohen and J. H. Wernick, "Nuclear Hyperfine Structure in Er^{166}," *Phys. Rev.* **134** (May 1964), pp. B503-B505.

169. R. L. Cohen, "Analysis of Mössbauer Hyperfine Structure in Thulium Metal Below the Néel Temperature," *Phys. Rev.* **169** (May 1968), pp. 432-436.

170. M. Eibschutz, G. Y. Chin, S. Jin, and D. Brasen "Observation of Phase Separation in a Cr-Co-Fe Alloy (Chromindur) by Mössbauer Effect," *Appl. Phys. Lett.* **33** (August 1978), pp. 362-363.

171. G. K. Wertheim and J. P. Remeika, "Nuclear Hyperfine Structure of Trivalent Fe^{57} in Corundum from the Mössbauer Effect," *Nuclear Magnetic Resonance and Relaxation in Solids*, ed. L. Van Gerven (Amsterdam: North Holland Publishing Co., 1965), pp. 146-160.

172. H. H. Wickman, "Experimental Studies of Spin Relaxation Phenomena," *Hyperfine Structure and Nuclear Radiations*, ed. B. Matthias and D. A. Shirley (Amsterdam: North-Holland Publishing Co., 1968), pp. 928-947.

173. See reference 172.

174. See reference 165.

175. M. Eibschutz and F. J. DiSalvo, "Observation of the Charge-Density Wave in lT−TaSe$_2$ by Mössbauer Resonance of an ^{57}Fe Impurity," *Phys. Rev.* **B15** (June 1977), pp. 5181-5183.

176. C. R. Kurkjian, "Mössbauer Spectroscopy in Inorganic Classes," *J. Non-Crystalline Solids* **3** (March 1970), pp. 157-194.

177. P. K. Gallagher, "Monitoring of Solid State Reactions," *Applications of Mössbauer Spectroscopy*, Vol. I, ed. R. L. Cohen (New York: Academic Press, 1976), pp. 199-239.

178. R. L. Cohen and K. W. West, "Generative and Stabilizing Processes in Tin-Palladium Sols and Palladium Sol Sensitizers," *J. Electrochem. Soc.* **120** (April 1973), pp. 502-508.

179. R. L. Cohen and R. L. Meek, "The Chemistry of Palladium-Tin Colloid Sensitizing Processes," *J. Colloid and Interface Science* **55** (April 1976), pp. 156-162.

180. R. L. Cohen, R. L. Meek, and K. W. West, "Sensitization with Palladium-Tin Colloids. I. Role of Rinse and Accelerator Steps," *Plating and Surface Finishing* **63** (May 1976), pp. 52-55.

181. R. L. Cohen and R. L. Meek, "Role of Rinsing in Palladium-Tin Colloid Sensitizing Processes. II. An Improved Processing Sequence," *Plating and Surface Finishing* **63** (June 1976), pp. 47-50.

182. R. L. Cohen, K. W. West, and M. Antler, "Search for Gold Cyanide Inclusions in Cobalt-Hardened Gold Electrodeposits," *J. Electrochem. Soc.* **124** (March 1977), pp. 342-345.

183. R. L. Cohen, F. B. Koch, L. N. Schoenberg, and K. W. West, "Characterization of Cobalt-Hardened Gold Electrodeposits by Mössbauer Spectroscopy," *J. Electrochem. Soc.* **126** (September 1979), pp. 608-615.

Chapter 2

Semiconductor Physics and Electronics— The Transistor

Semiconductor physics research has played a unique role at Bell Laboratories. It not only gave rise to the invention of the transistor, thereby revolutionizing the electronics industry, but it also stimulated advances in the techniques of preparing materials in single-crystal form of unprecedented purity. This made possible the preparation of a variety of materials of known chemical composition and structure, leading to research experiments with unambiguous interpretation and furthering the science of solid-state physics.

This chapter describes not only research on the physics of semiconductors involved in devices, for example, p-n junctions, transistors, photovoltaic cells, and light emitting diodes—but also research that has deepened the understanding of semiconductor physics, such as band structure, pressure effects and multivalley bands, the phonon drag, and electron-hole liquids. Other aspects of semiconductors are discussed elsewhere in this volume— semiconductor surfaces in Chapter 3, heterostructure lasers in Chapter 5, ion channeling and ion implantation in Chapter 8, semiconductor materials in Chapter 11, and crystal growth and impurity doping in Chapter 19.

In view of the historic importance of the invention of the transistor and the related Nobel Prize awarded to J. Bardeen, W. H. Brattain, and W. Shockley on December 10, 1956, for their research on semiconductors and their discovery of the transistor effect, this chapter contains a reproduction of a contemporary story of the "Genesis of the Transistor," and some personal reminiscences recorded by Brattain in 1975 expressly for this history.

Principal authors: J. K. Galt, T. H. Geballe, J. C. Hensel, and E. O. Kane

I. SEMICONDUCTOR RESEARCH UP TO 1948 – THE POINT CONTACT TRANSISTOR

In the mid-1940s the understanding of the physics of the rectifying properties of germanium and silicon, the principal semiconductors used as detectors in radar during World War II, was in a rudimentary state. Prior to this time, technological development proceeded mostly by the method of "cut and try." In 1945, scientists at Bell Laboratories realized that if semiconductor technology relevant to communications was to advance rapidly, a deeper understanding of the physical principles underlying semiconductors and their properties was imperative. It was also realized that little progress would be possible unless single-crystal specimens of high purity could be produced and the addition of very small amounts of specific impurities could be properly controlled. Multiple efforts were launched in the areas of physical research (experimental and theoretical investigations of semiconductors) and in metallurgy (the crystal growth and purification problem), and it was decided to concentrate on the Group IV semiconductors silicon and germanium (see Chapters 11 and 19 in this volume).

At the same time the theoretical picture of semiconductivity was coming into better focus. The understanding of semiconductor properties is based on the Bloch functions[1] and on A. H. Wilson's theory of energy bands, which introduced the idea of filled (valence) bands and empty (conduction) bands separated by a forbidden gap.[2] The rapid development of understanding in this period is beautifully summarized in the classic paper of G. L. Pearson and J. Bardeen, which concentrated mainly on the valence-band semiconductors, silicon and germanium.[3] The valence band in these materials is associated with electrons in covalent bonds. The four bonds are just enough to hold the four valence electrons per atom in a crystal structure, where each atom is surrounded by four nearest neighbors. It was also known that impurities with valence 5 (such as arsenic) could be incorporated in the crystal lattice substitutionally. The extra valence electron would go into the conduction band, giving rise to conductivity by electrons (n-type conduction). Similarly, trivalent impurities like boron could also be inserted in the lattice substitutionally. This would lead to conductivity by holes (p-type conduction) because one electron per boron atom is missing from the valence band. The hydrogenic effective-mass theory for these impurities was formulated, which yielded binding energies of the order of 0.01 electronvolts (eV) when scaled down from the binding energy of the electron of a free neutral hydrogen atom in the ground state by the large dielectric constants (12 to 16) and small effective masses (0.1 m_0, where m_0 is the free electron mass) characteristic of these materials.[4] The mobility of the carriers was measured and found to be large com-

Fig. 2-1. W. Shockley (seated), J. Bardeen (left), and W. H. Brattain (right), shown in an historic photograph taken in 1948.

pared to ionic conductors. The effects of lattice scattering and impurity scattering of the carriers were also studied at this time. Impurity scattering was found to be Rutherford scattering from charged impurities strongly reduced by screening due to the free carriers and the large dielectric constant. Lattice scattering was mainly caused by acoustic phonons as demonstrated by the $T^{3/2}$ temperature dependence of carrier mobility in pure samples.

The theory of lattice scattering was greatly advanced by the work of Bardeen and W. Shockley.[5] [Fig. 2-1] Their study showed that the scattering was related to the shift of the energy bands under uniform stress. This deformation-potential method made possible an empirical correlation of the mobility with measurements of band-edge shift caused by uniaxial stress. Phonon scattering causes a modulation of the electron density, which matches the phonon wavelength and has maxima in the troughs and minima at the peaks.

Experimental progress during the late 1940s did not lag. Initially it was deemed vital to pursue investigations into the physical properties of the semiconductor surfaces as well as the bulk, since the failure to differentiate carefully between bulk and surface effects had caused some considerable confusion in the past. Bardeen and W. H. Brattain initiated an extensive investigation of the properties of germanium surfaces—surface states, surface traps, and the nature of contacts. The major achievement of their study was the discovery of the phenomenon of current injection of minority carriers by a forward-biased point contact. This principle led to the development of the point contact transistor, the first working transistor.[6,7]

II. THE JUNCTION TRANSISTOR AND OTHER SEMICONDUCTOR AMPLIFIERS

Soon after the discovery of the point-contact transistor, Shockley developed a theory for the p-n junction in semiconductors and the junction transistor.[8] Because of the planar geometry of the p-n junction theoretical calculations and predictions of electrical characteristics were very much simplified. Two years later, Shockley, M. Sparks, and G. K. Teal verified experimentally Shockley's theoretical predictions and produced the first junction-transistor amplifier.[9] This formed the scientific basis for all the transistor technology that was to follow and the subsequent proliferation of integrated circuits in the electronics industry.

2.1 The p-n Junction

If one region of a semiconductor crystal such as germanium is doped with a trivalent impurity—for example, boron (resulting in p-type conductivity)—and the adjoining region is doped with a pentavalent impurity—for example, phosphorus (resulting in n-type conductivity)—a p-n junction is formed at the interface between the two regions. [Fig. 2-2] Such a junction acts as a rectifier. When no external potential is applied, some holes in the *p* region diffuse across the junction into the *n* region, and similarly, some electrons in the *n* region diffuse into the *p* region until a potential barrier is built, stopping the charge flow. When an external voltage is applied across the crystal with the *p* side made positive with respect to the *n* side (forward bias), the potential barrier is reduced. As a result, more electrons flow from the *n* region to the *p* region and also more holes flow in the opposite direction. When the *p* side is made negative with respect to the *n* side (reverse bias), only a very small current flows. This is caused by the small density of minority carriers (electrons in the *p* region and holes in the *n* region) normally present.

2.2 p-n Junction Transistors

A junction transistor is formed by putting two p-n junctions together back-to-back, giving rise to either a p-n-p or an n-p-n

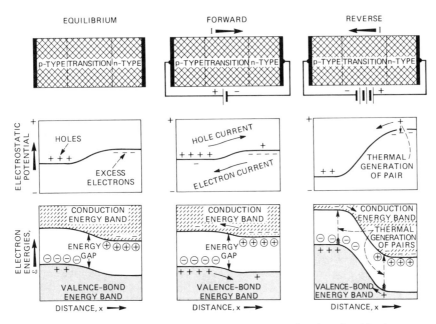

Fig. 2-2. Distribution of holes and electrons, and energy as a function of position in a p-n junction under applied biases. [Shockley, *Electrons and Holes in Semiconductors* (1950): 88].

transistor. Focusing on the n-p-n transistor, and following the nomenclature used by Shockley, Sparks, and Teal, one of the *n* regions is called an emitter, the *p* region is called the base, and the other *n* region is called the collector.[10] The emitter-base junction is forward-biased while the base-collector junction is reverse-biased. With this arrangement, electrons in the emitter region easily climb the small potential hill into the base region. Once in this region the electrons may diffuse so that some arrive at the base-collector junction. If the base layer is made very thin, very few of the electrons will combine with the holes in this *p* region and efficient transmission of electron current through the layer will occur. The current transmitted from the emitter through the base to the collector can be varied by applying a variable potential between the emitter and the base. Moreover, if the emitter region is made more highly conducting than the base region, most of the current across the emitter-base junction will consist of electrons. The behavior of this device is analogous to that of a vacuum-tube triode, with the emitter corresponding to the cathode, the base corresponding to the region around the grid wires, and the collector corresponding to the plate. Small ac voltage variations across the emitter-base junction results in a much larger voltage variation across a resistive load inserted in the circuit supplying the potential between the base and collector, thereby giving rise to large power gain.

The operation of a p-n-p junction transistor is very similar to that of the n-p-n transistor. In the p-n-p transistor the *n* region is the base and the *p* regions are the emitter and collector, respectively. Most of the current across the p-n and n-p junctions is carried by holes instead of electrons.

Shockley, Sparks, and Teal also discussed more complicated forms of junction transistors. One form, involving three junctions, is the p-n-p-n transistor called the hook-collector transistor. In this transistor the single n-type collector is replaced by a p-n junction, and holes injected by the p-n junction (biased forward) provoke enhanced electron flow, yielding current gain. A second type of transistor is the photo-transistor, which is constructed in the same way as the hook-collector transistor. The photo-transistor has four elements separated by three junctions, but the hole injection by the emitter junction is replaced by hole-electron pair generation produced by light shining in the surface of the *p* region. Electrical connections are made only to the two *n* regions.

2.3 Field Effect Transistors

An interesting example of the use of p-n junctions is in the junction field effect transistor (JFET) proposed by Shockley in 1952[11] and subsequently demonstrated by G. C. Dacey and I. M. Ross.[12,13] [Fig. 2-3] The initial objective of semiconductor research was to develop a solid-state amplifier based on the principle of field effect. Early attempts showed only a small effect caused by the unavoidable influence of the surface states as elucidated by Bardeen. Shockley correctly predicted that the p-n junction, when used as a gate of a field-effect transistor, would be free of surface state problems since the p-n junction gate can be located away from the surface.

The surface-state problems, however, were eventually resolved by an unexpected discovery. In 1959, D. Kahng and M. M. Atalla found that silicon and clean, thermally-grown SiO_2 interfaces contain a sufficiently small amount of surface states so that a true field-effect transistor can be built on this unique material system. The field-effect device they described also made use of p-n junctions, as well as surface inversion layers studied and characterized by W. L. Brown[14] and included in a device proposed by Ross.[15]

The inversion layer in the Kahng-Atalla device is a unique many-electron system. It is bound on one side by the SiO_2 with a potential barrier of 3.2 eV, and on the other side by the band bending in silicon, which is controlled by the voltage applied to the metal gate of the device. The bound states associated with the electron motion normal to the surface (their wave functions spread several tens of

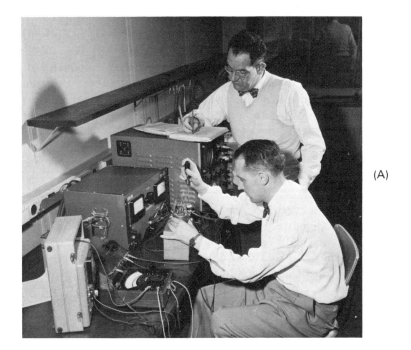

(A)

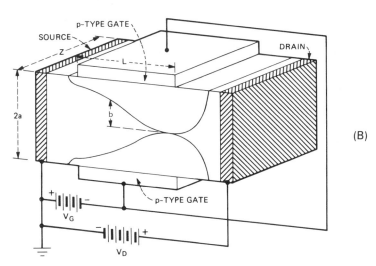

(B)

Fig. 2-3. (A) I. M. Ross (seated) and G. C. Dacey measuring the characteristics of a field-effect transistor. Ross later became executive vice president, and then president of Bell Laboratories. (B) Schematic of a field-effect transistor, the operation of which is described in Chapter 7. The space-charge layers that modulate the conductance of the n-type germanium are indicated by the shaded volumes extending into the crystal from the two p-type gates. [*Proc. IRE* **41** (1953): 970].

angstroms and their energy levels separate by several tens of mil-
lielectronvolts) were characterized in great detail by a combination of
magneto-transport, electron tunneling, and far infrared absorption
and emission experiments.[16] The two-dimensional character of the
inversion layer was also verified directly. Its cyclotron energy
depends only on the magnetic field perpendicular to the surface and
its plasmon energy goes to zero at long wavelengths.[17] The influence
of screening by the metal gate on the two-dimensional plasmon
dispersion was also confirmed. The inversion layer constitutes a
degenerate, two-dimensional, one-component plasma, whose density
can be varied continuously to about $2 \times 10^{13}/cm^2$ by varying the gate
voltage on the device. It behaves as a simple two-dimensional metal
in the high density ($\geq 10^{12}/cm^2$) limit, and goes into a nonmetallic
state at lower densities. The metal-to-nonmetal transition occurs at
approximately $5 \times 10^{11}/cm^2$, depending on the condition of the
$Si-SiO_2$ interface.[18] From measurement at low temperatures down to
0.05K, using silicon metal-oxide semiconductor field-effect transistors,
it was shown that there is no true metal-nonmetal transition in two
dimensions, but rather a continuous transition from exponential to
logarithmic localization.[19]

The Kahng-Atalla field-effect device, which became known as the
MOSFET (metal-oxide semiconductor field-effect transistor), was the
basic building block of metal-oxide semiconductor (MOS) integrated
circuits. The MOSFET represents fruition of the original objective of
the semiconductor research initiated at Bell Labs in 1946. (See "The
Genesis of the Transistor.")

2.4 The Read Diode

After the successful realization of a solid state triode, the transistor,
a search was launched for negative resistance in a solid state diode
structure as a potential source of high-frequency oscillation. Such a
negative resistance had been known to exist in a vacuum-tube diode
structure for some time, arising from carrier transit delays. Shockley
had proposed two possible mechanisms through which negative resistance effects could be obtained in three-layer structures.[20] However, it
was thought that oscillation of much higher frequency would be possible with a diode than with a triode, since the triode-based oscillators proved to be rather inefficient at higher frequencies.

It was first pointed out by W. T. Read that avalanche multiplication
has a desirable dynamic property as a cathode because the emitted
carrier current lags the applied field by 90 degrees.[21] Because of this
initial phase lag, any further phase lag due to carrier transit delay
immediately delivers forward oscillation energy. The diode oscillator
with a tailored drift region based on this principle has become
known as the Read Diode and has evolved into a practical and
efficient microwave source.

The first observation of significant microwave oscillation was made by R. L. Johnston, B. C. DeLoach, Jr., and B. G. Cohen in a silicon diode with quasiuniform doping, somewhat different from the original Read structure and mounted in a microwave cavity.[22] The Read structure was also shown to oscillate in a similar cavity by C. A. Lee and coworkers.[23] Read's proposal stimulated many careful fundamental investigations into the avalanche multiplication process. Another study by Lee and collaborators served not only the later development of practical microwave sources but also aided the development of avalanche radiation detectors.[24]

2.5 Acoustic-Wave Amplifiers

In 1960, while exploring possible means to amplify microwave signals, P. K. Tien proposed an acoustic-wave amplifier that was made of a semiconductor film that carries a current and a piezoelectric slab in which an acoustic wave propagates.[25] The thin semiconductor film is in close proximity with the piezoelectric slab. The piezoelectric fields generated by the acoustic wave in the slab are capable of interacting with the electrons in the film, thereby extracting kinetic energy from the electrons. This results in the amplification of the acoustic wave. Therefore, the amplifier is a solid-state version of the traveling wave tube, with the acoustic wave replacing the electromagnetic wave, which is normally carried by a slow wave circuit such as a helix. Shortly after Tien's study, another form of the acoustic wave amplifier, consisting of a single block of the piezoelectric semiconductor, was proposed by D. L. White.[26] The first acoustic wave amplifier was constructed and demonstrated by A. R. Hutson, J. H. McFee, and White in 1961.[27] Both types of amplifiers have been studied for application to real-time wideband signal processing, active delay lines, and radio-frequency amplification in television receivers.

Stimulated by these inventions, a large amount of research has been devoted to the acoustoelectric effect and the formation of high-field domains caused by that effect. In 1968, comprehensive, nonlinear calculation was carried out by Tien that provided all necessary data for the design of these devices.[28]

III. THE BELL SOLAR PHOTOVOLTAIC CELL

The invention of the silicon solar cell followed C. S. Fuller's pioneering study of impurity diffusion and p-n junction formation in germanium.[29] Pearson and P. W. Foy had previously made small-area junction rectifiers in silicon by alloying an aluminum wire with n-type silicon.[30] This junction demonstrated the advantages of silicon over germanium. Since silicon has a larger energy gap between the conduction band and valence band, it has a higher rectification ratio and can operate at much higher temperatures than germanium. By diffusing boron into n-type silicon, Pearson and Fuller succeeded in making large-area silicon rectifiers, and by making the junctions close to the surface, they achieved an efficiency of 6 percent.[31] (For a more detailed discussion of the silicon solar cell and other solar cells see section VII of Chapter 11.)

This work was followed by an analysis of the solar cell by M. B. Prince.[32] He showed that the expected efficiency of an ideal cell depended on the energy gap of the semiconductor. The energy gap of silicon was nearly optimum and an ideal efficiency of about 23 percent was expected. By the late 1970s, silicon solar-cell efficiency had been increased to 17 percent.[33]

The first application of the silicon solar cell was as a power source for a repeater of the Bell System Type P rural carrier. The test, conducted in 1957 in Americus, Georgia, lasted for six months.[34] An array of cells, delivering 9 watts in bright sunlight, charged a nickel-cadmium storage battery to provide continuous operation. The solar cell was also used in the 1960s as a power source in the Telstar satellites. Solar cells are now used extensively on all satellites for electric power generation. (See Chapter 7, section 2.1.)

IV. TRANSPORT PROPERTIES

Extensive studies on the transport properties of semiconductors were initiated by many researchers soon after the discovery of the transistor. Conductivity and Hall effect measurements were made on germanium and silicon single crystals in both the intrinsic (carriers thermally activated across the band gap) and the extrinsic (carriers thermally activated from shallow impurity states) regimes. When studies were carried out as a function of temperature, the carrier concentration, and in turn, the appropriate activation energies, as well as the carrier mobilities and lifetimes, were obtained. A classic example of this approach was the Haynes-Shockley drift experiment.[35] A "sweeping field" was set up in a rod of germanium by a direct current flowing from end to end. An emitter contact that injects a pulse of minority carriers was attached at some point along the length of the rod. Detection of the drifting carrier pulse downstream by a suitable collector contact gave the time of flight and, hence, the minority carrier mobility.

Transport experiments in selectively doped crystals of germanium and silicon provided the first knowledge about the nature of the shallow states introduced in the energy gap by the trivalent and pentavalent substitutional impurities. F. J. Morin and coworkers measured thermal activation energies and located the energy position in the band gap of the impurity ground states.[36] H. J. Hrostowski and R. H. Kaiser confirmed these "thermal" energies by measurements (in the infrared) of optical transitions from impurity ground states to excited states.[37]

4.1 Phonon Drag and Thermal Transport

After the discovery of the transistor, the availability of large single crystals of germanium and silicon, obtained by pulling from the melt and zone refining, created the opportunity to study transport phenomena in specimens with well-defined geometry and controlled chemical composition. (See also sections I and II of Chapter 19.) At that time, it was well known that an electric current could perturb thermal energy distribution among lattice modes. It was also known that thermoelectric power or, more correctly, the Seebeck voltage, Q, results from the tendency of the mobile charge carriers to diffuse from hot to cold when a thermal gradient exists in the lattice. The lattice remains in local equilibrium, and the diffusion continues until balanced by the buildup of an electric field of just sufficient magnitude to counteract the diffusion.

It was discovered experimentally by T. H. Geballe at Bell Laboratories and by H. P. R. Frederikse at Purdue University that there was a spectacular rise in Q of germanium and silicon at low temperatures.[38] This was almost immediately interpreted in terms of the drag exerted on the charge carriers by the asymmetric distribution phonons that travel from hot to cold in the thermal gradient.[39] This possibility was first considered by L. Gurevich and has become known as the phonon-drag effect.[40]

C. Herring simplified the problem by transforming it to a problem by means of the Kelvin relation, $Q = \pi/T$, where π is the Peltier heat flux transported per electron in isothermal current flow, and T is the absolute temperature.[41] He obtained quantitative expressions for phonon-phonon and phonon-electron scattering times. The importance of anisotropy in the velocity of sound in removing divergencies to which energy and momentum conservation lead in an isotropic model was recognized. Those phonons of interest that drag the electrons have wavelengths as much as an order of magnitude longer than the thermal-energy phonons that carry the bulk of the heat in thermal conductivity experiments. Herring further established that it is meaningful to define a relaxation time for phonon-drag, long-wavelength, low-energy phonons because they chiefly interact with the bath of thermal energy phonons and relax back to equilibrium independently of the occupation of the low energy modes.

Early studies of the phonon-electron scattering times in doped n-type germanium and p-type silicon were undertaken by W. P. Mason and T. P. Bateman.[42] They used ultrasonic techniques at 500 megahertz (MHz) and obtained values for the intervalley scattering time. The phonon-drag phonons typically have frequencies in the range of 10^{11} hertz (Hz), higher than can be generated by microwave techniques, and lower than can be studied by conventional thermal experiments. Thus, the phonon-drag experiments opened up a new region of the vibrational spectrum for study. Geballe and G. W. Hull used single crystals cut into the shapes of tuning forks with tines of different cross-sectional areas to measure the phonon-drag contribution to Q. It was possible to establish almost identical thermal gradients in each of the tines of the tuning fork by a simple null method. The relaxation times of the phonons traveling down the parallel paths differed because boundary scattering in the one with the smaller cross-sectional area occurred more frequently. It was also possible to measure the effect of sample dimensions on thermal conduction all the way up to 100K (a sensitivity that to date has not been exceeded) due to the very large relaxation times of the phonon-drag phonons.

The application of a magnetic field in different orientations with respect to the crystal axes and to the thermal gradient led to the measurement of a number of magneto-thermoelectric longitudinal and transverse effects. The study of these effects facilitated sorting the contributions of phonon drag and electron diffusion, and clarified the role of different types of scattering that affect phonon drag.[43]

Unfortunately, for the possible applications of phonon-drag phenomena to devices such as thermoelectric generators, a saturation effect was found for concentrations of carriers greater than 10^{16} to 10^{17} per cubic centimeter.[44] This is due to the fact that there is only a finite amount of nonequilibrium momentum in the phonon system to be fed into the electronic system so that the amount per carrier becomes less with increasing carrier concentration.

Another cause of phonon scattering resulting from fluctuations in mass caused by the random distribution of isotopes in naturally occurring elemental germanium was suspected following the ideas of Pomeranchuk[45] and Slack.[46] This was verified by experiments in the sensitive temperature region near 20K.[47] [Fig. 2-4] A small amount of enriched Ge[74] obtained from the Oak Ridge National Laboratory was purified to semiconductor purity by H. C. Theuerer and pulled into a single crystal by P. Freeland. Its thermal conductivity became, at the maximum, three times greater than that of the crystals of highest purity grown from natural germanium. The anticipated, even greater, increase was found to be suppressed by the strong dispersion discovered about the same time in the transverse acoustic spectrum of germanium.

Many of the questions raised by the pioneering experiments of Geballe are being answered by high-frequency phonon techniques that have moved up to frequencies of 7×10^{11} Hz. These techniques involve the use of thin, superconducting, tunnel-junction transducers that act as generators and detectors of gap-frequency phonons.[48] The different acoustic branches can also be distinguished when these techniques are combined with time-of-flight techniques. The first reso-

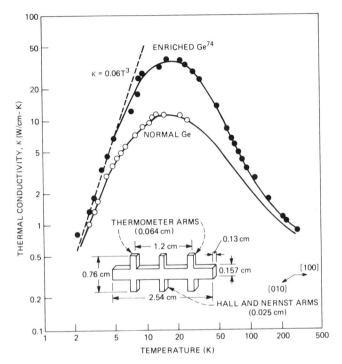

Fig. 2-4. Isotope effect on thermal conduction in germanium. [Geballe and Hull, *Phys. Rev.* **110** (1958): 774].

nance spectroscopy experiments using these techniques were performed by R. C. Dynes, V. Narayanamurti, and M. Chin on antimony donors in germanium.[49] These techniques have also been applied by Narayanamurti, R. A. Logan, and Chin to study electron phonon coupling in epitaxial layers of GaAs.[50] These measurements have shown directly the disequilibrium between the long wavelength phonons (which couple to the electrons) and the thermal reservoir, and are related to many of the early concepts of Herring. The polarization dependence of the isotope scattering in germanium has been vividly demonstrated using ballistic phonon techniques by J. C. Hensel and Dynes.[51]

V. SEMICONDUCTOR SPECTROSCOPY

5.1 Band Structure in Semiconductors

Band structure is fundamental to all semiconductor physics. The first goal in understanding band structure of germanium and silicon—delineation of the conduction and valence band edges—seemed relatively modest at the beginning, but turned out to require a surprising degree of sophistication to achieve. The experimental breakthrough came with the cyclotron resonance technique, following its proposal by Shockley in the early 1950s.[52] With the announcement of cyclotron resonance experiments in 1953 (carried out by scientists at the University of California at Berkeley and at the Lincoln Laboratory of MIT[53]), the quantitative understanding of semiconductor physics advanced by an enormous step. It was found that electrons were in multivalley energy bands with highly anisotropic effective masses. In addition, the hole was found to play as important a role as the electron in conductivity. Never before had the hole's existence been demonstrated so graphically as it was by its own identifiable lines in the cyclotron resonance spectrum. Holes were found in a pair of degenerate bands, one having a light effective mass and the other a heavy effective mass. These novel effective masses were then shown to be responsible for a number of interesting transport effects. As part of a study of band structure at Bell Labs, C. S. Smith measured the piezoresistance coefficients of germanium and silicon, and found them to be very large in certain crystal directions.[54] Mason pointed out the potential usefulness of those semiconductors as strain gauges.[55] W. G. Pfann and R. N. Thurston conceived a variety of strain gauges that, unlike conventional metal strain gauges, utilized the sensitivity of these semiconductors to transverse and shear strains.[56]

The theoretical techniques for handling these rather exotic holes and electrons were developed in large part by J. M. Luttinger and W. Kohn, working at Bell Labs in the summer of 1954, and appeared in their paper in 1955.[57] The simple "hydrogenic" theory of impurity states was then extended to the more realistic situation, giving quantitative confirmation between theory and experiment. Small discrepancies were identified with "central cell" corrections.

Perhaps the most advanced application of this Kohn-Luttinger effective mass formalism is their theory of the "free" (band) carrier moving in the presence of an external magnetic field. The theory predicts the result that cyclotron resonance (and, indeed, all magneto-optical phenomena) involving holes would exhibit "quantum" anomalies at very low temperatures. Observation of these quantum spectra by R. C. Fletcher, W. A. Yager, and F. R. Merritt,[58] and by Hensel and K. Suzuki[59] provided a very rigorous test of the effective mass approach, a cornerstone of semiconductor physics.

The unpaired electron of the donor state is paramagnetic, making it a natural candidate for spin resonance experiments. A series of spin resonance experiments conducted in silicon by Fletcher and coworkers,[60] and by G. Feher,[61] provided further information about the donor state, and demonstrated the onset of delocalization of donor electrons with increasing impurity concentration. This work provided a catalyst to P. W. Anderson's thinking on disordered systems, which was part of the work for which he was awarded the Nobel Prize in physics in 1977. A high point of the resonance experiments was Feher's invention of the ENDOR (Electron-Nuclear Double Resonance) technique, which made it possible to map out the donor wave function by resolving the electron's hyperfine interactions with the Si^{29} nuclei that were randomly located on silicon lattice sites with an abundance of about 5 percent.

In the late 1950s, one of the landmark experiments in semiconductor spectroscopy was J. R. Haynes' discovery of the recombination luminescence from free excitons and from excitons bound to impurity states in silicon and germanium.[62] These experiments not only provided valuable information about germanium and silicon (for example, the identification of the momentum-conserving phonons in these "indirect" transitions fixed the zone boundary phonon energies) but also paved the way for the explosive growth of luminescence spectroscopy that was soon to follow. In his last paper, Haynes reported an intriguing luminescence from strongly pumped silicon at liquid helium temperatures, which he attributed to recombination of free biexcitons.[63] Subsequently, it became known that, in reality, he observed the electron hole liquid (see section 5.6 in this chapter).

5.1.1 Optical Studies and Band Structure

The important role of optical studies in clarifying the quantitative understanding of electronic band structure was first recognized by J. C. Phillips.[64] Structure in the fundamental reflectivity was seen to be caused by optical energy extrema (optical critical points, where the curve of optical energy versus momentum has zero slope) which generally occur at high symmetry points in k-space (crystal momentum space). Parallel with this development, Phillips also applied the pseudopotential concept to energy band studies, and obtained the striking result that the silicon and germanium band structures could be very accurately described in terms of only three Fourier coefficients of the pseudopotential. Optical critical point energies were then used to provide a purely empirical determination of energy band structure that is still remarkable for its accuracy and broad applicability. In the early 1970s the investigation of optical critical points was greatly advanced by the electroreflectance studies of D. E. Aspnes.[65]

Another valuable concept introduced by Phillips is the dielectric definition of ionicity.[66] [Fig. 2-5] It is based on the dielectric properties of simple compounds with eight valence electrons per formula unit (for example, zincblende materials and rock salt compounds). From the dielectric ionicity, it is possible to predict very accurately which compounds form in the rock salt and which form in the zinc-

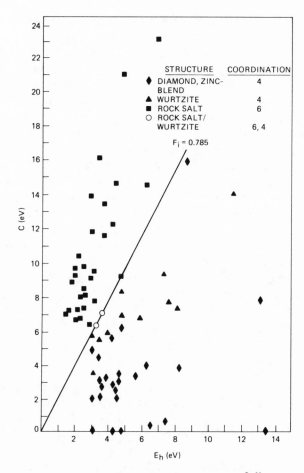

Fig. 2-5. Binary compounds with formula $A^n B^{8-N}$ (where N = valence) are separated into two distinct groups when their ionic energy gap, C, is plotted against their homopolar energy gap, E_n. The group below the line crystallizes with fourfold coordinated structures; those above the line crystallize with sixfold or eightfold coordinated structures. The compounds MgS, MgSe, and MgTe fall on the line and are found in both structures. The partial ionic character, F_i [$= C/(C+E_h)^{1/2}$], has the value 0.785 for the line. The compounds falling below the line have F_i values below 0.785; those falling above the line have F_i values greater than 0.785.

blende structure. Materials on the borderline transform from zinc-blende to rock salt under pressure. Many other fundamental properties of electrons and phonons are found to correlate well with the ionicity.

5.1.2 *Effect of Pressure on the Conduction Band of a Multivalley Semiconductor*

The large effort in semiconductor physics research led naturally to pressure experiments. It was found that the energies of the different minima in the conduction band in a multivalley semiconductor varied at different rates with increasing pressure.[67] One experiment that stands out is the unambiguous determination of the mechanism of the Gunn effect by A. R. Hutson and coworkers.[68] When a dc potential is applied to a short sample of n-type GaAs, the current-voltage curve follows Ohm's law at low voltages. With increasing voltage, oscillations occur sharply at a certain threshold voltage. This phenomenon, which has device applications in solid-state microwave generators, was first observed by J. B. Gunn at IBM.[69] The high-pressure experiment at Bell Labs showed that the threshold for the effect decreases as the interband separation decreases with increasing pressure, and that the effect disappears when half of the electrons have been transferred to the lower mobility band, as predicted by the proposed electron transfer mechanism for the Gunn effect.

5.2 Pair Spectra

Rapid advances in optical techniques were largely responsible for opening new frontiers of semiconductor research in the 1960s. This avenue turned out to be particularly well suited for investigations of compound semiconductors in which interest was widening rapidly. In the early stages traditional tools were employed, such as luminescence, reflectance, and absorption. Later, differential methods came into vogue—for example, electroreflectance, piezoelectroreflectance, and wavelength modulation. Uniaxial stress was another new spectroscopic technique pioneered at Bell Labs that contributed greatly to the spectroscopy of semiconductors.

The optical research effort was spearheaded by the research of D. G. Thomas and J. J. Hopfield [Fig. 2-6] on the II-VI compound CdS, a well-known but hitherto poorly understood luminescent material.[70] They clarified the role played by excitons, both bound and free, through the introduction of the concept of the polariton, a mixed photon-exciton mode, analogous to the photon-phonon excitation characteristic of infrared-active vibrations. Later, they turned their attention to the III-V compound GaP, technologically important for its luminescence in the visible part of the electromagnetic spectrum. As a result of this effort many of the long-standing mysteries of luminescence phenomena in solids were cleared away. Thomas and Hopfield set out with the objective of understanding the radiative and nonradiative recombination processes and their relation to the chemistry of impurities in GaP crystals. Studies of the photolumines-

Fig. 2-6. J. J. Hopfield (left) and D. G. Thomas conducted theoretical and experimental studies of impurities in III-V compounds, leading to the development of efficient light-emitting semiconductor diodes.

cent spectroscopy of nominally pure GaP at low temperatures revealed an amazingly complicated spectrum with about 100 sharp lines in the green part of the visible spectrum near the bandgap. The presence of many lines in such a simple system led to a theoretical analysis in 1962 by Hopfield, Thomas, and M. Gershenzon.[71] The crystals, although pure by the standards of the time, contained residual donors and acceptors that trapped negative and positive charges, respectively, at low temperatures.

An analysis of the behavior of donor-acceptor pairs irradiated with ultraviolet light led to a satisfactory explanation of the complicated spectra, not only in terms of the number and location of the lines, but also of their intensities. [Fig. 2-7] In terms of the interactions of the charged entities involved—electrons, holes, donors, and acceptors— isoelectronic impurities (for instance, nitrogen substituting for phosphorus in GaP) were found to introduce trapping states important in producing fluorescence.[72] Two major mechanisms curtailing luminescence were also discovered. Studies by D. F. Nelson and coworkers displayed curtailed luminescence caused by nonradiative Auger recombination on certain traps.[73] Nonradiative multiphonon capture of electrons on levels strongly coupled to the crystal lattice was another luminescence-curtailing mechanism discovered by C. H. Henry.[74]

Through studies of pair spectra, the ionization energies of virtually all the substitutional donors and acceptors in GaP have been accurately determined. Pair spectra have also been used as an analytical

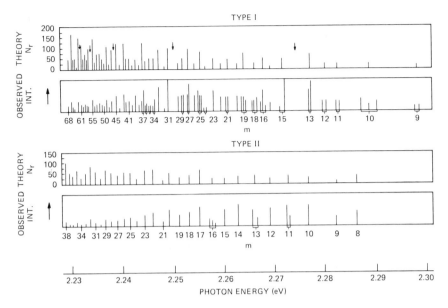

Fig. 2-7. Donor-acceptor pair spectra in GaP. Light is emitted in fluorescence as many sharp lines of different energies. The emission of light arises from the recombination of electrons and holes trapped on distant donor-acceptor pairs. The discrete energies of emission result from the discrete distances of separation of the donor-acceptor pairs as they lie on the lattice sites of the crystal, because a Coulomb energy term with an r^{-1} dependence is added to the fixed atomic energy levels. Two patterns of lines have been found. Type I corresponds to a donor atom and an acceptor atom on the same type of lattice site—both on gallium or both on phosphorus sites. Type II corresponds to a donor on one type of lattice site and an acceptor on the other. The intensity of the lines is related to the number of pairs at a particular separation distance. Experiment compares well with theory for both types of spectra. [Hopfield, Thomas, and Gerschenzon, *Phys. Rev. Lett.* **10** (1963): 163].

tool to identify unknown donors and acceptors not intentionally introduced. In the pure material mentioned earlier, the sharp line spectra arose from acceptor-donor pairs composed of carbon and sulphur. This simple, yet elegant, explanation of these very complicated spectra represented a major advance toward understanding radiative recombination in semiconductors and was very important to the development of efficient electroluminescent diodes.

5.3 Light Emitting Diodes

In the late 1950s, attention was focused on the compound gallium phosphide, which has an energy gap of about 2.3 eV. The energy gap is the energy separating the conduction band from the valence band. When an electron drops from the conduction band to an empty state, or hole, in the valence band, the recombination process can result in *electroluminescence*. With an energy gap of 2.3 eV, this semiconductor can potentially generate light in the wavelength range corresponding to the red and green part of the visible spectrum, where the red and green photon energies are 1.8 eV and 2.4 eV, respectively. From the late 1950s to the late 1960s, scientists investigated this material and demonstrated the feasibility of the light emitting diode (LED) device technology. Significant advances were made, especially in the fields of controlled addition of chemical impurities to the crystal and in the physics of radiative recombination. It was demonstrated that the radiative mechanism responsible for efficient light generation was associated with isoelectronic impurities. [Fig. 2-8] (For more on this topic, see section 5.2 of this chapter.) The impurities trap excitons and provide the momentum required for radiative recombination. In addition, p-n junctions were made that demonstrated the generation of both red and green light at commercially attractive levels.

In the late 1960s the work on LEDs gradually moved into the device technology area, where a mass-production technology was developed using large-area crystal substrates grown by a high-pressure liquid encapsulation Czochralski method. Efficient junctions were formed by a newly developed high-capacity liquid-phase epitaxial process, representing the first commercial application of this technique. This led to the production of red as well as green indicators, illuminators, numeric displays, and optically coupled isolators using GaP as well as ternary compounds by Western Electric and many other manufacturers. These devices find wide application in the Bell System as reliable, low-power lamps and numeric displays for telephones, consoles, test panels, and station apparatus, and as efficient low-noise couplers and isolators in various transmission and switching systems.

5.4 Thin Layers

The 1960s was an era distinguished by increased optical sophistication and consolidation. A completion of the picture of semiconductors seemed almost attainable. Still, the quest for new horizons continued into the 1970s. A. Y. Cho succeeded, by using molecular beam epitaxy, in growing lattices with a controlled periodicity by alternating layers of GaAs and GaAlAs. R. Dingle, W. Wiegmann, and Henry grew multilayered films in which they observed quantum states of confined electrons.[75] Electrons (or holes, as the case may be) are found to be confined to a layer and behave as a two-dimensional electron gas, the lowering of dimensionality giving rise to a variety of interesting phenomena. Another example of an analogous two-dimensional system is the electrons confined to a surface inversion layer of silicon in a MOSFET device, as discussed earlier in this section. This problem has undergone extensive study by D. C. Tsui and S. J. Allen.[76]

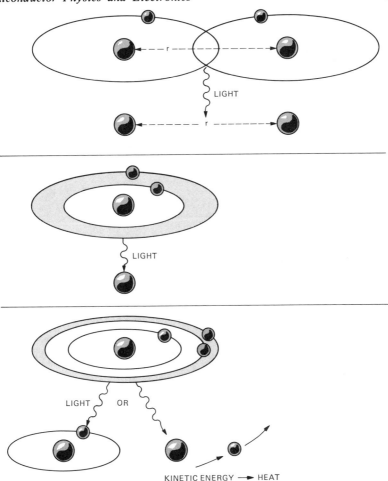

Fig. 2-8. Three means of hole-electron recombination. At the top, an electron (−) is bound to a donor impurity (D+) and a hole (+) to an acceptor (A⁻). The donor and acceptor are separated by a distance r. The overlap between electron and hole allows recombination to occur and light to be generated. In the center illustration, a hole and an electron are both bound to an "isielectronic trap" (ISO) causing a much greater overlap. Rapid recombination occurs and generates light. In the bottom illustration, a hole and electron are bound to a neutral donor, with an extra electron bound to the donor. Recombination of the hole and electron can occur to give off light (left), leaving the extra electron on the donor. ϕr, instead, the energy of the hole and electron can be given to the extra electron (right), which is ejected with kinetic energy and no light is generated. The latter process is dominant. All of these processes occur at low temperatures and help in understanding effects observed at room temperature.

5.5 Deep Levels

Interest in certain long-neglected but very important areas of semi-conductor physics reawakened in the 1970s. One such area is that of defects and impurities with energy levels deep in the gap. After two decades of preoccupation with shallow impurity states, attention turned to deep levels, especially for the wide-gap materials GaAs and GaP. These states are of particular interest for the very same reason that they are difficult to study—the nonradiative nature of recombination through them not only spoils light-emitting devices but precludes their study using the usual luminescence methods.

However, this experimental problem was solved by a capacitance technique[77] that was used to obtain information about nonradiative centers in GaP by H. Kukimoto, Henry, and Merritt.[78] D. V. Lang subsequently developed a practical spectroscopic capacitance technique called deep-level transient spectroscopy that proved extremely useful in studying nonradiative processes in large numbers of semiconductor devices.[79] Among the results that have been obtained using this technique are the observation of recombination-enhanced defect migration in p-n junctions,[80] the identification of multiphonon capture as an important mechanism for nonradiative capture,[81] and the discovery of centers responsible for low temperature, persistent impurity photoconductivity in III-V semiconductors.[82]

These experimental studies stimulated efforts to understand theoretically deep levels in semiconductors. G. A. Baraff and M. Schlüter developed theoretical methods for calculating the electronic energy states of deep levels.[83] A major triumph of this theoretical understanding was the prediction[84] and subsequent observation[85] that the deep levels associated with a lattice vacancy in silicon should behave in a very peculiar way, namely, as if two electrons had a net attraction instead of the normal repulsion felt by electrons for each other. This was the first direct observation of the apparent electron-electron attraction effect, caused by an interaction with the lattice strain energy, which had been suggested earlier on more general grounds by P. W. Anderson.[86]

The success of the study of deep levels in crystalline semiconductors led to efforts to understand deep gap states in amorphous semiconductors, where such states play a major role in the observed transport and optical properties of the material. An extension of the deep-level transient spectroscopy method to the case of hydrogenated amorphous silicon made possible the first direct measurement of the spectrum of deep gap states in this technologically important material.[87]

5.6 Electron-Hole Liquids

Certainly one of the more exotic developments in semiconductor physics was the discovery of the condensation of excitons into an electron-hole liquid in many semiconductors. The idea was originally presented by L. V. Keldysh[88] in an address at the 1968 International Semiconductor Conference held in Moscow and was verified in substance a few months later by experiments conducted in the Soviet Union.[89] Experimental[90] and theoretical[91] collaborations at Bell Labs have done much to elucidate the nature of this very unusual phenomenon. It has been found that at liquid helium temperatures, photogenerated free excitons, the "gaseous phase," can condense into a liquid state when the average density exceeds a certain well-defined value. [Fig. 2-9] The nature of the condensate, after the theoretical model of W. F. Brinkman and coworkers,[92] is that of a metallic liquid, made up of "free" electrons and holes, in the form of drops. The overall analogy with the vapor-liquid transformation of a conventional gas is striking.

VI. MOLECULAR BEAM EPITAXY

An outgrowth of the study of semiconductor single crystal surfaces was the work on the interaction of beams of gallium atoms and arsenic molecules on heated GaAs surfaces initiated by J. R. Arthur in the mid-1960s. Utilizing modulated beams, Arthur observed that while the sticking coefficient for gallium was unity, the sticking coefficient of arsenic (from As_2 molecules) was small and highly dependent on the gallium coverage of the crystal surface.[93] By making the arsenic beam intensity much higher than gallium, he was able to achieve a deposit of one arsenic atom on the surface for each added gallium atom. This observation provided the basis for an epitaxial growth technique for stoichiometric GaAs that did not require precise control over the As/Ga beam intensity ratios, provided the arsenic beam was significantly more intense than the gallium beam. [Fig. 2-10] This very versatile vacuum-epitaxial growth technique was further developed largely by Cho and is called molecular beam epitaxy (MBE).[94] (This technique, and its application to heterostructure lasers, varactor diodes, IMPATT diodes, and other semiconductor devices, is discussed in some detail in Chapter 19 of this volume.) [Fig. 2-11]

Cho's work demonstrating extremely smooth epitaxial layers and heterostructures of GaAs and $Al_xGa_{1-x}As$ by MBE was a precursor to studies of ultrathin, or superlattice, structures by A. C. Gossard and coworkers.[95] Two classes of new crystal structures were prepared. In the first, alternate layers of GaAs and AlAs were grown. It was demonstrated that artificial crystal structures with a periodicity of one monolayer could be obtained by suitable shuttering of aluminum and gallium beams. Although these structures had rather small domain sizes (approximately 100Å), structures in which the individual layers were several monolayers thick had very large domains.

The second class of superlattice structures has somewhat thicker (50-100Å) alternating layers of GaAs and $Al_xGa_{1-x}As$. The GaAs has a

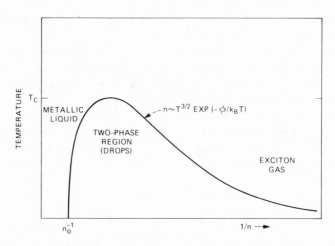

Fig. 2-9. Phase diagram representing the two-phase system of electron-hole liquid drops and exciton gas. Exciton gas alone exists at low average density (above the curve, at the right); the two-phase coexistence region exists at high densities (above the curve, to the left). The critical temperature, T_c, in germanium is 6.7°K.

narrower band gap than $Al_xGa_{1-x}As$. A sandwich consisting of a thin GaAs layer between $Al_xGa_{1-x}As$ layers is a two-dimensional quantum well for holes and electrons. The absorption spectra of undoped superlattice crystals, consisting of a stack of such sandwich structures, clearly show the well-defined, confined hole and electron states.[96]

A further elaboration of quantum well structures is the modulation-doped superlattice reported by Dingle, H. L. Störmer, and coworkers.[97] In these, only the $Al_xGa_{1-x}As$ layers are doped and the carriers are in their minimum energy state when confined in the quantum well. Thus, the GaAs layers contain the carriers and the $Al_xGa_{1-x}As$ layers contain the immobile fixed charges. These new anisotropic crystals have electron mobilities greater than GaAs because impurity scattering has been eliminated. Together with modulation-doped interfaces between single pairs of layers, they have provided materials for a number of studies of spectroscopy and transport in two-dimensional electron gases. In 1980, K. Von Klitzing showed that a two-dimensional electron gas in a silicon inversion layer exhibits the quantized Hall effect.[98] The electrical resistance of the modulation-doped superlattices also showed strong quantum effects in response to magnetic fields, with the resistance parallel to the layers dipping close to zero over certain ranges of field. At the same time, their Hall resistance became precisely quantized in integral submultiples of Planck's constant divided by the square of the electron charge (h/e^2). These effects, observed previously only in silicon at higher fields, challenged theorists and offered new

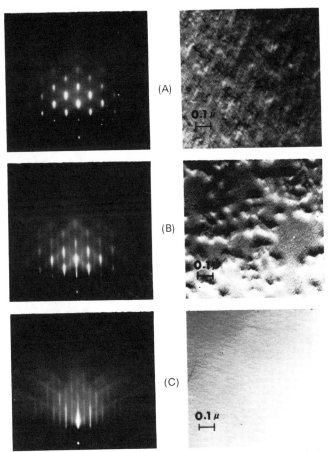

Fig. 2-10. Reflection electron diffraction patterns of GaAs [001] (40 keV, 100 degrees azimuth) and the corresponding electron micrographs (38,400X) of Pt-C replicas of the same surface. (A) Br_2-methanol chemically polished GaAs substrate heated in vacuum to 580°C for 5 minutes. The diffraction pattern consists of spots, and the surface is micro-faceted. (B) A layer of GaAs of average thickness of 150Å was grown on the surface of the substrate in (A) with molecular beam epitaxy. The diffraction pattern becomes more streaked and patches of smooth areas are formed on the substrated. (C) A 1-micrometer GaAs layer was grown on the surface of the substrate in (A). The diffraction pattern is uniformly streaked normal to the crystal surface, and the morphology appears completely featureless. The additional diffraction features ("half-order" streaks) that appear in (B) and (C) are due to the formation of reconstructed unit-cells of the surface atoms, which have a unit-mesh length twice the dimension of the bulk.

approaches to a precise measurement of h/e^2 and the fine structure constant and for realization of a new fundamental standard of resistance. Conductivity perpendicular to the layered structures was also

Fig. 2-11. J. R. Arthur (left) and A. Y. Cho pioneered in the development of Molecular Beam Epitaxy, a process particularly suited for thin-film growth.

studied and revealed the ability to control the detailed profile of potential barriers by crystal growth of graded layers. Asymmetric barriers with graded bandgaps were created that produced unipolar rectification, involving motion only of semiconductor charge carriers of one sign. The layered structures may result in new devices that utilize these high-mobility and anisotropic-conductivity characteristics.

VII. SEMICONDUCTOR RESEARCH SUPPLEMENT – THE STORY OF THE "GENESIS OF THE TRANSISTOR"

The story of the "Genesis of the Transistor" is reproduced in three parts:

1. "The Genesis of the Transistor," by W. S. Gorton, Assistant to the Director of Physical Research, J. B. Fisk, dated December 27, 1949.

2. A letter from J. B. Fisk to R. Bown, Director of Research, dated February 17, 1950.

3. Personal reminiscences by W. H. Brattain, recorded by Brattain in 1975 for this History.

7.1 "The Genesis of the Transistor"

December 27, 1949

MEMORANDUM FOR RECORD

The history of the transistor begins with the decision to study intensively the properties of silicon and germanium. This decision was made in 1946 as a result of a series of conferences intended to establish a plan for semiconductor research, which was then being resumed after a war-time lapse.

Although silicon and germanium were the simplest semiconductors, and most of their properties could be well understood in terms of existing theory, there were still a number of matters not completely investigated. It was also thought wise to develop techniques with these well-known substances before experimenting with a wider variety of materials. *The Plan was thus directed definitely toward establishing fundamental understanding of phenomena and proper experimental techniques and not toward the solution of problems of technological rather than scientific importance.*

Work was begun actively in January 1946 under the direction of W. Shockley. J. Bardeen worked on the theory, G. L. Pearson conducted the experiments on bulk properties, and W. H. Brattain those on surface properties. This work was aided by results obtained by J. H. Scaff and H. C. Theuerer during the war, as well as those obtained by other laboratories.

From the point of view of the communications art, it appeared that the most important development likely to arise from semiconductor research, and quite possibly from any branch of solid state research, would be a useful semiconductor amplifier. *This consideration influenced the emphasis of the work in various parts of the solid state area.* Very early in the program it was predicted by Shockley from the existing theories for silicon and germanium that appreciable resistance modulation of thin layers of semiconductor could be produced by inducing a net charge on them with a strong electric field. This proposed form of modulation, which became known as the *"field effect,"* was electronic, rather than thermal as in the case of a thermistor, and it appeared that it might lead to new and useful semiconductor amplifiers. Since the then-hypothetical field effect did not violate any of the basic laws of nature, it constituted a theoretical *"existence proof"* of an electronic semiconductor amplifier and thus served to focus attention on such possibilities. A number of experimental tests of the proposal were carried out by J. R. Haynes, H. J. McSkimin, W. A. Yager and R. S. Ohl. All gave negative results; in the case of the experiment of Ohl the expected effect was more than one thousand times the minimum detectable indication of the measuring instruments.

These results led to a re-examination of the theory and the postulation by J. Bardeen of the trapping of electrons in the surface layers of, or adsorbed layers on, semiconductors, especially silicon and germanium.[1] This concept, referred to as electrons in surface states, led to the idea that a space-charge layer may exist at the free surface of a semiconductor independent of a metal contact. It provided an explanation of several puzzling facts about point-contact rectifiers using germanium and silicon. These included (1) lack of dependence of rectifier characteristic on work function of metal, (2) lack of contact potential difference between samples of n- and p-type germanium and between n- and p-type silicon, and (3) current-voltage characteristics observed by S. Benzer of Purdue University between two similar pieces of germanium. The theory suggested that at sufficiently low temperatures electrons might be frozen in the surface states so that the field effect could be observed. Experiments by Pearson and Bardeen showed that this was the case.[2] The effect was much smaller than had been predicted from properties of bulk samples, but there was evidence that the remaining discrepancy was due to an abnormally low mobility of electrons in these films.

The nature of surfaces and surface phenomena have always posed some of the most difficult problems in solid state physics. Bardeen's theory afforded a means of investigating the electronic behavior of the surface and of determining the properties and origin of the surface states—results which would constitute important contributions to the science of surface phenomena. There was also the possibility that if action of the surface states could be prevented, then the field effect would become efficient, and electronic semiconductor amplifiers might become practical. Research on the nature of surface state effects was thus seen to have the usual combination of advantages of being physical research of fundamental scientific importance, of involving skills, instruments and materials which were available almost uniquely at Bell Telephone Laboratories, and of having, at the same time, the possibility of leading to developments of great practical importance. The obvious decision was, therefore, made to stress research on surface states, and as described below, the phenomena which led up to the invention of the transistor were discovered in the course of this fundamental research program.

Experiments to test further predictions of the surface state theory were suggested by Bardeen, Shockley and Brattain. By varying the impurity content of silicon, Brattain found that he could systematically change the contact potential in accordance with the changes in the surface state effected by changing the impurity content.[3] The change was found to be in accordance with Shockley's prediction that increasing the impurity content of silicon would increase the difference between the contact potential of the n-type (where the impurity produces an excess of electrons) and the contact potential of the p-type (where the impurity produces a defect of electrons). A large number of experiments, particularly by Pearson and H. R. Moore, to obtain experimental confirmation of Bardeen's surface-state theory and direct evidence of the existence of his predicted space-charge layer at the free surface of a semiconductor failed. The effects looked for were small and were generally masked by extraneous phenomena.

An experiment which did indicate the presence of a space-charge layer was carried out by Brattain. He found that shining light on n-type silicon produces a change in contact potential which is interpreted as a defect of electrons at the surface, and on p-type an excess of electrons.[4] The former effect is generally described as bringing *holes* to the surface. In order to investigate a possible temperature effect, the surface was cooled to a low temperature. A large hysteresis in the effect was observed, which was considered as possibly due to the condensed water on the surface which was noticed at the end of the experiment. In order to avoid this effect, the surface was immersed in a liquid dielectric. A greatly enhanced effect of light was observed. Various dielectric liquids were tried, and then electrolytes.[5] The effect was larger with the electrolytes.

In the experiments involving electrolytes, R. B. Gibney suggested changing the dc bias which had been incorporated in the circuit to counteract the contact potential.[6] The results indicated that the electrolyte was transmitting a strong electric field to the surface layer of the silicon and that the experiment was another test of the field effect mentioned earlier in this memorandum.[7] Gibney and Brattain pointed out that the effect could be used to control the passage of current through the silicon and, consequently, that a suitable arrangement could be made to function as an amplifier.[8] They also remarked that a solid, instead of a liquid, dielectric could be used, the only requirement being a sufficient ionic mobility to furnish ions for the requisite dipole layer at the surface of the semiconductor.

Bardeen suggested an experiment by which the amplification effect with an electrolyte could be studied. Instead of using a thin semiconductive film, as had been used in earlier tests of the field effect, he suggested using a block of semiconductor of one conductivity type on which there was a thin surface layer of opposite conductivity type. This avoided the use of thin films with questionable electrical properties. This suggestion was made to Brattain, and he and Bardeen immediately tried the experiment with a block of p-type silicon on which a surface layer of n-type silicon had been produced by oxidation. A contact was made to the layer by a metal point, and a large-area low-resistance contact was made to the base of the block. The point contact was surrounded by, but insulated from, a drop of electrolyte. When a voltage is applied between the point and the base electrode in the high-resistance direction for the n-p barrier between the layer and the body, current flows to the point mainly in the thin surface layer. It was found that the magnitude of this current could be controlled by a potential applied to the electrolyte. The strong electric field applied to the layer by the electrolyte changed its resistance in the way predicted by Shockley's theory of the field effect. Current amplification and, at very low frequencies, power amplification were obtained, but not voltage amplification. This experiment was performed on November 21, 1947.[9]

The semiconductor was next changed, at Bardeen's suggestion, to high-back-voltage germanium furnished by Scaff and Theuerer. Experiments were continued by Brattain and Bardeen, with the aid of Gibney on chemical problems. Although the effect was again limited by the electrolyte to very low frequencies, amplification of voltage, as well as current and power, was achieved. Although there was no prior reason to suspect a p-type layer on the n-type germanium block, the sign of the effect indicated that holes were flowing near the surface, and that the magnitude of the hole current was enhanced by a negative potential applied to the electrolyte.

In order to increase the frequency response, Bardeen suggested replacing the electrolyte by a metal contact.[10] Gibney prepared a surface by anodizing it and then evaporating a number of gold spots on it. It was hoped that a field produced by a gold spot could be used to modulate the current flowing near the surface. When the experiment was tried by Brattain, a new effect, now known as *transistor action*, was observed.[11] It was found that current flowing in the forward direction from one contact influenced the current flowing in the reverse direction in a neighboring contact in such a way as to produce voltage amplification. This suggested that holes were flowing from the contact biased in the forward direction to the contact biased in the reverse direction. At first there was no power amplification. It was estimated that power amplification could be achieved if the separation between the rectifying contacts were of the order of 0.001 inch.

This arrangement was set up, and a voltage gain of 15 was secured at 1,000 cycles per second; the gain was slightly larger at 100 cycles per second.[12] The experiments were continued, and on December 23, 1947, a speech amplifier giving a power amplification of 18 or more, with good quality, was demonstrated by W. H. Brattain and H. R. Moore to R. Bown, H. Fletcher, W. Shockley, J. Bardeen, G. L. Pearson and R. B. Gibney.[13] The arrangement was operated as an oscillator on December 24, 1947.[14]

The elements of one of the arrangements were given to H. S. Black. His group found that amplification occurred up to at least 107 cycles per second.[15]

Brattain found that the practical spacing of the rectifying points had to be less than 0.010 inch and that the optimum was about 0.002 inch.[16] The points could be improved by electrical forming.[17]

At the suggestion of J. R. Pierce the device was designated the *transistor*; it was disclosed to a meeting of the BTL Research Department Technical Staff in the auditorium at Murray Hill on June 22, 1948. It was demonstrated to the press on June 30, 1948, in the West Street auditorium. The first scientific publication was in the form of three letters to the editor, published in the *Physical Review* for July 15, 1948.

(Original signed by)
W. S. GORTON

---

1 This theory of trapped electrons is recorded in Notebook 20780, pages 38-53, March 18-April 23, 1946. It is published in *Physical Review* **47**, 717, 1947 (May 15).

* (one of p-type and one of n-type). Note added by W. H. Brattain, 1975.

2 Notebook 20912, pages 1-11, April 22, 1946.
Notebook 20780, pages 47-53, April 23, 1946.

3 Notebook 21373, pages 88-108, May 20, 1947. (W. H. Brattain and W. Shockley, *Phys. Rev.* **72**, 345, 1947.)

4 Notebook 18194, page 78, April 2, 1947. (W. H. Brattain, *Phys. Rev.* **72**, 345, 1947)

5 Notebook 18194, pages 138-141, November 13-17, 1947.

6 Notebook 18194, page 142, November 17, 1947.

7 This whole matter was discussed in conference with P. J. W. Debye. It was agreed that the concept was correct and that the experiment had been a test of Shockley's suggestion. (Recollection of W. H. Brattain.)

8 Notebook 18194, pages 151-153, November 20, 1947.

9 Notebook 20780, pages 61-67, November 22, 1947.

10 Notebook 20780, pages 69-70, November 23, 1947.

11 Notebook 18194, pages 190-192, December 15, 1947. (NOTE. Bardeen and Brattain were working in very close cooperation at this time and had been so working for some weeks previously. Bardeen had spent much time in the laboratory watching the experiments as they were made, and often suggesting them and participating in them. This arrangement facilitated interpretation and discussion and enabled the ideas of both to be tried out with a minimum of delay.)

* Footnote added by W. H. Brattain in 1975:
  We were using glycoborate at the electrolyte and noticed an anodic oxide film growing on the surface of the germanium so we anodized the surface of a piece of germanium, washed off the glycoborate and evaporated the gold spots on it. As it turned out the germanium oxide was soluble in water and we had also washed it off! So these experiments were done on a freshly anodized surface of germanium, and the first transistor was made on one of these samples anodized in this way!

12 Notebook 18194, pages 193-194, December 16, 1947.

13 Notebook 21780, pages 708, December 24, 1947.

14 Notebook 21780, page 9, December 24, 1947.

15 Notebook T23265, page 2, January 20, 1948, and subsequent entries to February 10, 1948.

16 Notebook 21780, pages 56-61, January 26, 1948.

17 Notebook 21780, pages 26, 31, January 15, 1948.

7.2 J. B. Fisk's Letter to R. Bown

February 17, 1950

MR. RALPH BOWN:

I send you herewith Mr. W. S. Gorton's memorandum of December 27, 1949, entitled "The Genesis of the Transistor". This has been written in compliance with your request of June 22, 1948, to him to prepare an account of the thinking, work, and events which resulted in the transistor.

Mr. Gorton had repeated interviews with Messrs. W. Shockley, J. Bardeen, W. H. Brattain, and G. L. Pearson; he also read the significant portions of pertinent notebooks, especially the references cited in the memorandum. The memorandum was written, submitted to those named, altered, often extensively, and resubmitted. Count has been lost of the number of times this process was repeated. The final result was submitted to you on September 12, 1949.

After you had referred the manuscript to Mr. H. A. Burgess, Mr. Gorton discussed it with him and Mr. H. C. Hart. The note to footnote No. 11 was added, and they then approved the account in toto. The changed memorandum was again submitted to Messrs. Shockley, Bardeen, Brattain, and Pearson; it was approved by them and constitutes the attached memorandum.

Throughout the work Mr. Gorton repeatedly raised the question as to whether full credit was being given to all to whom it was due; he was assured that it was. It is to be noted that the names of twelve persons appear in the memorandum as having taken substantial part in the work.

The interviews showed that memory was beginning to get hazy in a few respects but discussion and time cleared it up. To counterbalance any such effect it is thought that the account has benefited from the better perspective due to the passage of time. Taking everything into account, including the fact that all of the pertinent documents were at hand for study, I think we may reasonably regard this account of the genesis of the transistor as definitive.

(Original signed by)
J. B. FISK

Copy to
Mr. H. A. Burgess-Mr. H. C. Hart
Mr. W. Shockley
Mr. J. Bardeen
Mr. W. H. Brattain
Mr. G. L. Pearson

7.3 Walter H. Brattain's Personal Reminiscences, Recorded by Brattain in 1975

When the question was asked, "What should we name it?", Bardeen and I were told, "You did it; you name it." We were aware that deForest had called his three-electrode vacuum tube an audion, and that this name did not survive. We also knew that whatever we named it might not take. We knew a two-syllable name would be better than three or more syllables. J. A. Becker had originated names for other semiconductor devices, namely, varistor for the rectifier and thermistor for the temperature-sensitive device. We wanted a name that would fit into this family. We had many suggestions, some ending in "-tron," which we did not like. Bardeen and I were about at the end of our rope when one day J. R. Pierce walked by my office and I said to him, "Pierce, come in and sit down. You are just the man I want to see."

I told him all about our dilemma, including that we wanted something to fit in with varistor and thermistor. Now Pierce knew that the point contact device was a dual of the vacuum tube, circuitwise; i.e., the device was short circuit unstable and the vacuum tube was open circuit unstable. (This, by the way, was a stumbling block for electronic engineers when they first tried to use the new device.) He mentioned the most important property of the vacuum tube, "transconductance," thought a minute about what the dual of this parameter would be and said, "transresistance," and then said "Transistor," and I said, "Pierce, that is it!"

The sequel to this is: some years later, I came across a story by J. J. Coupling entitled "The Transistor" in a science fiction journal and read it. The last phrase in the story was "and an obscure individual by the name of J. R. Pierce named it." Pierce had written many science fiction stories, and he signed them all J. J. Coupling. I knew this and was somewhat chagrined that maybe we had not given him proper credit. Though everybody knew who had named it.

My late wife, Karen, said, when she first heard the name, that it would probably be shortened to "sistor" before too long. When the Award of Nobel Prize to Bardeen, Shockley, and me was announced, my father was out in the Bitteroot Mountains of Idaho. The only way my mother could send him a message was by forest reserve telephone to tell Ross Brattain, etc... She wanted him to get the news before everybody else on the line knew, so her message was "Tell Ross Brattain the transistor won a Nobel Prize." The message my father received was, "Your sister won a Nobel Prize!" My father did have a sister, but he knew that she had not won this prize. When we went to the first International Semiconductor Conference held at the University of Reading in England (1950), the English scientists were not using our name for the device. We asked them if by chance they did not think the name "transistor" was appropriate. Their answer was that they thought we had copyrighted the name and were, therefore, being very proper in not using it. We told them this was not so, that they could use the name if they wished!

William Shockley's work on the theory of the p-n junction (first discovered by Russell Ohl in a silicon ingot made for him by Scaff and Theuerer in 1939 or 1940) led to his investigation of the n-p-n or p-n-p transistor.

The impact of all these results on solid state research was tremendous! Single crystals for germanium by Teal and Little; the p-n junction, a surface or phase boundary in a single crystal well understood from first principles; zone refining, etc. by Pfann, making possible single crystals of an unheard of purity; in addition to the impact on the electronic technology.

REFERENCES

1. F. Bloch, "Uber die Quantenmechanik der Elektronen in Kristallgittern," *Z. Physik* **52** (1928), pp. 555-600.
2. A. H. Wilson, "The Theory of Electronic Semi-Conductors," *Proc. Royal Soc. London* **133** (1931), pp. 458-491.
3. G. L. Pearson and J. Bardeen, "Electrical Properties of Pure Silicon and Silicon Alloys Containing Boron and Phosphorus," *Phys. Rev.* **75** (March 1949), pp. 865-883.

4. See, for example, C. Kittel, *Introduction to Solid State Physics*, 4th ed. (New York: John Wiley, 1971), p. 331.

5. J. Bardeen and W. Shockley, "Deformation Potentials and Mobilities in Non-Polar Crystals," *Phys. Rev.* **80** (October 1950), pp. 72-80.

6. J. Bardeen and W. H. Brattain, "The Transistor, A Semiconductor Itriode," Letter to the Editor, *Phys. Rev.* **74** (July 15, 1948), pp. 230-231.

7. W. H. Brattain and J. Bardeen, "Nature of the Forward Current in Germanium Point Contacts," *Phys. Rev.* **74** (July 1948), pp. 231-232.

8. W. Shockley, "The Theory of p-n Junctions in Semiconductors and p-n Junction Transistors," *Bell System Tech. J.* **28** (July 1949), pp. 435-489.

9. W. Shockley, M. Sparks, and G. K. Teal, "p-n Junction Transistors," *Phys. Rev.* **83** (July 1951), pp. 151-162.

10. See reference 9.

11. W. Shockley, "A Unipolar 'Field-Effect' Transistor," *Proc. IRE* **40** (November 1952), pp. 1365-1376.

12. G. C. Dacey and I. M. Ross, "The Field Effect Transistor," *Bell System Tech. J.* **34** (November 1955), pp. 1149-1189.

13. G. C. Dacey and I. M. Ross, "Unipolar 'Field-Effect' Transistor," *Proc. IRE* **41** (August 1953), pp. 970-979.

14. W. L. Brown, "n-Type Surface Conductivity on p-Type Germanium," *Phys. Rev.* **91** (August 1953), pp. 518-527.

15. I. M. Ross, U. S. Patent No. 2,791-760; filed February 18, 1955, issued May 7, 1957.

16. F. Gornik and D. C. Tsui, "Voltage-Tunable Far-Infrared Emission from Si Inversion Layers," *Phys. Rev. Lett.* **37** (November 22, 1976), pp. 1425-1428.

17. S. J. Allen, D. C. Tsui, and R. A. Logan, "Observation of the Two-Dimensional Plasmon in Silicon Inversion Layers," *Phys. Rev. Lett.* **38** (April 25, 1977), pp. 980-983.

18. D. C. Tsui and S. J. Allen, "Localization and the Minimum Metallic Conductivity in Si Inversion Layers," *Phys. Rev. Lett.* **34** (May 19, 1975), pp. 1293-1295.

19. D. J. Bishop, D. C. Tsui, and R. C. Dynes, "Nonmetallic Conduction in Electron Inversion Layers at Low Temperatures," *Phys. Rev. Lett.* **44** (1980), pp. 1153-1156.

20. W. Shockley, "Negative Resistance Arising from Transit Time in Semiconductor Diodes," *Bell System Tech. J.* **33** (July 1954), pp. 799-826.

21. W. T. Read, Jr., "A Proposed High-Frequency, Negative-Resistance Diode," *Bell System Tech. J.* **37** (March 1958), pp. 401-446.

22. R. L. Johnston, B. C. DeLoach, Jr., and B. G. Cohen, "A Silicon Diode Microwave Oscillator," *Bell System Tech. J.* **44** (February 1965), pp. 369-372.

23. C. A. Lee, R. A. Logan, R. L. Batdorf, J. J. Kleimack, and W. Wiegmann, "Ionization Rates of Holes and Electrons in Silicon," *Phys. Rev.* **134** (May 1964), pp. A761-A773; C. A. Lee, R. L. Batdorf, W. Wiegmann, and G. Kaminsky, "The Read Diode—An Avalanching, Transit-Time, Negative-Resistance Oscillator," *Appl. Phys. Lett.* **6** (March 1, 1965), pp. 89-91.

24. C. A. Lee, L. R. Batdorf, W. Wiegmann, and G. Kaminsky, "Time Dependence of Avalanche Processes in Silicon," *J. Appl. Phys.* **38** (June 1967), pp. 2787-2796.

25. P. K. Tien, U. S. Patent No. 3,158,819; filed April 26, 1961, issued November 24, 1964.

26. D. L. White, U. S. Patent No. 3,173,100; filed April 26, 1961, issued March 9, 1965.

27. A. R. Hutson, J. H. McFee, and D. L. White, "Ultrasonic Amplification in CdS," *Phys. Rev. Lett.* **7** (September 15, 1961), pp. 237-239.

28. P. K. Tien, "Nonlinear Theory of Ultrasonic Wave Amplification and Current Saturation in Piezoelectric Semiconductors," *Phys. Rev.* **171** (July 1968), pp. 970-986.

29. C. S. Fuller, "Diffusion of Donor and Acceptor Elements into Germanium," Letter to the Editor, *Phys. Rev.* **86** (April 1952), pp. 136-137.

30. G. L. Pearson and P. W. Foy, "Silicon p-n Junction Diodes Prepared by the Alloying Process," *Phys. Rev.* **87** (July 1952), p. 190.

31. G. L. Pearson and C. S. Fuller, "Silicon p-n Junction Power Rectifiers and Lightning Protectors," *Proc. IRE* **42** (April 1954), p. 760; D. M. Chapin, C. S. Fuller, and G. L. Pearson, "A New Silicon p-n Junction Photocell for Converting Solar Radiation into Electrical Power," Letter to the Editor, *J. Appl. Phys.* **25** (May 1954), pp. 676-677.

32. M. B. Prince, "Silicon Solar Energy Converters," *J. Appl. Phys.* **26** (May 1955), pp. 534-540.

33. J. G. Fossum, R. D. Nashby, and E. L. Burgess, "Development of High-Efficiency P+−N−N+ Back-Surface-Field Silicon Solar Cells," *Thirteenth IEEE Photovoltaic Specialists Conference* (1978), pp. 1294-1299.

34. G. L. Pearson, "Conversion of Solar to Electrical Energy," *Am. J. Phys.* **25** (December 1957), pp. 591-598.

35. J. R. Haynes and W. Shockley, "Investigation of Hole Injection in Transistor Action," *Phys. Rev.* **75** (February 1949), p. 691.

36. T. H. Geballe and F. J. Morin, "Ionization Energies of Groups III and V Elements in Germanium," *Phys. Rev.* **95** (August 1954), pp. 1085-1086; F. J. Morin, J. P. Maita, R. G. Shulman, and N. B. Hannay, "Impurity Levels in Silicon," *Phys. Rev.* **96** (November 1954), p. 833.

37. H. J. Hrostowski and R. H. Kaiser, "Absorption Spectrum of Arsenic Doped Silicon" *J. Phys. Chem. Solids* **7** (November 1958), pp. 236-239; idem, "The Solubility of Oxygen in Silicon," *J. Phys. Chem. Solids* **9** (March 1959), pp. 214-216.

38. T. H. Geballe, "The Seebeck Effect in Germanium," *Phys. Rev.* **92** (November 1953), p. 857; T. H. Geballe and G. W. Hull, "Seebeck Effect in Germanium," *Phys. Rev.* **93** (June 1954), pp. 1134-1140; H. P. R. Frederikse, "Thermoelectric Power in Germanium Single Crystals," *Phys. Rev.* **91** (July 1953), p. 491; H. P. R. Frederikse, "Thermoelectric Power of Germanium Bel Room Temperature," *Phys. Rev.* **92** (October 1953), pp. 248-252.

39. C. Herring, "Theory of Thermoelectric Power of Semiconductors," *Phys. Rev.* **92** (November 1953), pp. 857-858.

40. L. Gurevich, "Thermoelectric Properties of Conductors. I," *J. Phys.* (U.S.S.R.) **9** (1945), pp. 477-488.

41. C. Herring, "Theory of the Thermoelectric Power of Semiconductors," *Phys. Rev.* **96** (December 1954), pp. 1163-1187.

42. W. P. Mason and T. P. Bateman, "Ultrasonic Attenuation and Velocity Changes in Doped n-Type Germanium and p-Type Silicon and Their Use in Determining an Intrinsic Electron and Hole Scattering Time," *Phys. Rev. Lett.* **10** (March 1, 1963), pp. 151-154; idem, "Ultrasonic Wave Propagation in Doped n-Germanium and p-Silicon," *Phys. Rev.* **134A** (June 1964), pp. 1387-1396.

43. C. Herring, T. H. Geballe, and J. E. Kunzler, "Phonon-Drag Thermomagnetic Effects in n-Type Germanium. I. General Survey," *Phys. Rev.* **111** (July 1958), pp. 35-57; C. Herring, T. H. Geballe, and J. E. Kunzler, "Analysis of Phonon-Drag Thermomagnetic Effects in n-Type Germanium," *Bell System Tech. J.* **38** (May 1959), pp. 657-747.

44. See reference 38.

45. I. Pomeranchuk, *J. Phys.* (U.S.S.R.) **4** (1942), p. 259.

46. G. A. Slack, "Effect of Isotopes on Low-Temperature Thermal Conductivity," *Phys. Rev.* **105** (February 1957), pp. 821-831.

47. T. H. Geballe and G. W. Hull, "Isotopic and Other Types of Thermal Resistance in Germanium," Letter to the Editor, *Phys. Rev.* **110** (May 1958), pp. 773-775.

48. W. Eisenmenger and A. H. Dayem, "Quantum Generation and Detection of Incoherent Phonons in Superconductors," *Phys. Rev. Lett.* **18** (January 23, 1967), pp. 125-127.

49. R. C. Dynes, V. Namayanamurti, and M. Chin, "Monochromatic Phonon Propagation in Ge:Sb Using Superconducting Tunnel Junctions," *Phys. Rev. Lett.* **26** (January 25, 1971), pp. 181-184.

50. V. Narayanamurti, R. A. Logan, and M. A. Chin, "Direct Observation of Phonons Generated During Nonradiative Capture in GaAs p-n Junctions," *Phys. Rev. Lett.* **40** (January 2, 1978), pp. 63-66.

51. J. C. Hensel and R. C. Dynes, "Interaction of Non-Equilibrium, Ballistic Phonons in a Heat Pulse with the Electron-Hole Liquid in Ge: The Phonon Wind," *Proc. of the 3rd Int'l Conf. of Phonon Scattering in Condensed Matter,* held at Brown Univ., Providence, R.I., ed. H. J. Maris (New York: Plenum Press, 1980), pp. 395-400.

52. W. Shockley, "Cyclotron Resonances, Magnetoresistance, and Brillouin Zones in Semiconductors," Letter to the Editor, *Phys. Rev.* **90** (May 1, 1953), p. 491.

53. G. Dresselhaus, A. F. Kip, and C. Kittel, "Observation of Cyclotron Resonance in Germanium Crystals," Letters to the Editor, *Phys. Rev.* **92** (November 1, 1953), p. 827; idem, "Spin-Orbit Interaction and the Effective Masses of Holes in Germanium," Letters to the Editor, *Phys. Rev.* **95** (July 15, 1954), pp. 568-569; B. Lax, H. J. Zeiger, R. Dexter, and E. S. Rosenblum, "Directional Properties of the Cyclotron Resonance in Germanium," Letters to the Editor, *Phys. Rev.* **93** (March 15, 1954), pp. 1418-1420; R. N. Dexter, H. J. Zeiger, and B. Lax, "Anisotropy of Cyclotron Resonance of Holes in Germanium," Letters to the Editor, *Phys. Rev.* **95** (July 15, 1954), pp. 568-569.

54. C. S. Smith, "Piezoresistance Effect in Germanium and Silicon," *Phys. Rev.* **94** (April 1954), pp. 42-49.

55. W. P. Mason, "Semiconductors in Strain Gauges," *Bell Laboratories Record* **37** (1959), pp. 7-9.

56. W. G. Pfann and R. N. Thurston, "Semiconducting Stress Transducers Utilizing the Transverse and Shear Piezoresistance Effects," *J. Appl. Phys.* **32** (October 1961), p. 2008.

57. J. M. Luttinger and W. Kohn, "Motion of Electrons and Holes in Perturbed Periodic Fields," *Phys. Rev.* **97** (February 1955), pp. 869-883.

58. R. C. Fletcher, W. A. Yager, and F. R. Merritt, "Observation of Quantum Effects in Cyclotron Resonance," *Phys. Rev.* **100** (October 1955), pp. 747-748.

59. J. C. Hensel and K. Suzuki, "ThAb-3 Quantum Resonance Spectroscopy in the Valence Bands of Germanium," *Proc. of the Tenth International Conf. on the Physics of Semiconductors,* ed. S. P. Keller, J. C. Hensel, and F. Stern (Springfield, Va.: U.S.A.E.C., 1970), pp. 541-551.

60. R. C. Fletcher, W. A. Yager, G. L. Pearson, and F. R. Merritt, "Hyperfine Splitting in Spin Resonance of Group V Donors in Silicon," Letters to the Editor, *Phys. Rev.* **95** (August 1, 1954), p. 844.

61. G. Feher and E. A. Gere, "Polarization of Phosphorus Nuclei in Silicon," Letters to the Editor, *Phys. Rev.* **103** (July 15, 1956), pp. 501-503.

62. J. R. Haynes, "Experimental Proof of the Existence of a New Electronic Complex in Silicon," *Phys. Rev. Lett.* **4** (April 1, 1960), pp. 361-363.

63. J. R. Haynes, "Experimental Observation of the Excitonic Molecule," *Phys. Rev. Lett.* **17** (October 17, 1966), pp. 860-862.

64. J. C. Phillips, "The Fundamental Optical Spectra of Solids," *Solid State Physics, Vol. 18: Advances in Research and Applications* (1966), pp. 55-164.

65. D. E. Aspnes and A. A. Studna, "Schottky-Barrier Electroreflectance: Application to GaAs," *Phys. Rev.* **B7** (May 15, 1973), pp. 4605-4625.

66. J. C. Phillips, "Ionicity of the Chemical Bond in Semiconductors," *Proc. of the Tenth International Conf. on the Physics of Semiconductors,* ed. S. P. Keller, J. C. Hensel, and F. Stern (Springfield, Va.: U.S.A.E.C., 1970), pp. 22-29.

67. W. Paul and D. M. Warschauer, "Role of Pressure in Semiconductor Research," *Solids Under Pressure* (New York: McGraw-Hill Book Co., Inc., 1963).

68. A. R. Hutson, A. Jayaraman, A. G. Chynoweth, A. S. Coriell, and W. L. Feldmann, "Mechanism of the Gunn Effect from a Pressure Experiment," *Phys. Rev. Lett.* **14** (April 19, 1965), pp. 639-641.

69. J. B. Gunn, "Instabilities of Current in III-V Semiconductors," *IBM J. Research and Development* **8** (April 1964), pp. 141-159.

70. D. G. Thomas and J. J. Hopfield, "Optical Properties of Bound Exciton Complexes in Cadmium Sulfide," *Phys. Rev. Lett.* **128** (December 1, 1962), pp. 2135-2148.

71. J. J. Hopfield, D. G. Thomas, and M. Gerschenzon, "Pair Spectra in GaP," *Phys. Rev. Lett.* **10** (March 1, 1963), pp. 162-164.

72. D. G. Thomas, "A Review of Radiative Recombination at Isoelectric Donors and Acceptors," *J. Phys. Soc. Japan* **21** Supplement (1966), pp. 1265-1276.

73. D. F. Nelson, J. D. Cuthbert, P. J. Dean, and D. G. Thomas, "Auger Recombination of Excitons Bound to Neutral Donors in Gallium Phosphide and Silicon," *Phys. Rev. Lett.* **17** (December 19, 1966), p. 1262.

74. C. H. Henry, "Deep Level Spectroscopy, Low Temperature Defect Motion and Nonradiative Recombination in GaAs and GaP," *J. Elect. Materials* **4** (1975), pp. 1037-1052.

75. A. Y. Cho, "Growth of Periodic Structures by the Molecular Beam Method," *Appl. Phys. Lett.* **19** (December 1, 1971), pp. 467-468; R. Dingle, "Confined Carrier Quantum States in Ultrathin Semiconductor Heterostructures," *Festkorperprobleme XV (Advances in Solid State Physics)* ed. H. J. Queisser (Braunschweig: Pergamon/Vieweg, 1975), pp. 21-48.

76. S. J. Allen, D. C. Tsui, and J. V. Dalton, "Far-Infrared Cyclotron Resonance in the Inversion Layer of Silicon," *Phys. Rev. Lett.* **32** (January 21, 1974), pp. 107-110.

77. R. Williams, "Determination of Deep Centers in Conducting Gallium Arsenide," *J. Appl. Phys.* **37** (August 1966), pp. 3411-3416; C. T. Sah and J. W. Walker, "Thermally Stimulated Capacitance for Shallow Majority-Carrier Traps in the Edge Region of Semiconductor Junctions," *Appl. Phys. Lett.* **22** (April 15, 1973), pp. 384-385.

78. H. Kukimoto, C. H. Henry, and F. R. Merritt, "Photocapacitance Studies of the Oxygen Donor in GaP. I. Optical Cross Sections Energy Levels, and Concentration," *Phys. Rev.* **B7** (March 1973), pp. 2486-2499.

79. D. V. Lang, "Deep-Level Transient Spectroscopy: A New Method to Characterize Traps in Semiconductors," *J. Appl. Phys.* **45** (July 1974), pp. 3023-3032.

80. D. V. Lang and L. C. Kimerling, "Observation of Recombination-Enhanced Defect Reactions in Semiconductors," *Phys. Rev. Lett.* **33** (August 19, 1974), pp. 489-492.

81. C. H. Henry and D. V. Lang, "Nonradiative Capture and Recombination by Multiphonon Emission in GaAs and GaP," *Phys. Rev.* **B15** (January 1977), pp. 989-1016.

82. D. V. Lang and R. A. Logan, "Large-Lattice-Relaxation Model for Persistent Photoconductivity in Compound Semiconductors," *Phys. Rev. Lett.* **39** (September 5, 1977), pp. 635-639.

83. G. A. Baraff and M. Schlüter, "Self-Consistent Green's-Function Calculation of the Ideal Si Vacancy," *Phys. Rev. Lett.* **41** (September 25, 1978), pp. 892-895.

84. G. A. Baraff, E. O. Kane, and M. Schlüter, "Theory of the Silicon Vacancy: An Anderson Negative-*u* System," *Phys. Rev.* **B21** (June 1980), pp. 5662-5686.

85. G. D. Watkins and J. R. Troxell, "Negative-*u* Properties for Point Defects in Silicon," *Phys. Rev. Lett.* **44** (March 3, 1980), pp. 593-596.

86. P. W. Anderson, "Model for the Electronic Structure of Amorphous Semiconductors," *Phys. Rev. Lett.* **34** (April 14, 1975), pp. 953-955.

87. J. D. Cohen, D. V. Lang, and J. P. Harbison, "Direct Measurement of the Bulk Density of Gap State in *n*-Type Hydrogenated Amorphous Silicon," *Phys. Rev. Lett.* **45** (July 21, 1980), pp. 197-200.

88. L. V. Keldysh, *Proceedings of the Ninth International Conference on the Physics of Semiconductors, Moscow, 1968* (Nanka, Leningrad, 1968), p. 1303.

89. Ya. E. Pokrovskii and K. I. Svistunova, "Occurrence of a Condensed Phase of Nonequilibrium Carriers in Germanium," JETP Lett. 9 (April 5, 1969), pp. 261-262; V. M. Asmin and A. A. Rogachev, "Condensation of Exciton Gains in Germanium," JETP Lett. 9 (April 5, 1969), pp. 248-251; V. S. Vavilov, V. A. Zayats, and V. N. Murzin, "Resonant Absorption Scattering and Fusion of Electron-Hole Drops in Germanium in the Region of their Plasma Frequency," JETP Lett. 10 (October 5, 1969), pp. 192-195.

90. J. C. Hensel, T. G. Phillips, and G. A. Thomas, "The Electron-Hole Liquid in Semiconductors: Experimental Aspects," *Solid State Physics: Advances in Research and Applications* **32** ed. H. Ehrenreich, F. Seitz, and D. Turnbull (New York: Academic Press, 1977), pp. 1-86.

91. T. M. Rice, "The Electron-Hole Liquid in Semiconductors: Theoretical Aspects," *Solid State Physics: Advances in Research and Applications* **32** ed. H. Ehrenreich, F. Seitz, and D. Turnbull (New York: Academic Press, 1977), pp. 1-86.

92. W. F. Brinkman, T. M. Rice, P. W. Anderson, and S. T. Chui, "Metallic State of the Electron-Hole Liquid, Particularly in Germanium," *Phys. Rev. Lett.* **28** (April 10, 1972), pp. 961-964.

93. J. R. Arthur, Jr., "Interaction of Ga and As_2 Molecular Beams with GaAs Surfaces," *J. Appl. Phys.* **39** (July 1968), pp. 4032-4034.

94. A. Y. Cho, "GaAs Epitaxy by a Molecular Beam Method: Observations of Surface Structure on the (001) Face," *J. Appl. Phys.* **42** (April 1971), pp. 2074-2081; idem, "Film Deposition by Molecular-Beam Techniques," *J. Vac. Sci. Technol.* **8** (1971), p. S31.

95. A. C. Gossard, P. M. Petroff, W. Wiegmann, R. Dingle, and A. Savage, "Epitaxial Structure with Alternate-Atomic-Layer Composition Modulation," *Appl. Phys. Lett.* **29** (September 15, 1976), pp. 323-325; P. M. Petroff, A. C. Gossard, W. Wiegmann, and A. Savage, "Crystal Growth Kinetics in $(GaAs)_n-(AIAs)_m$ Superlattices Deposited by Molecular Beam Epitaxy," *J. Crystal Growth* **44** (1978), pp. 5-13.

96. R. Dingle, W. Wiegmann, and C. H. Henry, "Quantum States of Confined Carriers in Very Thin $Al_xGa_{1-x}As-GaAs-Al_xGa_{1-x}As$ Heterostructures," *Phys. Rev. Lett.* **33** (1974), p. 827; R. Dingle, A. C. Gossard, and W. Wiegmann, "Direct Observation of Superlattice Formation in a Semiconductor Heterostructure," *Phys. Rev. Lett.* **34** (May 26, 1975), pp. 1327-1330.

97. R. Dingle, H. L. Stormer, A. C. Gossard, and W. Wiegmann, "Electron Mobilities in Modulation-Doped Semiconductor Heterojunction Superlattices," *Appl. Phys. Lett.* **33** (October 1, 1978), pp. 665-667; D. C. Tsui and A. C. Gossard, "Resistance Standard Using Quantization of the Hall Resistance of $GaAs-Al_xGa_{1-x}As$ Heterostructures," *Appl. Phys. Lett.* **38** (January 1981), pp. 550-552; C. L. Allyn, A. C. Gossard, and W. Weigmann, "New Rectifying Semiconductor Structure by Molecular Beam Epitaxy," *Appl. Phys. Lett.* **36** (March 1980), pp. 373-376.

98. K. von Klitzing, G. Dorda, and M. Pepper, "New Method for High-Accuracy Determination of the Fine-Structure Constant Based on Quantized Hall Resistance," *Phys. Rev. Lett.* **45** (August 11, 1980), pp. 494-497.

Chapter 3

Surface Physics —
Wave Nature of the Electron

Motivation for fundamental studies of metallic surfaces arose in the early years of Bell Laboratories because of the increasing use of the vacuum tube in telephone repeaters. In the light of the role that surface states played in the discovery of the point contact transistor, research in surface physics was accelerated. This chapter starts with the historic Davisson-Germer experiment, which established the wave nature of the electron, and with a discussion of electron emission from solids, including secondary emission and field emission.

Semiconductor surface research immediately following the discovery of the transistor was limited to "real" surfaces immersed in air or electrolytes. These studies dealt with surface charge, contact potential, surface photovoltage, and surface states. The development of ultrahigh vacuum techniques made possible studies using atomically clean surfaces, such as low energy electron diffraction (LEED), the two-electron Auger emission, surface crystallography, and surface electronic structure on semiconductor and metallic surfaces. The research on the interaction of higher energy ions with semiconductor surfaces, including ion implantation, is discussed in Chapter 8. Related work on molecular beam epitaxy (MBE) is discussed in Chapters 2 and 19.

I. THE DAVISSON-GERMER EXPERIMENT

The historic experiment by C. J. Davisson and L. H. Germer was an outgrowth of an investigation of electron emission from a clean metal surface. They began this experiment to understand the effect on electron emission when a very clean metal was subsequently coated with an oxide. Starting with the discovery of elastic scattering of electrons from the metal surface, Davisson and Germer [Fig. 3-1] investigated the angular distribution of the elastically scattered electrons.[1] [Fig. 3-2] This led them to study the variation of the intensity with orientation of the scattering crystal. The unambiguous demonstration of the

---

Principal authors: H. D. Hagstrum, E. G. McRae, J. E. Rowe, and N. V. Smith

Fig. 3-1. C. J. Davisson (left) and L. H. Germer with the tube used in their electron diffraction work.

wave nature of electrons deduced from such electron diffraction was the basis for the award of the 1937 Nobel Prize in physics, which Davisson shared with G. P. Thomson of the University of Aberdeen, Scotland.

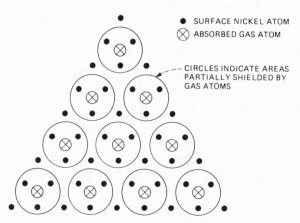

Fig. 3-2. The arrangement of a superstructure of absorbed gas atoms on a nickel surface as proposed by Davisson and Germer.

The story of the Davisson-Germer experiment is best recounted in quotations from Davisson's Nobel lecture of December 13, 1937, in the related excerpt from the Davisson and Germer paper published in the *Physical Review* in December 1927 describing the "well-known accident," and in some quotations from K. K. Darrow's paper published in the *Bell System Technical Journal* 1951 Festschrift issued in celebration of Davisson's seventieth birthday.*

1.1 Quotations from Davisson's Nobel Lecture, December 13, 1937

The case for a corpuscular aspect of light, now exceedingly strong, became overwhelmingly so when in 1922 A. H. Compton showed that in certain circumstances light quanta—photons, as they were now called—have elastic collisions with electrons in accordance with the simple laws of particle dynamics. What appeared, and what still appears to many of us, as a contradiction in terms had been proved true beyond the least possible doubt—light was at once a flight of particles and a propagation of waves; for light persisted, unreasonably, to exhibit the phenomenon of interference.

In 1924 there appeared the brilliant idea which was destined to grow into that marvelous synthesis, the present-day quantum mechanics. Louis de Broglie put forward in his doctor's thesis the idea that even as light, so matter has a duality of aspects; that matter like light possesses both the properties of waves and the properties of particles. ...perhaps no idea in physics has received so rapid or so intensive development as this one. De Broglie himself was in the van of this development but the chief contributions were made by the older and more experienced Schrödinger.

In these early days—eleven or twelve years ago—attention was focused on electron waves in atoms. The wave mechanics had sprung from the atom, so to speak, and it was natural that the first applications should be to the atom. No thought was given at this time, it appears, to electrons in free flight. It was implicit in the theory that beams of electrons like beams of light would exhibit the properties of waves, that scattered by an appropriate grating they would exhibit diffraction, yet none of the chief theorists mentioned this interesting corollary. The first to draw attention to it was Elsasser, who pointed out in 1925 that a demonstration of diffraction would establish the physical existence of electron waves. The setting of the stage for the discovery of electron diffraction was now complete.

It would be pleasant to tell you that no sooner had Elsasser's suggestion appeared than the experiments were begun in New York which resulted in a demonstration of electron diffraction—pleasanter still to say that the work was begun the day after copies of de Broglie's thesis reached America. The true story contains less of perspicacity and more of chance. The work actually began in 1919 with the accidental discovery that the energy spectrum of secondary electron emission has, as its upper limit, the energy of the primary electrons, even for primaries accelerated through hundreds of volts; that there is, in fact, an elastic scattering of electrons by metals.

Out of this grew an investigation of the distribution-in-angle of these elastically scattered electrons. And then chance again intervened; it was discovered, purely

---

* Chester J. Calbick, a young collaborator of Davisson and Germer, wrote another interesting account entitled "The Discovery of Electron Diffraction by Davisson and Germer," *The Physics Teacher* **1** (1963), p. 63.

by accident, that the intensity of elastic scattering varies with the orientations of the scattering crystals. Out of this grew, quite naturally, an investigation of elastic scattering by a single crystal of predetermined orientation. The initiation of this phase of the work occurred in 1925, the year following the publication of de Broglie's thesis, the year preceding the first great developments in the wave mechanics. Thus the New York experiment was not, at its inception, a test of the wave theory. Only in the summer of 1926, after I had discussed the investigation in England with Richardson, Born, Franck and others, did it take on this character.

From first to last a considerable number of colleagues contributed to the investigation. Chief among these were my two exceptionally able collaborators, Dr. C. H. Kunsman and Dr. L. H. Germer. Dr. Kunsman worked with me throughout the early stages of the investigation, and Dr. Germer, to whose skill and perseverance a great part of the success of the definitive experiments is due, succeeded Dr. Kunsman in 1924. Figure 3-2

I would like also at this time to express my admiration of the late Dr. H. D. Arnold, then Director of Research in the Bell Telephone Laboratories, and of Dr. W. Wilson, my immediate superior, who were sufficiently farsighted to see in these researches a contribution to the science of communication. Their vision was in fact accurate, for today in our, as in other, industrial laboratories electron diffraction is applied with great power and efficacy for discerning the structures of materials.

1.2 Davisson's "Well-Known Accident"

The accident mentioned in Davisson's Nobel lecture is described in Davisson and Germer's *Physical Review* paper published in December 1927.[2]

> During the course of his work a liquid-air bottle exploded at a time when the target was at a high temperature; the experimental tube was broken, and the target heavily oxidized by the in-rushing air. The oxide was eventually reduced and a layer of the target removed by vaporization, but only after prolonged heating at various high temperatures in hydrogen and in vacuum. When the experiments were continued, it was found that the distribution-in-angle of the scattered electrons had been completely changed. This marked alteration in the scattering-pattern was traced to a re-crystallization of the target that occurred during the prolonged heating. Before the accident and in previous experiments we had been bombarding many small crystals, but in the tests subsequent to the accident we were bombarding only a few large ones. The actual number was of the order of ten.

1.3 Quotations from Karl K. Darrow's "The Scientific Work of C. J. Davisson"

In 1951, a Festschrift edition of the *Bell System Technical Journal* was issued to celebrate Davisson's seventieth birthday. Darrow's essay entitled, "The Scientific Work of C. J. Davisson," is one of the papers in that Festschrift.[3] (Darrow joined Western Electric in 1917 and became a member of Bell Labs upon its incorporation in 1925. He became famous for his scholarly reviews of physics research. At the time this paper was written, he was also the secretary of the American Physical Society, a post he retained after retiring from Bell Labs in 1956.) Darrow gives an account of the Davisson-Germer experiment, authenticated by Davisson:

I can tell its history in words which I wrote down while at my request he related the story. This happened on the twenty-fifth of January 1937: I have the sheet of paper which he signed after reading it over, as also did our colleague L. A. MacColl, who was present to hear the tale. This is authentic history such as all too often we lack for other discoveries of comparable moment. Listen now to Davisson himself relating, even though in the third person, the story of the achievement.

The attention of C. J. Davisson was drawn to W. Elsasser's note of 1925, which he did not think much of because he did not believe that Elsasser's theory of his (Davisson's) prior results was valid. This note had no influence on the course of the experiments. What really started the discovery was the well-known accident with the polycrystalline mass, which suggested that single crystals would exhibit interesting effects. When the decision was made to experiment with the single crystal, it was anticipated that "transparent directions" of the lattice would be discovered. In 1926 Davisson had the good fortune to visit England and attend the meeting of the British Association for the Advancement of Science at Oxford. He took with him some curves relating to the single crystal, and they were surprisingly feeble (surprising how rarely beams had been detected!). He showed them to Born, to Hartree and probably to Blackett; Born called in another Continental physicist (possibly Franck) to view them, and there was much discussion of them. On the whole of the westward transatlantic voyage Davisson spent his time trying to understand Schroedinger's papers, as he then had an inkling (probably derived from the Oxford discussions) that the explanation might reside in them. (The reader is reminded that the "transatlantic voyage" was by steamship.)

In the autumn of 1926, Davisson calculated where some of the beams ought to be, looked for them and did not find them. He then laid out a program of thorough search, and on January 6, 1927, got strong beams due to the line-gratings of the surface atoms, as he showed by calculation in the same month.

In 1937 the Nobel prize was conferred on Davisson, and he had the opportunity of enjoying the ceremonies and festivities which are lavished upon those who go to Stockholm and receive it. He shared the prize with G. P. Thomson, who must not be entirely neglected even in an article dedicated explicitly to Davisson. There was little in common between their techniques, for Thomson consistently used much faster electrons which transpierced very thin polycrystalline films of metal and produced glorious diffraction-rings. He too founded a school of crystal analysts.

1.4 Observation of Spin Polarization Effects

Davisson and Germer are cited in textbooks for their pioneering work in 1927 on the diffraction of low-energy electrons from nickel single-crystal surfaces, leading to the confirmation of the wave nature of particles. It is only because of a mistake in the analysis of experimental data that they did not open another very exciting and novel field of research. In fact, in 1975, C. E. Kuyatt[4] of the National Bureau of Standards pointed out that in 1929, Davisson and Germer published a paper on the search for polarization of electron waves by reflection.[5] Mainly because of the negative results, this paper remained completely unnoticed for four decades. In the setup of the experiment described in their original paper, the electron waves scattered at 45 degrees from the first nickel crystal should show, if polarized, an asymmetry in the scattering from the second nickel crystal as this is rotated around the axis of the beam between the two crystals. This experiment is analogous to the one used for demonstrating the polarization of light by reflection from solid surfaces, as noted by Davisson and Germer. But this similarity is true only within certain limits that were not realized by Davisson and Germer. They expected to observe two maxima and two minima in the scattering as the second crystal is rotated through 360 degrees, as in the case of light polarization. Actually, for the electron spin with quantum number 1/2, only one maximum and one minimum should be observed. The erroneous conclusion reached by their 1929 paper is striking because polarization effects up to about 30 percent are obvious from the numerical results reported in the same publication. But for more than 45 years researchers in the field of low energy electron diffraction (LEED) did not realize this misinterpretation.

At the time of this writing, experiments involving spin polarization effects in LEED look very promising for investigating surface-related problems and for providing another detector for the spin polarization of electrons that may be more efficient than Mott scattering.[6] To this field, too, Davisson and Germer made their own contributions but, unfortunately, this time without recognizing its relevance.

II. ELECTRON EMISSION FROM SOLIDS

2.1 Primary Emission

Scientists at Bell Labs have long been interested in solids as emitters of electrons. The investigation of electron emission from a clean metal surface by Davisson and Germer was prompted by a desire for a better understanding of the effect on electron emission when a metal was coated with an oxide. In the late 1920s, H. E. Ives and his associates were interested in producing photoelectric cells of high efficiency as light detectors in connection with the development of the commercial system of picture transmission then in operation over certain Bell System lines.[7] They studied alkali-metal photoelectric cells of various structures and the effects of varying the treatment and temperature of the material and the nature of the radiation used.

J. A. Becker performed experiments with oxide-coated cathodes designed to yield information about the enhancement of electron emission resulting from coating the metal with barium oxide. He found, for example, that when current is drawn from the oxide, oxygen is deposited on the surface. If the oxygen is beneath the absorbed barium, it increases the activity; if it is above the barium, it decreases the activity. Together with W. H. Brattain, Becker correlated experimental values of the thermionic work-function with the theoretical Richardson equation.[8,9] Their correlation resulted in some modification of Richardson's equation.

In 1949, N. B. Hannay, D. MacNair, and A. H. White investigated the semiconducting properties of (Ba,Sr)O cathodes. They found that the electrical conductivity was directly proportional to the thermionic emission over a range of three orders of magnitude of activation, except in the cases where the oxide coating was probably inhomogeneous.[10] In 1955, L. A. Wooten and coworkers pointed out difficulties of measurement that had not been adequately realized in prior studies.[11] The fact that minor impurities might play an important role in the activity of oxide coatings was indicated when they found that very pure barium oxide or strontium oxide coatings on platinum supports led to very low emission. (For more on this topic see Chapter 17, section III.)

2.2 Secondary Emission

K. G. McKay and J. B. Johnson applied increasingly sophisticated techniques to the study of secondary electrons during the early 1950s. McKay, using pulsed bombardment, found that the resulting transient not only gave a value for the yield, but also values for the resistivity, the dielectric constant, and part of the energy distribution function of the secondaries.[12] In order to work with a clean substance of known structure, McKay and Johnson bombarded the (100) cleavage face of a single crystal of magnesium oxide (MgO) with electrons, establishing for this case also the inverse relationship between secondary emission and temperature.[13]

A theory of secondary electron emission proposed by P. A. Wolff in 1954 showed satisfactory agreement with experimental results and provided a valid and useful model for the phenomenon.[14]

2.3 Auger Electron Emission Spectroscopy of Solids

A novel type of secondary emission from solids, involving interaction with two electrons in the metal surface, was discovered by J. J. Lander. This was designated as Auger electron emission because of its similarity to the Auger effect discovered in cloud-chamber X-ray experiments by P. Auger of France in 1925. In the Auger effect, a singly ionized atom spontaneously becomes doubly ionized. The spontaneous step is a two-electron transition in which one electron drops into the hole produced in the initial ionization, while the second electron is ejected. The energy of the ejected electron is related through energy conservation to the other three levels of the two-electron transition.

Lander's paper, "Auger Peaks in the Energy Spectra of Secondary Electrons from Various Materials," published in 1953, marked the beginning of modern methods of surface chemical analysis.[15] Lander showed conclusively that certain narrow peaks of the energy distribution of secondary electrons from solids occur at energies that are related in a specific way to the core energy levels of surface atoms. Core-level spectra are highly characteristic (distinctly different for each different chemical element), and so offer a means of chemical identification.

Besides making the first identification of Auger transitions at surfaces, Lander gave one of the first demonstrations of the utility of electron-stimulated (as opposed to X-ray stimulated) Auger spectroscopy.

In the early 1950s, Bell Labs was an especially good environment for Lander's work. McKay had just completed a review that gathered many instances of secondary-emission features of the type later identified as Auger transitions.[16] G. H. Wannier helped formulate a description of Auger transitions in solids that accurately exhibited the potentialities of Auger electron spectroscopy. G. A. Harrower later demonstrated the coexistence of Auger spectra and "energy loss" spectra associated with electrons involved in ionization events.[17]

In time, Lander's pioneering work was recognized by scientists in other laboratories. With suitable modifications, Lander's experiments led to practical means of surface chemical analysis, an essential prerequisite for further progress in surface science. [Fig. 3-3] Auger electron spectroscopy is used as the chief means of surface chemical analysis in practically every laboratory devoted to surface science.

Another kind of surface investigative technique depending on the Auger effect was introduced by H. D. Hagstrum in 1954.[18] In this technique, low-energy, positive ions of the noble gases are used to bombard metal or semiconductor surfaces. An ion impinging on a surface induces an Auger-type transition in which one of the two electrons involved neutralizes the ion and the other is collected. A series of experiments by Hagstrum led to a general understanding of the electron transitions that occur when excited or ionized atoms interact with a surface. A computer program was developed that made possible the derivation of a function approximating the local density of states in the surface region of a solid from the measured energy distribution of the ejected Auger electrons.

2.4 Field Emission

The field emission microscope invented by E. W. Mueller of Pennsylvania State University has been a powerful tool in the study of the distribution and effect of coatings on cathodes. In this instrument, electrons are emitted from a sharp metal point along diverging paths in an evacuated tube. These electrons impinge on a curved fluorescent screen at the far end of the tube, producing a pattern that may be photographed. As the point is heated, surface atoms migrate and crystal facets with different emissivities develop.

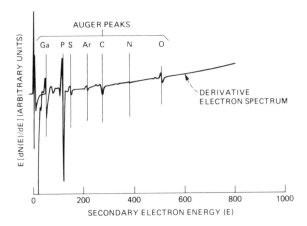

Fig. 3-3. Typical Auger spectrum of impurity atoms embedded in GaP. The derivative technique used for detection is much more sensitive than the original detection method used by Lander.

Beginning in the early 1950s, the patterns from clean surfaces were the subject of a series of papers by Becker[19] and others. In 1953, Becker reported that magnification of the image of the point was about 10^6, with a resolution of about 20×10^{-8}cm. The excitement of the early discoveries with this instrument is conveyed in Becker's early papers. [Fig. 3-4] At 2800K, the surface of the tungsten point is hemispherical. Only the (110), (111), and (100) regions consist of small flat planes. In fields of 50 million volts per cm and at 1200K, these planes enlarge. The edges of the planes are seen to be in violent agitation. Hence, surface atoms are mobile at temperatures above one-third of the melting point. Barium atoms show surface mobility at 400K on the (110) and 800K on the (100) planes.

In 1958, L. A. D'Asaro studied field emission from p-type silicon,[20] and in the 1960s, J. R. Arthur used field emission microscopy to study surfaces of the semiconductors gallium arsenide and germanium.[21,22] In a slice of a gallium arsenide crystal cut parallel to the octahedral (111) plane, gallium atoms form the outer layer on one surface, the (111), and arsenic atom on reverse surface, the (111). Arthur found that surface migration of both gallium and GaAs was more rapid on the (111) "B," or arsenic, face, which became thermally disordered above 300°C. The (111) "A" face remained ordered up to 400°C. On both faces, gallium decreased the work function by about 0.5 volts, while arsenic reduced the emitting area without altering the work function appreciably. Arthur also discovered that the intensity of emission from germanium, whether p-type or n-type, was strongly sensitive to surface treatment. In related work, F. G. Allen used photoemission techniques to study the work function in clean GaAs surfaces.

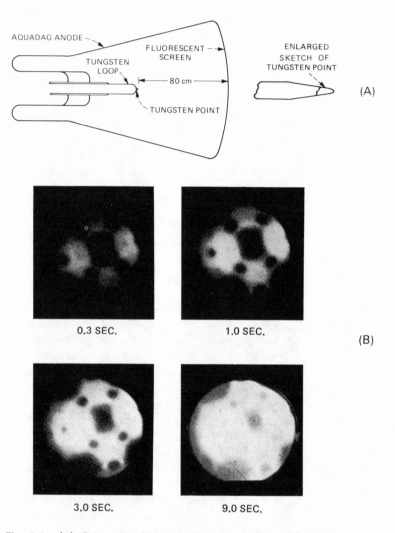

Fig. 3-4. (A) Schematic of field emission microscope. (B) Field emission patterns produced by the surface of the hemispherical tungsten point with varying exposure times.

In the early 1970s, T. Utsumi and O. Nishikawa at Bell Labs used a Mueller field *ion* microscope to study alloy formation when a tungsten or molybdenum point came in contact with molten gallium.[23] In the field ion microscope, neutral atoms are injected into the tube and ionized by the large electric field near the charged point, from which they then travel to the screen. The shorter wavelength associated with the greater mass results in better resolution of the pattern. Nishikawa and Utsumi combined the field ion microscope with field ion spectroscopy to measure the kinetic energy distribution of field-ionized noble gases on both clean surfaces and nitrogenabsorbate-covered surfaces of tungsten.[24,25]

In the mid-1970s, M. Campagna and others developed a technique for measuring the polarization of emitted electrons as a function of the surface crystallographic direction in the field emission microscope.[26] The novelty of this technique relies on the possibility of obtaining atomically clean metal surfaces by controlled ultrahigh vacuum field evaporation. The field emission cathode is located in the center of a superconducting coil, so that under the influence of the axial magnetic field, the divergent beam of electrons forms a distorted image on the screen. The measurements provide unique, direct information on magnetic interactions near surfaces. Problems related to chemisorption on transition metals can also be investigated by this technique because the spin-polarization of the emitted electrons has been found to be strongly sensitive to surface conditions.

III. SEMICONDUCTOR SURFACE RESEARCH DURING 1948-1960

Semiconductor surface research at Bell Laboratories can be divided into two distinct periods. The research activity during 1948-1960, carried on by W. H. Brattain and others, was concerned with the properties of surfaces like those used in devices—the "real" surfaces. In the research begun after 1960, the emphasis was on clean or chemically well-characterized surfaces.

Surfaces used in semiconductor research in the earlier period were generally produced by cutting, grinding or sandblasting, polishing, and etching. The chemical state of such a surface depends on the etchant used. It may be atomically ordered and in some cases may be covered with a thin oxide layer 10-30Å thick, particularly if exposed to long periods in air. During this period, the research concentrated on elucidating the static and kinetic features of the electronic structure of surfaces produced in this way.

3.1 Surface Charge, Contact Potential, and Surface Voltage

As a semiconductor surface is approached from the deep bulk of the solid, the space-charge region is entered. This region is typically about 10^{-5} cm in extent, and is associated with a surplus or deficit of free carriers. The space-charge layer is the result of charges residing at the interface between the bulk of the semiconductor and the surface oxide, as well as in the oxide itself. Surface electronic states in intimate contact with the bulk, the "fast" (microsecond) states, reside at the oxide-semiconductor interface. "Slow" (second) states in poor electrical contact with the bulk reside inside and at the outer surface of the oxide layer. Charge in the slow states results in a potential drop, V_D, across the oxide. For a given bulk impurity doping, the space-charge barrier potential, V_S, uniquely determines the shape of the barrier and the carrier distribution (via the Poisson equation). In the absence of an external field, the charges in all surface states and in the space-charge layer are equal and opposite.

The existence of a space-charge layer at the free surface of a semiconductor was first predicted by J. Bardeen in 1949.[27] In 1953, experimental evidence of its existence came from the work on contact potential and surface photovoltage by Brattain and Bardeen.[28] It was discovered that the barrier potential associated with the space charge layer (V_S) could be reproducibly varied by varying the gaseous ambient. The Brattain-Bardeen cycle of gaseous ambients involved the use of wet and dry oxygen and nitrogen, as well as ozone, applied in a particular sequence. This caused a variation of V_S of as much as 0.5 electronvolts ascribed to the addition and removal of ions at the outer surface of the oxide film. Recombination rates of holes and electrons and surface trapping were studied, and a particular model of surface states as donors and acceptors was proposed.

3.2 Surface Photovoltage and Surface States

Brattain and Bardeen also varied the barrier potential by applying light using the surface photovoltage effect. They demonstrated a direct correlation between the surface photovoltage and the work function of the surface.[29] C. G. B. Garrett and Brattain produced a detailed theory of the surface photovoltage effect that accounted for the experimental data and contributed significantly to the quantitative understanding of the space-charge layer.[30] [Fig. 3-5]

The barrier voltage associated with the space-charge region, the region itself, and the surface conductance can be varied by applying a capacitatively coupled external electric field.[31] Garrett and Brattain used field effect, surface photovoltage, and surface conductivity measurements in a combined experiment and compared their results with theory.[32] W. L. Brown used the variation of conductance with external field to determine both the surface potential and the distribution of charge in the surface states.[33] He recognized that observation of the unique minimum in conductance leads to quantitative results. Low-frequency field-effect measurements in various gaseous ambients,[34] and the measurement of surface conductance in strong inversion layers,[35] were also performed during the period of 1948-1960.

W. Shockley made a theoretical study of the symmetrical truncation of a crystal with perfect periodicity from bulk to surface.[36] He found that localized states split off from the upper and lower bands, forming the so-called Shockley surface states in the forbidden gap. Surface states on the free surface of germanium were first demonstrated in the field-effect measurements of Shockley and G. L. Pearson.[37] That surface states can be slow or fast (poor versus good electrical contact with the bulk) was evident in the early work of Brattain and Bar-

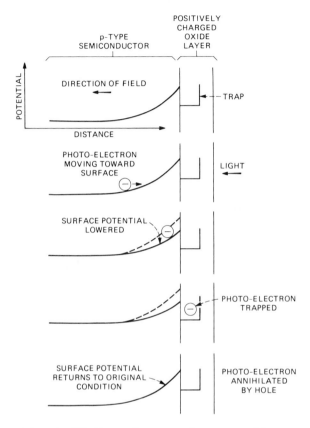

Fig. 3-5. Life history of an extra electron created in p-type material by illumination of the sample, from its birth in the photoexcitation process to its death in recombination at the surface, starting with a positive charge in the oxide layer and higher at the surface than at the side, as shown in the top part of the diagram. In the next part of the diagram, an extra electron created by photoexcitation begins moving in the direction of the arrow. The other steps are shown in the remaining parts of the diagram.

deen.[38] That these surface states differ greatly in capture times was shown by Garrett and Brattain when they observed that the surface photovoltage disappeared after illumination in times of seconds or minutes.[39] Relaxation of the fast surface states was studied with high-frequency applied fields by H. C. Montgomery, who developed this means of eliminating the effects of slow states.[40] A quantitative analysis of this experiment was given by Garrett.[41] Surface recombination velocity was shown to be very sensitive to treatment of the surface.[42] Its connection with surface noise was studied by Montgomery.[43]

3.3 Semiconductors in an Electrolytic Ambient

Work with the semiconductor in an electrolytic ambient has proved very fruitful. Brattain and Garrett elucidated the rectification properties of the semiconductor-electrolyte interface.[44] They studied reactions for anodic and cathodic bias, as well as the surface properties that had been investigated for the gas-semiconductor interface. The surface states introduced by various metallic ions from an electrolyte were studied by P. J. Boddy and Brattain.[45] Adsorption of gases on semiconductor surfaces, as well as the oxidation kinetics of these surfaces, were studied extensively by J. T. Law.[46]

IV. SURFACE RESEARCH – CONTROLLED SURFACE IN ULTRAHIGH VACUUM

Several factors contributed to the nature of surface research in the late 1970s. Advances in ultrahigh vacuum techniques in glass systems had progressed to the point that fundamental scientific experiments on surfaces appeared practical. Moreover, experimentation was greatly facilitated by the availability of commercial ultrahigh vacuum system components. This was accompanied by the application of new spectroscopic techniques having greater surface specificity, such as ultraviolet photoemission at energies in the range of 10 to 100 eV, extended X-ray absorption spectroscopy, electron energy loss spectroscopy, high-energy ion scattering, and the application of high-speed computer methods to low energy electron diffraction.

A surface is a collection of interacting atoms that may be considered a phase of matter in close association with, but nevertheless distinguishable from, the bulk solid under it. It is characterized by the geometric arrangement of its atoms (surface crystallography), the chemical nature of the atoms present (chemical composition and adsorption), and the energy level and charge density structure of the electrons in the surface region (surface electronic structure).

The study of the interaction of atoms with surfaces has both kinetic and static aspects. Several important parameters are the probability that an atom incident on a surface will stay on, or stick to the surface, the migration and nucleation of adsorbed species, and the thermal desorption of the foreign atom. Each of these phenomena was studied extensively by J. A. Becker in the late 1940s and 1950s using a variety of techniques. Among these were thermionic emission, thermal and field desorption, work function measurement, and field emission microscopy. This work led to a much better understanding of the charge state of adsorbed species by their effect on surface potential or work function; of the specificity of adsorption and migration phenomena to particular crystallographic planes; and to the binding energy of adsorbate atoms to crystal surfaces in more than one crystallographic site. Becker reviewed much of this work in 1955.[47]

Becker's work represented an early effort to attack surface problems using more than one technique. (For more on Becker's studies see section 2.4 of this chapter.)

During the late 1950s, J. T. Law studied the adsorption of gases on cleaned semiconductor surfaces.[48] These studies led to Law's work on the oxidation of silicon, in which measurements of kinetics were made and models of the growth of oxide films were presented.[49]

An important aspect of the interaction of atoms with surfaces is the development of tools for the chemical analysis of such surfaces. The principal means for analysis is Auger electron spectroscopy (AES) described in section 2.3 of this chapter.

Researchers also benefited from the greatly increased understanding of the nature of the solid state. In 1962, E. O. Kane proposed a theory of photoelectric emission from semiconductors that was based on density-of-state and energy-band considerations and that did not involve scattering of the excited electrons either from the bulk material or at the surface.[50] Theorists also began to apply self-consistent calculations of energy levels specifically to the surface region of the solid.

The geometric structure of the surface layer was explored with low-energy electron diffraction by J. J. Lander, G. W. Gobeli, and A. U. MacRae, among others.[51] A variety of surface superlattices were studied. It was found, for example, that in an annealed Si(111) surface, the translational periodicity of the surface layers is seven times that of the bulk substrate. The implications of these new structural forms, seen on almost all semiconductors, were far-reaching for the understanding of chemical bonding.

F. G. Allen and Gobeli characterized other physical properties of the elemental and the III-V compound semiconductors.[52,53] Particularly noteworthy were their experimental measurements of the work function, bulk photoelectric threshold, and energy gap surface state distribution on Si(111). Gobeli and Allen performed a series of experiments on the photoelectric emission from cleaved (111) surfaces of single silicon crystals in a vacuum, using both pure and doped crystals. Their results were in agreement with the Kane theory, and gave rise to an understanding of the surface transport and rectification properties of these materials.

Beginning in the late 1960s, advanced techniques of surface science, particularly Auger spectroscopy and electron diffraction, were applied with notable success to the problems of growing and characterizing the surfaces of nearly perfect crystals of GaAs in ultrahigh vacuum by Arthur and A. Y. Cho.[54] Insights into the kinetic processes involved in the growth of these compounds were obtained, and for the first time, geometric characterization of a surface under growth conditions was achieved. This technique, molecular beam epitaxy (MBE), has resulted in improved capabilities in the areas of heterojunction lasers, and microwave and optical component fabrication.[55] Molecular beam epitaxy holds great promise as a tool for the development of practical integrated optical devices. (For more on MBE see section VI of Chapter 2.)

The greatest progress in controlling and documenting a surface and its characteristics has been made for the free surface of a solid in a vacuum or in a controlled gaseous environment. This has occurred because it has been possible to develop the methods of cleaning the surface and of diagnosing its properties to the necessary level of sophistication. The research on semiconductor surfaces carried on after 1960 at Bell Labs falls into this category.

4.1 Surface Crystallography — Low Energy Electron Diffraction

Low energy electron diffraction (LEED) is a tool for determining the geometric arrangement of surface atoms. The study of this phenomenon as a crystallographic tool for surface studies goes back to the first experiments by Davisson and Germer on the wave nature of matter. Even in that early work, the effect of surface condition was clearly evident. It was found that the condensation of an unknown gas (probably CO) on the nickel crystal produced a superstructure on the surface with a repeat distance twice that of the surface metal atoms. This resulted in extra diffraction spots between those caused by the surface nickel atoms. Thus began a study of adsorption super-structures on solid surfaces, which proceeded very slowly until the advent of improved instrumentation in the early 1960s. At that time, Germer, Lander, MacRae, and others undertook intensive studies in this field.

The determination of the periodicity and symmetry of the adsorp-tion superstructure from the LEED data is not difficult. It is a neces-sary first step in every complete surface study leading to a full analysis of the arrangement of the surface atoms. Observations of LEED pattern changes or the disappearance of the pattern also make possible studies of surface or two-dimensional phase transformations, and order-disorder transformations both in adsorbed layers and on clean surfaces. Such adsorbed layers may be the initial foothold of an epitaxial deposit.

A particularly interesting discovery made during this period is the metastable (2-by-1) structure on the cleaved Si(111) surface that, when heated, reverts irreversibly to the (7-by-7) structure. The (7-by-7) structure has a superstructure unit mesh (the two-dimensional equivalent of the unit cell of a three-dimensional crystal) 49 times as large in area as that of the underlying semiconductor surface.[56]

Once the surface symmetry and mesh dimensions have been deter-mined, the specific determination of atom positions at a surface is still a difficult task. This requires the study of the way in which the intensity of the diffracted beams varies with electron energy (or wavelength) of the incident beams. Such observations were made in the early Davisson and Germer work, but a detailed understanding required the development of LEED theory and computing methods. P. M. Morse, who spent the summer of 1929 at Bell Labs, pursued the problem beyond a simple single-scattering kinematic theory of electron diffraction. Although his theoretical analysis did not account for structure observed between the principal Bragg peaks in the plots of intensity versus voltage, it did point to the necessity of a multiple scattering approach as represented in this case by the band structure of the crystal. In 1966, E. G. McRae applied a general multiple-scattering theory developed by M. Lax to the specific case of LEED intensities, giving the first exact solution for a model in which atomic potentials are represented specifically.[57] McRae's study led to qualitative understanding of the extra (non-Bragg) structure in the I-V plot. His "layer" method of computing diffraction intensities is an extension of early ideas of Darwin and Wannier. This method, or a variation, is used in practically all numerical LEED computations leading to specific atom positions.[58] The study of beam intensities in LEED as a function of temperature led to the first observation that vibrational amplitudes for surface atoms exceed those of the bulk, and to the determination of a surface Debye temperature.[59]

The original Davisson and Germer studies demonstrated the potential of using the LEED technique in various forms. During the following two decades, D. W. Farnsworth and his students at Brown University used LEED to measure the intensity of electrons diffracted from surfaces by standard current, measuring techniques. In the late 1950s, E. J. Scheibner, who was later joined by Germer, put a display-type LEED apparatus (first suggested by Ehrenberg in 1934) into practical form.[60] [Fig. 3-6] Lander and coworkers (and independently, Peria at the University of Minnesota) further improved display-type LEED by using spherical grids and phosphor screens.[61] This was the form that Germer arranged to have made commercially available. It was based on a design he provided after his retirement from Bell Labs, and it had a stimulating effect on LEED research because of its visual display of the diffraction pattern.

4.2 Surface Electronic Structure

The third basic characterization of a solid surface, viewed as a collection of interacting atoms, is its electronic structure or chemical binding. The questions may arise: How can this structure differ from the bulk electronic structure? And what are the best ways to describe the electronic states of adsorbed foreign atoms? Prominent among the techniques used to answer these questions is ultraviolet photo-

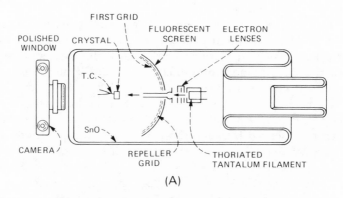

(A)

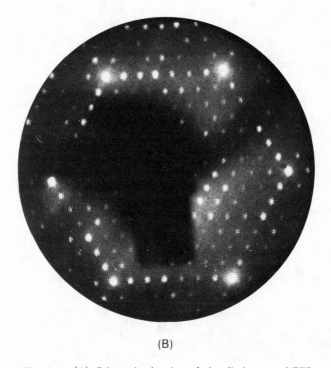

(B)

Fig. 3-6. (A) Schematic drawing of the display-type LEED apparatus developed by Schiebner, Germer, Hartman, and Lander. (B) Cathode-ray display of a typical LEED pattern.

emission spectroscopy (UPS). Also important are ion neutralization spectroscopy (INS) and electron energy-loss spectroscopy (ELS). In pursuing these spectroscopic investigations, it has been most important for experimentalists to work in close coordination with theoreticians.

The energy spectrum of photoelectrons emitted from a solid surface is related closely to the energy level distributions of electronic states in both the bulk and at the surface. The surface sensitivity is enhanced by working in the photon energy range above about 20 eV, where the photoelectron mean-free path is only a couple of atomic spacings. Early work on photoelectric emission was performed at Bell Labs by Ives and collaborators. In 1928, Ives, A. R. Olpin, and A. L. Johnsrud published a paper that contained measurements of the energy spectra of photoelectrons, and their distribution in angle.[62]

Photoemission languished in the physics community for several decades, and was taken up again at Bell Labs in the early 1960s by Gobeli, Allen, and Kane, as noted in section IV of this chapter. In 1964, Kane proposed that measurements of the angular distributions of photoelectrons should yield directly the dispersion relations (that is, the energy-versus-wavevector curves) for electronic states.[63]

In the early 1970s, UPS was studied by J. E. Rowe, H. D. Hagstrum, N. V. Smith, and their respective coworkers. Rowe and H. Ibach pursued photoemission from surface states on several different crystal faces of silicon.[64] From Si(111) they saw not only the "dangling" bond states associated with the fundamental gap, but were also able to observe additional surface states within the valence band energy range associated with back-bonding orbitals. These states had been predicted by J. A. Appelbaum and D. R. Hamann in what were the first self-consistent calculations of energy states in the surface region of a solid.[65] [Fig. 3-7] The experimental results were confirmed and extended by Rowe and Ibach using energy loss spectroscopy (ELS).[66] Similar studies were performed on adsorbate-covered surfaces by detailed examination of the new peaks that appear in the photoelectron energy spectra. For example, experimental studies by Ibach and Rowe, and by T. Sakurai and Hagstrum,[67] coupled with theoretical calculations and interpretation by Appelbaum and Hamann and by K. C. Pandey and J. C. Phillips,[68] revealed the existence of a variety of structurally different forms of chemisorbed hydrogen on silicon.

Additional theoretical and experimental work was applied to the study of the metal-semiconductor interface, or Schottky barrier, formed by sequential deposition of fractions of aluminum monolayers on silicon.[69] Theoretical studies of atomic geometries showed that a threefold bonding of aluminum atoms to silicon occurs. Experimental measurements of surface states after aluminum deposition showed that the Schottky-barrier energy levels were caused by a thin layer ($\sim$2Å) rather than the thicker layer ($\sim$15Å to 20Å) suggested previously.[70]

One of the most important solid-solid interfaces in technology is formed by silicon dioxide on silicon. The stabilization of silicon sur-

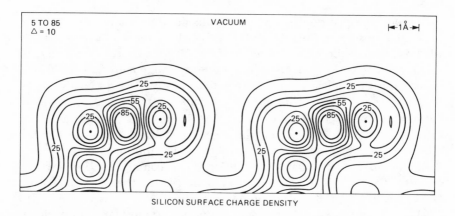

Fig. 3-7. Contours of charge density on a silicon surface. The numbers indicate equi-charged density contours in arbitrary units.

faces by thermally grown oxides was first demonstrated by M. M. Atalla, E. Tannenbaum, and Scheibner.[71] The oxide layer is used as a passivating element to protect the silicon device from the ambient environment and as an insulating layer to isolate individual electronic components on a single chip. In the late 1970s, a number of different techniques were developed and applied to the physical characterization of this structure. D. E. Aspnes and J. B. Theeten used ellipsometric techniques to determine the interface width.[72] O. L. Krivanek of the University of California at Berkeley, and D. C. Tsui and coworkers at Bell Labs, studied the same system by cross-sectional transmission electron microscopy,[73] while L. C. Feldman and coworkers analyzed the structure using high-energy Rutherford backscattering techniques.[74] The results of these studies indicated a very sharp interface, ~5Å thick, which included a region of strained silicon single crystal. These results confirmed the high degree of perfection at this interface that makes it very useful in technological applications.

Smith, whose initial efforts had concentrated on that part of the photoemission spectra which could be understood in terms of wave-vector conserving transitions within the bulk band structure, turned to the old problem of the angular distribution of the photoelectrons. In 1974, Smith, M. M. Traum, and F. J. DiSalvo demonstrated for the first time that the electronic energy dispersion relations could indeed be mapped directly from angle-resolved photoemission experiments performed on the layer compounds TaS_2 and $TaSe_2$.[75] Their study consummated the proposal made ten years earlier by Kane.[76] The energy band structure derived was in remarkable agreement with the theoretical band calculations of L. F. Mattheiss.[77] In the same year, Traum, Rowe, and Smith applied the angular-dependence technique to the dangling and back-bond surface states on Si(111).[78] The extension to adsorbate systems was performed by Smith and coworkers for chlorine atoms adsorbed on Si(111).[79] Results were obtained for the two-dimensional surface band structure of this system that agreed well with theoretical calculations by M. Schlüter and coworkers.[80] [Fig. 3-8] In short, a very detailed description of the surface electronic structure and chemisorptive bond could be obtained.

Since 1975, much of the photoemission work has been done using synchrotron radiation from the Tantalus storage ring at the University of Wisconsin, Madison. The intense continuum nature of synchrotron radiation makes it an attractive source, and its inherent polarization was used, for example, in the additional selection rules needed to infer the atomic position of chlorine on the Si(111) surface.[81]

The surface-sensitive ion-neutralization spectroscopy (INS) was developed by Hagstrum [Fig. 3-9] as a result of extensive studies of

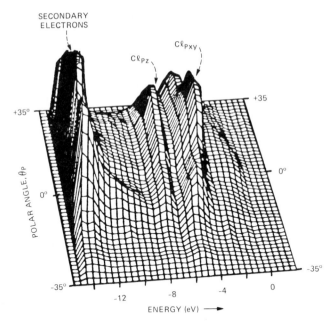

Fig. 3-8. Photoelectrons emitted from an ordered monolayer of chlorine atoms (1-1, as observed by low energy electron diffraction) on a silicon surface. The three-dimensional plot shows intensity as a function of the emitted electron energy and the angle between, normal to the surface and the direction of the emitted electrons. The maximum electron energy is 16.3 eV (21.2 eV photon energy minus 4.9 eV work function). The two principal intensity peaks, $Cl_{p\perp}$ and $Cl_{p\|}$, result from electrons in two different atomic states of chlorine — one perpendicular to the surface and the other parallel to the surface, respectively. The peak at the left is caused by multiple scattering.

Fig. 3-9. H. D. Hagstrum pioneered in research involving surface phenomena in ultrahigh vacuum. In the early 1960s, he designed and built an all-metal, multi-experiment apparatus. Hagstrum's speciality has been the study and use of electron ejection accompanying the surface interaction of slowly moving atoms that carry surface potential energy (ions or metastables) upon which the most surface-specific probes of electronic structure are based. Using his newly developed ion-neutralization spectroscopy, Hagstrum was the first to observe the surface resonance of electrons in the chemical bonds holding adsorbate atoms to otherwise atomically clean surfaces.

the electronic transitions that can occur when a slow atomic particle, carrying potential energy by virtue of its being ionized or excited, encounters a solid surface. It is based on a two-electron, Auger-type electron ejection process. Hagstrum developed a method for using the experimental data to obtain the surface spectroscopic information and observed the surface electronic resonance caused by an adsorbed atom.[82] The method has been applied to the adsorption of the chalcogens on nickel crystalline surfaces. It has been shown that the coordination of the "surface molecule" is mirrored in the orbital energy spectrum obtained.[83]

In 1977, researchers at Northwestern University and at the University of Kent discovered giant Raman scattering molecules adsorbed from solution onto silver electrodes in an electrochemical environment.[84] (For more on Raman scattering see Chapter 5, section 6.2.) Estimates of the magnitude of the scattering, assuming that only the first few adsorbed monolayers were contributing, concluded that it was enhanced by roughly six orders of magnitude over normal gas-phase Raman scattering. At Bell Labs, J. G. Bergman and coworkers used radioactive tracer measurements to confirm that the giant Raman scattering was indeed taking place from about one monolayer, or roughly 10^{15} molecules per square-centimeter on the electrode.[85] This surface-enhanced scattering can be compared with conventional, non-resonant, Raman scattering cross sections of molecules in the study of surface structure or catalysis, where scattering from approximately 10^{15} molecules per square-centimeter is normally swamped by the intense scattering of the substrate. This new technique of surface vibrational spectroscopy appears to be capable of yielding essential information about adsorbant-adsorbate systems that is difficult or impossible to obtain either by traditional electronic level spectroscopy or by LEED. The knowledge of surface vibrational frequencies and intensities can yield direct and positive identification of adsorbed species and give important insight into how and to which bonding sites they are adsorbed.

In 1979, Rowe and coworkers observed the surface-enhanced Raman effect on a silver surface prepared and dosed with an adsorbate at ultrahigh vacuum. This study paved the way for an understanding of the mechanism behind the large observed enhancements.[86] The results of the study were consistent with the excitation of localized dipolar plasmon resonances of small (100Å to 1000Å scale) silver particles, which Rowe determined must be present on the surface in order to obtain enhanced signals. This effect had been suggested originally by M. Moscovits at the University of Toronto,[87] and later analyzed by S. L. McCall, P. M. Platzman, and P. A. Wolff,[88] and confirmed experimentally by C. A. Murray and coworkers[89] and D. A. Zwemer and coworkers.[90] Using a classical spheroid model, they showed that the silver particles act as antennas for intensifying both the incident exciting optical laser light and the reradiated Raman-shifted light. The predicted magnitude, distance, and frequency dependence of the signal was also consistent with the data.

4.3 Multiple Experiments in One Apparatus

The work of Bell Labs scientists in surface physics has emphasized the importance of performing multiple experiments on the same solid state specimen in one ultrahigh vacuum apparatus.[91] [Fig. 3-10] In

Fig. 3-10. H. D. Hagstrum's ultrahigh vacuum apparatus containing facilities for freeing a specimen from contaminants and maintaining the purity while several surface physics experiments are performed.

one type of multiple experiment, the surface is characterized, inspected, and probed by a variety of means that yield information on several different aspects of the surface and its interactions. Thus, LEED specifies surface crystallography, Auger electron spectroscopy (AES) specifies the atoms present in the surface region (the surface chemistry), and an electron spectroscopy such as ultraviolet photoemission spectroscopy (UPS) probes surface electronic structure. A second type of multiple experiment, although it may include the first, emphasizes the probing of a particular aspect of a surface by a variety of means. Thus, surface electronic structure has been studied by more than one electron spectroscopy such as UPS, INS, or electron energy loss spectroscopy (ELS).[92] Similarly, surface geometrical structure has been probed by ion backscattering, by LEED, by high energy electron diffraction (HEED), and by the diffraction of low energy, nearly monoenergetic beams of helium atoms from silicon surfaces by M. J. Cardillo and G. E. Becker.[93] The atomic beams of helium were obtained from a free-jet expansion of helium out of a high-pressure (7 atm) nozzle through a small (~30 μm) aperture. Combined with LEED and AES, atom diffraction allows a more complete determination of the surface structure.[94] Each spectroscopy, or method, has its peculiar set of characteristics. The use of a combination of them provides considerably more information about a given aspect of a surface than can be obtained with one method alone.

Multiple experiments of either type or, as is usually the case, a combination of the two, is an essential part of good surface experimentation. This is rooted in the fact that the atomic system studied in the first monolayer or two of a well-characterized surface cannot be transported from one experiment to another as can a bulk crystalline solid. In most cases, the two-dimensional crystal must be created and studied in the same vacuum environment. Multiple experiments come close to being ideal for performing research on controlled surfaces in a vacuum.

The story of the investigation of electron emission during the first fifty years of the history of Bell Labs is one of progress from the study of materials whose physical nature and chemical purity was inadequately known, to powerful techniques involving high-vacuum, electron spectroscopic techniques, temperature measurement over wide ranges, and purity of materials unavailable to the early workers in the field. The development of the computer has made possible correlations between theory and experiment that might have been prohibitively time-consuming in the past. Understanding of the processes involved in electron emission continues to increase at an accelerated rate.

REFERENCES

1. C. J. Davisson and L. H. Germer, "The Scattering of Electrons by a Nickel Crystal," *Phys. Rev.* **29** (June 1927), p. 908.
2. C. J. Davisson and L. H. Germer, "Diffraction of Electrons by a Crystal of Nickel," *Phys. Rev.* **30** (December 1927), pp. 705-740.
3. K. K. Darrow, "The Scientific Work of C. J. Davisson," *Bell System Tech. J.* **30** (October 1951), pp. 786-797.
4. C. Kuyatt, "Observation of Polarized Electrons by Davisson and Germer," *Phys. Rev.* **B12** (November 1, 1975), pp. 4581-4583.
5. C. Davisson and L. H. Germer, "A Test for Polarization of Electron Waves by Reflection," *Phys. Rev.* **33** (May 1929), pp. 760-772.
6. M. R. O'Neill, M. Kalisvaari, F. B. Dunning, and G. K. Walters, "Electron-Spin Polarization in Low-Energy Electron Diffraction from Tungsten (001)," *Phys. Rev. Lett.* **34** (May 5, 1975), pp. 1167-1170.
7. H. E. Ives, "The Alkali Metal Photoelectric Cell," *Bell System Tech. J.* **5** (April 1926), pp. 320-335.
8. J. A. Becker, "Phenomena in Oxide Coated Filaments," *Phys. Rev.* **34** (November 1929), pp. 1323-1351.
9. J. A. Becker and W. H. Brattain, "The Thermionic Work Function and the Slope and Intercept of Richardson Plots," *Phys. Rev.* **45** (May 1934), pp. 694-705.
10. N. B. Hannay, D. MacNair, and A. H. White, "Semi-Conducting Properties in Oxide Cathodes," *J. Appl. Phys.* **20** (July 1949), pp. 669-681.

11. L. A. Wooten, G. E. Moore, and W. G. Guldner, "Measurement of Excess Ba in Practical Oxide Coated Cathodes," *J. Appl. Phys.* **26** (August 1955), pp. 937-942; G. E. Moore, L. A. Wooten, and J. Morrison, "Excess Ba Content of Practical Oxide Coated Cathodes and Thermionic Emission," *J. Appl. Phys.* **26** (August 1955), pp. 943-948.

12. K. G. McKay, "A Pulse Method of Determining the Energy Distribution of Secondary Electrons from Insulators," *J. Appl. Phys.* **22** (January 1951), pp. 89-94.

13. J. B. Johnson and K. G. McKay, "Secondary Electron Emission of Crystalline MgO," *Phys. Rev.* **91** (August 1953), pp. 582-587.

14. P. A. Wolff, "Theory of Secondary Electron Cascade in Metals," *Phys. Rev.* **95** (July 1954), pp. 56-66.

15. J. J. Lander, "Auger Peaks in the Energy Spectra of Secondary Electrons from Various Materials," *Phys. Rev.* **91** (September 1953), pp. 1382-1387.

16. K. G. McKay, *Advances in Electronics* (New York: Academic Press, Inc., 1948).

17. G. A. Harrower, "Auger Electron Emission in the Energy Spectra of Secondary Electrons from Mo and W," *Phys. Rev.* **102** (April 1956), pp. 340-347.

18. H. D. Hagstrum, "Theory of Auger Ejection of Electrons from Metals by Ions," *Phys. Rev.* **96** (October 1954), pp. 336-365; idem, "Theory of Auger Neutralization of Ions at the Surface of a Diamond-Type Semiconductor," *Phys. Rev.* **122** (April 1961), pp. 83-113.

19. J. A. Becker and C. D. Hartman, "Field Emission Microscope and Flash Filament Techniques for the Study of Structure and Adsorption on Metal Surfaces," *J. Phys. Chem.* **57** (February 1953), pp. 153-159; J. A. Becker and R. G. Brandes, "On the Adsorption of Oxygen on Tungsten as Revealed in the Field Emission Electron Microscope," *J. Chem. Phys.* **23** (July 1955), pp. 1323-1330; idem, "Adsorption on Metal Surfaces and Its Bearing on Catalysis," *Advances in Catalysis and Related Subjects: Volume VII*, ed. W. G. Frankenberg, V. I. Komarewsky, and E. K. Rideal (New York: Academic Press, 1955); idem, "Study of Surfaces by Using New Tools," *Solid State Physics: Advances in Research and Application, Vol. 7.*, ed. F. Seitz and D. Turnbull (New York: Academic Press, 1958), pp. 379-424.

20. L. A. D'Asaro, "Field Emission from Silicon," *J. Appl. Phys.* **29** (January 1958), pp. 33-34.

21. J. R. Arthur, "Energy Distribution of Field Emission from Germanium," *Surf. Sci.* **2** (1964), pp. 389-395.

22. J. R. Arthur, "Gallium Arsenide Surface Structure and Reaction Kinetics: Field Emission Microscopy," *J. Appl. Phys.* **37** (July 1966), pp. 3057-3064.

23. T. Utsumi and O. Nishikawa, "Field-Ion-Microscope Studies of the Interface Between Solid-Liquid Metals in Vacuum," *Appl. Phys. Lett.* **21** (August 1, 1972), pp. 110-112.

24. O. Nishikawa and T. Utsumi, "Field Ion Microscope Study on the Interaction of Gallium with Metals. I. Pseudomorphic Structure and Superstructures on Tungsten," *J. Appl. Phys.* **44** (March 1973), pp. 945-954; idem, "Field Ion Microscope Study on the Interaction of Gallium with Metals. II. Alloy Formation with Molybdenum and Anisotropic Binding Force in Mo_3Ga," *J. Appl. Phys.* **44** (March 1973), pp. 955-964.

25. T. Utsumi and N. V. Smith, "Field-Ion Spectroscopy of Electronic States at Clean and Adsorbate-Covered Tungsten Surfaces," *Phys. Rev. Lett.* **33** (November 18, 1974), pp. 1294-1297.

26. M. Campagna, T. Utsumi, and D. N. E. Buchanan, "Study of the Spin Polarization of Field-Emitted Electrons from Magnetic Materials," *J. Vac. Sci. and Technology* **13** (Jan./Feb. 1976), pp. 192-195.

27. J. Bardeen, "Surface States and Rectification at a Metal Semiconductor Contact," *Phys. Rev.* **71** (May 1949), pp. 717-727.

28. W. H. Brattain and J. Bardeen, "Surface Properties of Germanium," *Bell System Tech. J.* **32** (January 1953), pp. 1-41.

29. See reference 28.
30. C. G. B. Garrett and W. H. Brattain, "Physical Theory of Semiconductor Surfaces," *Phys. Rev.* **99** (July 1955), pp. 376-387.
31. W. Shockley and G. L. Pearson, "Modulation of Conductance of Thin Films of Semi-Conductors by Surface Charges," Letter to the Editor, *Phys. Rev.* **74** (July 15, 1948), pp. 232-233.
32. W. H. Brattain and C. G. B. Garrett, "Combined Measurements of Field Effect, Surface Photo-Voltage and Photoconductivity," *Bell System Tech. J.* **35** (September 1956), pp. 1019-1040; C. G. B. Garrett and W. H. Brattain, "Distribution and Cross-Sections of Fast States on Germanium Surfaces," *Bell System Tech. J.* **35** (September 1956), pp. 1041-1058.
33. W. L. Brown, "Surface Potential and Surface Charge Distribution from Semiconductor Field Effect Measurements," *Phys. Rev.* **100** (October 1955), pp. 590-591.
34. H. C. Montgomery and W. L. Brown, "Field-Induced Conductivity Changes in Germanium," *Phys. Rev.* **103** (August 1956), pp. 865-870.
35. W. L. Brown, "n-Type Surface Conductivity on p-Type Germanium," *Phys. Rev.* **91** (August 1953), pp. 518-527.
36. W. Shockley, "On the Surface States Associated with a Periodic Potential," *Phys. Rev.* **56** (August 1939), pp. 317-323.
37. See reference 31.
38. See reference 28.
39. See reference 30.
40. H. C. Montgomery, "Field Effect in Germanium at High Frequencies," *Phys. Rev.* **106** (May 1957), pp. 441-445.
41. C. G. B. Garrett, "High-Frequency Relaxation Processes in the Field-Effect Experiment," *Phys. Rev.* **107** (July 15, 1957), pp. 478-487.
42. See reference 28.
43. H. C. Montgomery, "Electrical Noise in Semiconductors," *Bell System Tech. J.* **31** (September 1952), pp. 950-975; idem, "Comments on 'Effect of Gaseous Ambients Upon 1/f Noise in Ge Filaments,'" Letters to the Editor, *J. Appl. Phys.* **33** (June 1962), pp. 2143-2144.
44. W. H. Brattain and C. G. B. Garrett, "Experiments on the Interface Between Germanium and an Electrolyte," *Bell System Tech. J.* **34** (January 1955), pp. 129-176.
45. P. J. Boddy and W. H. Brattain, "Effect of Cupric Ion on the Electrical Properties of the Germanium-Aqueous Electrolyte Interface," *J. Electrochem. Soc.* **109** (1962), p. 812.
46. J. T. Law, "The Adsorption of Gases on a Germanium Surface," *J. Phys. Chem.* **59** (June 1955), pp. 543-549; J. T. Law and E. E. Francois, "Adsorption of Bases on a Silicon Surface," *J. Phys. Chem.* **60** (March 1956), pp. 353-358; J. T. Law, "The Interaction of Oxygen with Clean Silicon Surfaces," *J. Phys. Chem. Solids* **4** (1958), pp. 91-100.
47. J. A. Becker, "Adsorption on Metal Surfaces and Its Bearing on Catalysis," *Advances in Catalysis and Related Subjects: Volume VII*, ed. W. G. Frankenburg, V. I. Komarewsky, and E. K. Rideal (New York: Academic Press, 1955).
48. J. T. Law, "The Adsorption of Gases on a Germanium Surface," *J. Phys. Chem.* **59** (June 1955), pp. 543-549.
49. J. T. Law, "The Interaction of Oxygen with Clean Silicon Surfaces," *J. Phys. Chem. Solids* **4** (1958), pp. 91-100.
50. E. O. Kane, "Theory of Photoelectric Emission from Semiconductors," *Phys. Rev.* **127** (July 1962), pp. 131-141.
51. J. J. Lander, "Low Electron Diffraction and Surface Structural Chemistry," *Progress in Solid State Chemistry*, **2**, ed. H. Reiss (Oxford: Pergamon Press, 1965), pp. 26-116; A. U. MacRae and G. W. Gobeli, "Low Energy Electron Diffraction Studies," *Semiconductors and Semimetals: Volume 2. Physics of III-V Compounds*, ed. R. K. Willardson and A. C. Beer (New York: Academic Press, 1966), pp. 115-137.

52. F. G. Allen, "Field Emission: A Tool for Studying Semiconductor Surfaces," *Annals of the New York Acad. of Sciences*, **Vol. 101** (January 23, 1963), pp. 850-856.

53. F. G. Allen and G. W. Gobeli, "Work Function Photoelectric Threshold, and Surface States of Atomically Clean Silicon," *Phys. Rev.* **127** (July 1962), pp. 150-158; G. W. Gobeli and F. G. Allen, "Photoelectric Properties and Work Function of Cleared Germanium Surfaces," *Surf. Sci.* **2** (1964), pp. 402-408.

54. J. R. Arthur, Jr. "Interaction of Ga and As_2 Molecular Beams with GaAs Surfaces," *J. Appl. Phys.* **39** (July 1968), pp. 4032-4034; A. Y. Cho, "Morphology of Epitaxial Growth of GaAs by a Molecular Beam Method: The Observation of Surface Structures," *J. Appl. Phys.* **41** (June 1970), pp. 2780-2786; A. Y. Cho and J. R. Arthur, "Molecular Beam Epitaxy," *Progress in Solid State Chemistry*, 10, ed. J. O. McCaldin and G. Somorjai (Oxford: Pergamon Press, 1965), pp. 157-191.

55. H. C. Casey, Jr., A. Y. Cho, and P. A. Barnes, "Application of Molecular-Beam Epitaxial Layers to Heterostructure Lasers," *IEEE J. Quantum Elect.* **QE11** (July 1975), p. 467.

56. See reference 15.

57. E. G. McRae, "Multiple-Scattering Treatment of Low Energy Electron-Diffraction Intensities," Letters to the Editor, *J. Chem. Phys.* **45** (1966), pp. 3258-3276.

58. E. G. McRae, "Electron Diffraction at Crystal Surfaces. I. Generalization of Darwin's Dynamical Theory," *Surf. Sci.* **11** (1968), pp. 479-491.

59. A. U. MacRae and L. H. Germer, "Thermal Vibrations of Surface Atoms," *Phys. Rev. Lett.* **8** (June 15, 1962), pp. 489-490.

60. E. J. Scheibner, L. H. Germer, and C. D. Hartman, "Apparatus for Direct Observation of Low-Energy Electron Diffraction Patterns," *Rev. Sci. Instrum.* **31** (February 1960), pp. 112-114; L. H. Germer and C. D. Hartman, "Improved Low Energy Electron Diffraction Apparatus," *Rev. Sci. Instrum.* **31** (July 1960), pp. 776-777.

61. J. J. Lander, J. Morrison, and F. Unterwald, "Improved Design and Method of Operation of Low Energy Electron Diffraction Equipment," *Rev. Sci. Instrum.* **33** (July 1962), pp. 782-783.

62. H. E. Ives, A. R. Olpin, and A. L. Johnsrud, "The Distribution in Direction of Photoelectrons from Alkali Metal Surfaces," *Phys. Rev.* **32** (July 1928), pp. 57-80.

63. E. O. Kane, "Implications of Crystal Momentum Conservation in Photoelectric Emission for Band-Structure Measurement," *Phys. Rev. Lett.* **12** (January 27, 1964), pp. 97-98.

64. J. E. Rowe and H. Ibach, "Surface and Bulk Contributions to Ultraviolet Photoemission Spectra of Silicon," *Phys. Rev. Lett.* **32** (February 25, 1974), pp. 421-424.

65. J. A. Appelbaum and D. R. Hamann, "Surface States and Surface Bonds of Si (111)," *Phys. Rev. Lett.* **31** (July 9, 1973), pp. 106-109.

66. J. E. Rowe and H. Ibach, "Surface State Transitions of Silicon in Electron Energy-Loss Spectra," *Phys. Rev. Lett.* **31** (July 9, 1973), pp. 102-105.

67. H. Ibach and J. E. Rowe, "Hydrogen Adsorption and Surface Structures of Silicon," *Surf. Sci.* **43** (1974), pp. 481-492; T. Sakurai and H. D. Hagstrum, "Chemisorption of Atomic Hydrogen on the Silicon (111), 7 x 7 Surface," *Phys. Rev.* **B12** (December 1975), pp. 5349-5354.

68. J. A. Appelbaum and D. R. Hamann, "Self-Consistent Quantum Theory of Chemisorption: H on Si(111)," *Phys. Rev. Lett.* **34** (March 31,1975), pp. 806-809; K. C. Pandey and J. C. Phillips, "Energy Bands of Reconstructed Surface States of Cleaved Si," *Phys. Rev. Lett.* **34** (June 9, 1975), pp. 1450-1453.

69. H. I. Zhang and M. Schlüter, "Studies of the Si(111) Surface with Various Al Overlayers," *Phys. Rev.* **B18** (August 1978), pp. 1923-1935.

70. V. Heine, "Theory of Surface States," *Phys. Rev.* **138** (June 1965), pp. 1689-1696.

71. M. M. Atalla, E. Tannenbaum, and E. J. Scheibner, "Stabilization of Silicon Surfaces by Thermally Grown Oxides," *Bell System Tech. J.* **38** (1959), p. 749.

72. D. E. Aspnes and J. B. Theeten, "Spectroscopic Analysis of the Interface Between Si and Its Thermally Grown Oxide," *J. Electrochem. Soc.* **127** (1980), p. 1359.

73. O. L. Krivanek, D. C. Tsui, T. T. Sheng, and A. Kamgar, "A High-Resolution Electron Microscopy Study of the Si-SiO₂ Interface," in *The Physics of SiO₂ and Its Interfaces,* ed. S. T. Pantelides (New York: Pergamon Press, 1978).

74. N. W. Cheung, L. C. Feldman, P. J. Silverman, and I. Stensgaard, "Studies of the Si-SiO₂ Interface by MeV Ion Channeling," *Appl. Phys. Lett.* **34** (1979), p. 859.

75. N. V. Smith, M. M. Traum, and F. J. DiSalvo, "Mapping Energy Bands in Layer Compounds from the Angular Dependence of Untraviolet Photoemission," *Solid State Commun.* **15** (July 15, 1974), pp. 211-214.

76. See reference 63.

77. L. F. Mattheiss, "Band Structures of Transition-Metal-Dichalcogenide Layer Compounds," *Phys. Rev.* **B8** (October 1973), pp. 3719-3740.

78. M. M. Traum, J. E. Rowe, and N. V. Smith, "Angular Distribution of Photoelectrons from (111) Silicon Surface States," *J. Vac. Sci. Tech.* **12** (Jan./Feb. 1975), p. 298.

79. P. K. Larsen, N. V. Smith, M. Schlüter, H. H. Farrell, K. M. Ho, and M. L. Cohen, "Surface Energy Bands and Atomic Position of Cl Chemisorbed on Cleaved Si(111)," *Phys. Rev.* **B17** (March 1978), pp. 2612-2619.

80. M. Schlüter, J. E. Rowe, G. Margaritondo, K. M. Ho, and M. L. Cohen, "Chemisorption-Site Geometry from Polarized Photoemission: Si(111)Cl and Ge(111)Cl," *Phys. Rev. Lett* **37** (December 13, 1976), pp. 1632-1635.

81. G. Margaritondo and J. E. Rowe, "Atomic and Electronic Structure of Surfaces Studied with Synchroton Radiation," *J. Vac. Sci. Tech.* **17** (March/April 1980), pp. 561-573.

82. H. D. Hagstrum, "Ion-Neutralization Spectroscopy of Solids and Solid Surfaces," *Phys. Rev.* **150** (October 1966), pp. 495-515.

83. H. D. Hagstrum and G. E. Becker, "Orbital Energy Spectra of Electrons in Chemisorption Bonds: O, S, Se on Ni(100)," *J. Chem. Phys.* **54** (February 1, 1971), pp. 1015-1032.

84. D. L. Jeanmaire and R. P. van Duyne, "Surface Raman Spectroelectrochemisty. Part I, Heterocyclic, Aromatic, and Aliphatic Amines Adsorbed on the Anodized Silver Electrode," *J. Electroanal. Chem.* **84** (November 1977), pp. 1-20; M. G. Albrecht and J. A. Creighton, "Anomalously Intense Raman Spectra of Pyridine at a Silver Electrode," *J. Am. Chem. Soc.* **99** (July 1977), pp. 5215-5217.

85. J. G. Bergman, J. P. Heritage, A. Pinczuk, J. M. Worlock, and J. H. McFee, "Cyanide Coverage on Silver in Conjunction with Surface Enhanced Raman Scattering," *Chem. Phys. Lett.* **68** (December 15, 1979), pp. 412-415.

86. J. E. Rowe, C. V. Shank, D. A. Zwemer, and C. A. Murray, "Ultrahigh-Vacuum Studies of Enhanced Raman Scattering from Pyridine on Ag Surfaces," *Phys. Rev. Lett.* **44** (June 30, 1980), pp. 1770-1773.

87. M. Moskovits, "Surface Roughness and the Enhanced Intensity of Raman Scattering by Molecules Adsorbed in Metals," *J. Chem. Phys.* **69** (November 1978), pp. 4159-4161.

88. S. L. McCall, P. M. Platzman, and P. A. Wolff, "Surface Enhanced Raman Scattering," *Phys. Lett.* **A77** (June 9, 1980), pp. 381-383.

89. C. A. Murray, D. L. Allara, and M. Rhinewine, "Silver-Molecule Dependence of Surface Enhanced Raman Scattering," *Phys Rev. Lett.* **46** (January 5, 1981), p. 57-60.

90. D. A. Zwemer, C. V. Shank, and J. E. Rowe, "Surface-Enhanced Raman Scattering as a Function of Molecule-Surface Separation," *Chem. Phys. Lett.* **73** (July 15, 1980), p. 201-204.

91. H. D. Hagstrum, "Electronic Characterization of Solid Surfaces," *Science* **178** (October 20, 1972), pp. 275-282; idem, "The Development of Ion-Neutralization

Spectroscopy," *J. Vac. Sci. Tech.* **12** (Jan./Feb. 1976), pp. 193-195.

92. J. E. Rowe, "Photoemission and Electron Energy Loss Spectroscopy of GeO$_2$ and SiO$_2$," *Appl. Phys. Lett.* **25** (November 15, 1974), pp. 576-578.

93. M. J. Cardillo and G. E. Becker, "Diffraction of He Atoms at a Si(l00) Surface," *Phys. Rev. Lett.* **40** (April 24, 1978), pp. 1148-1151; idem, "Diffraction of He at Reconstructed Si(100) Surface," *Phys. Rev.* **B21** (February 1980), pp. 1497-1510.

94. L. C. Feldman, P. J. Silverman, and I. Stensgaard, "Structural Studies of the Reconstructed W(001) Surface with MeV Ion Scattering," *Surf. Sci.* **87** (1979), pp. 410-414; I. Stensgaard, L. C. Feldman, and P. J. Silverman, "Calculation of the Backscattering-Channeling Surface Peak," *Surf. Sci.* **77** (1978), pp. 513-522.

Chapter 4

Electronic Band Structure
of Metals

The measurement and calculation of the electronic band structure of metals started at Bell Laboratories in the 1950s. Materials purification methods developed for semiconductors were applied to metals, and the increased availability of sensitive and reliable electronics made rapid and accurate measurements possible. The development of high-speed computers and new approximations to the one-electron theory also brought about rapid advances in theoretical calculations.

Scientists at Bell Labs studied Fermi surfaces, cyclotron resonance, and oscillatory effects such as the deHaas-van Alphen effect, magnetothermal as well as magnetoacoustic effects, and band-structure calculations. Other research on metals is discussed elsewhere in this volume, in particular, magnetic properties of metals and alloys in Chapters 1 and 12, superconductivity in Chapters 9 and 15, and internal friction and dislocations in Chapter 19.

I. FERMI SURFACES

A metal is a good electrical conductor because its conduction electrons are free to move through the lattice of positive ions. The position of an individual electron in a metal is completely unknown, but because of the uncertainty principle, its momentum is well defined. Therefore, the description of the electronic structure of a metal involves the specification of the energy as a function of the momentum of each electron. The momentum may be represented by a point (or state) whose Cartesian coordinates are the components of momentum in three perpendicular directions; this is usually referred to as the representation in momentum-space. The Pauli exclusion principle permits only two electrons (one of positive and one of negative spin) to have the same momentum, so that to achieve minimum

Principal authors: L. F. Mattheiss, W. A. Reed, and W. M. Walsh

energy, the momentum states of increasing energy are successively filled until all the electrons are accounted for. The boundary between these filled states and the empty states of higher energy is a surface of constant energy called the Fermi surface. The Fermi surface reflects the *symmetry* of the crystal in position-space, but it generally has a very complicated *shape*, determined by the periodic potential field of the ionic lattice. As an example, the Fermi surface of tantalum retains the basic cubic symmetry of the crystal lattice even though it is composed of several complicated pieces or sheets.[1] [Fig. 4-1] The study of Fermi surfaces is of interest because the electrons at, or near, the Fermi surface determine the properties of a metal. The branch of solid state physics that studied these surfaces and the associated band structures became known as Fermiology.

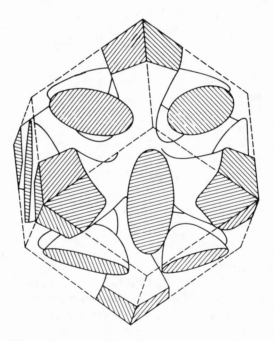

Fig. 4-1. The Fermi surface of a single crystal of tantalum. The outer hole sheets, or unoccupied electron states in momentum space, are shown in the shaded regions. The dashed lines are the boundaries of the first Brillouin zone for a body-centered cubic lattice. This model is based on the theoretical calculations of L. F. Mattheiss and is consistent with the experimental data of E. Fawcett and W. A. Reed. In contrast, the Fermi surface of a simple monovalent metal like sodium is a sphere. [Mattheiss, *Phys. Rev.* **139** (1965): A1901].

Many of the experimental techniques for studying Fermi surfaces originated in the late 1930s with electrical and magnetic measurements on semimetals. The data were very complicated and did not fit the simple theoretical models, which predicted spherical or ellipsoidal Fermi surfaces. However, in the mid-1950s two major breakthroughs, one experimental and one theoretical, initiated a period of intensive study of the electronic band structure of metals.[2]

The theoretical advance, by L. Onsager at Yale University, showed that the frequency of the oscillations observed in the field dependence of the magnetic susceptibility could be directly related to the extremal cross-sectional areas of the Fermi surface.[3] This meant that a study of the frequencies of oscillation of the susceptibility as a function of magnetic-field orientation could, in principle, completely map the Fermi surface of a metal.

The experimental advance was the measurement of the anomalous skin effect in copper by A. B. Pippard at Cambridge University in 1957.[4] These results showed that the Fermi surface, originally thought to be nearly spherical, was in reality a "jungle gym" of connected "balls and pipes." Pippard verified what many had previously suspected, namely, that Fermi surfaces could be quite complicated and that their study would lead to a deeper understanding of the properties of metals.

A variety of experimental techniques were developed to study Fermi surfaces. Each method is based upon the fact that an electron's energy is quantized in a magnetic field, and the trajectory of an electron in a crystal is confined to the intersection of the Fermi surface with a plane perpendicular to the magnetic field. To obtain usable data, it is necessary that the electrons traverse their orbits many times before scattering. In practical terms this means that the metal samples must be high-purity [less than 10 parts per million total impurities], nearly perfect single crystals, and that the experiments must be performed at low temperatures (1K to 4K) and in magnetic fields of 10 to 100 kilogauss.

II. CYCLOTRON RESONANCE

Since the mid-1950s cyclotron resonance has proved to be a powerful spectroscopic tool in solid state physics. The first experiments studied the motion of electrons and holes in semiconductors; later studies included semimetals and metals. At Bell Labs in the late 1950s, J. K. Galt had been measuring the cyclotron resonance in semimetals,[5] and it was natural for him to apply this technique to metals.[6] He recognized the need for high-purity single crystals, and with P. H. Schmidt initiated a program to grow pure single crystals of zinc and cadmium. However, the experimental geometry, which had been successful in the study of semimetals (with the magnetic field perpendicular to the sample surface) yielded confusing results in metals because of the very small skin depth. (For more on this topic see section 2.4 of Chapter 1.)

This impasse was overcome by the Soviet theorists M. Ya. Azbel' and E. A. Kaner, who showed that well-defined resonance series could be observed if the magnetic field was accurately aligned in the plane of extremely flat samples.[7] The theoretical prediction was soon qualitatively verified by E. Fawcett at the Royal Radar Establishment in England.[8] A. F. Kip and coworkers at the University of California at Berkeley,[9] and Galt at Bell Labs,[10] demonstrated the power of the new experimental geometry. The era of cyclotron resonance in metals was launched. During the 1960s Azbel'-Kaner cyclotron resonance was widely exploited, in parallel with other experimental techniques and increasingly sophisticated band-structure computations, to establish the electronic properties of nearly all the elemental metals and even some metallic compounds.

At Bell Labs, interest focused on the transition metals because the degree to which d electrons might be considered to be mobile had not been established. Cyclotron resonance measurements on tungsten by Fawcett and W. M. Walsh[11] proved to be consistent with the band structure computations of L. F. Mattheiss.[12] As a result of these studies, the previously emphasized distinction between d electrons and more free-electron-like states was shown to be meaningless because of extensive mixing (hybridization) of the electronic wave functions. The ultimate example of this itinerant nature of magnetic electrons was provided by observation by Azbel'-Kaner cyclotron resonance in ferromagnetic nickel by P. Goy of Ecole Normale Superiere in France and by C. C. Grimes.[13] [Fig. 4-2]

Cyclotron resonance is a temporal phenomenon requiring equality, or a harmonic relationship, between the periods of the orbiting electrical carriers and the electrical excitation. In 1962, related spatial resonance phenomenon was discovered by V. F. Gantmakher in the Soviet Union.[14] He showed that sharp anomalies in the radio frequency impedance of thin metal plates occurred when a parallel magnetic field caused cyclotron orbits, or multiples of orbits, to span the sample thickness. The phenomenon results from current being carried from the surface skin-effect region and refocused into an image-current sheet one orbit diameter away. If the image-current sheet intersects the opposite surface of the metal plate, the surface impedance is modified. Similarly, if the orbit only spans half the sample thickness (at twice the magnetic field strength) the image-current sheet excites a second set of orbits that produce a weaker secondary image at the second surface. Grimes used this very direct

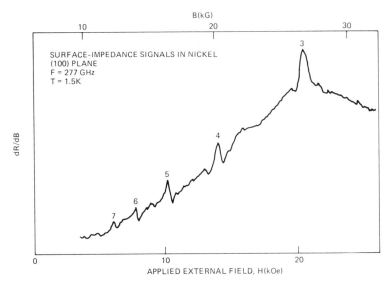

Fig. 4-2. Cyclotron resonance in nickel as a striking proof that the magnetism of transition metals results from fully itinerant electrons. The graph of the derivative of the surface resistance versus applied external field H shows a series of peaks that are subharmonically related in the internal magnetic induction B. [Goy and Grimes, *Phys. Rev.* **B7** (1973):299].

means of measuring orbit sizes and shapes to study several simple metals. Walsh and Grimes[15] then used the technique to deduce important details of the electronic structure of tungsten as calculated by Mattheiss and R. E. Watson.[16]

S. J. Allen extended the Azbel'-Kaner cyclotron resonance method in potassium to extremely high frequencies, ≤ 1750 GHz, with a far-infrared, laser-driven spectrometer. Allen was able to observe effects caused by electron phonon coupling and the breakdown of the Azbel'-Kaner theory. It was shown that at these high frequencies, the electrons do not escape the skin depth before the infrared field changes phase and the harmonics of cyclotron resonance, normally seen at low frequencies, are strongly attenuated.[17]

III. HIGH-FIELD GALVANOMAGNETIC EFFECTS

Galvanomagnetic effects occur when a conductor carrying a current is placed in a magnetic field. If an electron can traverse only a small fraction of its cyclotron orbit before scattering, the measurements are said to be in the low-field regime. Conversely, if an electron is able to complete one or more orbits before scattering, then the measurements are in the high-field regime.

To understand the galvanomagnetic properties of metals, it is important to understand the motion of an electron under the combined influence of the periodic field of the lattice, and the Lorentz force which results from the application of a magnetic field. From the definition of the Fermi surface and the Lorentz force, the electrons' motion may be described in a simple geometric way. Each electron at the Fermi surface has a constant energy, and a constant component of momentum along the magnetic field, since the Lorentz force is perpendicular to both the electrons' velocity and the magnetic field. Thus the motion (or orbits) of the electrons at the Fermi surface in a magnetic field is the perimeter of each plane-section of the Fermi surface perpendicular to the magnetic field.

The change in a conductor's resistance in a magnetic field is known as magnetoresistance. At room temperatures, this effect is small (less than 1 percent) and is only slightly dependent upon the orientation of the magnetic field relative to the sample's axis. However, it was observed by N. E. Alekseevskii and Yu. P. Gaidukov,[18] and by J. Yahia and J. A. Marcus,[19] that the magnetoresistance of high-purity single crystals at temperatures less than 4K could be very large (greater than 10^3) and highly dependent on the directions that the magnetic field and current made with the sample axes. These results could not be reconciled with the spherical or ellipsoidal Fermi-surface models that had been applied successfully in understanding the galvanomagnetic effects in semiconductors and semimetals. The answer to this puzzle was provided by a trio of Soviet theorists—I. M. Lifshitz, Azbel', and M. I. Kaganov.[20] They assumed that the Fermi surface of a material could be composed of more than one sheet, that these sheets could involve either electrons or holes, and that some of these sheets could possess a multiply connected topology that supported cyclotron orbits extending indefinitely in momentum space. These calculations showed that as the magnetic field increased, the magnetoresistance could either saturate at a small value (less than 10) or increase quadratically to large values (greater than 10^3) depending upon the nature of the cyclotron orbits permitted on the Fermi surface for that particular magnetic field direction. Rotating the magnetic field around some axis of a single crystal could produce large peaks and low valleys as different types of orbits were allowed. At Bell Labs, J. R. Klauder and J. E. Kunzler applied these results to copper and demonstrated experimentally most of the theoretical predictions.[21]

The galvanomagnetic studies were continued by W. A. Reed and Fawcett. They were aided by R. R. Soden, who was then applying the art of float-zone refining to the fabrication of high-purity single crystals of the transition metals. Probably the most notable work of this collaboration resulted from their measurements on nickel.[22] This study demonstrated that *all* of the conduction electrons in nickel were free to move throughout the crystal (itinerant), and that the previous idea of localized *d* electrons was incorrect. They also demonstrated that the magnetic field "felt" by the electrons was the magnetic induction $\vec{B}$, not the magnetic intensity *H*.

IV. THE OSCILLATORY EFFECTS

When a metal is placed in a magnetic field the free energy of the electrons is quantized and the electrons are distributed among these discrete levels. As the magnetic field is increased the energy of some of these levels will become greater than the Fermi energy and the electrons in these levels will redistribute themselves into the lower energy levels. This redistribution of the electron population as a function of magnetic field reveals itself in any measurable quantity that depends upon the free energy. The oscillation of this quantity will be periodic in B^{-1}. The effects most used to study Fermi surfaces are the deHaas-van Alphen effect, the magnetothermal effect, and the magnetoacoustic effect.

4.1 deHaas-van Alphen Effect

In 1930, L. D. Landau calculated the magnetic susceptibility of an electron gas and found a term that oscillated in the magnetic field.[23] At that time he dismissed this term because he felt that it could not be observed experimentally. However, in 1930 W. J. deHaas and P. M. van Alphen observed these oscillations in bismuth. Although a number of scientists continued to measure the deHaas-van Alphen effect over the intervening years, it was not until 1952, when Onsager made the connection between the frequency of the oscillations and the cross-sectional area of the Fermi surface, that the measurement of the oscillatory magnetic susceptibility and the complementary oscillatory effects (magnetothermal, magnetoacoustic, galvanomagnetic, and so on) became powerful tools for measuring the Fermi surfaces of metals.

In 1963, deHaas-van Alphen measurements were started at Bell Labs by J. H. Condon. While studying beryllium, he noticed that the shape of the susceptibility oscillations were distorted, but the distortions were not dependent upon the sample shape. This observation was at variance with a paper by Pippard, which explored the ramifications of the fact that the oscillatory free energy was a function of the magnetic induction $\vec{B}$, and not the magnetic intensity *H* as had been previously assumed.[24] This became known as the *B-H* effect. Condon developed an explanation of his results in beryllium by postulating that during parts of the oscillation the sample broke up into magnetic domains, similar to the domains observed in ferromagnetic materials.[25] Condon and R. E. Walstedt subsequently verified this explanation by measuring the nuclear magnetic resonance in silver.[26] They observed two resonances, corresponding to two values of the magnetic induction, when the domains existed and only one resonance when the domains were absent. The *B-H* effect was also studied in beryllium by Reed and Condon using the high-field magnetoresistance oscillations.[27] [Fig. 4-3]

4.2 Magnetothermal Effect

In 1960, W. S. Boyle, Kunzler, and F. S. L. Hsu demonstrated the magnetothermal effect in bismuth.[28] They measured the temperature fluctuations of a single crystal that had a weak thermal link to a bath of liquid helium and observed thermal oscillations periodic in B^{-1}. This technique was applied by J. E. Graebner and Kunzler to the high-field superconductor V_3Ge,[29] by Graebner and E. S. Greiner to the metallic oxide ReO_3,[30] by M. H. Halloran and coworkers to niobium and tantalum,[31] and by Graebner, Greiner, and W. D. Ryden to the conducting transition-metal dioxides RuO_2, IrO_2 and OsO_2.[32]

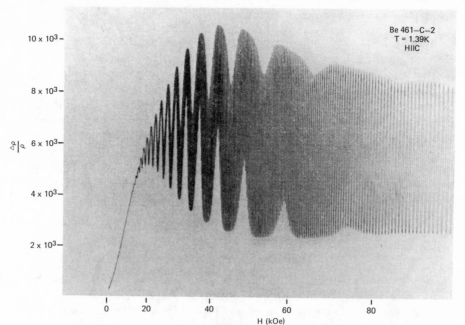

Fig. 4-3. The high-field magnetoresistance of beryllium, showing the effects of quantum oscillations and the fact that these oscillations depend on the magnetic induction *B* (internal field) and not the magnetic intensity *H* (applied field). [Reed and Condon, *Phys. Rev.* **B1** (1970): 3506].

4.3 Magnetoacoustic Effects

As in previously mentioned effects, the absorption of high-frequency sound (approximately 10 MHz) by electrons in a high-purity metal single crystal undergoes periodic oscillations as the strength of the magnetic field is varied. R. W. Morse at Brown University was one of the first to apply this technique to the measurement of Fermi surfaces.[33] Measurement of magnetoacoustic oscillations was initiated at Bell Labs by D. Gibbons and continued by L. R. Testardi. Testardi's measurements on rhenium,[34] coupled with the calculations of Mattheiss,[35] were instrumental in the understanding of the band structure of this metal.

V. BAND STRUCTURE CALCULATIONS

A basic problem in representing the electronic states of metals is caused by their dual nature. They resemble bound atomic states near the nuclei and freely propagating plane waves in the interstitial regions. A practical theoretical formulation combining these characteristics was derived by J. C. Slater at M.I.T. which he called the augmented-plane-wave method.[36] Mattheiss furthered the development of this method with Slater's group,[37] and initiated a program of band structure calculations when he joined Bell Labs in 1963. He used the augmented-plane-wave method to calculate the band structure of transition metals and compounds that were being investigated. His band calculations for the A15 compounds (for example, V_3Si),[38] tungsten,[39] rhenium,[40] niobium and tantalum,[41] the metallic oxides ReO_3 and RuO_2, IrO_2 and OsO_2,[42] and the layer compounds (for example, $NbSe_2$),[43] provided a useful framework for interpreting the experimental data and furthering the understanding of the electronic structure of metals and compounds.

REFERENCES

1. L. F. Mattheiss, "Fermi Surface in Tungsten," *Phys. Rev.* **139** (September 1965), pp. A1893-A1904.
2. W. A. Harrison, "The Fermi Surface," *Science* **134** (September 1961), pp. 915-920; A. R. MacIntosh, "The Fermi Surface of Metals," *Scientific American* **209** (July 1963), pp. 110-120; A. B. Pippard, "Experimental Analysis of the Electronic Structure of Metals," *Reports on Progress in Physics* **XXXIII** (1960), pp. 176-266.
3. L. Onsager, "Interpretation of the deHaas-van Alphen Effect," *Phil. Mag.* **43** Serial 7 (1952), pp. 1006-1008.
4. A. B. Pippard, "An Experimental Determination of the Fermi Surface in Copper," *Phil. Trans. Roy. Soc. London*, **250** Series A (1957-1958), pp. 325-357.
5. J. K. Galt, W. A. Yager, F. R. Merritt, B. B. Cetlin, and A. D. Brailsford, "Cyclotron Absorption in Metallic Bismuth and Its Alloys," *Phys. Rev.* **114** (June 1959), pp. 1396-1413.

6. J. K. Galt and F. R. Merritt, "Cyclotron Resonance Observations in Zinc," *The Fermi Surface*, ed. W. A. Harrison and M. B. Webb (New York: John Wiley, 1960), pp. 159-165.

7. M. Ya. Azbel' and E. A. Kaner, "The Theory of Cyclotron Resonance in Metals," *Soviet Phys. JETP* **3** (December 1956), pp. 772-774.

8. E. Fawcett, "Cyclotron Resonance in Tin and Copper," *Phys. Rev.* **103** (1956), pp. 1582-1583.

9. A. F. Kip, D. N. Langenberg, B. Rosenblum, and G. Wagoner, "Cyclotron Resonance in Tin," *Phys. Rev.* **108** (October 1957), pp. 494-495; A. F. Kip, D. N. Langenberg, and T. W. Moore, "Cyclotron Resonance in Copper," *Phys. Rev.* **124** (October 1961), pp. 359-372.

10. J. K. Galt, F. R. Merritt, and J. R. Klauder, "Cyclotron Resonance in Cadmium," *Phys. Rev.* **139** (August 1965), pp. A823-A837.

11. E. Fawcett and W. M. Walsh, Jr., "Cyclotron Resonance in Tungsten," *Phys. Rev. Lett.* **8** (June 1962), pp. 476-478.

12. See reference 1.

13. P. Goy and C. C. Grimes, "Cyclotron Resonance in Nickel," *Phys. Rev.* **B7** (January 1973), pp. 299-306.

14. V. F. Gantmakher, "A Method of Measuring the Momentum of Electrons in a Metal," *Sov. Phys. JETP* **15** (November 1962), pp. 982-983.

15. W. M. Walsh, Jr., and C. C. Grimes, "Evidence of Spin-Orbit Coupling in Metallic Tungsten," *Phys. Rev. Lett.* **13** (October 1964), pp. 523-525.

16. L. F. Mattheiss and R. E. Watson, "Estimate of the Spin-Orbit Parameter 5d in Metallic Tungsten," *Phys. Rev. Lett.* **13** (October 1964), pp. 526-527.

17. S. J. Allen, Jr., L. W. Rupp, Jr., and P. H. Schmidt, "Probing the Electron-Phonon Interaction in Potassium by Far-Infrared Cyclotron Resonance," *Phys. Rev.* **B7** (1973), pp. 5121-5140; S. J. Allen, Jr., "Excitation of High-Frequency Cyclotron Waves in a Semi-Infinite Metal in the Far Infrared: Ordinary Waves," *Phys. Rev.* **B9** (1974), pp. 4121-4129.

18. N. E. Alekseevskii and Yu. P. Gaidukov, "Anistropy of the Electrical Resistance of a Gold Monocrystal in a Magnetic Field at 4.2°," Letters to the Editor, *Sov. Phys. JETP* **8** (February 1959), pp. 383-384.

19. J. Yahia and J. A. Marcus, "Galvanomagnetic Properties of Gallium at Low Temperatures," *Phys. Rev.* **113** (January 1959), pp. 137-146.

20. I. M. Lifshitz, M. Ya. Azbel', and M. I. Kaganov, "On the Theory of Galvanomagnetic Effects in Metals," Letters to the Editor, *Sov. Phys. JETP* **3** (August 1956), pp. 143-145.

21. J. R. Klauder and J. E. Kunzler, "Higher Order Open Orbits and the Interpretation of Magnetoresistance and Hall Effect Data for Copper," *The Fermi Surface*, ed. W. A. Harrison and M. B. Webb (New York: John Wiley, 1960), pp. 125-133.

22. W. A. Reed and E. Fawcett, "Fermi Surface of Nickel from Galvanomagnetic Measurements," *J. Appl. Phys.* **35** Pt. 2 (March 1964), pp. 754-759.

23. L. D. Landau, "Diamagnetismus der Metalle," *Zeit. für Physik* **64** (1930), pp. 629-637.

24. A. B. Pippard, "Commentary on a Conjecture of Schoenberg's Concerning the deHaas-van Alphen Effect," *Proc. Roy. Soc. London*, **272** Series A, (March 1963), p. 192.

25. J. H. Condon, "Nonlinear deHaas-van Alphen Effect and Magnetic Domains in Beryllium," *Phys. Rev.* **145** (May 1966), pp. 526-535.

26. J. H. Condon and R. E. Walstedt, "Direct Evidence for Magnetic Domains in Silver," *Phys. Rev. Lett.* **21** (August 26, 1968), pp. 612-614.

27. W. A. Reed and J. H. Condon, "Effect of Magnetic Breakdown and Nonlinear Magnetization on the High-Field Magnetoresistance of Be," *Phys. Rev.* **B1** (April 1970), pp. 3504-3510.

28. W. S. Boyle, F. S. L. Hsu, and J. E. Kunzler, "Spin Splitting of the Landau Levels in Bismuth Observed by Magnetothermal Experiments," *Phys. Rev. Lett.* **4** (March 15, 1960), pp. 278-280.

29. J. E. Graebner and J. E. Kunzler, "Magnetothermal Oscillations and the Fermi Surface of β-Tungsten V_3Ge," *J. Low Temp. Phys.* **1** (October 1969), pp. 443-450.

30. J. E. Graebner and E. S. Greiner, "Magnetothermal Oscillations and the Fermi Surface of ReO_3," *Phys. Rev.* **185** (September 1969), pp. 992-994.

31. M. H. Halloran, J. H. Condon, J. E. Graebner, J. E. Kunzler, and F. S. L. Hsu, "Experimental Study of the Fermi Surfaces of Niobium and Tantalum," *Phys. Rev.* **B1** (January 1970), pp. 366-372.

32. J. E. Graebner, E. S. Greiner, and W. D. Ryden, "Magnetothermal Oscillations in RuO_2, OsO_2, and IrO_2," *Phys. Rev.* **B13** (March 1976), pp. 2426-2432.

33. R. W. Morse, A. Myers, and C. T. Walker, "Fermi Surfaces of Gold and Silver from Ultrasonic Attenuation," *Phys. Rev. Lett.* **4** (June 15, 1960), pp. 605-606.

34. L. R. Testardi and R. Soden, "Magnetoacoustic Study of the Rhenium Fermi Surface," *Phys. Rev.* **158** (June 1967), pp. 581-590.

35. L. F. Mattheiss, "Band Structure and Fermi Surface for Rhenium," *Phys. Rev.* **151** (November 1966), pp. 450-464.

36. J. C. Slater, "Wave Functions in a Periodic Potential," *Phys. Rev.* **51** (May 1937), pp. 846-851.

37. L. F. Mattheiss, J. H. Wood, and A. C. Switendick, "A Procedure for Calculating Electronic Energy Bands Using Symmetrized Augmented Plane Waves," *Methods in Computation Physics, Advances in Research and Applications, Vol. 8: Energy Bands of Solids* (New York: Academic Press, 1968), pp. 63-147.

38. L. F. Mattheiss, "Energy Bands for V_3X Compounds," *Phys. Rev.* **138** (April 1965), pp. A112-A128.

39. See reference 1.

40. See reference 34.

41. L. F. Mattheiss, "Electronic Structure of Niobium and Tantalum," *Phys. Rev.* **B1** (January 1970), pp. 373-380.

42. L. F. Mattheiss, "Band Structure and Fermi Surface of ReO_3," *Phys. Rev.* **181** (May 1969), pp. 987-1000; idem, "Electronic Structure of RuO_2, OsO_2, and IrO_2," *Phys. Rev.* **B13** (March 1976), pp. 2433-2450.

43. L. F. Mattheiss, "Band Structures of Transition-Metal-Dichalcogenide Layer Compound," *Phys. Rev.* **B8** (October 1973), pp. 3719-3740.

Chapter 5

Quantum Electronics – The Laser

Quantum electronics can be said to have originated with the invention of the maser by C. H. Townes and his students at Columbia University in the 1950s, although the basic physics of stimulated emission of radiation and population inversion had been understood decades earlier.

Townes and A. L. Schawlow collaborated in research that applied maser principles to the optical region of the electromagnetic spectrum and resulted in the development of the laser. This first laser opened the way for others: the helium-neon laser, the semiconductor heterostructure that is of special interest in optical communications, the high-power CO_2 laser, dye lasers for very short pulses, and the spin-flip Raman laser, among others.

With the availability of the laser as a tool for high-resolution spectroscopic research, Bell Labs scientists have made contributions in a number of fields of research—for example, Raman scattering, coherent optical effects, radiation pressure studies, nonlinear optics including second harmonic generation, and optical parametric amplification. Laser applications are also discussed in Chapter 6 and Chapter 19.

I. MICROWAVE SPECTROSCOPY AND MASERS

The development of microwave techniques during World War II gave impetus to the exploration of the properties of matter in the microwave region of the electromagnetic spectrum. Before the war C. E. Cleeton and N. H. Williams at the University of Michigan used a magnetron for microwaves down to 6 millimeters.[1] Bell Laboratories entry into this field was marked by the work of C. H. Townes in 1945-1946 on the microwave absorption spectroscopy of gases. The characteristic rotational frequencies of molecules lie in the microwave

Principal authors: P. A. Fleury, A. G. Fox, J. A. Giordmaine, B. F. Levine, R. C. Miller, M. B. Panish, C. K. N. Patel, and P. W. Smith range. In addition, certain special molecular motions, such as the tunneling of the nitrogen atom through the plane of hydrogen atoms in NH_3, also occur at microwave frequencies.[2] By measuring the absorption frequencies of molecules such as OCS, ClCN, and BrCN, Townes and coworkers derived information concerning bond distances, dipole moments, and chemical bonding, and nuclear properties such as masses and quadrupole moments.[3]

Townes continued his microwave spectroscopy program after he accepted an academic appointment to the physics department of Columbia University. The research by Townes and his graduate students at Columbia led to the development of the concept of microwave amplification by stimulated emission of radiation (the maser). In particular, their studies of the NH_3 maser had an important impact on molecular spectroscopy research.[4] The maser produced a more profound impact a few years later when the concept of stimulated emission of radiation was applied to the optical region of the electromagnetic spectrum.

At Bell Labs, attention turned to the possibility of designing a solid state maser amplifier with very low noise possibilities capable of operating at liquid helium temperature. In 1956, acting on a suggestion of N. Bloembergen of Harvard University, H. E. D. Scovil, G. Feher, and H. Seidel designed and constructed the first continuous-wave solid state maser using Gd^{3+} ions in lanthanum ethylsulfate.[5] A broadband traveling-wave maser was later developed by R. N. DeGrasse, E. O. Schultz-DuBois, and Scovil.[6] A form of this maser was used in the low-noise preamplifier of the earth station at Andover, Maine, used in the Telstar communication satellite studies.

In the 1970s, a renaissance in the subject of microwave gas spectroscopy occurred, particularly in astrophysics (see section 1.3 of Chapter 7). More than forty molecules have been discovered in the interstellar medium in our galaxy, among which is OCS,[7] the spectrum of which was studied by Townes at Bell Laboratories 30 years earlier.

II. PHYSICAL PRINCIPLES AND CONDITIONS FOR LASER ACTION – THE He-Ne LASER

Recognizing the potentially important role that microwave spectroscopy and the maser were likely to play in physics research and in communications devices, scientists at Bell Labs Physical Research Laboratory set up a consulting arrangement with Townes in 1957. Among the many scientists with whom Townes interacted, his collaboration with A. L. Schawlow turned out to be the most fruitful. [Fig. 5-1] Prior to joining Bell Labs Physical Research Department in 1953, Schawlow had spent two post-doctoral years with Townes at

Fig. 5-1. (Left) A. L. Schawlow adjusts a ruby optical maser during an experiment at Bell Laboratories in 1960. (Right) C. H. Townes with a ruby maser amplifier used for radio astronomy. [MIT photo, circa 1957].

Columbia University, where they wrote a book on microwave spectroscopy. Schawlow's initial research activities at Bell Laboratories were in the field of superconductivity.

Schawlow and Townes examined the conditions needed to achieve amplification by stimulated emission of radiation in the optical region of the electromagnetic spectrum, which is over four orders of magnitude higher in frequency than oscillation in the ammonia maser. In a December 1958 publication, they promulgated the physical principles and requirements for such amplification in the visible or infrared regions of the spectrum.[8] [Fig. 5-2] These included the pumping intensity needed to produce an inverted population density sufficient for amplification, the optical cavity configuration needed to get adequate mode selection, expected output characteristics, and possible materials for use.

In 1959, A. Javan described the basic principles for a gaseous helium-neon (He-Ne) continuous-wave laser system.[9] [Fig. 5-3] He proposed using a low-power gas discharge to excite helium atoms by means of inelastic collisions with electrons to a long-lived metastable state, 2^3S. The energy of this helium metastable state is essentially resonant with the neon-$2s$ levels. Javan reasoned that under the right experimental conditions, the helium metastables should serve as

Infrared and Optical Masers

A. L. SCHAWLOW AND C. H. TOWNES[*]
Bell Telephone Laboratories, Murray Hill, New Jersey
(Received August 26, 1958)

The extension of maser techniques to the infrared and optical region is considered. It is shown that by using a resonant cavity of centimeter dimensions, having many resonant modes, maser oscillation at these wavelengths can be achieved by pumping with reasonable amounts of incoherent light. For wavelengths much shorter than those of the ultraviolet region, maser-type amplification appears to be quite impractical. Although use of a multimode cavity is suggested, a single mode may be selected by making only the end walls highly reflecting, and defining a suitably small angular aperture. Then extremely monochromatic and coherent light is produced. The design principles are illustrated by reference to a system using potassium vapor.

INTRODUCTION

AMPLIFIERS and oscillators using atomic and molecular processes, as do the various varieties of masers,[1-4] may in principle be extended far beyond the range of frequencies which have been generated electronically, and into the infrared, the optical region, or beyond. Such techniques give the attractive promise of coherent amplification at these high frequencies and of generation of very monochromatic radiation. In the infrared region in particular, the generation of reasonably intense and monochromatic radiation would allow the possibility of spectroscopy at very much higher resolution than is now possible. As one attempts to extend maser operation towards very short wavelengths, a number of new aspects and problems arise, which require a quantitative reorientation of theoretical discussions and considerable modification of the experimental techniques used. Our purpose is to discuss theoretical aspects of maser-like devices for wavelengths considerably shorter than one centimeter, to examine the short-wavelength limit for practical devices of this type, and to outline design considerations for an example of a maser oscillator for producing radiation in the infrared region. In the general discussion, roughly reasonable values of design parameters will be used. They will be justified later by more detailed examination of one particular atomic system.

* Permanent address: Columbia University, New York, New York.
[1] Gordon, Zeiger, and Townes, Phys. Rev. 99, 1264 (1955).
[2] Combrisson, Honig, and Townes, Compt. rend. 242, 2451 (1956).
[3] N. Bloembergen, Phys. Rev. 104, 329 (1956).
[4] E. Allais, Compt. rend. 245, 157 (1957).

CHARACTERISTICS OF MASERS FOR MICROWAVE FREQUENCIES

For comparison, we shall consider first the characteristics of masers operating in the normal microwave range. Here an unstable ensemble of atomic or molecular systems is introduced into a cavity which would normally have one resonant mode near the frequency which corresponds to radiative transitions of these systems. In some cases, such an ensemble may be located in a wave guide rather than in a cavity but again there would be characteristically one or a very few modes of propagation allowed by the wave guide in the frequency range of interest. The condition of oscillation for n atomic systems excited with random phase and located in a cavity of appropriate frequency may be written (see references 1 and 2)

$$n \geq h V \Delta\nu / (4\pi\mu^2 Q_c), \qquad (1)$$

where n is more precisely the difference $n_1 - n_2$ in number of systems in the upper and lower states, V is the volume of the cavity, $\Delta\nu$ is the half-width of the atomic resonance at half-maximum intensity, assuming a Lorentzian line shape, μ is the matrix element involved in the transition, and Q_c is the quality factor of the cavity.

The energy emitted by such a maser oscillator is usually in an extremely monochromatic wave, since the energy produced by stimulated emission is very much larger than that due to spontaneous emission or to the normal background of thermal radiation. The frequency range over which appreciable energy is distributed is given approximately by[1]

$$\delta\nu = 4\pi kT(\Delta\nu)^2 / P, \qquad (2)$$

Fig. 5-2. Page 1 of the historic paper by A. L. Schawlow and C. H. Townes. [*Phys. Rev.* **112** (1958): 1940].

efficient carriers of energy. Through a collision process, the helium metastables would excite the nearly resonant neon levels to produce the population inversion required for laser action on the $2s \rightarrow 2p$ neon transition. The optimum conditions for laser action were determined experimentally by W. R. Bennett and Javan.

Laser oscillations were first demonstrated in 1960 by T. H. Maiman at the Hughes Research Laboratories.[10] Maiman used a pulsed flash lamp, placing transiently ions from the ground state of Cr^{+++} in a ruby crystal to an excited state to produce oscillations. In 1961, Javan, Bennett, and D. R. Herriott demonstrated the first gas laser and the first continuously operating laser, thus experimentally verifying

POSSIBILITY OF PRODUCTION OF NEGATIVE TEMPERATURE IN GAS DISCHARGES

A. Javan

Bell Telephone Laboratories, Murray Hill, New Jersey

(Received June 3, 1959)

In a recent paper[1] Schawlow and Townes have discussed a possibility for obtaining maser action in the optical region. In their proposed scheme, negative temperature is obtained by optical pumping. One may expect also that under favorable conditions the excitation of atomic levels by electrons in a discharge can lead, in principle, to a state of negative temperature. However, severe restrictions exist if densities of the excited atoms as large as those needed for maser action are required. The present Letter considers briefly these limitations and certain types of systems which appear to be most favorable for practical application of this proposal. Pure gases behave quite differently than certain kinds of gas mixtures. First let us consider the former case.

For the purposes of rough estimates of various discharge conditions as described below, let us make a simplifying assumption that the main source of population of an excited state is due to collisions of the first kind between the electrons and atoms in the ground state leading directly to the excited level under consideration. It can be shown that, at least in cases discussed below, other details such as cascade processes and collision of electrons with other excited atoms do not appreciably effect our order-of-magnitude estimates.

The $^3S_1$ metastable of He also lies in energy fairly close to the excitation energy of the upper maser level of Ne discussed above. The presence of a partial pressure of He is expected to enhance considerably the negative temperature in the levels of Ne.

The transfer of excitation of the type described above may play an appreciable role within the levels of the same atom. An important example of this is expected to occur in the levels of Ne. Let us consider the group of four levels $2s_5$, $2s_4$, $2s_3$, and $2s_2$. The level $2s_4$ is the one emphasized in the above for the upper of the two maser levels. These four levels all fall fairly close in energy. The level $2s_2$ is also allowed for an optical transition to the ground state. The transfer of excitation within these levels is expected to result in particular built up of large population in the level $2s_5$, this level having the lowest energy within this group. Thus, an even more favorable transition in Ne appears to be the $2s_5 - 2p_{10}$. This transition lies at 10343 wave number.

Details of the above proposals will be published upon their experimental verifications.

I would like to acknowledge helpful discussions with Dr. W. R. Bennett, Jr., Dr. S. J. Buchsbaum, Professor C. H. Townes, Dr. J. P. Gordon, and Dr. A. L. Schawlow.

[1]A. L. Schawlow and C. H. Townes, Phys. Rev. 112, 1940 (1958).

Fig. 5-3. Javan's proposed scheme for obtaining population inversion in atomic energy levels of neon, resulting in the helium-neon laser. [Adapted from *Phys. Rev. Lett.* 3 (July 15, 1959)].

Javan's predictions.[11] [Fig. 5-4] Initially the He-Ne laser operated on any of five different wavelengths in the near infrared, and used a low-power gas discharge. [Fig. 5-5] Fifteen milliwatts of continuous power were generated in the strongest line, which was the $2s_2 \rightarrow 2p_4$ transition at 1.15 μm. The spectral linewidth was thousands of times sharper than the best spectroscopic lines then available in the visible region.

In the He-Ne laser, planar mirrors were used inside the vacuum envelope. The mirrors required repeated and delicate adjustments, making this arrangement somewhat complex to build and use. A considerable simplification was accomplished by the introduction of Brewster-angle windows and concave mirrors by W. W. Rigrod and coworkers.[12] The Brewster-angle windows allowed the laser mirrors to be placed outside the discharge tube with negligible transmission

Fig. 5-4. (Left to right) A. Javan, W. R. Bennett, Jr., and D. R. Herriott adjusting
the helium-neon laser, 1961.

losses, and the concave mirrors made alignment of the laser resonators much easier.

Subsequently, A. D. White and J. D. Rigden studied the visible spectral characteristics of the He-Ne discharge and obtained laser action in the red region of the spectrum at 0.633 μm on the $3s_2 \rightarrow 2p_4$ neon transition.[13] As of the time of this publication, the He-Ne red laser is probably still the most widely known laser on the market. It is estimated that there are more than 200,000 He-Ne lasers in use as teaching tools, and in laboratory instruments, measuring systems, scanners, optical data storage systems, and video-disc readers.

2.1 Early Solid State Lasers

When T. H. Maiman announced the operation of the first laser in mid-1960, he reported a lifetime shortening from 3.8 to 0.6 milliseconds and an R_1 to R_2 line-intensity change from 2:1 to 50:1 as evidence of laser action in ruby crystals.[14] At the time some investigators regarded the sufficiency of this evidence as controversial. This led a group of Bell Labs researchers to verify Maiman's report. The result, published by R. J. Collins and coworkers, gave confirmation of laser

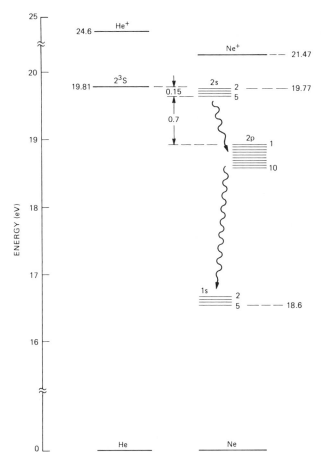

Fig. 5-5. Energy-level diagram of helium and neon atoms. Note the coincidence of the metastable 2^3S level of helium and the 2S levels of neon. [Javan, Bennett, Jr., and Herriott, *Phys. Rev. Lett.* **6** (February 1, 1961): 106].

action—sharp directionality, line narrowing of a factor of 30, and spatial coherence over a lateral dimension of 100 wavelengths in the source.[15] In addition, the first observations of relaxation oscillations in a laser were made.

Extending the research by G. H. Dieke and his collaborators at Johns Hopkins University on rare earth ions in $LaCl_3$ and other host crystals, which aimed at identifying the energy levels and visible transitions of the rare earth ions, L. F. Johnson initiated spectroscopic studies into the near infrared. Spectroscopic observations of the fluorescent emission in neodymium-doped crystals, supplied by K. Nassau, showed that upon excitation with a mercury lamp, the dominant emission arises from the de-excitation from the Nd-$^4F_{3/2}$ level, the strongest transition being to the $^4I_{11/2}$ terminal state. This observation, coupled with the long lifetime of the upper level, led Johnson and Nassau to use neodymium as the active ion for a near infrared solid state laser. Furthermore, since the terminal state for this transition lies at approximately 2000 cm^{-1} above the ground state, it will not be populated at 300K. Thus, room temperature continuous-wave operation with a solid state laser seemed a possibility. Because of the high crystal quality of $CaWO_4$, this was initially the preferred host. Pulsed laser action at 1.064 μm with Nd:$CaWO_4$ was first observed by Johnson and Nassau in 1961.[16] Soon thereafter, Johnson and coworkers observed continuous-wave operation with this same system at room temperature.[17]

During 1961, D. F. Nelson and W. S. Boyle worked on making a continuous-wave ruby laser. Since pulsed ruby lasers typically used megawatts of optical pump power, extensive changes in the ruby rod size, shape, and doping were required. In order to implement the new idea of end-pumping, the rod was made trumpet-shaped, having an input cone of sapphire to intensify the pump in the attached ruby rod, which had 10 times less chromium than pulsed rods. When cooled with liquid nitrogen and pumped with 900W, the laser emitted 4 milliwatts (mW) continuously.[18] In 1962, G. D. Boyd and coworkers obtained continuous-wave operation of U:CaF_2.[19] The demonstration of continuous-wave, solid state laser action emphasized the potential of such systems for a variety of applications in communications and physical research.

Extending the spectroscopic studies to transition metal ions in insulating crystals, Johnson, R. E. Dietz, and H. J. Guggenheim found strong infrared fluorescence from several ions other than chromium. In 1963, they obtained laser emission from nickel, cobalt, and vanadium ions.[20] However, the mode of operation was quite unlike any other system—the terminal state of the laser transition was a vibrational state of the lattice. Since laser oscillation occurred in a broad vibrational sideband rather than in a narrow electronic line, these phonon-terminated lasers offered the attractive possibility of continuous tuning over a broad wavelength range. Such continuous tunability was demonstrated in MgF_2:Ni by Johnson, Guggenheim, and R. A. Thomas in 1966.[21] The application of similar principles to liquids led to the development of tunable dye lasers.[22]

2.2 Modes of Oscillation in the Laser Resonating System

In their seminal work, Schawlow and Townes realized that any realistic laser resonator would have dimensions that were large compared to the wavelength of light, and that it would be difficult to limit significant amplification to only one, or just a few modes. Nevertheless, they envisioned the selection that has been adopted on almost all lasers—using a gain medium that is long and narrow with good reflectors at the ends and the sides left open. This leaves only those few modes that propagate precisely back and forth between the mirrors with low loss, and thus produce oscillations. All other modes have much higher loss because of their eventual escape through the sides of the open resonator structure. A. G. Fox and T. Li proposed using a computer to simulate what would happen to a wave bouncing back and forth between mirrors.[23] Although a strictly analytical solution was not possible, they were able to obtain computer results that showed that if energy was initially launched in the resonator in the form of a uniform plane wave, higher-order mode components were rapidly lost, and the field always stabilized on the lowest-order mode representing a wave directed along the resonator axis. This wave had a nearly planar phase front but had a field distribution that had a maximum in the center and decreased to relatively low values at the edges of the mirror. Thus, the energy losses at the edges were much lower than for a uniform plane wave, and the resulting loss-per-round-trip transit was an order of magnitude lower than the estimates previously made.

At the same time, Boyd and J. P. Gordon were investigating a confocal interferometer for use as an optical resonator.[24] They extended the self-consistent field approach of Fox and Li by working on a suggestion of W. D. Lewis that the modes of a confocal resonator might be susceptible to analytic solution. They found that the modes of a confocal resonator with rectangular mirrors could be described approximately by Hermite-Gaussian functions. The simplicity of their results made it easy to predict the cross section of the beam not only within the resonator, but also as it was transmitted through the mirrors to points outside. These modes were shown to retain the same Hermite-Gaussian intensity profile at every point along the path of propagation. Thus, the modes of a confocal resonator can also be considered to be the characteristic modes of propagation in free space. The unique properties of the confocal resonator, which has the lowest loss of all resonator geometries, are due to the periodic refocusing of the diffracting wave at each mirror. These analytic studies were continued by Boyd and H. W. Kogelnik, who produced a more general theory covering mirrors of unequal size and curvature.[25] They also discovered that there were stable and unstable resonator classes depending on the ratios of mirror curvatures and spacings. In stable resonators bundles of light rays are periodically refocused, while in unstable resonators light rays diverge.

These theoretical studies contributed to an improved understanding of how the optical field intensities for the various modes are distributed throughout a laser resonator. That these modes really exist was confirmed when the first He-Ne laser that oscillated continuously was made to operate with curved mirrors external to the glass envelope containing the gain medium. The first pure-mode patterns were observed by Kogelnik and Rigrod using a He-Ne laser with Brewster-angle windows.[26] [Fig. 5-6] By changing the mirror spacings and curvatures, and adjusting their alignments, it was possible to observe the mode patterns in detail, to measure combination tones produced by the beating of different mode frequencies, and to determine the ranges of mirror spacings that permit or prevent oscillation. The predictions of the theories in all details were well borne out.

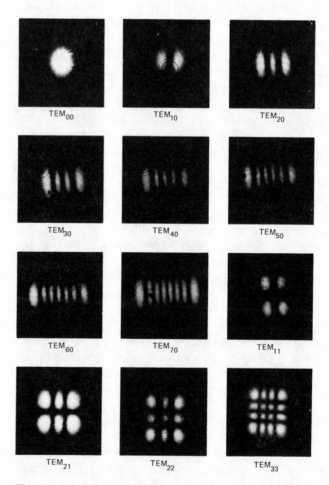

Fig. 5-6. Mode patterns of coherent beams produced in a laser oscillator. The photographs show the cross-sectional distributions of light, first observed in a helium-neon gas laser.

In the years that followed, the Hermite-Gaussian description of resonator modes emerged as a simple but powerful tool for the analysis of the propagation of laser beams through practical optical systems. The techniques that were developed have since found widespread use. Among them are the mode-matching procedures described by Kogelnik, which are used to transform an incoming laser beam into a beam with the properties required for a given optical system.[27] Other examples are the simplification of the laws governing the propagation of laser beams by the introduction of a complex beam parameter that describes both the diameter and the wavefront curvature of the beam, and the discovery of Kogelnik's ABCD law[28] that provides a simple and unexpected relationship between the laser beam parameters in any optical system and the paraxial ray matrix of that system.

Most of our understanding of the behavior of laser beams and laser resonators developed in the first half-dozen years after its advent. A summary of this knowledge is given in the review article by Kogelnik and Li, which has become a standard text.[29]

2.3 Mode Locking and Pulse Generation

A typical laser consists of an optical resonator formed by two parallel plate mirrors and contains a laser gain medium. The frequency band over which laser oscillation can occur is determined by the frequency region where the gain of the laser medium exceeds the resonator losses. Often such an optical resonator can support many modes within this oscillation band, and, therefore, the laser output consists of radiation at a number of closely spaced frequencies. The total output of such a laser as a function of time will depend on the amplitudes, frequencies, and relative phases of all of these oscillating modes. If nothing fixes these parameters, random fluctuations and nonlinear effects in the laser medium will cause them to change with time, and the output will vary correspondingly. If the oscillating modes are forced to maintain equal frequency spacings with a fixed phase relationship to each other, the output as a function of time will vary in a well-defined manner. The laser is then said to be "mode-locked" or "phase-locked."

Although there were indications of mode locking in earlier studies, the first paper to demonstrate clearly the fundamental properties of mode locking was published in 1964 by L. E. Hargrove, R. L. Fork, and M. A. Pollock.[30] They obtained a continuous train of equally spaced, short pulses from a He-Ne laser by mode locking with an internal acoustic loss modulator, with the laser modes locked into a condition of fixed-amplitude, equal-frequency spacing, and well-defined phase relations. M. DiDomenico, following a suggestion by

E. I. Gordon, completed an independent theoretical description of mode locking by internal loss modulation at the resonator mode-spacing frequency.[31] Earlier, W. E. Lamb had described how the non-linear properties of the laser medium could cause the modes of a laser to lock with equal frequency spacing. This idea was later discussed by M. H. Crowell for the case of many oscillating modes.[32] Crowell's experiments with a 6328Å He-Ne laser demonstrated the self-locking of laser modes caused solely by the nonlinear behavior of the laser medium. In 1967, a new mode-locking technique was proposed and demonstrated by P. W. Smith, who showed that mode locking could be obtained by moving one laser mirror at a constant velocity.[33]

Shortly thereafter, a new theory of self-locking based on the transient response of the laser medium to the incident radiation was proposed by Fox and Smith, and further developed by Smith.[34] Fox and coworkers demonstrated the first use of a section of laser medium excited to the low-laser state as a saturable absorber to produce mode locking.[35] In 1968, Smith published the first demonstration of the simultaneous locking of longitudinal and transverse laser modes.[36] Under these conditions, light energy is confined to a small region of space and travels a zigzag path as it bounces back and forth in the laser resonator.

By using a number of isotopes of cadmium in a He-Cd laser, W. T. Silfvast and Smith demonstrated the inverse dependence of mode-locked pulsewidth on laser bandwidth, and obtained a continuous train of 120 psec pulses—at the time, the shortest pulses available in a mode-locked continuous-wave laser.[37]

During 1970, interest developed in mode-locking, high-pressure, transversely excited (TE) CO_2 lasers. The first mode-locking experiments were reported by O. R. Wood and coworkers.[38] They obtained nanosecond (nsec) pulses with 1 megawatt (MW) peak power. Later, Smith and coworkers reported the first mode locking of a waveguide CO_2 laser.[39] In 1971, P. K. Runge reported the use of a flowing dye as a saturable absorber to mode lock a 6328Å He-Ne laser.[40]

The broad molecular levels that permit the broad tunability of organic-dye lasers provided a means of overcoming the bandwidth limitation that restricted the generation of short optical pulses in continuous lasers. The first attempt at mode locking a continuous-wave dye laser to generate ultrashort optical pulses was described by A. Dienes, E. P. Ippen, and C. V. Shank using an active mode-locking scheme in 1971.[41] Synchronously pumped mode locking was reported by Shank and Ippen in 1973.[42] (See also section 1.6.3 of Chapter 6.) These schemes produced pulses of the order of 50 psec. A dramatic reduction in optical pulse width was achieved using the passive cw mode-locking technique devised by Ippen, Shank, and Dienes.[43] In fact, the first optical pulses shorter than a picosecond were reported by Shank and Ippen in 1974.[44] (For more on this topic, see Chapter 6, section 1.6.3 — "Subpicosecond Molecular Spectroscopy.") A new time-resolved spectroscopy has been developed with better than an order-of-magnitude time resolution over the best achieved in other systems. These techniques have been extensively applied to study picosecond phenomena in semiconductors as well as chemical and biological systems.

Ultrashort pulses are also produced in color center lasers by a technique called "synchronous mode locking." Most of the mode-locking experiments at Bell Labs have used a laser with F_2^+ centers in the host potassium fluoride (KF) crystal, tunable from about 1.23 μm to 1.48 μm, and pumped with a Nd:YAG laser operating at 1.064 μm. The KF-F_2^+ laser produced 300 million pulses per second, each 3 to 5 psec wide.

The transit time of a pulse through a length of optical fiber depends on the wavelength—this is the phenomenon of group velocity dispersion. In general, the effect of dispersion is to broaden severely very short pulses upon transit through long fibers. However, in the silica glass fibers, there is one special wavelength, usually near 1.3 μm, where the dispersion disappears. (Conveniently, this zero-dispersion point can be tailored to lie in a region of low transmission loss.) By tuning the mode-locked KF laser to the zero-dispersion wavelength, D. M. Bloom and coworkers were able to directly demonstrate distortionless propagation of 5 psec pulses in fibers several kilometers long.[45] This important result indicated directly the ultimate capacity of the fibers to transmit information at very high rates.

2.4 Temporal Coherence of Laser Radiation

The laser has stimulated various theoretical models for the dynamic behavior of quantum mechanical oscillators. These models are of interest because they describe an instructive interface between quantum and purely classical phenomena, and because they provide a basis for calculating the intensity and phase fluctuations that make up laser noise, as well as the higher-order correlation properties that are part of a complete description of laser light. Representative of work in this area is the intensity fluctuation calculation of D. E. McCumber,[46] the general quantum noise source model of the laser by M. Lax,[47] and the treatment of a similar model by J. P. Gordon.[48]

An important result is the calculation by Lax and M. Zwanziger that predicted the full intensity fluctuation distribution for a laser near threshold for arbitrary sampling time.[49]

Observations of laser noise behavior include the study by T. L. Paoli and J. E. Ripper of spiking behavior arising directly from quantum intensity fluctuations in semiconductor lasers.[50]

III. LASERS FOR OPTICAL COMMUNICATION

The discovery of laser action in solid state and gaseous media occurred at a time when the research activities on semiconductor p-n junction devices were widespread. Therefore, it is not surprising that these two fields were quickly combined to demonstrate laser action resulting from the injection of a non-equilibrium electron population across a p-n junction. Among the early proposals for a semiconductor laser was one from France by P. Aigrain,[51] one from the Soviet Union by N. G. Basov, B. M. Yul, and Yu. M. Popov,[52] and one from Bell Labs by W. S. Boyle and D. G. Thomas.[53] The stage was set for this development when the concepts for stimulated emission in semiconductors were clarified by M. G. A. Bernard and G. Duraffourg in 1961,[54] and by the reports of highly efficient radiative recombination of carriers in GaAs by J. I. Pankove and M. J. Massoulie of RCA[55] and R. J. Keyes and T. M. Quist of IBM.[56] By the end of 1962, R. N. Hall and coworkers, at General Electric,[57] N. Holonyak and S. F. Bevacqua, also at General Electric,[58] M. I. Nathan and coworkers at IBM,[59] and Quist and coworkers at M.I.T.'s Lincoln Laboratory[60] had all observed laser action at 77K by injecting electrons across a p-n junction in a GaAs crystal. The resonant cavity was between two faces of the crystal that were perpendicular to the junction plane.

Considerable excitement was generated by the demonstration of laser action by electron injection because of the potential for very simple pumping, and the extreme simplicity and small size of the injection laser. The dimensions of this laser were about 25 μm by 400 μm by 100 μm, and if the laser could be operated continuously, the pumping current could be achieved with the application of 1.5 volts. Unfortunately, a common and discouraging feature of all of the early injection lasers was an extremely high threshold current density of about 50,000 amps/cm^2 at room temperature (which is about 20 amps for the cross-sectional area given above). Most studies were done at liquid nitrogen temperature (77K), and the usual mode of operation was with very short current pulses and low duty cycles (less than one percent). Those early injection lasers have become known as homostructure lasers because they are composed of a single semiconducting compound. The highest temperature at which a homostructure laser has been operated continuously is 205K. This was achieved at Bell Labs in 1967 by J. C. Dyment and L. A. D'Asaro.[61] They carefully heat-sinked a GaAs injection laser that had been fabricated in the form of a narrow stripe only 12 μm wide. However, it was clear that the fundamental problem of the very high room temperature threshold current density had to be solved before the injection laser could become a useful device.

3.1 The Heterojunction Semiconductor Laser

In late 1967, M. B. Panish and S. Sumski began studies of the phase chemistry and liquid epitaxy of $Al_xGa_{1-x}As$.[62] At the same time Panish and I. Hayashi [Fig. 5-7] began studies of possible injection laser structures incorporating one or more heterojunctions between GaAs and $Al_xGa_{1-x}As$. These semiconductors are a good choice for a high quality heterojunction because they have the same crystal structure and almost identical lattice parameters. Furthermore, the energy gap of $Al_xGa_{1-x}As$ increases as x increases, while the refractive index decreases as x increases. As a result, a structure consisting of a layer of GaAs sandwiched between layers of n-type and p-type $Al_xGa_{1-x}As$ is simultaneously an optical waveguide and a confinement region for carriers injected into the GaAs layer. Panish and Hayashi called the laser incorporating the sandwich structure a double heterostructure (DH) injection laser. Since the major reasons for the high room-temperature, threshold-current current density of homostructure lasers had been the inability of the weak waveguide to confine and efficiently use injected carriers, the DH laser, which did not suffer from these defects, had a much lower threshold current density. [Fig. 5-8]

By mid-1968, Hayashi, Panish, and coworkers had achieved room temperature threshold current densities as low as 8600 amps/cm² with an intermediate structure designated as a single heterostructure laser. By June 1970, they achieved continuous room temperature lasing

Fig. 5-7. I. Hayashi (left) and M. B. Panish discuss a semiconductor laser designed in 1970 that operates continuously at room temperature.

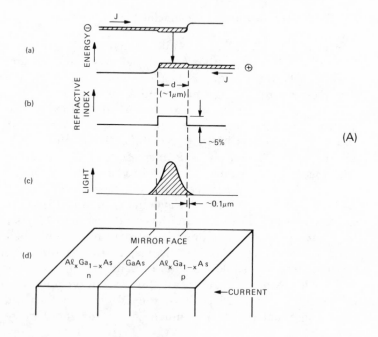

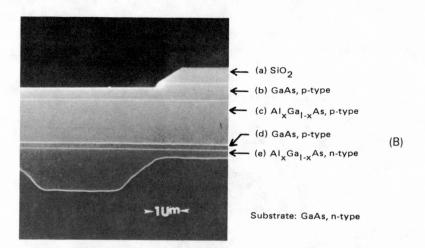

Fig. 5-8. (A) Schematic representation of a heterojunction laser, showing (a) the band edges with forward bias, (b) refractive index changes, (c) optical field distribution, and (d) physical structure of a double heterostructure laser diode. [*Appl. Sol. State Sci.—Adv. Mat. Dev. Res.* **4** (1974): 269]. (B) Scanning electron photomicrograph of the face of a channel substrate heterostructure laser. Layers (c), (d), and (e) correspond to the double heterostructure shown schematically in (A). Layer (a) is an insulator to define the stripe contact. Layer (b) permits easier contact to a metallic layer that will be added later. Note the addition of a channel in the substrate. This provides the real refractive index guiding parallel to the plane of the layers.

with a DH laser that had a room temperature threshold current density of 1600 amps/cm^2.[63] Similar results were achieved in the Soviet Union at almost exactly the same time.[64] Since that time a variety of heterostructure lasers have been studied in order to achieve even lower threshold current densities (to about 500 amps/cm^2 at room temperature) and improved optical mode and electrical behavior. All of the structures proposed for communications applications incorporate the original idea of R. A. Furnanage and D. K. Wilson to use a narrow strip region to permit efficient heat sinking and low overall current.[65] The simplest version of the strip, as proposed by Dyment and D'Asaro is formed by proton bombardment of adjoining regions to render them nonconducting.[66]

As a result of the studies of heterostructure lasers and the almost simultaneous development of extremely low-loss optical fibers, the injection laser has become the prime choice as the optical source for lightwave communications systems. For this reason extensive studies have been made of the way that heterostructure lasers degrade. Of primary importance was the observation by B. C. De Loach and coworkers of the dark-line defect: a region of enhanced nonradiative recombination that grew rapidly during laser operation and rapidly increased the laser threshold current.[67]

W. D. Johnston and B. I. Miller showed that the dark-line defect could be generated by optical excitation of undoped double heterostructure material.[68] Studies by P. Petroff and R. L. Hartman, and by D. V. Lang and L. C. Kimerling showed that the dark-line defects were dislocation networks that grew from threading dislocations by climb, driven by the energy released by the nonradiative recombination of minority carriers.[69]

R. L. Hartman and A. R. Hartman showed that strain reduction was the key to a vast reduction in this short-life degradation mechanism.[70] The remaining gradual degradation mechanisms have not been fully elucidated, but by 1976, growth and fabrication processing had been refined to the point where W. B. Joyce and coworkers were able to report extrapolated room-temperature laser-lifetimes of one million hours based upon elevated temperature tests.[71]

3.2 Heterostructure Lasers and Optical Fibers

While numerous improvements were being made to GaAs double-heterostructure lasers, interest began to grow in moving the wavelength away from 0.87 μm, at which the laser was oscillating, to wavelengths where the newly developed optical fibers had their lowest loss and minimum pulse dispersion. Among the materials examined were the III-V ternary and quaternary mixed crystals with combinations of aluminum, gallium, or indium on the sublattice of atoms of valence III, and phosphorus, arsenic, or antimony on the sublattice of atoms of valence V. The first successful laser based on one of these new materials was made by R. E. Nahory and Pollack in 1975.[72] This laser consisted of a recombination layer of $GaAs_{1-x}Sb_x$, and had a room temperature threshold of 2100 amps/cm^2, much lower than an earlier version developed in Japan.[73] Later in 1975, Nahory and coworkers, using the proton bombardment-stripe geometry, succeeded in operating these lasers continuously at room temperature.[74] The thresholds were as low as those of comparable GaAs devices. The operating laser wavelength ranged from 1.0 to 1.06 μm, depending on the value of x. This first demonstration that complex, mixed crystal systems could be used successfully in continuous room temperature lasers was a strong stimulus for the investigation of other materials. Only a few months later, workers at Lincoln Laboratory reported a continuous $In_{1-x}Ga_xAs_yP_{1-y}/InP$ laser,[75] and at RCA an $In_{1-x}Ga_xAs/In_{1-y}Ga_yP$ laser[76] was constructed.

In 1971, Kogelnik and Shank demonstrated a very compact mirror-free laser structure that they named the distributed feedback (DFB) laser.[77] The DFB structure is compatible with integrated optics, and helps to stabilize and purify the spectrum of the laser emission. DFB structures are made by introducing high-resolution periodic variations of the effective refractive index into the laser medium. A typical example is a corrugation with a 1000Å period of the active layer of a semiconductor laser. Such a periodic structure provides the required feedback for laser action through backward Bragg scattering. The first demonstrations of stimulated emission in DFB structures were made with dye laser media. These were soon followed by the exploration of a considerable variety of DFB structures suitable for semiconductor junction lasers at Bell Laboratories[78] and elsewhere.

IV. LASERS FOR INDUSTRIAL APPLICATIONS – THE CO$_2$ LASER

Prior to 1963, gas lasers were primarily low-power systems and the laser community considered only the solid state lasers in the visible and the near infrared for high-power application. But in 1963, C. K. N. Patel [Fig. 5-9] discovered laser action in CO_2 on its vibrational-rotational transitions near 10 μm under continuous-wave and pulsed conditions.[79] This discovery is significant because, unlike prior schemes that utilized atomic energy levels for laser action, the CO_2 laser used the molecular vibrational-rotational bands. From initial calculations, Patel noted that molecular lasers operating on vibrational-rotational transitions would be the key to gas lasers for high-power applications. [Fig. 5-10] In 1964 he introduced a continuous-flow laser system and demonstrated that vibrational energy transfer from N_2 to CO_2 was extraordinarily efficient.[80] In part, this is attributable to the very long lifetimes of the vibrationally

Fig. 5-9. C. K. N. Patel standing near his CO_2 laser apparatus.

excited N_2 molecules that can be produced efficiently in an ordinary nitrogen discharge and to the near coincidence of the relevant N_2 and CO_2 vibrational energy levels. Patel found that at typical gas pressures almost all of the vibrationally excited N_2 molecules can transfer their energy to the CO_2 molecules. In the He-Ne case, the electronic energy is exchanged. [Fig. 5-11] Laser action on vibrational-rotational transitions of molecules is efficient because of the very rapid equilibration of the excitation energy of a vibrational state among its closely spaced, but discrete, rotational levels. [Fig. 5-12] This leads to a laser system where the optical gain and laser action can occur on a large number of closely spaced transitions. Even though the optical gain on any of the transitions is relatively small, the power output is very high. Since all the vibrational level lifetimes are very long (compared with atomic laser systems), once a molecular gas laser medium becomes excited, it can store enormous amounts of energies that can be extracted in short-time pulses to give very high power pulses. The CO_2 lasers, in continuous-wave as well as pulsed mode, operate in the 9 μm to 11 μm region of the infrared. This is a spectral region of great interest, even though the radiation is invisible to the human eye, since the 8 μm to 14 μm spectral region constitutes a low atmospheric loss window for laser transmission.

In 1965, Patel and his colleagues demonstrated that the CO_2 laser was a very high continuous-wave power system by obtaining an output of more than 200 watts (W), and an operating efficiency as high as 10 percent.[81] Further work has focused on increasing the CO_2 laser power output by using a variety of excitation mechanisms. By 1979

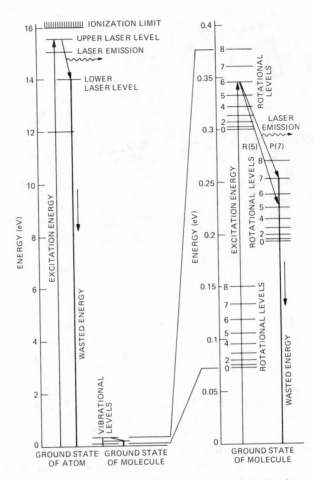

Fig. 5-10. Energy-level diagrams of an atom and a molecule are compared. In an atom (left), the electronic energy levels between which infrared transitions can occur are situated near the atomic ionization limit—far above the ground state of the atom. As a result, the atom has to be excited to a very high energy to produce laser action, which in turn results in the emission of a photon with a comparatively small amount of energy.

the maximum continuous-wave power output for a CO_2 laser had exceeded 100 kilowatts (kW) and the pulsed-power output exceeded 10^{12}W, with single-pulse energy of more than 10,000 joules. The applications of such high powers to communications, metal working (cutting, welding, drilling, and so on), paper and cloth cutting, optical fiber drawing, laser induced fusion, high-resolution spectroscopy in the infrared region, as high-power pump sources for obtaining laser action in far infrared region by optical pumping (see section 5.3), isotope separation, laser surgery, and noncivilian (weapons) pur-

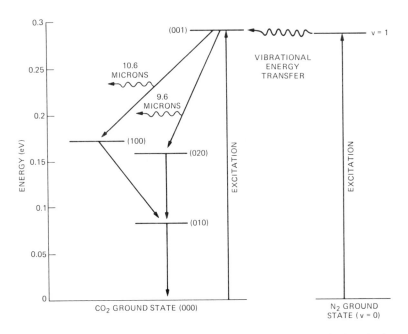

Fig. 5-11. Addition of nitrogen gas to a carbon dioxide laser results in the selective excitation of the carbon dioxide molecules to the upper laser level. Since nitrogen is a diatomic molecule, it has only one degree of vibrational freedom; hence, one vibrational quantum number (ν) completely describes its vibrational energy levels. Nitrogen molecules can be efficiently excited from the $\nu=0$ level to the $\nu=1$ level by electron impact in a low-pressure nitrogen discharge. Since the energy of excitation of the $N_2(\nu=1)$ molecule nearly equals the energy of excitation of the $CO_2(001)$ molecule, an efficient transfer of vibrational energy takes place from the nitrogen to the carbon dioxide in collisions between $N_2(\nu=1)$ molecules and $CO_2(000)$ molecules. In such a collision the nitrogen molecule returns from the $\nu=1$ level to its ground state by losing one quantum of its vibrational energy, thereby exciting the carbon dioxide molecule from its ground state to the 001 level. The carbon dioxide molecule can then radiatively decay to either the 100 level or the 020 level, in the process emitting infrared light at 10.6 or 9.6 microns, respectively.

poses have all been explored vigorously. In the area of high-resolution spectroscopy, the CO_2 and other molecular lasers (see section 5.2) have proved to be the only sources in the 5 μm-12 μm region. Their use in infrared spectroscopy has exceeded the use of any other laser system for spectroscopic uses. In the area of laser surgery, the CO_2 laser has become the laser of choice with some 20,000 operations performed by more than 1000 surgeons by 1981. Further, each year newer applications of laser surgery have been forthcoming with dozens of CO_2 laser surgery conferences held each year.

In the 19 years following the discovery of the CO_2 laser and the demonstration of its high efficiency, about 3,000 technical papers and

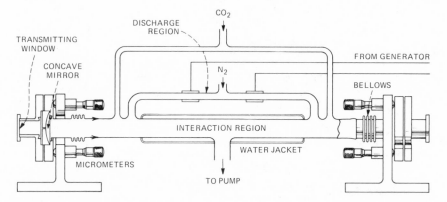

Fig. 5-12. Continuous-flow system was used by C. K. N. Patel to verify the hypothesis that a carbon dioxide-nitrogen laser would be more efficient than a pure carbon dioxide laser. Strong laser oscillation was obtained in this system on the vibrational-rotational transitions of carbon dioxide even though no electric discharge was present in the interaction region, thereby proving the effectiveness of using vibrationally excited nitrogen molecules for selective excitation of carbon dioxide molecules to the upper laser level.

more than a dozen books were published on various aspects of CO_2 lasers. Moreover, the CO_2 laser became one of the most commercially useful laser systems in the world.

4.1 Yttrium Aluminum Garnet (YAG) Laser

In 1964, J. E. Geusic, H. M. Marcos, and L. G. Van Uitert showed that neodymium-doped yttrium aluminum garnet (YAG) crystals should have a lower threshold for laser action than solid state laser systems previously investigated.[82] One of the main advantages of this system is the presence of pump bands revealed by absorption spectroscopy that are favorable for tungsten sources. Continuous operation of a Nd:YAG laser pumped at room temperature with a tungsten lamp was achieved with a threshold (360W input power) about one-fifth that for the $CaWO_4$ system. This laser has been further developed, and has found wide use in the "smart weapons" of the military, such as target designators, range finders, and target seekers. Its use in industrial applications also is growing, and popular roles for it include hole drilling and welding, particularly where close control is important.

V. OTHER LASER TYPES

5.1 Lasers Based on Atomic Transitions

The successful operation of the He-Ne laser was soon followed by the discovery of many other lasers in the visible, infrared, and even the far infrared. Along with the new lasers came new principles of operation. Early in 1962, Bennett and Patel independently demonstrated that, due to direct inelastic impact excitations, gain was still present for the 1.15 μm neon-transition in He-Ne laser, even in the absence of helium in the discharge.[83] Later in 1962, Patel and coworkers obtained laser action on a number of lines near 2 μm using direct electron excitation of the pure, neutral noble gases helium, neon, argon, krypton, and xenon.[84] By 1964, Patel and collaborators had made neon lasers that operated in the middle and far infrared, including one at 133 μm.[85] In the same year E. I. Gordon and E. F. Labuda, in a joint publication with W. B. Bridges of the Hughes Research Laboratories, announced continuous-wave laser action in the visible from ionized argon, krypton, and xenon noble gases.[86]

Subsequent accomplishments in ion lasers were made in the area of metal-vapor lasers. In the late 1960s, Silfvast[87] achieved high-efficiency, continuous-wave oscillation in cadmium vapor at 0.4416 μm while he was at the University of Utah. Subsequently, laser action at approximately fifty wavelengths in the visible in ionized selenium was reported by Silfvast and M. B. Klein.[88,89] This laser, and others in lead, tin, and zinc, are based upon a new excitation mechanism for gas lasers (Penning ionization), which Silfvast proposed and verified in the He-Cd discharge.

In 1971, Silfvast and L. H. Szeto demonstrated a simplified design for metal-vapor lasers that led to inexpensive construction and long-lived operation of the He-Cd laser.[90] This type of laser became the second most reliable laser (in terms of operating lifetime) available at the time. Ion lasers are used widely for a variety of research investigations and industrial applications where blue or green light is desirable. They also have proved to be the most popular form for use in entertainment applications such as light shows.

An early attempt at an X-ray laser was made by M. A. Duguay and P. M. Rentzepis.[91] Their scheme called for the use of high-power ultrashort X-ray pulses to create vacancies preferentially in the innermost electronic shells of an atom. The experimental difficulties encountered when this approach was tried led E. J. McGuire and Duguay to propose a photoionization scheme in alkali earth atoms irradiated by laser fields tuned to specific transitions in the ion.[92] Although these experiments did not achieve their objectives, they have paved the way for other, possibly more successful, work in this important field.

5.2 Lasers Involving Vibrational-Rotational Molecular Transitions

Laser action on the vibrational-rotational transitions of molecules other than CO_2, such as CO, N_2O, and CS_2, operating at different wavelength regions, were also demonstrated by Patel and his colleagues.[93-96] The general nature of the efficiency of vibrational energy transfer in N_2-CO, N_2-N_2O, and N_2-CS_2 lasers was established.

5.3 Optically Pumped Molecular Gas Lasers

Although of great scientific interest, the far infrared (FIR) region (where λ = 10 μm to 1000 μm), lying between the traditional optics region and the area of microwave technology, has always presented great technical difficulty. The lack of radiation sources in this region has been one of the chief reasons for this impediment. Black-body radiation is very weak in this wavelength range and electron devices used for microwave generation will not operate at the high frequencies involved.

In 1970, T. Y. Chang and T. J. Bridges invented the FIR optically pumped laser.[97,98] In this device an efficient gas discharge laser in the near infrared, usually the CO_2 laser operating near 10 μm, excites a vibrational-rotational transition in a molecular gas contained in a separate cavity. This excitation produces a population inversion in the rotational levels of the vibrational states involved, and allows laser action to take place, typically in the FIR region. The first observed laser excitations were in methyl fluoride at 452, 496, and 541 μm. Both pulsed and continuous-wave operation were found to be possible. With this lasing mechanism, there is a choice of a large number of molecular lasing gases with no fear of decomposition, since no electrical discharge is present. By 1979, about 1,000 FIR lasing lines had been reported in over 30 different molecular gases spread over the spectral range from 30 μm to 2,000 μm.[99]

5.4 Dye Lasers

Shortly after the achievement of laser action on atomic transitions, it became apparent that a tunable laser would open up a whole new vista of applications for coherent light, including the generation of short optical pulses in continuously operated lasers. A number of approaches were taken to develop a conveniently tunable laser. The most successful approach in the visible region of the spectrum has been the organic dye laser. Organic dyes are ideal systems for achieving tunable laser action because stimulated emission takes place between broad molecular levels rather than narrow atomic transitions as in gas laser systems.

At Bell Labs, work on tunable dye lasers began with the use of a pulsed nitrogen laser as a pump for a dye-laser system. In 1970, C. V. Shank and coworkers used an excited-state complex (exciplex) molecular system to achieve the broadest range of tunability ever observed from a single molecule, with the emission ranging from the near ultraviolet to the yellow region of the visible spectrum.[100] In 1972, a continuously operated dye laser with highly improved efficiency was reported by A. Dienes, E. P. Ippen, and Shank,[101] using a new, folded, three-mirror configuration proposed by H. W. Kogelnik and coworkers.[102] In this configuration, which became used in most commercial dye laser and color-center laser systems, astigmatic aberrations caused by oblique folding angles were compensated by proper dye cell design. Another significant improvement in continuous-wave dye laser performance followed the invention of the free-flowing jet stream by P. K. Runge and R. Rosenberg.[103] This system is a dye-laser cell without windows and eliminates the degrading effects of performance due to thermal heating of the dye material. The first demonstration of such a laser was by Shank and coworkers in 1973.[104] At the time of this writing the folded-mirror configuration and free-flowing dye material are used in all commercial laser systems.

5.5 Color-Center Lasers

While the organic dyes have provided a medium for tunable lasers and the generation of short pulses in the visible spectrum, they are not easily applied to longer wavelengths. L. F. Mollenauer and collaborators have developed tunable color-center lasers as viable, and in many ways unique, substitutes for dye lasers at the longer wavelengths.[105] Color-center lasers have been used in high resolution molecular spectroscopy, in the characterization of fiber and integrated optic devices, in fundamental experiments on the propagation of very short pulses in optical fibers, and in investigations into the basic physics of semiconductors.

There are two distinct types of laser-active color centers. Both are based on electrons trapped at halide ion vacancies in an optically polished slab of alkali halide crystal, such as NaCl. Centers involving a single vacancy associated with an impurity alkali ion are known as F_A centers. (The F is from the German "Farbe," meaning color.) Pulsed, non-tunable laser action with $F_A(Li)$ centers in KCl was first demonstrated in 1965 by B. Fritz and E. Menke of the Physikalische Institut der Technische Hochschule, Stuttgart.[106] The F_A-center lasers developed at Bell Labs in 1973 are tunable from about 2.2 μm to 3.3 μm. The more powerful F_2^+-center lasers, developed in the late 1970s, have a pair of adjacent vacancies sharing a single electron. This center can be created, usually by radiation damage, in just about any alkali halide host. Using various hosts, a tuning range of 0.82 μm to 2.5 μm has been observed.

Like their dye laser counterparts, the color-center lasers are excited, or "pumped," with light from another (but fixed-frequency) laser. When the excited crystal is placed in a tuned optical resonator, its broad, spontaneous emission is suppressed, and most of the light emerges as a laser beam at the wavelength of the resonator. Tuning is usually accomplished with either a diffraction grating or a prism.

VI. LASERS IN PHYSICAL RESEARCH

6.1 High - Resolution Spectroscopy

Optical experiments conducted after the introduction of the laser taught a great deal about the nature of light. The early experiments of D. F. Nelson and coworkers were the first to establish clearly the spatial coherence of laser radiation.[107] Several fundamental contributions to optics were made at a time when questions of optical coherence had not yet been widely discussed and were still not completely understood. Among these experiments were the beating of helium-neon laser light from two adjacent resonator modes by A. Javan, E. A. Ballik, and W. L. Bond,[108] the demonstration of laser-light granularity by J. D. Rigden and E. I. Gordon,[109] the observation of spectral-line splitting from microwave modulation of laser light by I. P. Kaminow,[110] and the achievement of phase locking of two independent optical sources by L. H. Enloe and J. H. Rodda.[111]

The Lamb dip in laser power output, observed as a single axial mode of oscillation is tuned through the center of a Doppler-broadened line, was first observed by R. A. McFarlane, W. R. Bennett, and W. E. Lamb.[112] The Lamb dip has become of considerable value in laser frequency stabilization. Also accompanying the development of new lasers during this early period was the accumulation of much detailed information on radiative lifetimes, collision cross sections, transition probabilities, and other basic parameters of neutral and ionized rare gases.

Studies of argon ion lasers, first operated continuously by Gordon, Labuda, and Bridges, improved the understanding of the mechanism of inversion in ion lasers. Gordon and coworkers determined gain, electron density, and level populations under continuous-wave conditions and showed the importance of multiple-step, electron-impact excitation of argon ions.[113]

During the early 1960s, extensive effort was devoted to studies of the optical properties of ions in solids. Motivated in part by the discovery of solid state laser action, this work led to a wealth of new spectroscopic data and line assignments and produced numerous studies of fluorescence efficiencies, line broadening mechanisms, energy exchange in crystals with high doping concentrations, Stark and Zeeman effects, charge compensation of doped ions, and other related subjects. One example was the study of the mechanism of line broadening of the ruby R lines by D. E. McCumber and M. D.

Sturge.[114] This work established the dominant contributions to the linewidth from phonon Raman scattering and from crystal inhomogeneities at temperatures above and below 77K, respectively. Nelson and Sturge studied absorption and emission of the R lines of ruby, and verified the principle of detailed balance, the only precise verification ever made in a solid.[115]

6.1.1 Two-Photon Spectroscopy

In 1970, L. S. Vasilenko and coworkers in the Soviet Union discussed theoretically a simple technique for obtaining Doppler-free two-photon spectra from gases.[116] Their basic idea was to use two laser beams of equal frequency propagating in opposite directions. For such a case, the Doppler shift of one beam is equal, but of opposite sign, to the Doppler shift of the opposing beam. The sum frequency is independent of the velocity of atoms and Doppler effects are eliminated. It was not until 1974 that appropriate dye lasers became available so that Doppler-free, two-photon spectroscopy could be experimentally demonstrated. At about this time, work on high-resolution two-photon spectroscopy at Bell Labs was undertaken by J. E. Bjorkholm and P. F. Liao. In most of their work they used two precisely tunable, single-mode, continuous-wave dye lasers and cells filled with sodium vapor.

Two-photon absorption obtained with equal frequency laser beams is usually very weak because the required laser frequency may be far from the frequency of a resonance transition of the atom. Bjorkholm and Liao demonstrated that at the price of slightly increased linewidth, two-photon absorption could be enormously enhanced by using two lasers of different frequencies.[117] Strong resonant enhancement of the absorption occurs when one of the lasers is tuned near the frequency of a resonance transition. Since $\nu_1 \neq \nu_2$, the Doppler broadening is not totally eliminated; however, in most cases the residual effect is small since $(\nu_1 - \nu_2) \ll (\nu_1 + \nu_2)$. In sodium, residual Doppler-broadening near resonance amounts to less than 30 MHz, whereas the width of the Doppler-broadened transition is 3.4 GHz. For tunings outside the Doppler width of the resonance transition, the absorption could be enhanced by up to a factor of 10^6.

Shortly thereafter, Liao and Bjorkholm experimentally demonstrated that optically induced shifts of atomic energy levels can be very significant in two-photon spectroscopy.[118] In their experiments, ac Stark effect shifts exceeding 1 GHz were observed. With the use of an atomic beam of sodium, they also demonstrated experimentally the appearance of ac Stark splitting in two-photon spectra.[119]

Theoretical and experimental studies of two-photon resonant enhancement were extended to the case where one laser frequency was inside a Doppler-broadened resonance transition.[120] By tuning one laser onto resonance, Liao and Bjorkholm demonstrated two-photon absorption 6×10^9 larger than that obtained with equal frequency lasers. Moreover, when one laser was tuned within the Doppler-width of the resonance transition, totally Doppler-free signals were once again obtained.

Using the strong, Doppler-free absorption obtained with this technique (called two-photon spectroscopy with a resonant intermediate state), Liao and Bjorkholm observed the "forbidden" (and consequently, extremely weak) 3S → 4F transition in sodium.[121] This yielded the first measurement of the 4F state fine-structure splitting; it also showed that, in contrast to the D states of sodium, the 4F level is not inverted. The results helped to demonstrate that the F states of sodium were essentially hydrogenic.

Since the first observation of photon echoes in 1964,[122] lasers have been widely used to observe coherent optical transient effects. Most of these observations were made using single-photon resonances. In collaboration with J. P. Gordon, Liao and Bjorkholm made one of the first observations of optical transients associated with a two-photon transition and explained theoretically the observed two-photon optical free-induction decay.[123] Liao, N. Economu, and R. R. Freeman used the Doppler-free character of two-photon coherent states to make high-resolution measurements of atomic linewidth, and demonstrated that such measurements could be made with simple broadband lasers.[124]

6.2 Raman and Brillouin Scattering

From the first demonstration of laser action in 1960, it was clear to some that the laser's high intensity, collimation, and monochromaticity would make it relatively simple to perform high-precision spectroscopy in a way that was impossible utilizing prelaser techniques.

The advent of the continuous-wave He-Ne laser, the argon ion laser, and subsequently tunable coherent light sources further stimulated research in the area of Raman and Brillouin light scattering that resulted in many contributions to the understanding of the physics of solids, liquids, and gases. These investigations included studies of inelastic scattering by molecular vibrations, optical and acoustical phonons, magnons, plasmons, polaritons, and other collective excitations.

Laser Raman spectroscopy was pioneered and exploited by S. P. S. Porto. In 1961, Porto, together with D. L. Wood, carried out the first Raman experiment using a laser—their ruby laser fired three times a minute.[125] This was soon followed by the first demonstration of the utility of a continuously operating laser as a Raman source, reported by Kogelnik and Porto using a red He-Ne laser.[126] In Brillouin scattering, which is based on the elasto-optic effect, theoretical work by Nelson and M. Lax led to the prediction that a rotation of volume element in a birefringent crystal produces effects comparable to strain.[127] This prediction was verified experimentally in magnitude and symmetry by Nelson and P. D. Lazay using rutile crystals.[128] The research served to point out the shortcoming in using strain as the independent variable in characterizing elastic deformation in elasto-optic effect experiments of previous workers.

6.2.1 *Alkali Halides and Semiconductors*

In 1965, J. M. Worlock and Porto made the first use of resonance enhancement in the Raman effect to observe scattering from color-center impurities in alkali halides.[129] Subsequently, Porto, B. Tell, and T. C. Damen found even more dramatic resonance effects in cadmium sulfide, manifested by as many as eighth-order phonon replicas in the Raman spectrum.[130] Since then, resonant Raman and Brillouin scattering have been widely employed to probe electron-phonon interactions in semiconductors, insulators, and macromolecules.

In 1967, G. B. Wright and A. Mooradian of Lincoln Laboratory reported spontaneous light scattering from plasmon-phonon excitations.[131] Patel and R. E. Slusher,[132] Tell and R. J. Martin,[133] and J. F. Scott and coworkers[134] examined related phenomena in both III-V and II-VI semiconductors. Worlock and collaborators used light scattering to determine the size as well as the growth, decay, and spatial distribution of transient electron-hole droplets produced in cold semiconductors by pulsed-laser radiation.[135] J. Doehler, J. C. V. Mattos, and Worlock were also able to measure droplet velocities by laser-Doppler velocimetry.[136]

6.2.2 *Spin Waves*

In 1965, inelastic light scattering from spin waves (or magnons) in magnetically ordered solids was discovered. The original experiments in MnF_2 and FeF_2 by P. A. Fleury and coworkers revealed not only the theoretically predicted one-magnon process, but an additional process caused by magnon pairs.[137] Theoretical analysis by Fleury and R. Loudon showed that a combination of these effects carried all the information necessary to specify the spin Hamiltonian because both Brillouin zone-center and zone-boundary magnon energies could be measured by one-magnon and two-magnon scattering, respectively.[138] Refinements of this theory led to predictions and observations of magnon-magnon interaction effects and of the differing influences of long- and short-range magnetic order on the light scattering spectrum.[139] During the 1970s, light scattering became established as a quantitative technique to probe spin dynamics in both transparent and opaque magnetic materials.

6.2.3 Phase Transitions

Light scattering has had the largest impact in the study of phase transitions. Several early experiments in this area were carried out at Bell Labs. The first light scattering observations of soft-mode behavior were made in $KTaO_3$ and $SrTiO_3$ by Fleury and Worlock.[140] They devised an electric field modulation technique to obviate the selection rules that forbid Raman activity in the paraelectric phase of such high-symmetry materials. These experiments also revealed that soft-mode frequencies could be tuned appreciably with application of modest fields, and that phonon-phonon interaction effects could be enhanced and controlled in the same way.[141] Subsequently, Kaminow carefully detailed the soft-mode behavior in the ferroelectrics KDP and $LiTaO_3$.[142] DiDomenico, Porto, and S. H. Wemple reported mode softening in $BaTiO_3$.[143] During the following decade, researchers around the world applied light scattering to the study of structural transitions, making it probably the most widely used technique to probe phase transition dynamics. Many of these generalized Raman processes were made observable by the development of the double-grating spectrometers. Porto and his colleagues in industry were the catalysts for this development.

Starting in the early 1970s, researchers at Bell Labs perfected new instrumentation that permitted even higher resolution and contrast so that very weak scattering features such as interacting soft modes and dynamic central peaks could be followed right through the critical temperature. The use of a single-mode argon laser tuned precisely to the frequency corresponding to a strong and narrow absorption line in molecular iodine vapor permitted stray light rejection by more than seven orders of magnitude.[144] Development of computer-assisted normalization techniques permitted quantitative recovery of the most subtle lineshape behavior in quite demanding quasielastic light-scattering spectra.[145] These advances allowed a host of previously inaccessible phenomena in structural phase transitions, glasses, and surface wave excitations on metals to be studied by laser light scattering.[146]

6.2.4 Polaritons

In 1965, C. H. Henry and J. J. Hopfield used Raman techniques to observe the spontaneous Raman scattering in GaP by polaritons, an excitation of a mixed photon-phonon nature characteristic of all infrared active modes.[147] By measuring the energy shift of the scattered light versus scattering angle, Henry and Hopfield were able to plot the polariton dispersion curve (energy versus momentum). This data demonstrated clearly that as momentum increases, the polariton changes from a photon to an optical phonon.

An important outgrowth of this experiment was a study by W. L. Faust and Henry in 1966 of frequency mixing of visible and infrared laser light in GaP.[148] Frequency mixing can be viewed as driving the polariton mode at the difference of the two applied laser frequencies through a nonlinear interaction. This result enabled Nelson and E. H. Turner to determine the absolute sign of the nonlinear coefficient for GaP[149] and served as the basis for all subsequent absolute sign determinations of nonlinear coefficients.

6.3 Coherent Optical Effects

Coherent resonant interaction of laser light with atoms and molecules leads to nonlinear propagation phenomena. Analogous to echo and other transient behavior in nuclear magnetic resonance, these effects provide information on relaxation times and the interaction of the resonant absorbers with their environment. This information is valuable in studies of molecular and atomic collision processes. Coherent optical effects are observed in laser-light pulse propagation when the pulse field is sufficiently high to drive the atomic dipoles through a substantial angle during the pulse duration, and when the inverse pulse duration is large compared to both the radiative decay rate and the homogeneous linewidth. Self-induced transparency occurs when the laser pulse drives the atomic dipoles through an angle of 360 degrees, thus absorbing and reradiating the incident 2π pulse. The phenomena of self-induced transparency (SIT) was predicted and observed in 1969 by S. L. McCall and E. L. Hahn at the University of California at Berkeley.[150] Patel and Slusher at Bell Labs observed in 1967 and 1970 the delay, pulse sharpening, and absence of attenuation characteristic of SIT in the propagation of CO_2 laser pulses through SF_6.[151] In this same system, in 1970, P. K. Cheo and C. H. Wang observed optical free induction decay and edge echo effects with rectangular optical pulses.[152]

6.3.1 Self-Induced Transparency

Although McCall and Hahn at Berkeley, and Patel and Slusher at Bell Labs, had demonstrated nonlinear transmission and delays, Slusher and H. M. Gibbs were the first to see breakup and peaking and significant pulse compression characteristics of SIT and to make a careful comparison of SIT theory with experimental data from a well-defined system.[153] Also, pulses were slowed down to as little as 1/1000 times the speed of light and were drastically reshaped. G. J. Salamo, together with Gibbs, McCall, and C. C. Churchill, studied the effects of degeneracies on SIT and found them much less destructive than expected.[154] Other interesting observations include SIT on-resonance self-focusing and collisions of SIT pulses.

The SIT reshaping features are of potential technical importance in the processing of information pulses. The nonlinear transmission feature would provide an optical discriminator to separate large signal pulses from small noise pulses in optical repeaters. SIT permits nanosecond delays in millimeter lengths, as compared with meter lengths in vacuum. Integrated optics delay lines, pulse compression, and peak amplification may prove to be useful in multiplexing.

The importance of the π pulse in quantum oscillators is illustrated by the tendency for certain mode-locked lasers to favor oscillation in the form of a π pulse shuttling back and forth in the resonator, as has been noted by A. G. Fox and P. W. Smith.[155]

6.3.2 Photon Echoes

The first coherent optical effect, the photon echo, was reported in ruby by N. A. Kurnit, I. D. Abella, and S. R. Hartmann of Columbia University in 1964.[156] The resonant atoms are coherently excited by one pulse; after a delay time, a second pulse effectively reverses the time so that atoms that had been oscillating the fastest and were ahead in phase are now behind in phase. After the second pulse, all of the dipoles are again in phase, and a burst of light, the echo, is emitted in the direction of the first of two pulses. By measuring the echo intensity as the delay time is changed, it is possible to determine the rate of relaxation of the macroscopic dipole moment or the polarization excited by the first pulse.

Patel and Slusher extended the photon echo technique to gases by using CO_2 laser pulses to study the dephasing of SF_6 vibrational transitions by collisions with SF_6 and foreign gases.[157] Hahn, N. S. Shiren, and McCall pointed out the strong changes in photon echoes that occur when the absorption is high and SIT effects are important.[158] In 1976, B. Golding and J. E. Graebner observed phonon echoes in glass, which surprisingly has two-level tunneling states at 0.02K.[159] They also succeeded in observing microwave photon echoes in amorphous polymers, showing that the tunneling states exist in polymers as well as glasses and other amorphous systems, thus opening a new route to the study of polymer dynamics.[160] P. Hu and S. Geschwind have used two-photon, or Raman excitation, to produce Raman echoes between two states of CdS not coupled by a one-photon transition; consequently, the echo does not radiate itself, and a Raman process must be used to observe it.[161]

6.3.3 *Nonlinear Transmission and Optical Bistability*

Optical bistability with continuous-wave coherent light, a phenomenon of great device potential, was predicted by McCall in 1974.[162] Such a two-state device might consist of a Fabry-Perot inter- ferometer containing a nonlinear medium. The two-mirror optical cavity transmits very little light unless the mirrors are separated by an integral number of wavelengths of the incident light, in which case the transmission is very high. The nonlinear medium can introduce an effective change in plate separation, making the transmission very low at low intensities. At high-enough intensities, the effect of the medium can be removed by its nonlinear interaction with the incident light, and the cavity transmits almost completely. A property of a Fabry-Perot cavity is that energy is stored inside the cavity. The intensity inside a transmitting cavity can be 100 times higher than the incident and transmitted intensities. Consequently, once the cavity is switched on, it can continue to transmit far lower input intensities than were required to turn it on. This hysteresis characteristic of the transmitted versus incident light is known as optical bistability. It was first demonstrated in 1976 by Gibbs, McCall, and T. N. C. Venkatesan in sodium vapor.[163] It was also observed in room temperature ruby by Venkatesan and McCall.[164] In 1979, Gibbs, McCall, and coworkers have demonstrated optical bistability in GaAs using a molecular beam epitaxial sandwich only 5 μm thick.[165]

Bistable optical devices have also been developed using a hybrid configuration in which the nonlinearity is produced by an electro-optic modulator within the Fabry-Perot resonator. The modulator is driven by the electrical signal from a detector that samples the output light. The advantage of such a hybrid device is that the artificial nonlinearity created with the detector-electro-optic modulator combination can be far larger than the intrinsic nonlinearities of optical materials. Thus, devices requiring only nanowatts of optical power can be made.

The first hybrid bistable optical device was demonstrated by Smith and Turner at Bell Labs in 1976.[166] In the years following, rapid progress was made both in terms of demonstrating a variety of useful operating characteristics,[167] and in developing integrated optical versions that are capable of switching with light energies of less than one picojoule.[168,169]

An optical bistable device could be used as an optical memory element. In addition to bistability, other characteristics may be observed by adjusting the detunings between the laser, the resonant transition, the cavity, and the number of nonlinear atoms. Small modulations of the incident beam can be amplified; that is, some of the dc input intensity is converted to ac output intensity. Thus, with only optical inputs into a passive device, it is possible to obtain the optical analog of the electron tube or transistor amplifiers. Under other conditions, the device functions as an optical clipper, discriminator, or limiter. Under special cases, the device undergoes regenerative pulsations and converts continuous-wave laser power into a train of light pulses.[170]

6.3.4 *Other Coherent Interactions*

Coherent light from a laser was used by H. M. Gibbs at Bell Labs to demonstrate optical precession in which the electric dipole moments of the atoms are alternately excited and de-excited by the coherent pulse.[171] The coherence of the light is crucial to the production of coherent effects. In superfluorescence, a two-level system is initially completely in its upper state, so no macroscopic polarization or coherence exists. With special geometries, such as a long, thin cylinder, the decaying atoms become correlated through their common radiation field, resulting in coherent emission. Q. H. F. Vrehen, H. M. J. Hikspoors, and Gibbs observed beats demonstrating coherence between two such near-frequency superfluorescence pulses.[172] Their studies also showed that under certain conditions, the emission occurs in one coherent pulse rather than in a series of pulses of decreasing intensity.[173]

The research of Bell Laboratories scientists on the nonlinear interactions of coherent light with atoms and molecules has not only made important contributions to techniques for studying physical properties of matter, but has also greatly advanced our understanding of optical propagation of short, intense pulses and of optical switching—two fields of interest to the emerging technology of lightwave communications.

6.4 Radiation Pressure and Optical Levitation

Stable optical trapping and manipulation of small particles by the forces of radiation pressure from lasers was discovered by A. Ashkin in the early 1970s. It was shown that optical beam configurations exist that can be used to trap and manipulate dielectric particles in various media such as liquid,[174] air,[175] and vacuum.[176] This type of trapping is called optical levitation when the light traps particles in opposition to the force of gravity.[177] Optically levitated particles can serve as sensitive probes of electric, diamagnetic, and optical forces. It is useful with dielectric particles in the 1-μm to 100-μm range in those fields of physics where small particles play an important role, such as light scattering,[178] cloud physics,[179] and laser fusion.[180] Studies of optical levitation led to the discovery by Ashkin and J. M. Dziedzic of extremely sharp dielectric surface wave resonances of dielectric spheres.[181] These surface wave resonances were subsequently shown to be in agreement with scattering theory[182] and can be used to measure the average radius of micron-sized spheres with an accuracy of 1 part in 10^5 to 10^6, which is better than previous optical size measurements by at least a factor of 10^2 to 10^3. Levitation techniques were also used in the discovery of a new nonlinear photoelectric effect.[183] Support of the hollow-shell type laser fusion targets has been demonstrated.[184]

Radiation pressure from lasers can also be used to manipulate and possibly trap neutral atoms. There are two basic forces acting on atoms—the resonance radiation pressure forces that are large near an atomic resonance. The first is the spontaneous scattering force, and the second is the dipole force. The use of the scattering force for atomic beam deflection and for exerting significant pressure on atomic vapors was first proposed by Ashkin in 1970.[185] This force has since been observed by Bjorkholm, Ashkin, and D. B. Pearson.[186] In 1978, the dipole force was directly observed for the first time by Bjorkholm and coworkers in an atomic beam trapping experiment in which a beam of neutral atoms was trapped within the high intensity region of a light beam.[187] The same force can be used to focus or defocus a neutral atomic beam when the laser light is tuned below or above the atomic resonance, respectively. Increases of the on-axis atomic beam intensity as large as a factor of 30 and decreases to less than 10^{-2} have been experimentally demonstrated. It has also been shown experimentally that the minimum spot size to which an atomic beam can be focused is limited by the quantum fluctuations that are inherent in resonance-radiation pressure.[188] These fluctuations exist because of the quantized nature of light and have been discussed in detail theoretically.[189] Because the resonance-radiation pressure forces are highly frequency-selective, new ways to optically separate isotopes become apparent. The use of light pressure from lasers to stably trap and cool atoms in a small localized region of a light beam at temperatures as low as 10^{-3}K to 10^{-4}K has recently been proposed[190] and analyzed theoretically.[191]

The work on the dynamics of particles moving under the influence of light pressure forces not only provides a new way of studying the basic interaction of light with neutral matter, but also gives a new means of optical manipulation and trapping of small particles that should continue to find new and unusual experimental uses.

VII. NONLINEAR OPTICS

One of the most active fields to develop from laser studies has been nonlinear optics (NLO). The subject of increasing emphasis at Bell Labs since its inception in 1961, nonlinear optics has had an impact on a number of areas of solid state physics, photochemistry, and electromagnetic propagation, as well as on tunable light sources and optical technology. The earliest observation of an NLO effect at Bell Labs, in 1961, was the generation of blue fluorescence in Eu^{2+}-doped CaF_2 by simultaneous two-photon absorption from ruby laser light. In this observation of two-photon fluorescence, W. Kaiser and C. G. B. Garrett[192] found the measured Eu^{2+} cross section for this process consistent with estimates obtained by D. A. Kleinman.[193] Two-photon and the related three-photon fluorescence processes that produce displays with brightness proportional to the square and cube of the incident light intensity were introduced in 1967 by J. A. Giordmaine and coworkers.[194] This technique has been widely used in measurements of the duration of picosecond light pulses by intensity correlation. The correlation method was used by M. A. Duguay in 1971 to photograph ultrashort light pulses in flight.[195] [Fig. 5-13]

7.1 Second Harmonic Generation

Efficient optical second harmonic generation (SHG), unlike two-photon absorption, requires the satisfaction of precise phase matching conditions on the refractive index of the fundamental frequency and its second harmonic. Experiments by Giordmaine in 1962 demonstrated the concept of optical birefringent phase matching.[196] This method provides greatly increased efficiency for second harmonic generation by matching the velocities of the incident and harmonic light. These experiments were followed by a general theory by Kleinman, delineating the nonlinear interaction of plane waves in birefringent crystals.[197] Subsequent experiments by Ashkin, Boyd, and Dziedzic,[198] by Boyd and coworkers,[199] and theory by Boyd and Kleinman[200] resulted in a detailed understanding of the interaction of Gaussian light waves as well as the conditions for optimization of SHG and parametric interactions in focused beams. The strong dependence of efficient SHG on optical dispersion and birefringence imposes severe requirements on crystal perfection and uniformity. The nature of this dependence has been described by F. R. Nash and coworkers.[201] The successful search for better NLO crystals and improved understanding of nonlinear wave interactions made it possible for J. E. Geusic and coworkers to demonstrate a useful 1-watt, continuous-wave, green-light source based on conversion of 1.06 μm laser light to the harmonic at 0.53 μm with 100 percent efficiency.[202]

The sensitivity of SHG to the optical dispersion and birefringence, which are usually poorly known in new materials, can lead to difficulties in even approximate measurements of the nonlinear susceptibilities. S. K. Kurtz and J. Jerphagnon have shown how to over-

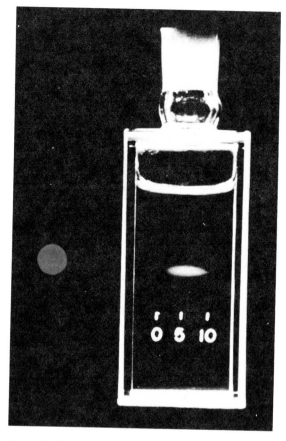

Fig. 5-13. Stop-motion photograph of an ultrashort pulse of light (bullet shape) in flight. The light bullet was moving from right to left through a cell containing milky water. Despite the tremendous shutter speed (10 picoseconds) the light bullet is somewhat blurred, obscuring a substructure known to be present in the pulse. Scale in millimeters.

come many of these problems in measurements with crystal plate-lets.[203] In addition, Kurtz has introduced a useful method for estimating susceptibilities of power samples.[204]

SHG by individual molecules, or double-quantum light scattering, has been discussed by R. Bersohn, Y.-H. Pao, and H. L. Frisch.[205] Their work delineates the relative contribution of both coherent and incoherent scattering processes to this rather weak nonlinear effect.

7.1.1 Nonlinear Optical Materials

Advances in physical understanding and demonstrations of new phenomena in nonlinear optics have largely been dependent on the discovery and synthesis of materials with large nonlinear optical coefficients and other essential optical properties. The first successful phase-matchable material, KDP, discovered by Giordmaine, was crucial to early experiments.[206] This was followed by the discovery of $LiNbO_3$ by Boyd and coworkers, which was an order of magnitude larger in nonlinear coefficient and led to the first optical parametric oscillator.[207] (See also Section 7.2 in Chapter 16). Measurements of the nonlinear properties of III-V and II-VI binary semiconductors have been crucial for a basic understanding of the mechanism of nonlinear optical susceptibilities. These and other measurements have been summarized by Kurtz.[208] High nonlinearity and optical anisotropy were also found in ternary compounds such as the chalcopyrite semiconductors by G. D. Boyd and coworkers.[209]

C. K. N. Patel's discovery of efficient SHG at 10.6 μm in tellurium using the high-power CO_2 laser made possible the investigation of nonlinear properties of a large number of solids that are opaque in the visible region.[210] Tellurium is the material with the largest known nonlinear optical coefficient in a phase-matchable system. These studies were subsequently extended to longer wavelengths by D. A. McArthur and R. A. McFarlane.[211] The nonlinear optics studies in the infrared also led to novel schemes of phase matching in materials that do not possess natural birefringence. These novel phase-matching techniques include reflection phase matching and the use of plasma dispersion.[212]

Early observations of the nonlinear optical properties of organic compounds were reported by P. M. Rentzepis and Pao[213] and by Jerphagnon.[214] B. F. Levine and C. G. Bethea measured an extensive series of organic molecules and elucidated the importance of bond conjugation and intramolecular charge transfer in producing large nonlinearities.[215] They found organic materials with nonlinearity an order of magnitude larger than $LiNbO_3$. Organic compounds will undoubtedly become more important for future nonlinear optical devices because the molecules can be engineered to optimize performance in ways not possible with inorganic compounds.

7.1.2 Theories of Nonlinear Optical Susceptibility

A number of theories of the nonlinear susceptibility of inorganic crystals have made available increasingly precise predictions of nonlinear dielectric properties. Kleinman provided important early insights on the form of the nonlinear susceptibility tensor that relates nonlinear polarization to the square of the electric field.[216] R. C.

Miller established the scaling of the nonlinear susceptibility with respect to the linear dielectric constant.[217] Miller's rule has proved to be a particularly valuable guide in the search for new nonlinear optical materials. Garrett and F. N. H. Robinson were able to provide a physical basis for Miller's rule and useful estimates of optical nonlinearity in terms of an anharmonic oscillator model.[218] This resulted in a unified phenomenological description of numerous aspects of infrared nonlinear behavior, Raman scattering, the electro-optic effect, and pyroelectricity.

J. C. Phillips' dielectric theory of electronegativity and ionicity has provided a basic new approach to understanding optical nonlinear response.[219] This theory connects quantitatively the optical properties of binary crystals to parameters describing fractional ionicity and covalency. Levine[220] has shown how to apply the theories of Phillips and of J. A. Van Vechten[221] to relate the nonlinear susceptibility to the linear refractive index. A novel aspect of Levine's theory is the central role played by the bond charge. The linear and nonlinear dielectric responses are expressed wholly in terms of the dynamic response of bond charges. Levine has also been able to extend the Phillips-Van Vechten approach to ternary and more complicated compounds. Values of nonlinear susceptibilities measured in various laboratories are in good agreement with the values predicted from linear dielectric properties on the basis of Levine's model. Miller and W. A. Nordland used laser interference techniques to find unexpected sign changes among the nonlinear susceptibility coefficients of various crystals.[222] Their discovery turned out to be an essential clue in completing the model. It is now recognized that the optical nonlinearity in binary crystals arises from two sources—difference in electronegativity and the difference in ionic radius of the atomic constituents. Contributions from the two sources have opposite signs, accounting, for example, for the relatively small nonlinearity of beryllium oxide.

An alternative approach to calculating nonlinear susceptibilities was developed by M. DiDomenico and S. H. Wemple.[223] They were able to calculate NLO and electro-optical properties in terms of a polarization potential tensor that relates band shifts to crystal polarization in ferroelectrics (for example, lithium niobate).

J. G. Bergman and coworkers pointed out the high incidence of acentricity and nonlinear optical behavior in oxides with nonbonded electron pairs.[224] This property provides another guideline in the search for new materials.

7.1.3 *Nonlinear Optical Phenomena and Applications*

A totally unexpected discovery was the susceptibility of crystals such as lithium niobate to laser-induced refractive index changes, first

observed by Ashkin and coworkers.[225] This optical damage, only partially reversible, was attributed by F. S. Chen[226] and by Johnston[227]
to displacement of photoexcited carriers by spontaneous or photoin-
duced fields, followed by their trapping outside the illuminated
region. G. E. Peterson, A. M. Glass, and N. J. Negran were able to
identify iron impurities as the origin of these laser-induced index
changes in lithium niobate as well as in similar materials.[228]

Chen, J. T. La Macchia, and D. B. Fraser were the first to demonstrate the use of optically induced index of refraction changes in
lithium niobate for making volume holograms.[229] Index changes in
lithium niobate and other ferroelectric crystals continues to be widely
studied as a means of optical information storage, and also continues
to be a limiting factor in the design of nonlinear optical devices in
ferroelectric crystals.

Optical nonlinearities arising from conduction electrons and giving
rise to various four-photon mixing phenomena have been observed
by Patel, Slusher, and Fleury in semiconductors.[230] P. A. Wolff and G.
A. Pearson explained these relatively strong nonlinearities as caused
by nonparabolicity of the conduction band associated with an
increase in effective mass of the electron as it is accelerated by the
optical electric field.[231] This requires a nonlinear term in its equation
of motion.

Nonlinear optical response in electron-gas plasmas leading to
light-off-light scattering, a related third-order effect, has been
analyzed by P. M. Platzman and N. Tzoar.[232] The scattering of pairs
of laser photons into pairs of different frequency by this mechanism
appears to be feasible.

The important third-order nonlinearity associated with the polarizability of bound electrons in laser host solids can contribute to self-
phase modulation and rapid spectral broadening during the buildup
of picosecond light pulses. This effect has been studied extensively
in glass by Duguay and S. L. Shapiro.[233]

Nonlinear optical effects of laser light have been utilized in various
studies of solids and liquids. For example, I. Freund and L. Kopf
made extensive measurements of the order-disorder phase transition
in ammonium chloride by SHG.[234] Below the transition temperature
of 243K, the ordered phase is acentric and exhibits SHG; no SHG is
expected in the completely disordered phase at higher temperatures.
From observations of the temperature and angular dependence of
SHG near 243K, Freund and Kopf observed directly changes in the
order parameter and discovered evidence of domain structure and
residual long-range order at temperatures above 243K. In another
application of NLO, Rentzepis and Giordmaine observed SHG in optically active liquids and established a relationship between molecular
nonlinear susceptibility and optical rotatory power.[235]

W. L. Faust and C. H. Henry contributed a necessary step in under-standing the electro-optic effect in piezoelectric crystals, that is, a change in the optical index on application of a dc or low-frequency electric field. They observed sum and difference frequency mixing of visible laser light with a number of infrared laser frequencies near the reststrahl in gallium phosphide.[236] This work clarified the separate contributions to electro-optic mixing arising from the depen-dence of electric susceptibility on electric field (pure electronic effect) and lattice displacement (Raman effect). Kaminow and Johnston reported this type of resolution of the sources of the electro-optic effect in lithium niobate and lithium tantalate.[237] Boyd and coworkers made microwave measurements of nonlinear susceptibility in various crystals and sorted out the lattice, electronic, and hybrid contribu-tions.[238] Their studies were based on Garrett's extended anharmonic oscillator model.[239] Levine, Miller, and Nordland studied second-harmonic generation at frequencies near the exciton resonance.[240] They were able to determine the exciton contribution to the non-linear optical susceptibility and to compare it with the theoretical cal-culation based on a modified hydrogenic wave function. Examples of materials exhibiting the electro-optic effect include $LiTaO_3$, shown by R. T. Denton, T. S. Kinsel, and Chen to be useful as an efficient light modulator at visible wavelengths,[241] and GaAs in the $Ga_{1-x}Al_xAs$ heterostructure lasers for the near infrared wavelengths, studied by F. K. Reinhart.[242] The latter was an outgrowth of an earlier discovery by Nelson and Reinhart of electro-optic modulation of light passing through the optical waveguide formed in the plane of a reverse-biased GaP p-n junction.[243]

A. Hasegawa and F. Tappert found theoretically that the nonlinear refractive index can compensate the pulse-broadening effect of group dispersion in low-loss optical fibers.[244] This leads to a stationary non-linear optical pulse (called the envelope soliton) in a single-mode fiber with negative group-velocity dispersion. The first experimental observations of pulse compression of picosecond pulses and soliton behavior in fibers was reported by L. F. Mollenauer, R. H. Stolen, and J. P. Gordon.[245]

Laser studies of the pyroelectric effect have proceeded along with nonlinear optical work. Of particular interest is the recognition by R. L. Abrams and Glass that pyroelectric detection in strontium barium niobate is sufficiently fast to respond to modulation frequencies of at least 30 MHz.[246]

D. H. Auston and Glass used a mode-locked glass laser at 1.06 μm to show that the pyroelectric and electro-optic effects in $LiNbO_3$ can occur on a picosecond time scale.[247] Using the optical rectification produced by these two mechanisms, they produced an 8 psec 300-volt electrical pulse and used it to switch an ultrafast Pockel's cell.

Future high-speed optical communication links may use integrated optical components for direct optical switching, modulating, and data processing. Work on nonlinear optical effects in waveguides is, therefore, of great interest. J. P. Van der Ziel and coworkers studied phase-matched second-harmonic generation from $\lambda = 2\,\mu$m to $\lambda = 1\,\mu$m in $Ga_xAl_{1-x}As$ waveguides and in multilayers grown by molecular beam epitaxy.[248] Levine, Bethea, and R. A. Logan studied phase-matched second-harmonic generation from $\lambda = 1.06\,\mu$m to $0.53\,\mu$m using electric field-induced optical harmonic generation in waveguides filled with an organic liquid.[249] Reinhart, Logan, and J. C. Shelton used the electro-optic effect in $Ga_xAl_{1-x}As$ waveguides to construct efficient optical modulators and rib waveguide switches.[250] These components have the potential of operating in the gigahertz range.

7.2 Optical Parametric Amplification

With the availability of optical nonlinearities, it was natural to explore at optical frequencies the parametric amplification phenomena familiar at radio and microwave frequencies. Taking advantage of high-quality lithium niobate crystals grown by Nassau,[251] Giordmaine and Miller built the first optical parametric oscillator and demonstrated the coherence and broad tunability characteristic of this light source.[252] [Fig. 5-14] They also observed a preference for certain frequencies of oscillation, or clustering—a feature of oscillators doubly resonant at signal and idler frequencies. Boyd and Ashkin demonstrated continuous-wave amplification in $LiNbO_3$ and showed theoretically that continuous optical parametric amplification should be achievable.[253] The achievement of tunable continuous-wave oscillation in barium sodium niobate by R. G. Smith and coworkers was an important milestone.[254] Further improvements in stability and frequency control were also reported by Smith.[255] J. E. Bjorkholm was the first to demonstrate a singly resonant parametric oscillator and pointed out the tuning and other advantages of this type of source, obtained at the price of increased threshold.[256] The question of stability of single-mode operation of the singly resonant oscillators was analyzed by L. B. Kreuzer, who found single-mode oscillation stable at pump powers higher than required for optimum efficiency.[257] Now commercially available, parametric oscillators provide a useful tunable source for optical spectroscopy.

Noise in parametric amplification, analogous to fluorescence in a laser medium, was described in principle by the early theories of W. H. Louisell, A. Yariv, and A. E. Siegman,[258] and Gordon, Louisell, and L. R. Walker,[259] which were developed in the context of microwave frequencies. Kleinman carried out a detailed analysis applicable to

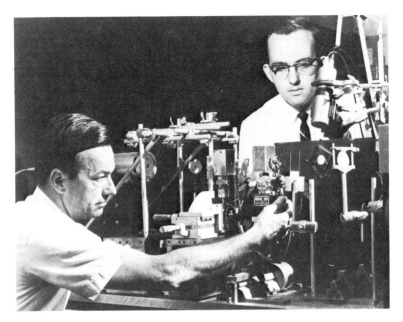

Fig. 5-14. R. C. Miller (left) and J. A. Giordmaine checking the alignment of a $LiNbO_3$ single crystal used by them in the first demonstration of a tunable optical parametric oscillator.

the optical region, calculating the frequency and directional distribution of spontaneous parametric noise emitted from crystals.[260] This understanding makes possible the use of spontaneous noise observations to measure the nonlinear optical properties.

The possibility of exploring optical nonlinearities at much higher frequencies was suggested by Freund and Levine, who used an extension of Kleinman's theory to predict that parametric fluorescence could be observed even at X-ray frequencies.[261] Although the equivalent nonlinear susceptibility in the X-ray region is minute by comparison with optical values, it is compensated by a greatly enhanced zero-point fluctuation of the electromagnetic field at X-ray frequencies, which can be considered to beat with the source to produce the fluorescence. In the early 1970s, P. M. Eisenberger and McCall observed X-ray down-conversion and verified momentum-phase matching requirements similar to those in the optical region.[262]

The significance of this X-ray phenomenon for solid state physics lies in the possibility, pointed out by Freund and Levine,[263] and by Eisenberger and McCall, of the related X-ray down-conversion process yielding an optical and an X-ray photon, rather than two X-ray photons. It can be shown that this type of scattering process is equivalent to Bragg scattering solely from the valence or outer shell electrons seen by the optical frequency. Crystal analysis by this modified diffraction method offers, in principle, a selective mapping of outer-shell electron density distributions.

7.3 Stimulated Raman Scattering and Lasers

In an early laser scattering experiment, Giordmaine and W. Kaiser demonstrated the scattering of light from driven optical phonons during the stimulated Raman scattering (SRS) vibration.[264] This type of scattering has provided the basis for coherent anti-Stokes Raman scattering, a sensitive new method of high-speed optical spectroscopy. The decay of driven optical phonons to generate intense lattice excitations of a few angstroms wavelength, as well as the usefulness of SRS-generated light in resonance experiments, were illustrated by experiments of M. J. Colles and Giordmaine.[265]

An SRS phenomenon with potentially important applications in laser fusion development is the generation by Raman compression of optical pulses with very high peak power—higher than available from practical laser sources. M. Maier, Kaiser, and Giordmaine demonstrated this effect for the first time in backward-scattering experiments in a Raman active liquid.[266] In this work, compression of a short optical pulse was achieved by depletion of a longer, counterpropagating pump pulse, producing a higher intensity than present originally in the laser pump.

The nonlinear scattering of light from acoustic waves was studied by Boyd, Nash, and Nelson.[267] They mixed two infrared waves at a wavelength 10.6 μm with an acoustic wave at 15.7 MHz to generate a phase-matched infrared wave near the optical harmonic wavelength of 5.3 μm. This experiment led to the idea of multiple-phase matching of higher-order acousto-optic interaction as a way of enhancing the strength, and to the observation of a triply phase-matched, five-wave, acousto-optic interaction.[268] E. P. Ippen's achievement of SRS in liquid-filled optical fibers with low-power, quasi-continuous-wave lasers,[269] and the observation of similar nonlinear effects in silica core fibers by Stolen, Ippen, and A. R. Tynes greatly extends the potential usefulness of SRS light sources.[270] SRS observations of aqueous solutions by Colles, G. W. Walrafen, and K. W. Wecht appear to reveal resolved spectral details not accessible by spontaneous Raman scattering in materials having broadband spectra.[271]

The advantage of using guided-wave structures such as optical fibers to enhance the stimulated Raman effect was first pointed out by Ashkin in 1970.[272] This was demonstrated by Ippen's achievement of SRS in liquid-filled optical fibers with low-power quasi-continuous-wave lasers[273] and the observation of similar nonlinear effects in silica core fibers by Stolen, Ippen, and Tynes.[274] Fiber Raman lasers have proved most useful in their simplest form, in which single-pass stimulated scattering generates a series of pulses in the 1.1 to 1.5 μm spectral region for fiber dispersion studies.[275] [Fig. 5-15] There has been extensive study of various fiber Raman lasers employing feedback and tuning, as well as investigations of other nonlinear effects such as stimulated Brillouin scattering, four-photon mixing, and self-phase modulation.

One of the most important stimulated emission processes is that associated with Raman scattering from electrons in a semiconductor in a magnetic field. The large Raman cross sections for scattering of infrared light from single particle excitations, distinct from collective excitations or plasmons, were pointed out by Wolff[276] and Y. Yafet.[277] Wolff suggested that inelastic laser light scattering, in which the light is shifted in frequency by twice the electron cyclotron frequency, should have a large cross section. In this process, the electron Landau-level quantum number changes by two. Yafet analyzed the related process in which the electron Landau level does not change but in which the electron spin flips. Both processes produce tunable light scattering as the magnetic field is changed, the spin-flip process having less tunability but increased cross section and narrower

Fig. 5-15. The fiber Raman laser used in the experiments by Stolen and coworkers.

linewidth. These predictions were confirmed and additional hybrid scattering observed in spontaneous Raman scattering experiments of Slusher, Patel, and Fleury in indium antimonide.[278]

Patel and E. D. Shaw reported the first stimulated spin-flip Raman scattering oscillator (SFR laser) and demonstrated its value as a tunable infrared spectroscopic source.[279] Pumped by the 10.6 μm carbon dioxide laser and 5.3 μm carbon monoxide laser sources, the SFR laser provides tunability over the 9.0 μm to 14.6 μm and 5.30 μm to 6.2 μm regions. The potential for ultrahigh resolution spectroscopy is shown by the linewidth of less than 1 KHz measured by Patel near 5.3 μm, the narrowest reported for any infrared tunable source.[280]

Using a variety of high-power molecular lasers, Patel and his colleagues succeeded in making the spin-flip Raman laser the first source of high continuous-wave and pulsed tunable laser power in the 5 μm to 17 μm region.[281] The tunability of the spin-flip Raman laser in the 16 μm to 17 μm range is of special importance in future energy research because the technique of uranium isotopic enrichment using UF_6 requires a tunable high-power laser source in this wavelength region.[282]

In addition to demonstrating the spectroscopic applications of the spin-flip Raman laser through a series of experiments, the same research group has applied the spin-flip Raman lasers and other molecular lasers to the problems of gaseous pollution detection. These studies are summarized in section 1.7 of Chapter 6.

REFERENCES

1. C. E. Cleeton and N. H. Williams, "The Shortest Continuous Radio Waves," *Phys. Rev.* **50** (December 1936), p. 1091.
2. C. H. Townes, "Resolution and Pressure Broadening of the Ammonia Spectrum Near One-cm Wavelength," *Phys. Rev.* **70** (July 1946), p. 109; idem, "Electrostatic Field Strengths in Molecules and Nuclear Quadrupole Moments," *Phys. Rev.* **71** (June 1947), pp. 909L-910L.
3. C. H. Townes, A. N. Holden, J. Bardeen, and F. R. Merritt, "The Quadrupole Moments and Spins of Br, Cl, and N Nuclei," *Phys. Rev.* **71** (1947), pp. 644-645; C. H. Townes, A. N. Holden, and F. R. Merritt, "Rotational Spectra of Some Linear Molecules Near 1-Cm Wave-Length," *Phys. Rev.* **71** (January 1947), p. 64; C. H. Townes and F. R. Merritt, "Stark Effect in High Frequency Fields," *Phys. Rev.* **72** (December 1947), pp. 1266-1267; J. Bardeen and C. H. Townes, "Calculations of Nuclear Quadrupole Effects in Molecules," *Phys. Rev.* **73** (January 1948), pp. 47-105.
4. J. P. Gordon, H. J. Zeiger, and C. H. Townes, "Molecular Microwave Oscillator and New Hyperfine Structure in the Microwave Spectrum of NH_3," *Phys. Rev.* **95** (July 1954), pp. 282-284.
5. H. E. D. Scovil, G. Feher, and H. Seidel, "Operation of a Solid State Maser," *Phys. Rev.* **105** (January 1957), pp. 762-763.
6. R. N. DeGrasse, E. O. Schulz-DuBois, and H. E. D. Scovil, "The Three-Level Solid State Traveling Wave Maser," *Bell System Tech. J.* **38** (March 1959), pp. 305-334.

7. K. B. Jefferts, A. A. Penzias, R. W. Wilson, and P. M. Solomon, "Detection of Interstellar Carbonyl Sulfide," *Astrophys. J.* **168** (September 1971), pp. L111-L113.

8. A. L. Schawlow and C. H. Townes, "Infrared and Optical Masers," *Phys. Rev.* **112** (December 1958), pp. 1940-1949.

9. A. Javan, "Possibility of Production of Negative Temperature in Gas Discharges," *Phys. Rev. Lett.* **3** (July 15, 1959), pp. 87-89.

10. T. H. Maiman, "Stimulated Optical Radiation in Ruby," *Nature* **187** (August 6, 1960), pp. 493-494.

11. A. Javan, W. R. Bennett, Jr., and D. R. Herriott, "Population Inversion and Continuous Optical Maser Oscillation in a Gas Discharge Containing a He-Ne Mixture," *Phys. Rev. Lett.* **6** (February 1, 1961), pp. 106-110; U.S. Patent No. 3,149,290; filed December 28, 1960, issued September 15, 1964.

12. W. W. Rigrod, H. Kogelnik, D. J. Brangaccio, and D. R. Herriott, "Gaseous Optical Maser with External Concave Mirrors," *J. Appl. Phys.* **33** (February 1962), pp. 743-744.

13. A. D. White and J. D. Rigden, "Continuous Gas Maser Operation in the Visible," *Proc. IRE* **50** (July 1962), p. 1697.

14. See reference 10.

15. R. J. Collins, D. F. Nelson, A. L. Schawlow, W. Bond, C. G. B. Garrett, and W. Kaiser, "Coherence, Narrowing, Directionality, and Relaxation Oscillations in the Light Emission from Ruby," *Phys. Rev. Lett.* **5** (October 1, 1960), pp. 303-305.

16. L. F. Johnson and K. Nassau, "Infrared Fluorescence and Stimulated Emission of Nd^{3+} in $CaWO_4$," *Proc. IRE* **49** (November 1961), pp. 1704-1706.

17. L. F. Johnson, G. D. Boyd, K. Nassau, and R. R. Soden, "Continuous Operation of a Solid-State Optical Maser," *Phys. Rev.* **126** (May 15, 1962), pp. 1406-1409.

18. D. F. Nelson and W. S. Boyle, "A Continuously Operating Ruby Optical Maser," *Appl. Opt.* **1** (March 1962), pp. 181-183.

19. G. D. Boyd, R. J. Collins, S. P. S. Porto, A. Yariv, and W. A. Hargreaves, "Excitation, Relaxation, and Continuous Maser Action in the 2.613-Micron Transition of $CaF_2:U^{3+}$," *Phys. Rev. Lett.* **8** (April 1, 1962), pp. 269-272.

20. L. F. Johnson, R. E. Dietz, and H. J. Guggenheim, "Optical Maser Oscillation from Ni^{2+} in MgF_2 Involving Simultaneous Emission of Phonons," *Phys. Rev. Lett.* **11** (October 1, 1963), pp. 318-320; idem, "Spontaneous and Stimulated Emission from CO^{2+} Ions in MgF_2; and ZnF_2," *Appl. Phys. Lett.* **5** (July 15, 1964), pp. 21-22; L. F. Johnson and H. J. Guggenheim, "Phonon-Terminated Coherent Emission from V^{2+} Ions in MgF_2," *J. Appl. Phys.* **38** (November 1967), pp. 4837-4839.

21. L. F. Johnson, H. J. Guggenheim, and R. A. Thomas, "Phonon-Terminated Optical Masers," *Phys. Rev.* **149** (September 1966), pp. 179-185.

22. P. P. Sorokin and J. R. Lankard, "Stimulated Emission Observed from an Organic Dye, Chloroaluminum Phthalocyanine," *IBM J. Res. and Dev.* **10** (January 1966), pp. 162-163.

23. A. G. Fox and T. Li, "Resonant Modes in a Maser Interferometer," *Bell System Tech. J.* **40** (March 1961), pp. 453-488.

24. G. D. Boyd and J. P. Gordon, "Confocal Multimode Resonator for Millimeter Through Optical Wavelength Masers," *Bell System Tech. J.* **40** (March 1961), pp. 489-508.

25. G. D. Boyd and H. Kogelnik, "Generalized Confocal Resonator Theory," *Bell System Tech. J.* **41** (July 1962), pp. 1347-1369.

26. H. Kogelnik and W. W. Rigrod, "Visual Display of Isolated Optical Resonator Modes," *Proc. IRE* **50** (February 1962), p. 220.

27. H. Kogelnik, "Matching of Optical Modes," *Bell System Tech. J.* **43** (January 1964), pp. 334-337.

28. H. Kogelnik, "Imaging of Optical Modes—Resonators with Internal Lenses," *Bell*

System Tech. J. **44** (March 1965), pp. 455-494; idem, H. Kogelnik, "On the Propagation of Gaussian Beams of Light Through Lenslike Media, Including Those with a Loss or Gain Variation," *Appl. Optics* **4** (December 1965), pp. 1562-1569.

29. H. Kogelnik and T. Li, "Laser Beams and Resonators," *Appl. Optics* **5** (October 1966), pp. 1550-1567; idem, "Laser Beams and Resonators," *Proc. IEEE* **54** (October 1966), pp. 1312-1329.

30. L. E. Hargrove, R. L. Fork, and M. A. Pollack, "Locking of He-Ne Laser Modes Induced by Synchronous Intracavity Modulation," *Appl. Phys. Lett.* **5** (July 1, 1964), pp. 4-5.

31. M. DiDomenico, Jr., "Small-Signal Analysis of Internal (Coupling-Type) Modulation of Lasers," *J. Appl. Phys.* **35** (October 1964), pp. 2870-2876.

32. M. H. Crowell, "Characteristics of Mode-Coupled Lasers," *IEEE J. Quantum Electronics* (April 1965), pp. 12-20.

33. P. W. Smith, "Phase Locking of Laser Modes by Continuous Cavity Length Variation," *Appl. Phys. Lett.* **10** (January 15, 1967), pp. 51-53.

34. A. G. Fox and P. W. Smith, "Mode-Locked Laser and the 180° Pulse," *Phys. Rev. Lett.* **18** (May 15, 1967), pp. 826-828; P. W. Smith, "The Self-Pulsing Laser Oscillator," *IEEE J. Quantum Electronics* **QE-3** (November 1967), pp. 627-635.

35. A. G. Fox, S. E. Schwarz, and P. W. Smith, "Use of Neon as a Nonlinear Absorber for Mode Locking a He-Ne Laser," *Appl. Phys. Lett.* **12** (June 1, 1968), pp. 371-373.

36. P. W. Smith, "Simultaneous Phase-Locking of Longitudinal and Transverse Laser Modes," *Appl. Phys. Lett.* **13** (October 1, 1968), pp. 235-237.

37. W. T. Silfvast and P. W. Smith, "Mode-Locking of the He-Cd Laser at 4416 and 3250Å," *Appl. Phys. Lett.* **17** (July 15, 1970), pp. 70-73.

38. O. R. Wood, R. L. Abrams, and T. J. Bridges, "Mode Locking of a Transversely Excited Atmospheric Pressure CO_2 Laser," *Appl. Phys. Lett.* **17** (November 1, 1970), pp. 376-378.

39. P. W. Smith, T. J. Bridges, E. G. Burkhardt, and O. R. Wood, "Mode-Locked, High-Pressure Waveguide CO_2 Laser," *Appl. Phys. Lett.* **21** (November 15, 1972), pp. 470-472.

40. P. K. Runge, "Mode-Locking of He-Ne Lasers with Saturable Organic Dyes," *Optics Comm.* **3** (August 1971), pp. 434-436.

41. A. Dienes, E. P. Ippen, and C. V. Shank, "A Mode-Locked cw Dye Laser," *Appl. Phys. Lett.* **19** (October 15, 1971), pp. 258-260.

42. C. V. Shank and E. P. Ippen, "Mode-Locking of Dye Lasers," *Dye Lasers*, ed. F. P. Schafer (New York: Springer-Verlag, 1973), pp. 121-143.

43. E. P. Ippen, C. V. Shank, and A. Dienes, "Passive Mode Locking of the cw Dye Laser," *Appl. Phys. Lett.* **21** (October 15, 1972), pp. 348-350.

44. C. V. Shank and E. P. Ippen, "Subpicosecond Kilowatt Pulses from a Mode-Locked cw Dye Laser," *Appl. Phys. Lett.* **24** (April 15, 1974), pp. 373-375.

45. D. M. Bloom, L. F. Mollenauer, C. Lin, D. W. Taylor, and A. M. DelGaudio, "Direct Demonstration of Distortionless Picosecond-Pulse Propagation in Kilometer-Length Optical Fibers," *Optics. Lett.* **4** (September 1979), pp. 297-299.

46. D. E. McCumber, "Intensity Fluctuations in the Output of cw Laser Oscillators, I," *Phys. Rev.* **141** (January 1966), pp. 306-322.

47. M. Lax, "Quantum Noise. IV. Quantum Theory of Noise Sources," *Phys. Rev.* **145** (May 6, 1966), pp. 110-129; idem, "Quantum Noise V: Phase Noise in a Homogeneously Broadened Maser," *Physics of Quantum Electronics*, ed. P. L. Kelley, B. Lax, P. E. Tannenwald (New York: McGraw-Hill, 1966), pp. 735-747; idem, "Quantum Noise. X. Density-Matrix Treatment of Field and Population-Difference Fluctuations," *Phys. Rev.* **157** (May 1967), pp. 213-231.

48. J. P. Gordon, "Quantum Theory of a Simple Maser Oscillator," *Phys. Rev.* **161** (September 1967), pp. 367-386.

49. M. Lax and M. Zwanziger, "Exact Photocount Distributions for Lasers near Threshold," *Phys. Rev. Lett.* **24** (April 27, 1970), pp. 937-940.

50. T. L. Paoli and J. E. Ripper, "Observation of Intrinsic Fluctuations in Semiconductor Lasers," *Phys. Rev.* **A2** (December 1970), pp. 2551-2555.

51. P. Aigrain, "Masers of Semi-Conducteurs," *Quantum Electronics, Proceedings of the Third International Congress, Paris, Vol. 2* (New York: Columbia Univ. Press, 1964), pp. 1761-1767.

52. N. G. Basov, B. M. Yul, and Yu. M. Popov, "Quantum-Mechanical Semiconductor Generators and Amplifiers of Electromagnetic Oscillations," *Sov. Phys. JETP* **10** (February 1960), p. 416.

53. W. S. Boyle and D. G. Thomas, U. S. Patent No. 3,059,117; filed January 11, 1960, issued October 16, 1962.

54. W. G. A. Bernard and G. Duraffourg, "Laser Conditions in Semiconductors," *Phys. Status Solidi* **1**, No. 7 (1961), pp. 699-703.

55. J. I. Pankove and M. J. Massoulie, "Injection Luminescence in Gallium Arsenide," *J. Electrochem. Soc.* **109** (March 1962), p. 67C.

56. R. J. Keyes and T. M. Quist, "Recombination Radiation Emitted by Gallium Arsenide," *Proc. IRE* **50** (August 1962), pp. 1822-1823.

57. R. N. Hall, G. E. Fenner, J. D. Kingsley, T. J. Soltys, and R. O. Carlson, "Coherent Light Emission from GaAs Junctions," *Phys. Rev. Lett.* **9** (November 1, 1962), pp. 366-368.

58. N. Holonyak, Jr. and S. F. Bevacqua, "Coherent (Visible) Light Emission from $Ga(As_{1-x}P_x)$ Junctions," *Appl. Phys. Lett.* **1** (December 1, 1962), pp. 82-83.

59. M. I. Nathan, W. P. Dumke, G. Burnes, F. H. Dill, Jr., and G. Lasher, "Stimulated Emission of Radiation from GaAs p-n Junctions," *Appl. Phys. Lett.* **1** (November 1, 1962), pp. 62-63.

60. T. M. Quist, R. H. Rediker, R. J. Keyes, W. E. Krag, B. Lax, A. L. McWhorter, and H. J. Zeigler, "Semiconductor Maser of GaAs," *Phys. Lett.* **1** (December 1, 1962), pp. 91-92.

61. J. C. Dyment and L. A. D'Asaro, "Continuous Operation of GaAs Junction Lasers on Diamond Heat Sinks at 200°K," *Appl. Phys. Lett.* **11** (November 1, 1967), pp. 292-294.

62. M. B. Panish and S. Sumski, "Ga-Al-As: Phase, Thermodynamic, and Optical Properties," *J. Phys. Chem. Solids* **30** (January 1969), pp. 129-137.

63. I. Hayashi, M. B. Panish, and P. W. Foy, "A Low-Threshold Room-Temperature Injection Laser," *IEEE J. Quantum Electron.* **QE-5** (April 1969), p. 211; I. Hayashi and M. B. Panish, *Device Research Conference*, Seattle, Washington, June 1970; I. Hayashi, M. B. Panish, P. W. Foy, and S. Sumski, "Junction Lasers Which Operate Continuously at Room Temperature," *Appl. Phys. Lett.* **17** (August 1, 1970), pp. 109-111.

64. Zh. I. Alferov, V. M. Andreev, D. Z. Garbuzov, Yu. V. Zhilyaev, E. P. Morozov, E. L. Portnoi, and V. G. Trofim, "Investigation of the Influence of the AlAs-GaAs Heterostructure Parameters on the Laser Threshold Current and the Realization of Continuous Emission at Room Temperature," *Sov. Phys. Semicond.* **4** (March 1971), pp. 1573-1575.

65. R. A. Furnanage and D. K. Wilson, U. S. Patent No. 3,363,195; filed July 1, 1963; issued January 1968.

66. J. C. Dyment, L. A. D'Asaro, J. C. North, B. I. Miller, and J. E. Ripper, "Proton-Bombardment Formation of Strip-Geometry Heterostructure Lasers for 300K cw Operation," *Proc. IEEE* **60** (June 1972), pp. 726-728.

67. B. C. DeLoach, B. W. Hakki, R. L. Hartman, and L. A. D'Asaro, "Degradation of CW GaAs Double-Heterojunction Lasers at 300K," *Proc. IEEE* **61** (July 1973), pp. 1042-1044.

68. W. D. Johnston, Jr., and B. I. Miller, "Degredation Characteristics of cw Optically Pumped $Al_xGa_{1-x}As$ Heterostructure Lasers," *Appl. Phys. Lett.* **23** (August 15, 1973), pp. 192-194.

69. P. Petroff and R. L. Hartman, "Defect Structure Introduced During Operation of Heterojunction GaAs Lasers," *Appl. Phys. Lett.* **23** (October 15, 1973), pp. 469-471; D. V. Lang and L.C. Kimerling, "Observation of Recombination-Enhanced Defect Reactions in Semiconductors," *Phys. Rev. Lett.* **33** (August 19, 1974), pp. 489-492.

70. R. L. Hartman and A. R. Hartman, "Strain-Induced Degradation of GaAs Injection Lasers," *Appl. Phys. Lett.* **23** (August 1, 1973), pp. 147-149.

71. W. B. Joyce, R. W. Dixon, and R. L. Hartman, "Statistical Characterization of the Lifetimes of Continuously Operated (Al,Ga)As Double-Heterostructure Lasers," *Appl. Phys. Lett.* **28** (June 1, 1976), pp. 684-686.

72. R. E. Nahory and M. A. Pollack, "Low-Threshold Room-Temperature Double-Heterostructure $GaAs_{1-x}Sb_{x/Al}Ga_{1-x}Sb_x$ Injection Lasers at 1-μm Wavelengths," *Appl. Phys. Lett.* **27** (November 15, 1975), pp. 562-564.

73. K. Sugiyama and H. Saito, "GaAsSb-AlGaAsSb Double-Heterojunction Lasers," *Japan J. Appl. Phys.* **11** (July 1972), pp. 1057-1058.

74. R. E. Nahory, M. A. Pollack, E. D. Beebe, J. C. Dewinter, and R. W. Dixon, "Continuous Operation of 1.0-μm-Wavelength $GaAs_{1-x}Sb_x/As_{1-x}Sb_x$ Double-Heterostructure Injection at Room Temperature," *Appl. Phys. Lett.* **28** (January 1, 1976), pp. 19-21.

75. J. J. Hsieh, J. A. Rossi, and J. P. Donnelly, "Room Temperature cw Operation of GaInAsP/InP Double-Heterostructure Diode Lasers Emitting at 1.1 μm," *Appl. Phys. Lett.* **28** (June 15, 1976), pp. 709-711.

76. C. J. Neuse, G. H. Olsen, M. Ettenberg, J. J. Gannon, and T. J. Zamerowski, "cw Room-Temperature $In_xGa_{1-x}As/In_yGa_{1-y}P$ 1.06 μm Lasers," *Appl. Phys. Lett.* **29** (December 15, 1976), pp. 807-809.

77. H. Kogelnik and C. V. Shank, "Stimulated Emission in a Periodic Structure," *Appl. Phys. Lett.* **18** (February 15, 1971), pp. 152-154.

78. H. Kogelnik and C. V. Shank, "Coupled-Wave Theory of Distributed-Feedback Lasers," *J. Appl. Phys.* **43** (May 1972), pp. 2327-2335; C. V. Shank, R. V. Schmidt, and B. I. Miller, "Double-Heterostructure GaAs Distributed-Feedback Laser," *Appl. Phys. Lett.* **25** (August 15, 1974), pp. 200-201; H. C. Casey, S. Somekh, and H. Ilegems, "Room Temperature Operation of Low-Threshold Separate Confinement Heterostructure Injection Laser with Distributed Feedback," *Appl. Phys. Lett.* **27** (August 1, 1976), pp. 142-144.

79. C. K. N. Patel, "Interpretation of CO_2 Optical Maser Experiments," *Phys. Rev. Lett.* **12** (May 25, 1964), pp. 588-590.

80. C. K. N. Patel, "Selective Excitation Through Vibrational Energy Transfer and Optical Maser Action in N_2-CO_2" *Phys. Rev. Lett.* **13** (November 23, 1964), pp. 617-619.

81. C. K. N. Patel, "CW High Power N_2-CO_2 Laser," *Appl. Phys. Lett.* **7** (July 1, 1965), pp. 15-17; C. K. N. Patel, P. K. Tien, and J. H. McFee, "cw High-Power CO_2-N_2-He Laser," *Appl. Phys. Lett.* **7** (December 1, 1965), pp. 290-292; C. K. N. Patel, "16 Watts Output Achieved in Infrared Laser," *Bell Laboratories Record* **43** (July-August 1965), p. 311; idem, "Helium Is Key to High Power Lasers," *Bell Laboratories Record* **43** (December 1965), p. 464.

82. J. E. Geusic, H. M. Marcos, and L. G. Van Uitert, "Laser Oscillations in Nd-Doped Yttrium Aluminum, Yttrium Gallium, and Gadolinium Garnets," *Appl. Phys. Lett.* **4** (May 15, 1964), pp. 182-184.

83. W. R. Bennett, Jr., "Recent Progress in Experiments with Gaseous Optical Maser," *Bull. Am. Phys. Soc.* **7** (January 24, 1962), p. 15; C. K. N. Patel, "Optical Power Output in He-Ne and Pure Ne Maser," *J. Appl. Phys.* **33** (November 1962), pp. 3194-3195.

84. C. K. N. Patel, W. R. Bennet, Jr., W. L. Faust, and R. A. McFarlane, "Infrared Spectroscopy Using Stimulated Emission Techniques," *Phys. Rev. Lett.* **9** (August 1, 1962), pp. 102-104.

85. C. K. N. Patel, W. L. Faust, R. A. McFarlane, and C. G. B. Garrett, "cw Optical Maser Action up to 133 μm (0.133 mm) in Neon Discharges," *Proc. IEEE* **52** (June 1964), p. 713.

86. E. I. Gordon, E. F. Labuda, and W. B. Bridges, "Continuous Visible Laser Action in Singly Ionized Argon, Krypton, and Xenon," *Appl. Phys. Lett.* **4** (May 15, 1964), pp. 178-180.

87. W. T. Silfvast, "Efficient cw Laser Oscillation at 4416 A in Cd (II)," *Appl. Phys. Lett.* **13** (September 1, 1968), pp. 169-171; idem, "New cw Metal-Vapor Laser Transitions in Cd, Sn, and Zn," *Appl. Phys. Lett.* **15** (July 1, 1969), pp. 23-25.

88. W. T. Silfvast and M. B. Klein, "cw Laser Action on 24 Visible Wavelengths in Se II," *Appl. Phys. Lett.* **17** (November 1, 1970), pp. 400-406.

89. M. B. Klein and W. T. Silfvast, "New cw Laser Transitions in Se II," *Appl. Phys. Lett.* **18** (June 1, 1971), pp. 482-485.

90. W. T. Silfvast and L. H. Szeto, "Simplified Low-Noise He-Cd Laser with Segmented Bore," *Appl. Phys. Lett.* **19** (November 16, 1971), pp. 445-447.

91. M. A. Duguay and P. M. Rentzepis, "Some Approaches to Vacuum UV and X-Ray Lasers," *Appl. Phys. Lett.* **10** (June 15, 1967), pp. 350-352

92. E. J. McGuire and M. A. Duguay, "Soft X-ray Gain in the Alkali Earths," *Applied Optics* **16** (January 1977), pp. 83-88.

93. C. K. N. Patel and R. J. Kerl, "Laser Oscillation on XE Vibrational- Rotational Transitions of CO," *Appl. Phys. Lett.* **5** (August 15, 1964), pp. 81-83.

94. C. K. N. Patel, "cw Laser on Vibrational-Rotational Transitions of CO," *Appl. Phys. Lett.* **7** (November 1, 1965), pp. 246-247.

95. C. K. N. Patel, "cw Laser Action in $N_2O(N_2-N_2O$ System)," *Appl. Phys. Lett.* **6** (January 1, 1965), pp. 12-13.

96. C. K. N. Patel, "cw Laser Oscillation in an N_2-CS_2 System," *Appl. Phys. Lett.* **7** (November 15, 1965), pp. 273-274.

97. T. Y. Chang and T. J. Bridges, "Laser Action at 452, 496, and 541 μm in Optically Pumped CH_3F," *Opt. Commun.* **1** (April 1970), pp. 423-426.

98. T. Y. Chang, T. J. Bridges, and E. G. Burkhardt, "CW Submillimeter Laser Action in Optically Pumped Methyl Fluoride, Methyl Alcohol, and Vinyl Chloride Gases," *Appl. Phys. Lett.* **17** (September 15, 1970), pp. 249-251; idem, "CW Laser Action at 81.5 and 263-4 μm in Optically Pumped Ammonia Gas," *Appl. Phys. Lett.* **17** (November 1, 1970), pp. 357-358.

99. D. T. Hodges, "A Review of Advances in Optically Pumped Far-Infrared Lasers," *Infrared Physics* **18** (December 1978), pp. 375-384.

100. C. V. Shank, A. Dienes, A. M. Trozzolo, and J. A. Myer, "Near UV to Yellow Tunable Laser Emission from an Organic Dye," *Appl. Phys. Lett.* **16** (May 15, 1970), pp. 405-407.

101. A. Dienes, E. P. Ippen, and C. V. Shank, "High Efficiency Tunable CW Dye Laser," *IEEE JQE* **8** (March 1972), pp. 388-389.

102. H. W. Kogelnik, E. P. Ippen, A. Dienes, and C. V. Shank, "Astigmatically Compensated Cavities for CW Dye Lasers," *IEEE JQE* **8** (March 1972), pp. 373-379.

103. P. K. Runge and R. Rosenberg, "Unconfined Flowing-Dye Films for CW Dye Lasers," *IEEE JQE* **8** (December 1972), pp. 910-911.

104. C. V. Shank, J. Edighoffer, A. Dienes, and E. P. Ippen, "Evidence for Diffusion Independent Triplet Quenching in the Rhodamine 6G Ethylene Glycol CW Dye Laser System," *Opt. Commun.* **7** (March 1973), pp. 176-177.

105. L. F. Mollenauer and D. H. Olson, "A Broadly Tunable CW Laser Using Color Centers," *Appl. Phys. Lett.* **24** (April 15, 1974), pp. 386-388; L. F. Mollenauer, "Dyelike Lasers for the 0.98-2 μm Region Using F_2^+ Centers in Alkali Halides,"

Optics. Lett. **1** (November 1977), pp. 164-165; L. F. Mollenauer, D. M. Bloom, and H. Guggenheim, "Simple Two-Step Photoionization Yields High Densities of Laser-Active F_2^+ Centers," *Appl. Phys. Lett.* **33** (September 15, 1978), pp. 506-509; L. F. Mollenauer and D. M. Bloom, "Color Center Laser Generates Picosecond Pulses and Several Watts CW over the 1.24-1.45 μm Range," *Optics. Lett.* **4** (August 1979), pp. 247-249.

106. B. Fritz and E. Menke, "Laser Effect in KCl with F_A(Li) Centers," *Solid State Comm.* **3** (1965), pp. 61-63.
107. See reference 15.
108. A. Javan, E. A. Ballik, and W. L. Bond, "Frequency Characteristics of a Continuous-Wave He-Ne Optical Maser," *J. Opt. Soc. Am.* **52** (January 1962), pp. 96-99.
109. J. D. Rigden and E. I. Gordon, "The Granularity of Scattered Optical Maser Light," *Proc. IRE* **50** (November 1962), pp. 2367-2368.
110. I. Kaminow, "Splitting of Fabry-Perot Rings by Microwave Modulation of Light," *Appl. Phys. Lett.* **2** (January 15, 1963), pp. 41-42.
111. L. H. Enloe and J. H. Rodda, "Laser Phase-Locked Loop," *Proc. IEEE* **53** (February 1965), pp. 165-166.
112. R. A. McFarlane, W. R. Bennett, Jr., and W. B. Lamb, Jr., "Single Mode Tuning Dip in the Power Output," *Appl. Phys. Lett.* **2** (May 15, 1963), pp. 189-190.
113. See reference 86.
114. D. E. McCumber and M. D. Sturge, "Linewidth and Temperature Shift of the R Lines in Ruby," *J. Appl. Phys.* **34** (June 1963), pp. 1682-1684.
115. D. F. Nelson and M. D. Sturge, "Relation Between Absorption and Emission in the Region of the R Lines of Ruby," *Phys. Rev.* **137** (February 1965), pp. 1117-1130.
116. L. S. Vasilinko, V. P. Chebotaev, and A. V. Shishaev, "Line Shape of Two-Photon Absorption in a Standing-Wave Field in a Gas," *JETP Lett.* **12** (August 5, 1970), pp. 113-116.
117. J. E. Bjorkholm and P. F. Liao, "Resonant Enhancement of Two-Photon Absorption in Sodium Vapor," *Phys. Rev. Lett.* **33** (July 15, 1974), pp. 128-131.
118. P. F. Liao and J. E. Bjorkholm, "Direct Observation of Atomic Energy Level Shifts in Two-Photon Absorption," *Phys. Rev. Lett.* **34** (January 6, 1975), pp. 1-4.
119. J. E. Bjorkholm and P. F. Liao, "AC Stark Splitting of Two-Photon Spectra," *Optics Commun.* **21** (April 1977), pp. 132-136.
120. J. E. Bjorkholm and P. F. Liao, "Line Shape and Strength of Two-Photon Absorption in an Atomic Vapor with a Resonant or Nearly Resonant Intermediate State," *Phys. Rev.* **A14** (August 1976), pp. 751-760.
121. P. F. Liao and J. E. Bjorkholm, "Measurement of the Fine-Structure Splitting of the 4F State in Atomic Sodium Using Two-Photon Spectroscopy with a Resonant Intermediate State," *Phys. Rev. Lett.* **36** (June 28, 1976), pp. 1543-1545.
122. N. A. Kurnit, I. D. Abella, and S. R. Hartmann, "Observation of a Photon Echo," *Phys. Rev. Lett.* **13** (November 9, 1964), pp. 567-568.
123. P. F. Liao, J. E. Bjorkholm, and J. P. Gordon, "Observation of Two-Photon Optical Free-Induction Decay in Atomic Sodium Vapor," *Phys. Rev. Lett.* **39** (July 4, 1977), pp. 15-18.
124. D. F. Liao, N. Economu, and R. R. Freeman, "Two-Photon Coherent Transient Measurements of Doppler-Free Linewidths with Broadband Excitation," *Phys. Rev. Lett.* **39** (December 5, 1977), pp. 1473-1476.
125. S. P. S. Porto and D. L. Wood, "Ruby Optical Maser as a Raman Source," *J. Opt. Soc. Am.* **52** (March 1962), pp. 251-252.
126. H. Kogelnik and S. P. S. Porto, "Continuous Helium-Neon Red Laser as a Raman Source," *J. Opt. Soc. Am.* **53** (December 1963), pp. 1446-1447.
127. D. F. Nelson and M. Lax, "New Symmetry for Acousto-Optic Scattering," *Phys. Rev. Lett.* **24** (February 23, 1970), pp. 379-380.

128. D. F. Nelson and P. D. Lazay, "Measurement of the Rotational Contribution to Brillouin Scattering," *Phys. Rev. Lett.* **23** (October 26, 1970), pp. 1187-1191.

129. J. M. Worlock and S. P. S. Porto, "Raman Scattering by F Centers," *Phys. Rev. Lett.* **15** (October 25, 1965), pp. 697-699.

130. S. P. S. Porto, B. Tell, and T. C. Damen, "Near-Forward Raman Scattering in Zinc Oxide," *Phys. Rev. Lett.* **16** (March 14, 1966), pp. 450-452.

131. G. B. Wright and A. Mooradian, "Raman Scattering from Donor and Acceptor Impurities in Silicon," *Phys. Rev. Lett.* **18** (April 10, 1967), pp. 609-610.

132. C. K. N. Patel and R. E. Slusher, "Light Scattering by Plasmons and Landau Levels of Electron Gas in InAs," *Phys. Rev.* **167** (March 1968), pp. 413-415.

133. B. Tell and R. J. Martin, "Raman Scattering by Coupled Optical-Phonon-Plasmon Modes in GaAs," *Phys. Rev.* **167** (March 1968), pp. 381-386.

134. J. F. Scott, T. C. Damen, R. C. C. Leite, and J. Shah, "Light Scattering from Plasmas and Single-Particle Excitations in Cadmium Sulfide near Resonance," *Phys. Rev.* **B1** (June 1970), pp. 4330-4333.

135. J. M. Worlock, T. C. Damen, K. L. Shaklee, and J. P. Gordon, "Determination of the Optical Properties and Absolute Concentrations of Electron-Hole Drops in Germanium," *Phys. Rev. Lett.* **33** (1974), p. 771.

136. J. Doehler, J. C. V. Mattos, and J. M. Worlock, "Laser-Doppler Velocimetry of Electron-Hole Drops in Germanium," *Phys. Rev. Lett.* **38** (March 28, 1977), pp. 726-729.

137. P. A. Fleury, S. P. S. Porto, L. E. Cheesman, and H. J. Guggenheim, "Light Scattering by Spin Waves in FeF_2," *Phys. Rev. Lett.* **17** (July 11, 1966), pp. 84-87.

138. P. A. Fleury and R. Loudon, "Scattering of Light by One- and Two-Magnon Excitations," *Phys. Rev.* **166** (February 1968), pp. 514-530.

139. P. A. Fleury, "Evidence for Magnon-Magnon Interactions in $RbMnF_3$," *Phys. Rev. Lett.* **21** (July 15, 1968), pp. 151-153; idem, "Paramagnetic Spin Waves and Correlation Functions in NiF_2," *Phys. Rev.* **180** (April 1969), pp. 591-593.

140. P. A. Fleury and J. M. Worlock, "Electric-Field-Induced Raman Effect in Paraelectric Crystals," *Phys. Rev. Lett.* **18** (April 17, 1966), pp. 665-667.

141. J. M. Worlock and P. A. Fleury, "Electric Field Dependence of Optical-Phonon Frequencies," *Phys. Rev. Lett.* **19** (November 13, 1967), pp. 1176-1179.

142. I. P. Kaminow and T. C. Damen, "Temperature Dependence of the Ferroelectric Mode in KH_2PO_4," *Phys. Rev. Lett.* **20** (May 13, 1968), pp. 1105-1108; I. P. Kaminow and W. D. Johnston, Jr., "Quantitative Determination of Sources of the Electro-Optic Effect in $LiNbO_3$ and $LiTaO_3$," *Phys. Rev.* **160** (August 1967), pp. 519-522.

143. M. DiDomenico, Jr., S. P. S. Porto, and S. H. Wemple, "Evidence from Raman Scattering for an Overdamped Soft Optic Mode in $BaTiO_3$," *Phys. Rev. Lett.* **19** (October 9, 1967), pp. 855-857.

144. G. E. Devlin, J. L. Davis, L. Chase, and S. Geschwind, "Absorption of Unshifted Scattered Light by a Molecular I_2 Filter in Brillouin and Raman Scattering," *Appl. Phys. Lett.* **19** (September 1, 1971), pp. 138-141.

145. K. B. Lyons and P. A. Fleury, "Digital Normalization of Iodine Filter Structure in Quasielastic Light Scattering," *J. App. Phys.* **47** (November 1976), pp. 4898-4900.

146. P. A. Fleury and K. B. Lyons, "Spectroscopic Observation of Very-Low-Energy Excitations in Glasses," *Phys. Rev. Lett.* **36** (May 17, 1976), pp. 1188-1191.

147. C. H. Henry and J. J. Hopfield, "Raman Scattering by Polaritons," *Phys. Rev. Lett.* **15** (December 20, 1965), pp. 964-966.

148. W. L. Faust and C. H. Henry, "Mixing of Visible and Near-Resonance Infrared Light in GaP," *Phys. Rev. Lett.* **17** (December 19, 1966), pp. 1265-1268.

149. D. F. Nelson and E. H. Turner, "Electro-Optic and Piezoelectric Coefficients and Refractive Index of Gallium Phosphide," *J. Appl. Phys.* **39** (June 1968), pp. 3337-3343.

150. S. L. McCall and E. L. Hahn, "Self-Induced Transparency," *Phys. Rev.* **183** (July 1969), pp. 457-485.

151. C. K. N. Patel and R. E. Slusher, "Self-Induced Transparency in Gases," *Phys. Rev. Lett.* **19** (October 30, 1967), pp. 1019-1022; C. K. N. Patel, "Investigation of Pulse Delay in Self-Induced Transparency," *Phys. Rev.* **A1** (April 1970), pp. 979-982.

152. P. K. Cheo and C. H. Wang, "Propagation of a Cavity-Dumped CO_2 Laser Pulse Through SF_6," *Phys. Rev.* **A1** (February 1970), pp. 225-230.

153. H. M. Gibbs and R. E. Slusher, "Peak Amplification and Breakup of a Coherent Optical Pulse in a Simple Atomic Absorber," *Phys. Rev. Lett.* **24** (March 23, 1970), pp. 638-641; idem, "Optical Pulse Compression by Focusing in a Resonant Absorber," *Appl. Phys. Lett.* **18** (June 1, 1971), pp. 505-507; R. E. Slusher and H. M. Gibbs, "Self-Induced Transparency in Atomic Rubidium," *Phys. Rev.* **A5** (April 1972), pp. 1634-1659; idem, "Self-Induced Transparency in Atomic Rubidium (Errata)," *Phys. Rev.* **A6** (September 1972), pp. 1255-1257; R. E. Slusher, "Self-Induced Transparency," *Progress in Optics*, Vol. XII, ed. E. Wolf (Amsterdam: North-Holland, 1974), pp. 53-100.

154. G. J. Salamo, H. M. Gibbs, and C. C. Churchill, "Effects of Degeneracy on Self-Induced Transparency," *Phys. Rev. Lett.* **33** (July 29, 1974), pp. 273-274; H. M. Gibbs, S. L. McCall, and G. J. Salamo, "Near-Ideal Self-Induced-Transparency Breakup in Highly Degenerate Systems," *Phys. Rev.* (September 1975), pp. 1032-1035.

155. A. G. Fox and P. W. Smith, "Mode-Locked Laser and the 180° Pulse," *Phys. Rev. Lett.* **18** (May 15, 1967), pp. 826-828.

156. N. A. Kurnit, I. D. Abella, and S.R. Hartmann, "Observation of Photon Echoes," *Phys. Rev. Lett.* **13** (November 9, 1964), pp. 567-568.

157. C. K. N. Patel and R. E. Slusher, "Photon Echoes in Gases," *Phys. Rev. Lett.* **20** (May 13, 1968), pp. 1087-1089.

158. E. L. Hahn, N. S. Shiren, and S. L. McCall, "Application of the Area Theorem to Photon Echoes," *Phys. Lett.* **37A** (November 22, 1971), pp. 265-267.

159. B. Golding and J. E. Graebner, "Phonon Echoes in Glass," *Phys. Rev. Lett.* **37** (September 27, 1976), pp. 852-855.

160. B. Golding, J. E. Graebner, and W. H. Haemmerle, "Microwave Photon Echoes from Polyethylene," *Phys. Rev. Lett.* **44** (March 31, 1980), pp. 899-902.

161. P. Hu, S. Geschwind, and T. M. Jedju, "Spin-Flip Raman Echo in n-Type CdS," *Phys. Rev. Lett.* **37** (November 16, 1976), pp. 1357-1360.

162. S. L. McCall, "Instabilities in Continuous-Wave Light Propagation in Absorbing Media," *Phys. Rev.* **A9** (April 1974),pp. 1515-1523.

163. H. M. Gibbs, S. L. McCall, and T. N. C. Venkatesan, "Differential Gain and Bistability Using a Sodium-Filled Fabry-Perot Interferometer," *Phys. Rev. Lett.* **36** (May 10, 1976), pp. 1135-1138.

164. T. N. C. Venkatesan and S. L. McCall, "Optical Bistability and Differential Gain Between 85 and 296°K in a Fabry-Perot Containing Ruby," *Appl. Phys. Lett.* **30** (March 15, 1977), pp. 282-284.

165. H. M. Gibbs, S. L. McCall, T. N. C. Venkatesan, A. Passner, A. C. Gossard, and W. Wiegmann, "Optical Bistability in Semiconductors," *Appl. Phys. Lett.* **35** (September 15, 1979), pp. 451-453.

166. P. W. Smith and E. H. Turner, "A Bistable Fabry-Perot Resonator," *Appl. Phys. Lett.* **30** (March 15, 1977), pp. 280-281.

167. P. W. Smith, E. H. Turner, and P. J. Maloney, "Electrooptic Nonlinear Fabry-Perot Devices," *IEEE J. Quantum Electron.* **QE-14** (March 1978), pp. 207-212.

168. P. S. Cross, R. V. Schmidt, R. L. Thornton, and P. W. Smith, "Optically Controlled Two Channel Integrated-Optical Switch," *IEEE J. Quantum Electron.* **QE-14** (August 1978), pp. 577-580; P. W. Smith, I. P. Kaminow, P. J. Maloney, and L. W. Stulz, "Self-Contained Integrated Bistable Optical Devices," *Appl. Phys. Lett.* **34** (January 1, 1979), pp. 62-65.

169. P. W. Smith, "Hybrid Bistable Optical Devices," *Optical Eng.* 19 (July/August 1980), pp. 456-462.

170. S. L. McCall, "Instability and Regenerative Pulsation Phenomena in Fabry-Perot Nonlinear Optic Media Devices," *Appl. Phys. Lett.* 32 (March 1, 1978), pp. 284-286.

171. H. M. Gibbs, "Spontaneous Decay of Coherently Excited Rb," *Phys. Rev. Lett.* 29 (August 21, 1972), pp. 459-462; idem, "Incoherent Resonance Fluorescence from a Rb Atomic Beam Excited by a Short Coherent Optical Pulse," *Phys. Rev.* A8 (July 1973), pp. 446-445; idem, "Test of Neoclassical Radiation Theory: Incoherent Resonance Fluourescence from a Coherently Excited State," *Phys. Rev.* A8 (July 1973), pp. 456-464.

172. Q. H. F. Vrehen, H. M. J. Hikspoors, and H. M. Gibbs, "Quantum Beats in Superfluourescence in Atomic Cesium," *Phys. Rev. Lett.* 38 (April 4, 1977), pp. 764-767.

173. H. M. Gibbs, Q. H. F. Vrehen, and H. M. J. Hikspoors, "Single-Pulse Superfluorescence in Cesium," *Phys. Rev. Lett.* 39 (August 29, 1977), pp. 547-550.

174. A. Ashkin, "Acceleration and Trapping of Particles by Radiation Pressure," *Phys. Rev. Lett.* 24 (January 26, 1970), pp. 156-159.

175. A. Ashkin, "Atomic-Beam Deflection by Resonance-Radiation Pressure," *Appl. Phys. Lett.* 25 (1970), p. 1321.

176. A. Ashkin and J. M. Dziedzic, "Optical Levitation by Radiation Pressure," *Appl. Phys. Lett.* 19 (October 15, 1971), pp. 283-285; idem, "Optical Levitation in High Vacuum," *Appl. Phys. Lett.* 28 (March 15, 1976), pp. 333-335.

177. A. Ashkin and J. M. Dziedzic, "Feedback Stabilization of Optically Levitated Particles," *Appl. Phys. Lett.* 30 (February 15, 1977), pp. 202-204.

178. A. Ashkin and J. M. Dziedzic, "Observations of Resonances in the Radiation Pressure on Dielectric Spheres," *Phys. Rev. Lett.* 38 (June 6, 1977), pp. 1351-1354.

179. A. Ashkin and J. M. Dziedzic, "Optical Levitation of Liquid Drops by Radiation Pressure," *Science* 187 (March 21, 1975), pp. 1073-1075.

180. A. Ashkin and J. M. Dziedzic, "Stability of Optical Levitation by Radiation Pressure," *Appl. Phys. Lett.* 24 (June 15, 1974), pp. 586-588.

181. See reference 179.

182. P. Chylek, J. T. Kiehl, and M. K. W. Ko, "Optical Levitation and Partial-Wave Resonances," *Phys. Rev.* A18 (November 1978), pp. 2229-2233.

183. A. Ashkin and J. M. Dziedzic, "Observation of a New Nonlinear Photoelectric Effect Using Optical Levitation," *Phys. Rev. Lett.* 36 (February 2, 1976), pp. 267-270.

184. See reference 181.

185. See references 175 and 176.

186. J. E. Bjorkholm, A. Ashkin, and D. B. Pearson, "Observation of Resonance Radiation Pressure on an Atomic Vapor," *Appl. Phys. Lett.* 27 (November 15, 1975), pp. 534-537.

187. J. E. Bjorkholm, R. R. Freeman, A. Ashkin, and D. B. Pearson, "Observation of Focusing of Neutral Atoms by the Dipole Forces of Resonance-Radiation Pressure," *Phys. Rev. Lett.* 41 (November 13, 1978), pp. 1361-1364.

188. D. B. Pearson, R. R. Freeman, J. E. Bjorkholm, and A. Ashkin, "Focusing and Defocusing of Neutral Atomic Beams Using Resonance-Radiation Pressure," *Appl. Phys. Lett.* 36 (January 1, 1980), pp. 99-101.

189. J. E. Bjorkholm, R. R. Freeman, A. Ashkin, and D. B. Pearson, "Experimental Observation of the Influence of the Quantum Fluctuations of Resonance-Radiation Pressure," *Optics. Lett.* 5 (March 1980), pp. 111-113.

190. A. Ashkin, "Trapping of Atoms by Resonance Radiation Pressure," *Phys. Rev. Lett.* 40 (March 20, 1978), pp. 729-732; A. Ashkin and J. P. Gordon, "Cooling and Trapping of Atoms by Resonance Radiation Pressure," *Opt. Lett.* 4 (June 1979), pp. 161-163.

191. J. P. Gordon and A. Ashkin, "Motion of Atoms in a Radiation Trap," *Phys. Rev.*

A21 (May 1980), pp. 1606-1617.

192. W. Kaiser and C. G. B. Garrett, "Two-Photon Excitation in $CaF_2:Eu^{2+}$," *Phys. Rev. Lett.* **7** (September 15, 1961), pp. 229-231.

193. D. A. Kleinman, "Laser and Two-Photon Processes," *Phys. Rev.* **125** (January 1962), pp. 87-88.

194. J. A. Giordmaine, P. M. Rentzepis, S. L. Shapiro, and K. W. Wecht, "Two-Photon Excitation of Fluorescence by Picosecond Light Pulses," *Appl. Phys. Lett.* **11** (October 1, 1967), pp. 216-218.

195. M. A. Duguay and J. W. Hansen, "Ultrahigh Speed Photography of Picosecond Light Pulses," *IEEE J. Quant. Electron.* **QE-7** (1971), pp. 37-39.

196. J. A. Giordmaine, "Mixing of Light Beams in Crystals," *Phys. Rev. Lett.* **8** (January 1, 1962), pp. 19-20.

197. D. A. Kleinman, "Theory of Second Harmonic Generation of Light," *Phys. Rev.* **128** (November 1962), pp. 1761-1775.

198. A. Ashkin, G. D. Boyd, and J. M. Dziedzic, "Observation of Continuous Optical Harmonic Generation with Gas Masers," *Phys. Rev. Lett.* **11** (July 1, 1963), pp. 14-17.

199. G. D. Boyd, R. C. Miller, K. Nassau, W. L. Bond, and A. Savage, "$LiNbO_3$: An Efficient Phase Matchable Nonlinear Optical Material," *Appl. Phys. Lett.* **5** (1964), pp. 234-236.

200. G. D. Boyd and D. A. Kleinman, "Parametric Interaction of Focused Gaussian Light Beams," *J. Appl. Phys.* **39** (July 1968), pp. 3597-3639.

201. F. R. Nash, G. D. Boyd, M. Sargent, III, and P. M. Bridenbaugh, "Effect of Optical Inhomogeneities on Phase Matching in Linear Crystals," *J. Appl. Phys.* **41** (May 1970), pp. 2564-2575.

202. J. E. Geusic, H. J. Levinstein, S. Singh, R. G. Smith, and L. G. Van Uitert, "Continuous 0.532-u Solid-State Source Using $Ba_2NaNb_5O_{15}$," *Appl. Phys. Lett.* **12** (May 1, 1968), pp. 306-308.

203. J. Jerphagnon and S. K. Kurtz, "Maker Fringes: A Detailed Comparison of Theory and Experiment for Isotropic and Uniaxial Crystals," *J. Appl. Phys.* **41** (March 1970), pp. 1667-1681.

204. S. K. Kurtz and T. T. Perry, "A Powder Technique for the Evaluation of Nonlinear Optical Materials," *J. Appl. Phys.* **39** (July 1968), pp. 3798-3813.

205. R. Bersohn, Y.-H. Pao, and H. L. Frisch, "Double-Quantum Light Scattering by Molecules," *J. Chem. Phys.* **45** (November 1966), pp. 3184-3198.

206. See reference 195.

207. See reference 200; also, J. A. Giordmaine and R. C. Miller, "Tunable Coherent Parametric Oscillation in $LiNbO_3$ at Optical Frequencies," *Phys. Rev. Lett.* **14** (June 14, 1965), pp. 973-976; idem, "Optical Parametric Oscillation in $LiNbO_3$," *Physics of Quantum Electronics*, ed. P. L. Kelley, B. Lax, and P. E. Tannenwald (New York: McGraw-Hill, 1966), pp. 31-42.

208. S. K. Kurtz, "Nonlinear Optical Materials," in *Laser Handbook*, Vol. 1, ed. F. T. Arecchi and E. O. Schulz-Dubois (Amsterdam: North Holland, 1972), pp. 923-974.

209. G. D. Boyd, E. Buehler, F. G. Storz, and J. H. Wernick, "Linear and Nonlinear Optical Properties of Ternary $A^{II}B^{IV}C^{V2}$ Chalcopyrite Semiconductors," *IEEE J. Quant. Electron.* **QE-8** (April 1972), pp. 419-426; G. D. Boyd, H. Kasper, and J. H. McFee, "Linear and Nonlinear Optical Properties of $AgGaS_2$, $CuGaS_2$, and $CuInS_2$, and Theory of the Wedge Technique for the Measurement of Nonlinear Coefficients," *IEEE J. Quant. Electron.* **QE-7** (December 1971), pp. 563-573; G. D. Boyd, J. H. McFee, F. G. Storz, and H. M. Kasper, "Linear and Nonlinear Optical Properties of Some Ternary Selenides," *IEEE J. Quant. Electron.* **QE-8** (December 1972), pp. 900-908.

210. C. K. N. Patel, "Efficient Phase-Matched Harmonic Generation in Tellurium with a CO_2 Laser at 10.6u," *Phys. Rev. Lett.* **15** (December 27, 1965), pp. 1027-1030; idem, "Parametric Amplification in the Far Infrared," *Appl. Phys. Lett.* **10** (November 1, 1966), pp. 332-334; idem, "Investigation of Nonlinear Phenomena and Scattering Processes at 10.6 Microns," *Modern Optics*, Vol. **XVII** (New York: Polytechnic Press, 1967), pp. 19-51; C. K. N. Patel, "Optical Harmonic Generation in the Infrared Using a CO_2 Laser," *Phys. Rev. Lett.* **16** (April 4, 1966), pp. 613-616; C. K. N. Patel, R. E. Slusher, and P. A. Fleury, "Optical Nonlinearities Due to Mobile Carriers in Semiconductors," *Phys. Rev. Lett.* **17** (November 7, 1966), pp. 1011-1014.

211. D. A. McArthur and R. A. McFarlane, "Optical Mixing in Cadmium Telluride Using the Pulsed Water Vapor Laser," *Appl. Phys. Lett.* **16** (June 1, 1970), pp. 452-454.

212. G. D. Boyd and C. K. N. Patel, "Enhancement of Optical Second-Harmonic Generation by Reflection Phase Matching in ZnS and GaAs," *Appl. Phys. Lett.* **8** (June 15, 1966), pp. 313-315; N. Van Tran and C. K. N. Patel, "Free-Carrier Magneto-Optical Effects in the Far Infrared Difference Frequency Generation in Semiconductors," *Phys. Rev. Lett.* **22** (March 10, 1969), pp. 463-466.

213. P. M. Rentzepis and Y.-H. Pao, "Laser-Induced Optical Second Harmonic Generation in Organic Crystals," *Appl. Phys. Lett.* **5** (October 15, 1964), pp. 156-158.

214. J. Jerphagnon, "Optical Second-Harmonic Generation in Isocyclic and Heterocyclic Organic Compounds," *IEEE J. Quantum Electron.* **QE-7** (January 1971), pp. 42-43.

215. B. F. Levine, "Studies of Molecular Characteristics and Interactions Using Hyperpolarizabilities as a Probe," in *Dielectric and Related Molecular Processes* 3 (London: The Chemical Soc., Burlington House, 1977), pp. 73-107; B. F. Levine and C. G. Bethea, "Second and Third Order Hyperpolarizabilities of Organic Molecules," *J. Chem. Phys.* **63** (1975), pp. 2666-2682.

216. D. A. Kleinman, "Nonlinear Dielectric Polarization in Optical Media," *Phys. Rev.* **126** (June 1962), pp. 1977-1979.

217. R. C. Miller, "Optical Second Harmonic Generation in Piezeoelectric Crystals," *Appl. Phys. Lett.* **5** (July 1, 1964),pp. 17-19.

218. C. G. B. Garrett and F. N. H. Robinson, "Miller's Phenomenological Rule for Computing Nonlinear Susceptibilities," *IEEE J. Quantum Electron.* **QE-2** (August 1966), pp. 328-329; F. N. H. Robinson, "Nonlinear Optical Coefficients," *Bell System Tech. J.* **46** (May-June 1967), pp. 913-956; C. G. B. Garrett, "Nonlinear Optics, Anharmonic Oscillators, and Pyroelectricity," *IEEE J. Quantum Electron.* **QE-4** (March 1968), pp. 70-84.

219. J. C. Phillips, "Ionicity of the Chemical Bond in Crystals," *Rev. Mod. Phys.* **42** (July 1970), pp. 317-356.

220. B. F. Levine, "Electrodynamical Bond-Charge Calculation of Nonlinear Optical Susceptibilities," *Phys. Rev. Lett.* **22** (April 14, 1969), pp. 787-790; idem, "A New Contribution to the Nonlinear Optical Susceptibility Arising from Unequal Atomic Radii," *Phys. Rev. Lett.* **25** (August 17, 1970), pp. 440-443.

221. J. A. Van Vechten, "Quantum Dielectric Theory of Electronegativity in Covalent Systems. I. Electronic Dielectric Constant," *Phys. Rev.* **182** (June 1969), pp. 891- 905.

222. R. C. Miller and W. A. Nordland, "Absolute Signs of Second-Harmonic Generation Coefficients of Piezoelectric Crystals," *Phys. Rev.* **B2** (December 1970), pp. 4896-4902.

223. M. DiDomenico, Jr., and S. H. Wemple, "Oxygen-Octahedra Ferroelectronics. I. Theory of Electro-Optical and Nonlinear Optical Effects," *J. Appl. Phys.* **40** (February 1969), pp. 720-734.

224. J. G. Bergman, G. D. Boyd, A. Ashkin, and S. K. Kurtz, "New Nonlinear Optical Materials: Metal Oxides with Nonbonded Electrons," *J. Appl. Phys.* **40** (June 1969), pp. 2860-2863.

225. A. Ashkin, G. D. Boyd, J. M. Dziedzic, R. G. Smith, A. A. Ballman, J. T. Levinstein, and K. Nassau, "Optically Induced Refractive Index Inhomogeneities in $LiNbO_3$ and $LiTaO_3$," *Appl. Phys. Lett.* **9** (July 1, 1966), pp. 72-74.

226. F. S. Chen, "Optically Induced Change of Refractive Indices in $LiTaO_3$ and $LiTaO_3$," *J. Appl. Phys.* **40** (July 1969), pp. 3389-3396.

227. W. D. Johnston, Jr., "Optical Index Damage in $LiNbO_3$ and Other Pyroelectric Insulators," *J. Appl. Phys.* **41** (July 1970), pp. 3279-3285.

228. G. E. Peterson, A. M. Glass, and N. J. Negran, "Control of the Susceptibility of Lithium Niobate to Laser-Induced Refractive Index Changes," *Appl. Phys. Lett.* **19** (September 1, 1971), pp. 130-132.

229. F. S. Chen, J. T. La Macchia, and D. B. Fraser, "Holographic Storage in Lithium Niobate," *Appl. Phys. Lett.* **13** (October 1, 1968), pp. 223-225.

230. See reference 209.

231. P. A. Wolff and G. A. Pearson, "Theory of Optical Mixing by Mobile Carriers in Semiconductors," *Phys. Rev. Lett.* **17** (November 7, 1966), pp. 1015-1017.

232. P. M. Platzman and N. Tzoar, "Nonlinear Interaction of Light in a Plasma," *Phys. Rev.* **136** (October 1964), pp. 11-16.

233. M. A. Duguay, J. W. Hansen, and S. L. Shapiro, "Study of the Nd:Glass Laser Radiation," *IEEE J. Quantum Electron.* **6** (November 1970), pp. 725-743.

234. I. Freund and L. Kopf, "Long-Range Order in NH_4Cl," *Phys. Rev. Lett.* **24** (May 4, 1970), pp. 1017-1021.

235. J. A. Giordmaine, "Nonlinear Optical Properties of Liquids," *Phys. Rev.* **138** (June 1965), pp. 1599-1606; P. M. Rentzepis, J. A. Giordmaine, and K. W. Wecht, "Coherent Optical Mixing in Optically Active Liquids," *Phys. Rev. Lett.* **16** (May 2, 1966), pp. 792-794.

236. W. L. Faust and C. H. Henry, "Mixing of Visible and Near-Resonance Infrared Light in GaP," *Phys. Rev. Lett.* **17** (December 19, 1966), pp. 1265-1268.

237. See reference 141.

238. G. D. Boyd, T. J. Bridges, M. A. Pollack, and E. H. Turner, "Microwave Nonlinear Susceptibilities Due to Electronic and Ionic Anharmonicities in Acentric Crystals," *Phys. Rev. Lett.* **26** (February 15, 1971), pp. 387-390.

239. See reference 217.

240. B. F. Levine, R. C. Miller, and W. A. Nordland, Jr., "Resonant Exciton Nonlinearities with Spatial Dispersion," *Phys. Rev.* **B12** (November 1975), pp. 4512-4521.

241. R. T. Denton, T. S. Kinsel and F. S. Chen, "Me/s Optical Pulse Code Modulator," *Proceedings of the IEEE* **54** (October 1966), pp. 1472-1473.

242. F. K. Reinhart and B. I. Miller, "Efficient $GaAs-Al_xGa_{1-x}As$ Double-Heterostructure Light Modulation," *Appl. Phys. Lett.* **20** (January 1, 1972), pp. 36-38.

243. D. F. Nelson and F. K. Reinhart, "Light Modulation by the Electro-Optic Effect in Reverse-Biased GaP p-n Junction," *Appl. Phys. Lett.* **5** (October 1, 1964), pp. 148-150.

244. A. Hasegawa and F. Tappert, "Transmission of Stationary Nonlinear Optical Pulses in Dispersive Dielectric Fibers. I. Anomalous Dispersion," *Appl. Phys. Lett.* **23** (August 1, 1973), pp. 142-144; idem, "Transmission of Stationary Nonlinear Optical Pulses in Dispersive Dielectric Fibers. II. Normal Dispersion," *Appl. Phys. Lett.* **23** (August 15, 1973), pp. 171-172.

245. L. F. Mollenauer, R. H. Stolen, and J. P. Gordon, "Experimental Observation of Picosecond Pulse Narrowing and Solitons in Optical Fibers," *Phys. Rev. Lett.* **45** (September 29, 1980), pp. 1095-1098.

246. R. L. Abrams and A. M. Glass, "Photomixing at 10.6 with Strontium Barium Niobate Pyroelectric Detectors," *Appl. Phys. Lett.* **15** (October 15, 1969), pp. 251-253.

247. D. H. Auston and A. M. Glass, "Optical Rectification by Impurities in Polar Crystals," *Phys. Rev. Lett.* **28** (April 3, 1972), pp. 897-900; idem, "Optical Generation of Intense Picosecond Electrical Pulses," *Appl. Phys. Lett.* **20** (May 15, 1972), pp. 398-399.

248. J. P. Van der Ziel, R. C. Miller, R. A. Logan, W. A. Nordland, Jr., and R. M. Mikulyak, "Phase-Matched Second-Harmonic Generation in GaAs Optical Waveguides by Focused Laser Beams," *Appl. Phys. Lett.* **25** (August 15, 1974), pp. 238-240.

249. B. F. Levine, C. G. Bethea, and R. A. Logan, "Phase-Matched Second Harmonic Generation in a Liquid-Filled Waveguide," *Appl. Phys. Lett.* **26** (April 1, 1975), pp. 375-377.

250. F. K. Reinhart and R. A. Logan, "Integrated Electro-Optic Intracavity Frequency Modulation of Double-Heterostructure Injection Laser," *Appl. Phys. Lett.* **27** (November 15, 1975), pp. 532-534; J. C. Shelton, F. K. Reinhart, and R. A. Logan, "Single-mode GaAs$-$Al$_x$Ga$_{1-x}$As Rib Waveguide Switches," *Appl. Optics* **17** (March 1978), pp. 890-891.

251. K. Nassau, H. J. Levinstein, and G. M. Loiacono, "Ferroelectric Lithium Niobate. 1. Growth, Domain Structure, Dislocations and Etching," *J. Phys. Chem. Solids* **27** (June/July 1966), pp. 983-988; idem, "Ferroelectric Lithium Niobate. 2. Preparation of Single Domain Crystals," *J. Phys. Chem. Solids* **27** (June/July 1966), pp. 989-996.

252. See reference 206.

253. G. D. Boyd and A. Ashkin, "Theory of Parametric Oscillator Threshold with Single-Mode Optical Masers and Observation of Amplification in LiNbO$_3$," *Phys. Rev.* **146** (June 1966), pp. 187-198.

254. R. C. Smith, J. E. Geusic, H. J. Levinstein, J. J. Rubin, S. Singh, and L. G. Van Uitert, "Continuous Optical Parametric Oscillation in Ba$_2$NaNb$_5$O$_{15}$," *Appl. Phys. Lett.* **12** (May 1, 1968), pp. 308-310.

255. R. G. Smith, "Optical Parametric Oscillators," *Laser Handbook*, ed. F. T. Arecchi and E. O. Schulz-Dubois (Amsterdam: North Holland, 1972), pp. 837-896.

256. J. E. Bjorkholm, "Efficient Optical Parametric Oscillation Using Doubly and Singly Resonant Cavities," *Appl. Phys. Lett.* **13** (July 15, 1968), pp. 53-56.

257. L. B. Kreuzer, "Single and Multimode Oscillation of the Singly Resonant Optical Parametric Oscillator," *Proc. Joint Conf. on Lasers and Opto-Electronics* (London: I.E.R.E., 1969), pp. 52-63.

258. W. H. Louisell, A. Yariv, and A. E. Siegman, "Quantum Fluctuations and Noise in Parametric Processes. I.," *Phys. Rev.* **124** (December 1961), p. 1646-1654.

259. J. P. Gordon, W. H. Louisell, and L. R. Walker, "Quantum Fluctuations and Noise in Parametric Processes. II," *Phys. Rev.* **129** (January 1963), pp. 481-485.

260. D. A. Kleinman, "Theory of Optical Parametric Noise," *Phys. Rev.* **174** (October 1968), pp. 1027-1041.

261. I. Freund and B. F. Levine, "Parametric Conversion of X-Rays," *Phys. Rev. Lett.* **23** (October 13, 1969), pp. 854-857.

262. P. M. Eisenberger and S. L. McCall, "X-Ray Parametric Conversion," *Phys. Rev. Lett.* **26** (March 22, 1971), pp. 684-688; idem, "Mixing of X-Ray and Optical Phonons," *Phys. Rev.* **A3** (March 1971), pp. 1145-1151.

263. I. Freund and B. F. Levine, "Optically Modulated X-Ray Diffraction," *Phys. Rev. Lett.* **25** (November 2, 1970), p. 1241.

264. J. A. Giordmaine and W. Kaiser, "Light Scattering by Coherently Driven Lattice Vibrations," *Phys. Rev.* **144** (April 1966), pp. 676-688.

265. M. J. Colles and J. A. Giordmaine, "Generation and Detection of Large-R-Vector Phonons," *Phys. Rev. Lett.* **27** (September 6, 1971), pp. 670-674.

266. M. Maier, W. Kaiser, and J. A. Giordmaine, "Intense Light Bursts in the Stimulated Raman Effect," *Phys. Rev. Lett.* **17** (December 26, 1966), pp. 1275-1277; idem, "Backward Stimulated Raman Scattering," *Phys. Rev.* **177** (January 1969), pp. 580-599.

267. G. D. Boyd, F. R. Nash, and D. F. Nelson, "Observation of Acoustically Induced Phase-Matched Optical Harmonic Generation in GaAs," *Phys. Rev. Lett.* **24** (June 8, 1970), pp. 1298-1301.

268. D. F. Nelson and R. M. Mikulyak, "Observation of a Triply Phase-Matched Five-Wave Acousto-Optic Interaction," *Phys. Rev. Lett.* **28** (June 12, 1972), pp. 1574-1577.

269. E. P. Ippen, "Low-Power Quasi-cw Raman Oscillator," *Appl. Phys. Lett.* **16** (April 15, 1970), pp. 303-305.

270. R. H. Stolen, E. P. Ippen, and A. R. Tynes, "Raman Oscillation in Glass Optical Waveguide," *Appl. Phys. Lett.* **20** (January 15, 1972), pp. 62-64; E. P. Ippen, C. K. N. Patel, and R. H. Stolen, U.S. Patent No. 3,705,992; filed December 13, 1971, issued December 12, 1972.

271. M. J. Colles, G. W. Walrafen, and K. W. Wecht, "Stimulated Raman Spectra from H_2, O, D_2, O, HDO and Solutions of $NaClO_4$ in H_2O and D_2O," *Chem. Phys. Lett.* **4** (February 1, 1970), pp. 621-624.

272. A. Ashkin and E. P. Ippen, U. S. Patent No. 3,793,541; filed December 21, 1970, issued February 19, 1974.

273. See reference 268.

274. See reference 269.

275. L. G. Cohen and C. Lin, "Pulse Delay Measurements in the Zero Material Dispersion Wavelength Region for Optical Fibers," *Appl. Opt.* **16** (December 1977), pp. 3136-3139.

276. P. A. Wolff, "Thomson and Raman Scattering by Mobile Electrons in Crystals," *Phys. Rev. Lett.* **16** (February 7, 1966), pp. 225-228.

277. Y. Yafet, "Raman Scattering by Carriers in Landau Levels," *Phys. Rev.* **152** (December 1966), pp. 858-862.

278. R. E. Slusher, C. K. N. Patel, and P. A. Fleury, "Inelastic Light Scattering from Landau-Level Electrons in Semiconductors," *Phys. Rev. Lett.* **18** (January 16, 1967), pp. 77-80.

279. C. K. N. Patel and E. D. Shaw, "Tunable Stimulated Raman Scattering from Conduction Electrons in InSb," *Phys. Rev. Lett.* **24** (March 2, 1970), pp. 451-455; C. K. N. Patel, E. D. Shaw, and R. J. Kerl, "Tunable Spin-Flip Laser and Infrared Spectroscopy," *Phys. Rev. Lett.* **25** (July 6, 1970), pp. 8-11.

280. C. K. N. Patel, "Linewidth of Tunable Stimulated Raman Scattering," *Phys. Rev. Lett.* **28** (March 13, 1972), pp. 649-652.

281. C. K. N. Patel, "Spin-Flip Raman Lasers and High Resolution Spectroscopy," *Proc. of the Sixth Int. Conference on Raman Spectroscopy*, ed. E. D. Schmid, R. S. Krishnan, W. Kiefer, and H. W. Schrotter (London: Heyden & Son., Ltd., 1978), pp. 369-379.

282. C. K. N. Patel, T. Y. Chang, and V. T. Nuyen, "Spin-Flip Raman Laser at Wavelengths up to 16.8 μm," *Appl. Phys. Lett.* **28** (May 15, 1976), pp. 603-605.

Chapter 6

Atoms, Molecules, and Plasmas

Studies of atoms, molecules, and plasmas cover a wide range of physics subfields to which Bell Laboratories scientists have made important contributions. In atomic and molecular physics the research activities have ranged from fundamental spectroscopy of the simplest of atoms and molecules—such as the Lamb shift in hydrogenic atoms, the hyperfine structure of the hydrogen molecule ion, and atomic collisions in a helium-neon discharge—to the radiation from ion-atomic and ion-molecular collisions that take place in the earth's atmosphere, and the opto-acoustic spectroscopy of polluting gases. The more massive biological molecules have also been studied at Bell Labs, including the application of the high-resolution technique of nuclear magnetic resonance to study DNA and hemoglobin, and the use of fluorometric screening tests for lead poisoning. Early plasma physics research included the discharge mechanisms in telephone relays and studies of the collective modes of ionized gases, electron beams, and solid-state plasmas, as well as plasma instabilities.

I. ATOMIC AND MOLECULAR PHYSICS

The study of atomic and molecular physics has been an important facet of the research at Bell Laboratories. Although these efforts were often motivated by the need to understand the atomic and molecular systems from which new laser systems were invented, many experiments whose sole aim was to probe the fundamental physics of atoms and molecules were also performed. Indeed, the invention of the laser gave rise to a renaissance of optical spectroscopy in the 1970s as the high power and spectral purity of laser sources were used to uncover new and detailed information about atomic systems. (For more on this topic, see section VI of Chapter 5.)

1.1 Lamb Shift in Hydrogenic Ions

A good example of fundamental atomic physics research was Bell Labs' collaboration with members of Rutgers University in determin-

Principal authors: W. E. Blumberg, A. Hasegawa, A. A. Lamola, P. F. Liao, P. M. Platzman, R. G. Shulman, R. E. Slusher, and C. M. Surko

ing the Lamb shift of hydrogenic atoms. The Lamb shift, or energy separation between the $2S_{1/2}$ and $2P_{1/2}$ excited states of the hydrogen atom, arises from the quantum nature of the electromagnetic field and was first measured by W. E. Lamb at Columbia University in 1946.[1] The various electron-photon interactions that contribute to this effect were explained by quantum electrodynamics (QED) field theory. Extensive measurements of the Lamb shift of hydrogen-like atoms, along with the anomalous magnetic moment of the electron, have provided the traditional observable parameters for testing the theoretical predictions and limitations of QED. A Lamb shift measurement of high precision performed by M. Leventhal and P. E. Havey of Bell Labs on $^6Li^{2+}$ showed the predictions of the theory to be in reasonable agreement with the data.[2]

Atoms of higher atomic number, Z, ionized to one remaining electron, are quantum-mechanically analogous to the hydrogen atom, but QED predicts an increase in the Lamb shift proportional to the fourth and higher powers of Z. This dependence allows higher sensitivity study of QED interactions and offers the possibility of observing new and unexpected atomic phenomena. Such highly ionized species can be produced from beams of high-energy ions, which became available at the Bell Labs-Rutgers University tandem accelerator about 1967. (See section 1.2 of Chapter 8.)

In the late 1960s, D. E. Murnick and Leventhal began experimenting with beams of 20 MeV to 35 MeV C^{5+} ions ($Z = 6$). New measurement techniques were developed that used electron adding in gas cells, electric field mixing in the beam, and efficient, soft X-ray detection. In collaboration with H. W. Kugel of Rutgers, these experiments were extended to O^{7+} beams ($Z = 8$), using energies in the range of 36 MeV to 48 MeV. Measurements with a 0.5 percent precision were obtained.[3]

In 1974, Kugel and coworkers started experiments on $F^{8+}(Z = 9)$ using an infrared gas laser to probe resonantly a beam of these excited hydrogenic ions.[4] Ion energies of 64 MeV were used, with resonance radiation provided by a pulsed hydrogen bromide chemical laser. A high-precision (1 percent) result was obtained by Doppler effect tuning made possible by varying the angle of the laser beam with respect to the high-velocity ion beam. Experiments on Cl^{16+} ions at 190 MeV were carried out at Brookhaven National Laboratory using discrete tuning of a high-power CO_2 laser to measure the Lamb shift to 0.5 percent precision.[5] In all cases studied so far, the QED theory prediction has been validated.

1.2 The Hydrogen Molecular Ion Hyperfine Structure

Another example of an experiment in fundamental physics is the research by K. B. Jefferts on the ionized hydrogen molecule H_2^+.

Jefferts was able to determine the hyperfine spectrum of the molecule and interpret it in terms of the prediction of exact quantum-mechanical calculation. In order to perform this experiment, Jefferts used time-varying electric and electromagnetic fields in a technique he had previously used at the University of Washington,[6] to form ion traps to prevent collision of the ions with container walls and to allow precision measurements of the radio frequency spectra. He first experimented with the simpler parahydrogen molecule ion having antiparallel protons. For this molecule the nuclear spin (I) is 0, and the electronic angular momentum is characterized by the quantum number $J = 0, 2, 4$, and so on. He then proceeded with the orthohydrogen molecule with parallel proton spins $(I = 1)$. The appropriate J values for the molecule are $J = 1, 3, 5$ and so on, resulting in a more complicated spectrum. In this ionized molecule, the complex interaction of the single electron with the nuclear spin and the various possible orbital momenta results in a spectrum of about 30 lines with frequencies ranging from 3 to 1410 megahertz (MHz).[7] [Fig. 6-1]

Jefferts' measurements and analysis marked the first understanding of the hyperfine structure of this simplest of all molecules. Prior to this, neither theoretical nor experimental determination of this basic molecular interaction had existed.

1.3 Optical Pumping of States with Nonzero Orbital Angular Momentum

In the early 1950s, A. Kastler of Ecole Normale Superiére proposed a method for producing orientation of atomic and nuclear angular momenta by illuminating atomic gases with polarized resonance radiation.[8] The absorption and subsequent emission of the radiation leaves the atoms in a nonequilibrium-oriented state; that is, specific atomic states receive excess population. When radio frequency and microwave radiation are applied to further perturb this excess population, the level structure of the atom can be determined. This data is used to determine nuclear spins, nuclear magnetic moments, electric quadrupole moments, and a host of important atomic parameters such as collision cross sections and excited-state lifetimes.

Early optical pumping experiments were done on states with zero orbital angular momentum, such as the $^1S_0$ ground states of the diamagnetic atoms mercury and chlorine or the $^2S_{1/2}$ ground states of the alkali atoms, which also have zero orbital angular momentum. In the late 1960s, H. M. Gibbs and coworkers at Bell Labs investigated optical pumping of two kinds of states with nonzero orbital angular momentum: the diamagnetic $^3P_0$ ground state of ^{207}Pb $(I = 1/2)$ and the paramagnetic P_J states of lead and thallium.[9] The objective was to determine whether any states of nonzero orbital angular momentum could exhibit long enough relaxation times, comparable to those in S states, to permit precision measurements. Gibbs found that the prob-

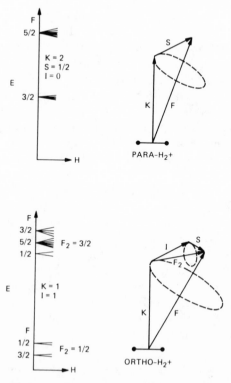

Fig. 6-1. Hyperfine energy levels and vector coupling schemes for the simplest molecule, H_2^+. In para-H_2^+, the nuclear spins of the two protons are antiparallel ($I = 0$); in ortho-H_2^+, the nuclear spins are parallel ($I = 1$). $K = 1$ and $K = 2$ refer to the rotational states of the molecule. S is the electron spin, and F is the total angular momentum. [Jefferts, *Phys. Rev. Lett.* **23** (1969): 1476].

ability for nuclear spin relaxation in a single-wall collision was low ($\leqslant 7$ percent), in sharp contrast with the alkali $^2S_{1/2}$ case where practically every collision completely disorients the electronic spin. This work demonstrated clearly that the nuclear orientation of an atom with nonzero orbital angular momentum, but with zero total angular momentum J, can relax very slowly. This slow relaxation is due to the short duration time of a collision compared with the period in the hyperfine frequency, even in a state with strong hyperfine coupling such as the $^3P_1$. In such cases, the well-established impact approximation predicts that I and J are decoupled during the collision; therefore, the nuclear orientation is unchanged since direct interactions with the nucleus are weak. With the attainment of long-lived nuclear polarization, it was possible to determine the nuclear moment of ^{207}Pb with high precision.

1.4 Radiation from Low-Energy, Ion-Atom, and Ion-Molecule Collisions

In 1968, N. H. Tolk initiated experimental investigations of low-energy (5 eV to 10 keV) ion-atom and ion-molecule collisions. His studies indicated that these collision processes can be very efficient in producing optical radiation arising from outer-shell electronic excitation of the colliding particles. These studies are of interest in understanding the atomic physics of high-altitude nuclear bursts and atmospheric reentry phenomena and have an impact on studies of auroral phenomena and on solar wind bombardment of comet gases. They also provide a fundamental insight into the detailed mechanism of the quasi-molecular collision process, where the particles are molecular entities for the duration of the collision but are not bound to each other.[10]

The results of these experiments contradicted a popularly accepted principle known as the "adiabatic criterion," which predicted a very low probability for the occurrence of inelastic collisions that would result in optical radiation.[11] Specifically, at low energies (defined as encompassing the energy threshold for the inelastic effect with an upper limit of a few tens of kilo-electronvolts), it was found that in many cases the absolute emission cross sections were as large as they had been measured to be at much higher energies. This implied a highly efficient mechanism for transferring the kinetic energy of the colliding heavy particles into internal electronic energy. In addition to the observation of a wealth of newly observed effects, in many instances there was found to be pronounced oscillatory structure in the emission cross sections measured as a function of ion-bombarding energy. In the early 1970s, Tolk and C. W. White at Bell Labs, in collaboration with S. H. Neff at Earlham College and W. Lichten at Yale University, observed strong optical polarization effects in low-energy Na^+-Ne collisions.[12] [Fig. 6-2]

These experimental results led to an explanation of low-energy, heavy particle collisions in terms of the quasi-molecule formed by the colliding particles during the collision. It was recognized that many quasi-molecular states may lead to the final atomic or ionic excited states involved in these collisions. If two or more of the molecular-state channels are assumed to lead to the same excited state, then the oscillations can be explained as arising from the quantum-mechanical phase interference between the two states. The existence of strong polarization effects constituted the first experimental observation of strong sublevel-state selection associated with collision quantum-mechanical phase-interference phenomena.[13]

1.5 Anticrossing Spectroscopy

In the mid-1970s T. A. Miller and R. S. Freund developed a spectroscopic method based upon energy level anticrossings to study

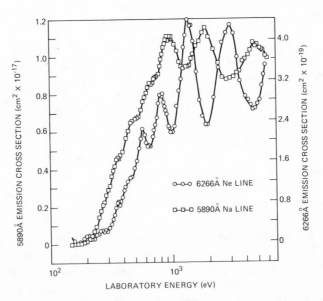

Fig. 6-2. Quantum-mechanical phase interference between coherently related matter waves. The variation of intensity of two spectral lines, arising from the collision of ionized sodium atoms (Na^+) on neutral helium gas, is shown as a function of the energy of the moving sodium ion. In the collision, a coherent superposition of quantum states occurs—the result of an exterial neon electron being associated with either an excited state of the sodium atom (rendering it neutral) or an excited state of neon. The upper levels of these excited states are near resonance, making possible quantum-mechanical phase interference. The phenomenon resembles the interference that occurs in R. A. Young's well-known two-slot experiment for electrons. [Tolk et al., *Phys. Rev.* **A13** (1976)].

interactions between singlet and triplet states of some of the simplest and, therefore, most fundamentally important atoms and molecules.[14] [Fig. 6-3] In this method the singlet and triplet levels are tuned toward one another by an external magnetic field. They would cross except that near the point of crossing, weak interactions mix their wavefunctions and each level becomes a mixture of singlet and triplet. Here the noncrossing rule of Wigner and von Neumann, one of the basic results of quantum mechanics, states that a pair of atomic or molecular energy levels cannot intersect or cross unless they are of completely different symmetry. Therefore, the levels repel each other when they approach as a function of a variable such as magnetic field. This behavior is called an avoided crossing or an anticrossing. The exact field of the anticrossing can be measured by monitoring the fluorescence emission intensities from either level as a function of magnetic field. This field, and a knowledge of the magnetic behavior of the energy levels, permit calculation of the zero-field separation of that pair of singlet and triplet levels.

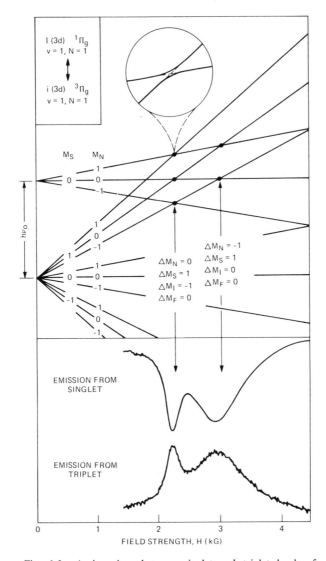

Fig. 6-3. Anticrossings between singlet and triplet levels of molecular deuterium. Within the circle at the top is a schematic illustration of an anticrossing, with the hypothetical energy levels in the absence of an interaction shown by dashed lines. The observed changes of visible light emission intensity are shown at the bottom. Their interpretation, in terms of energy levels and selection rules, is shown above. [Jost et al., *Chem. Phys. Lett.* **37**, (1976): 509].

Since singlet-triplet interactions are weakest when the nuclear charge is small, little was known about the strength of the interactions and the relative positions of the singlet and triplet energy levels in the simplest and most fundamental atoms and molecules. For example, although over 35,000 lines have been cataloged in the electronic spectrum of molecular H_2, not one of these lines is assigned to a singlet-triplet transition. Thus, while the energies of the various levels within the singlet or triplet manifold are known to an accuracy of 10^{-5} electronvolt (eV), the absolute energy of any triplet H_2 state with respect to the ground or any other singlet state was uncertain by over 10^{-2} eV. From experiments on several pairs of levels, Miller and Freund determined the absolute energies of all the triplet levels of H_2 with respect to the singlet states to an accuracy as good as the known levels within each manifold.

Besides determining the separation between singlet and triplet levels, the anticrossing technique also provided a unique method for measuring the strengths of the interactions between the singlet and triplet states. Numerous measurements of spin-orbit and hyperfine coupling constants of H_2 were made by this method. In addition to the results of H_2, anticrossing experiments have yielded similar information for singlet-triplet interactions in the helium atom and the D_2 molecules, and on double-quartet interactions in CN and O_2^+.

1.6 Laser Spectroscopy

During the 1960s and 1970s, the development of the laser into a readily available source of tunable narrow-band, powerful, coherent optical radiation resulted in a rebirth of optical atomic spectroscopy. The first demonstration of spectroscopy with tunable lasers was provided by C. K. N. Patel in 1963, when he measured the Doppler broadening and the atomic temperature of a xenon discharge using a xenon laser with a tuned frequency at 2.026 μm.[15] These seminal studies obtained a resolution of $1:10^8$. New methods of spectroscopy that were capable of revealing new information about atomic systems were developed in laboratories throughout the world.

1.6.1 Mechanism of Atomic Collisions in Helium-Neon Discharge

In 1971, P. W. Smith of Bell Labs collaborated with T. Hänsch of Stanford University on experiments investigating atomic collisions in helium-neon discharges.[16] These experiments were initially motivated by the desire to understand the helium-neon laser. In their experiment, two beams of light from a tunable laser pass in opposite directions through a sample discharge. The Doppler effect causes moving atoms to sense these two beams as having different optical frequencies. The atomic motion causes the atom to view the laser frequency as shifted from ω to $\omega(1 \pm v/c)$, where v is the atomic velocity along the beam and c is the speed of light. The plus sign is taken for one beam, while the minus is taken for the other counter-propagating beam. If the laser is tuned to the exact atomic resonance frequency of stationary atoms, atoms with zero longitudinal velocity will interact with both beams of light and the transmission of one beam will be modified by the other. If the laser is tuned away from exact resonance the Doppler shift will cause each beam to be resonant with a different velocity group of atoms and, hence, no transmission modification will result, unless collisions cause the atomic velocities to change. It was this sensitivity to atomic collisions that allowed the study of collisional processes within the discharge.

In 1980, P. F. Liao and J. E. Bjorkholm at Bell Labs, in collaboration with P. R. Berman of New York University, extended the techniques of atomic collision studies with lasers by using two different lasers.[17] One laser was used to pump only atoms with a specific velocity into an excited state. The second laser then probed transitions from that excited state to another state. If there were no collisions, tuning of the second laser would reveal a very narrow absorption line. Collisions caused the line to broaden, with a resulting shape that was determined by details of the collision process.

1.6.2 High-Resolution Spectroscopy

The ultrahigh frequency resolution available with stabilized lasers enabled accurate determination of many fundamental atomic parameters. As an example, the saturation spectroscopy techniques used by Smith and Hänsch in 1971 provided spectra whose linewidth was Doppler-free, because only the atoms with zero longitudinal velocity are observed in the absence of collisions. In 1972, a variant of this technique, called intermodulated fluorescence spectroscopy, was developed by M. S. Sorem and A. L. Schawlow at Stanford University.[18] In this technique, saturated absorption resonances are not monitored through changes in transmission, but by detecting changes in fluorescence. Furthermore, the two counter-propagating beams are modulated at different frequencies and only the component of the fluorescence that is modulated at either the sum or the difference frequency is recorded. In 1980 this technique was used by R. R. Freeman and coworkers to improve isotope shift measurement of the helium 2^3P-3^3D discharge by more than an order of magnitude.[19] They were also able to uncover details of hyperfine induced singlet-triplet mixing in ^3He.

Doppler-free two-photon spectroscopy was another technique developed in the 1970s. This technique, which is discussed in some detail in Section 6.1.1 of Chapter 5, allowed high-resolution studies of excited states such as the study of the $4f$ level in atomic sodium by Liao and Bjorkholm.[20]

The high optical power available made it possible to determine many new properties of very highly excited states, including states that lie near the ionization limit of an atom. Among these studies were the efforts of the group at M.I.T. headed by D. Kleppner to understand the effects of electric fields on highly excited states in atoms. At Bell Labs in 1978, Freeman and G. C. Bjorklund demonstrated the effects of electric fields on autoionizing states of multielectron atoms.[21] In 1979, Freeman and N. P. Economou discovered new electric-field-induced resonances in the normally featureless one-electron continuum above the ionization limit.[22] Similarly, the application of strong magnetic fields was found by Economou, Freeman, and Liao to produce structures in the continuum known as quasi-Landau levels.

1.6.3 Subpicosecond Molecular Spectroscopy

Early work in time-resolved spectroscopy of molecules used Nd:glass lasers that produced optical pulses in the 5 to 10 picosecond (ps) range. In 1974, the invention of the passively mode-locked dye laser by C. V. Shank and E. P. Ippen, [Fig. 6-4] and subsequent improvements, pushed the pulsewidth to 0.3 ps.[23] In 1981, R. L. Fork, B. I. Greene, and Shank were able to generate pulses as short as 90 femtoseconds (90×10^{-15}).[24] [Fig. 6-5]

The availability of continuous trains of subpicosecond optical pulses has opened up a new field of high-resolution, time-resolved

Fig. 6-4. C. V. Shank (left) and E. P. Ippen standing in front of their sub-picosecond dye laser.

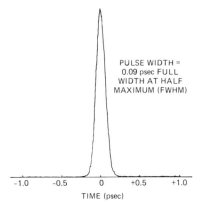

Fig. 6-5. Autocorrelation function of a 90-femtosecond (10^{-15} second) optical pulse. This is the first optical pulse ever generated and measured having a duration of less than 0.1 picosecond. [Fork, Greene, and Shank, *Appl. Phys. Lett.* **38** (1981): 672].

spectroscopy. These techniques have had an impact in solid state physics, chemistry, and biology, making it possible to obtain quantitative measurements instead of qualitative observations. Using these new techniques, the nonradiative relaxation rate in the molecule azulene was determined to be 1.9 ± 0.2 ps,[25] the first high-precision measurement for a very short life time associated with a nonlinear relaxation process. Further, the techniques have been applied to numerous molecular investigations, including rotational relaxation in the dye 3,3'-diethyloxadicarbocyanine-iodide (DODCI), picosecond photochemistry of bacteriorhodopsin, and measurements of time-resolved conformational dynamics in large molecules.

1.7 Opto-Acoustic Spectroscopy of Gases and Pollution Detection

In 1970, C. K. N. Patel and E. D. Shaw invented the spin-flip Raman laser (SFR laser), which provides tunable infrared radiation. (For more on this topic see Section 7.3 of Chapter 5.) The important characteristic of the tunable spin-flip Raman laser is its ability to produce higher power than any other tunable source known to date in the infrared spectrum, where most molecules have their fundamental absorption bands. The application of tunable lasers with a calorimetric absorption measurement technique has revolutionized the measurements of minute gaseous constituents. This work, first reported by L. B. Kreuzer and Patel,[26] relies upon the fact that in an absorption cell, the energy that is not transmitted because of absorption by the constituents is eventually converted into thermal energy. If the radiation going into the absorption cell is periodically interrupted, some energy is converted into sound that can easily be picked up using a sensitive microphone. This technique, called the spectrophone technique, was first demonstrated by Alexander Graham Bell,[27] J. Tyndall,[28] and W. C. Roentgen[29] toward the end of the 19th century. However, it took the discovery and invention of high-power tunable lasers for the technique to become a viable source of spectroscopy and a means of detecting extremely small concentrations of desired species. As in all calorimetric measurements, the sensitivity of this technique improves as the amount of available power increases. For the case of the spin-flip Raman laser, where continuous-wave power in excess of 1 watt is available between 5 and 7 μm, Patel showed that it is possible to detect nitric oxide pollution to a level of about 1×10^7 molecules per cubic centimeter (cc).[30] At atmospheric pressure this corresponds to a volumetric mixing ratio of 1 part in 10^{12}.

The spectrophone technique was first used in 1971 to measure nitric oxide in various samples, including ambient air samples collected in parking lots, near highways, and in the exhaust tailpipe of an automobile. This technique produces an output signal from the opto-acoustic cell that varies linearly with the concentration of the absorbing species over a very wide range. In the case of nitric oxide, this linearity has been shown to exist over a range from about 10^7 molecules per cc to about 10^{14} molecules per cc.[31] No other known measurement technique has this kind of linearity. The technique of using tunable laser radiation, together with the opto-acoustic detection technique, has wide applicability because all known polluting molecular gaseous species have absorptions in the infrared region of the spectrum.

Several important measurements of pollutants have been made with the opto-acoustic technique. In the early 1970s, Patel and his colleagues at Bell Labs and at Sandia Laboratories instrumented a balloon package with an SFR laser and opto-acoustic cell so that measurements of nitric oxide concentration could be made at an altitude of 28 kilometers.[32] [Fig. 6-6] This concentration is an important parameter because it is known that nitric oxide acts as a catalyst to destroy ozone. Ozone in the stratosphere serves as a protective filter that prevents harmful ultraviolet radiation from reaching the surface of the earth. The Bell Labs and Sandia Laboratories group measured not only the concentration of nitric oxide but also its evolution and decay caused by solar radiation (represented by the photon energy $h\nu$). The chemical reactions of interest are:

$$NO_2 + h\nu \rightarrow NO + O$$
$$NO_2 + O \rightarrow NO + O_2$$
$$NO + O_3 \rightarrow NO_2 + O_2$$

The measurements of the diurnal variation, together with the absolute concentration of nitric oxide, put the nitric oxide catalysis hypothesis on a firm observational basis.

Another application of opto-acoustic spectroscopy was the analysis of gases arising from the reduction of nitric oxide on platinum catalysts.[33] The gas concentrations and temperatures used in these laboratory measurements were similar to those that would be encountered in an automobile exhaust treatment catalyst. It was seen that under certain conditions high concentrations of hydrogen cyanide (HCN), approximately 700 parts per million, were being released. The toxicity of HCN is well known—its emission is clearly undesirable and potentially harmful. Subsequent studies by scientists from the Environmental Protection Agency confirmed these measurements. Thus, under certain conditions even automobiles with existing catalysts or future mandated catalysts could produce unacceptable concentrations of HCN.

II. PLASMA PHYSICS

A plasma is a collection of charged particles that are free to move either in response to mutual Coulomb interactions or in response to externally applied forces. One of the most striking characteristics of a plasma is the fact that the individual charged particles do not move independently, but owing to their mutual interactions, exhibit a wide range of collective motion. For example, as an ion moves in an ionized gas, a cloud of electrons moves with it to electrically shield the perturbation in the charge density. The radius of this shielding cloud of electrons is called the Debye length, λ_D. For the collection of charged particles to exhibit the collective behavior characteristic of a plasma, there must be many particles in a sphere with radius λ_D. The Debye length is proportional to the square root of the temperature of the plasma, and plasma temperatures can range from a few kelvin in solid state plasmas such as the electrons or holes in semiconductors, to 10^8K in the interior of stars or thermonuclear reactors. Plasma densities can also vary widely from values as low as 1 cm^{-3} to 10 cm^{-3} characteristic of interstellar plasmas, to densities approaching 10^{25} cm^{-3}, such as those predicted for small pellets of solid heated by intense laser light. Therefore, it is not surprising that plasmas are relevant to a wide range of physical phenomena.

2.1 Gas Discharges and the Arc Plasma

The earliest work in the area of plasma physics was related to the study of gas discharges. In the early 1920s, K. K. Darrow wrote a series of tutorial articles on "contemporary advances in physics," which were published in the *Bell System Technical Journal*. The fifth article in this series, published in 1925, was entitled "Electrical Phenomena in Gases."[34] As research on electron tubes progressed, high-frequency phenomena in discharges became more important. In 1932 and 1933 Darrow discussed these phenomena in a two-part article entitled "High Frequency Phenomena in Gases."[35]

2.1.1 Gas Discharge as a Circuit Element

In 1939, S. B. Ingram pointed out that the glow discharge initiated in a gas-filled tube by a cold cathode has a number of interesting and useful electrical properties.[36] For example, in contrast to the conven-

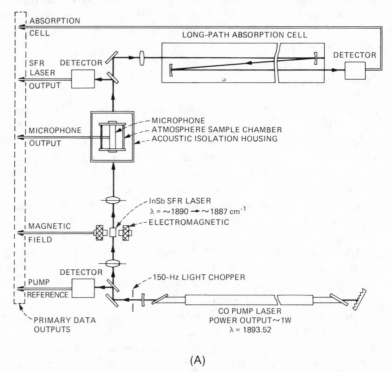

(A)

Fig. 6-6. (A) Schematic of the experimental setup used for spectroscopic determination of NO and H_2O in the stratosphere with a balloon-borne SFR laser. [C. K. N. Patel, *Optical and Quantum Electronics* **8** (1976): 147]. (B) Top: Relative output signal as a function of the SFR laser magnetic field for NO, taken before ultraviolet sunrise. The NO absorption signals are expected to occur at magnetic fields of 2545 and 2605 gauss. Calibration in equivalent NO molecules

tional vacuum-tube, the cold-cathode device can start immediately when a voltage is applied and does not deteriorate when used in standby service. In this device the background gas is ionized to produce a compensated plasma. Once this ionization (breakdown) is initiated, the tube voltage decreases and is nearly independent of the current through the device. Work on cold-cathode devices was continued in the 1940s,[37] and in the 1950s M. A. Townsend and W. A. Depp developed a cold-cathode relay suitable for telephone switching.[38] The resulting device used a hollow cathode because the geometry of a hollow cathode resulted in a low impedance circuit element particularly suited to switching applications. In 1958, A. D. White described an improved cathode geometry that maximized the cathode area.[39] The resulting hollow cathode tube produced a relatively uniform, high-density plasma. For switching purposes this relay (which was called the talking-path tube) provided a fast, low-impedance switch operable at a relatively low applied voltage. The talking-path tube was used as the basic switching element in the first field trial of an all-electronic switching office conducted in Morris,

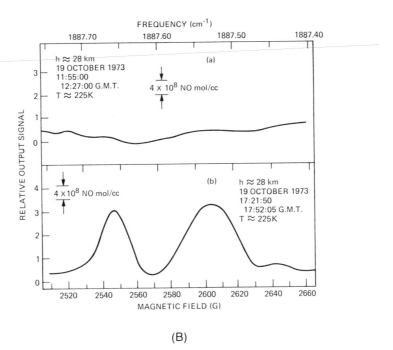

(B)

per cubic centimeter is given. Bottom: Relative output signal as a function of the SFR laser magnetic field for NO, taken after ultraviolet sunrise; NO absorption signals at magnetic fields of 2545 and 2605 gauss can be seen. Calibration in equivalent NO molecules per cubic centimeter is given, indicating an NO concentration of $(2 \pm 0.15) \times 10^9$ mol/cc. [Patel, Burkhardt, and Lambert, *Science* **184** (1974)].

Illinois, from 1960 to 1962.[40] However, an analysis of the data from this test determined that a mechanical device, the relay, offered superior reliability and use of the talking-path tube was discontinued.[41]

2.1.2 The Nature and Motion of Plasma Particles

In 1946 Bell Labs initiated investigations into fundamental processes in gas discharges. Some years before, R. W. Engstrom and W. S. Huxford at Northeastern University had observed that the pulsed operation of a Townsend discharge could be used to separate various ionization processes occurring in the discharge.[42] The Townsend discharge is a discharge in a low-pressure gas where the current is controlled by varying the flux of electrons emitted from the cathode.[43] In 1948, R. R. Newton at Bell Labs extended the theoretical analysis of such a discharge to show that, with increased time resolution, the measurements could be used to study specific processes such as ion-induced electron emission.[44] During the same period, J. A. Hornbeck carried out experimental studies of these relatively rapid phenomena,[45] while J. P. Molnar concentrated on slower processes in the discharge which, for example, involve metastable atoms and molecules.[46] They were able to identify specific ionic reactions and to measure electron and ion mobilities, the cross sections for the reaction of excited-state and ground-state atoms, and the lifetimes of metastable states.

Hornbeck provided precise measurements of the mobility of ions in rare gases (for example, helium, neon, and argon).[47] His studies covered a sufficiently large range of electric fields to enable him to examine changes in the mobility in the regime where the energy gained by ions between collisions is comparable to, or larger than, the thermal energy of neutral atoms in the background gas. This problem was considered from a theoretical viewpoint in a series of papers by G. H. Wannier.[48] He performed detailed computer calculations and obtained excellent agreement with the experimental mobility measurements over a wide range of applied electric fields. [Fig. -6-7] In addition to this, Wannier calculated detailed, three-dimensional, ion velocity distributions that provided great insight into the effect of the electric field on the ions in this nonlinear regime.

Hornbeck and Molnar discovered that molecular ions were a very important ion species in discharges in the rare gases.[49] They identified a process for the formation of these ions (now referred to as the Hornbeck-Molnar process), which can be written

$$X + X^* \rightarrow X_2^+ + e^-$$

where X^* denotes a rare gas atom in an excited electronic state. R. N. Varney extended the mobility measurements made by Hornbeck to

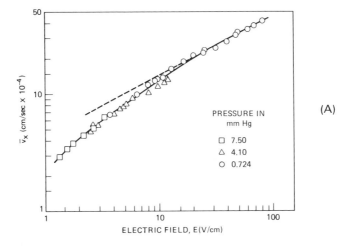

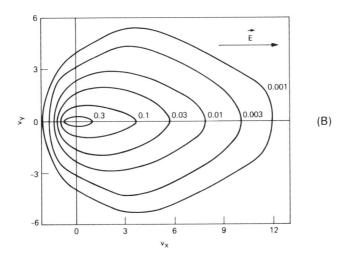

Fig. 6-7. (A). Drift velocity in an electric field of Ne^+ ions in neon gas. Comparison of observed results with an "asymptotic" straight line of slope ½. (B). Velocity distribution function of ions moving through the parent gas in a high field. [Wannier, *Bell System Tech. J.* **32** (1953): 190, 216].

measure the mobilities of krypton and xenon and the molecular ions of nitrogen and oxygen, and in 1954 he extended the analysis of the pulsed discharge.[50] In addition, Varney measured the activation energies for reactions involving molecular ions by studying the temperature dependence of the time-resolved currents.

K. B. McAfee used the pulsed-discharge technique to study the process of electron capture by neutral SF_6 molecules, and discovered that

SF$_6$ had an extremely large electron-capture cross section.[51] He found that the cross section for collision of these negative ions with neutral atoms was very large in SF$_6$ relative to that found for negative ions in other gases. A. J. Ahearn and N. B. Hannay studied the electron capture process in low-pressure SF$_6$ gas using a mass spectrometer.[52] The practical consequence was that it was very difficult to initiate a discharge in SF$_6$, and this gas became widely used in high-voltage engineering applications to prevent electrical breakdown.

Later, McAfee and D. Edelson were the first to install a mass-analyzer *in situ* in a plasma discharge to study the ions directly. Subsequent studies by McAfee and coworkers focused on more complicated reactions of ions and molecules that are important in plasma chemistry. For example, Edelson, J. A. Morrison, and McAfee considered the time-dependent diffusion in a discharge of multi-ion species.[53]

2.1.3 Breakdown Phenomena and the Plasma Arc

Plasma phenomena frequently occur even in mechanical switches, usually with deleterious results. Arcing in switches and relays has been a fundamental problem in the telephone system since the beginning of the industry. Consequently, the arc plasma has been the focus of considerable research activity at Bell Labs. From a plasma physics point of view, the arc plasma is a relatively dense and long-lived laboratory plasma of considerable interest and importance. In the arc plasma, ions can originate *from* the electrodes, as opposed to the Townsend discharge where ions originate from neutral gas atoms in the space *between* the electrodes. From a practical viewpoint, the erosion of material from electrical contacts and contact melting are phenomena to be avoided if at all possible. Prior to the late 1940s it was believed that an arc in air can exist only when the potential between the electrodes is of the order of 300 volts. Yet in telephone relays, discharges appeared to erode electrical contacts operating at a potential difference of only 48 volts. Some work at the turn of the century had indicated that low voltage arcs were possible, but this was somehow disregarded by workers in the field. Bell Labs researchers, motivated by problems concerning the erosion of electrical contacts, came to understand the physics of the low-voltage arc in detail. A crucial feature of these discharges is the fact that upon closure of a pair of contacts, a discharge occurs only when the electrodes are closer than a few thousand angstroms.

In 1948, L. H. Germer and F. E. Haworth studied the low-voltage discharge between close electrodes. They hypothesized that because the discharge occurs on a very short time scale, field emission might initiate the discharge but another process must be involved in the intense and rapid ejection of electrons.[54] Newton correctly explained this process as field emission assisted by the presence of individual positive ions close to the cathode.[55] J. J. Lander and Germer wrote the first of a series of papers on the erosion of electrical contacts in an arc. They found that these processes are related to the power dissipation at the metal surface that causes evaporation and melting.[56] In 1955, ion-assisted field emission was studied further by W. S. Boyle and P. P. Kisliuk,[57] and in 1956 the transition from a glow discharge to arc plasma was studied in detail by Boyle and Haworth.[58] These studies achieved a quantitative understanding of the arcing phenomenon. Germer and Boyle showed that two distinct types of arc are possible depending on the surface conditions of the electrodes.[59] [Fig. 6-8] Field emission and ohmic heating can lead to cathode erosion in the cathode arc. However, if the cathode surface is sufficiently smooth, the anode melts before appreciable cathode erosion, and in this case, material from both the cathode and anode can contribute to the discharge.

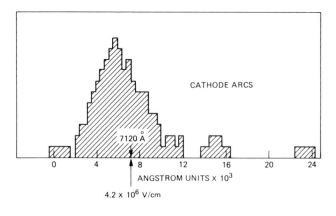

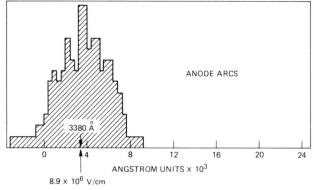

Fig. 6-8. Striking distances between palladium electrodes at 300 volts for arcs of the anode and cathode types. [Germer and Boyle, *J. Appl. Phys.* **27** (1956): 36].

The process of breakdown between close electrodes was studied further by Kisliuk and Germer in 1959. Germer showed experimentally that the number of ions involved was small enough to eliminate the possibility that the field of many ions together was important in enhancing electron emission.[60] This work was, in fact, a final confirmation of the single-ion model proposed by Newton a decade earlier. Kisliuk predicted theoretically that the ion-enhanced field emission would be important in breakdown in gases, liquids, and solids, but would not be effective in vacuum.[61] Because of the ion's relatively high velocity, it spends too little time close to the surface to enhance the field emission significantly in a vacuum.

Breakdown in gases with ac fields differs significantly from that observed when dc electric fields are applied. In 1955 D. J. Rose at Bell Labs and S. C. Brown at M.I.T. studied microwave breakdown in N_2, O_2, and air.[62] They were able to make a quantitative model of the observed phenomena and relate them to previous observations with dc fields.

2.2 The Collective Modes of Plasmas

2.2.1 Collective Modes of Ionized Gases and Electron Beams

The pioneering experiments on gas discharges conducted at the General Electric Company in the 1920s, and at Bell Laboratories in the 1930s and 1940s led to many basic discoveries concerning collective modes in plasmas. This research was motivated by interest in the discharge phenomena that occurred in the early electron tubes. The study of noise in these tubes and the quest for higher oscillating frequencies led to the study of a wide range of plasma phenomena which, for example, limit the power output and frequency response of the electron tube.

It was I. Langmuir at General Electric who, in 1928, coined the work "plasma" in the context used here. He showed that the approach of electrons to a Maxwellian velocity distribution depends on collective plasma modes,[63] and, with L. Tonks, he identified the two basic collective modes of oscillation of an unmagnetized plasma.[64] These modes are the electron plasma oscillation, with the frequency $\omega_{pe}/2\pi$ proportional to the square root of the electron density, and the ion acoustic wave, which is a type of sound wave where the pressure is mediated by the Coulomb force. The ion acoustic wave has a frequency $\omega_a/2\pi$ which is proportional to the wave vector K of the wave ($K = 2\pi/\lambda$) and to the square root of the electron temperature. As discussed below, these two collective modes are important to both linear and nonlinear phenomena in plasmas.

As mentioned above, the earliest considerations of plasma phenomena at Bell Laboratories were related to electron tubes. In

1934, G. L. Pearson discussed the effect of space-charge fluctuations associated with positive ions on vacuum tube noise,[65] and in 1938, A. J. Rack studied the effect of space charge and transit time on tube noise.[66] In 1939, F. B. Llewellyn and A. E. Bowen studied methods of producing high-frequency signals in electron tubes,[67] and in the same year J. R. Pierce discussed the effects of space charge in the design of intense electron beams.[68] In 1943, Llewellyn and L. C. Peterson wrote down the frequency-dependent equations that describe accurately the electron stream in a diode.[69] However, the final spark for much technological development and plasma physics discoveries was the invention in 1946 by R. Kompfner, who was then at Oxford University, of a new type of high-frequency amplifier called the traveling wave tube (TWT).[70]

Pierce immediately realized that the TWT had great potential as a broad-band amplifier.[71] In the course of analyzing and improving the basic design of the TWT, several important discoveries of significance to plasma physics were made. The collective modes of oscillation of the electron beam traveling along the axis of a helix are essential in the TWT geometry. The helical, slow-wave structure provides a way of phase matching electromagnetic radiation to these collective beam modes. Pierce's analysis of the TWT started with a detailed consideration of the collective modes of the electron beam.[72] [Fig. 6-9] His analysis of the coupled electron-beam, slow-wave structure problem included a component of the wave traveling anti-parallel to the direction of the beam propagation. This mode is the fundamental constituent of the "backward-wave, voltage-tuneable oscillator" developed by Kompfner and N. T. Williams.[73] Also included in these analyses were the situations where the beam travels through a background of positive ions, [74] where there are multiple electron streams,[75] and where the beam has a velocity spread, that is, a "finite temperature beam."[76] (For more on Pierce's work see the chapter on vacuum tube electronics in the forthcoming volume on communications science research.)

More than a decade later collective modes in strongly magnetized plasmas were studied in considerable detail by S. J. Buchsbaum. In 1961, he studied the absorption of radio-frequency radiation near the ion-cyclotron resonance frequency.[77] The ion cyclotron frequency, $\omega_{ci}/2\pi$, is the frequency of oscillation of a charged particle in the direction perpendicular to an applied magnetic field. In Buchsbaum's experiments on plasmas with more than one ion species, as the plasma density was increased the collective behavior shifted from the individual ion resonances to the hybrid, ion-ion resonance frequency that depends on the masses of all of the ions in the plasma. These results have been applied to the interpretation of heating fusion plasmas with radio-frequency waves near the ion-cyclotron frequency. The fact that the absorption of radiation may be controlled by the

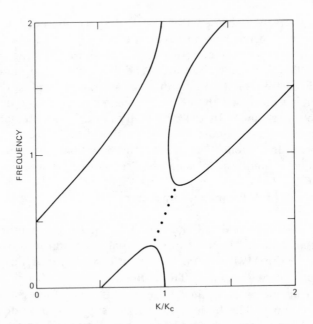

Fig. 6-9. Possible modes of oscillation of an electron beam coupled to a slow-wave circuit structure—the helix in a traveling wave tube. This calculation was one of the first analyses of the nonlinear interaction of modes in a plasma. Here K is the wave vector, which is inversely proportional to the wavelength ($K = 2\pi/\lambda$), and K_c ($2\pi/\lambda_c$) is the wave vector of an electromagnetic wave propagating down the slow wave structure in the absence of an electron beam. The frequency unit is the electron-beam velocity divided by the circuit wavelength. The dotted line represents two modes—one increasing in amplitude and one damped in space. The growing mode produces the microwave power in the traveling wave tube circuit. This type of calculation—one of the first analyses of the nonlinear interaction of modes in a plasma— has become a cornerstone of modern plasma physics.

relative concentration of various ion species may prove to be of significant practical value in heating fusion plasmas.

In 1964, Buchsbaum and A. Hasegawa [Fig. 6-10] found a series of narrow microwave absorption peaks near harmonics of the electron-cyclotron frequency.[78] They identified these absorption peaks as long-itudinal plasma oscillations propagating perpendicular to the magnetic field. The Buchsbaum-Hasegawa resonances, as they became called, are dependent upon the density gradients in the plasma and propagate, for example, near the axis of cylindrical arc discharges. They are closely related to the modes in a uniform plasma predicted theoretically by I. B. Bernstein and provide the first experimental observation of this rather general class of waves.[79] A similar micro-scopic wave that exists in the central region of a hot plasma was

Fig. 6-10. S. J. Buchsbaum (left) and A. Hasegawa identified the longitudinal modes of oscillation of an inhomogeneous magnetized plasma now known as the "Buchsbaum-Hasegawa resonances." Buchsbaum also developed theories of cyclotron resonance in plasmas containing multiple ion species and the propagation of waves in solid-state plasmas. He has held various technical leadership positions at Bell Labs and became executive vice president in 1980. Hasegawa has made many other fundamental contributions to plasma physics, including the development of the theory of Alfvén waves in a hot plasma and nonlinear theories of waves in magnetized plasmas.

described theoretically by Hasegawa and L. Chen in 1975.[80] This "kinetic Alfvén wave" is the analog in a hot plasma of the familiar Alfvén wave (which is a wave in a cold magnetized plasma named after the Swedish Nobel laureate H. Alfvén).[81] Since the kinetic Alfvén wave has a component of electric field parallel to the magnetic field, it is very effective in heating the plasma particles.[82]

2.2.2 Wave Damping and "Pseudowaves"

Another facet of wave propagation in plasmas is the mechanism for wave damping. L. D. Landau of the Soviet Union proposed a mechanism for wave damping in a collisionless plasma that involves the interaction of the wave with a group of ions or electrons moving with velocities nearly equal to the wave-phase velocity.[83] In 1981, P. M. Platzman and Buchsbaum included the effects of collisions in the theory of electron Landau damping and showed that the wave damping depends critically on the collisions of electrons trapped in the potential troughs of the wave.[84] Their paper was the first discussion of the importance of particles trapped in waves on wave damping—a subject that became recognized as central to many phenomena in plasma physics.

Because of the long-range nature of the Coulomb force, a type of sound wave called the ion-acoustic wave can propagate even in a collisionless plasma. G. M. Sessler and G. A. Pearson at Bell Labs studied ion-acoustic waves in weakly ionized plasmas with electron temperatures much larger than ion temperatures.[85] They found that in this case, the wave damping is predominantly caused by collisions of ions with neutral atoms. They also discovered that another disturbance propagates in the plasma with a phase velocity near the velocity of the ion-acoustic wave. However, in contrast to the ion-acoustic wave, this mode can exist at frequencies *above* the ion-plasma frequency. This disturbance, now known as the *pseudowave*, is the ballistic motion of groups of ions that was predicted in the second half of Landau's paper on damping. Pseudowaves are important because they damp more slowly than do ordinary waves generated in the plasma. The role of the Landau damping and collisional effects at the transition frequency from the collisional to the collisionless ion-acoustic wave was later studied theoretically by T. Huang, Chen, and Hasegawa.[86]

2.2.3 *Collective Modes of Solid-State Plasmas*

The charge carriers in semiconductors and metals, the electrons and holes, can act collectively in a manner similar to that of the electrons and ions in gas plasmas. This collective behavior has been the subject of numerous experiments designed both to study the nature of the collective modes in "solid-state plasmas" and to use these modes as tools to investigate other properties of semiconductors and metals.

There are many similarities between plasmas in solids and in gases, but there are also distinct differences. Plasmas in solids can be created with sufficiently high densities and at sufficiently low temperatures, T, that the quantum nature of the system is important. By the Pauli exclusion principle, each identical electron or hole must occupy a distinct state in phase space. When the plasma density is made high enough, the last occupied states must have a Fermi energy, E_f, which can be large compared with the thermal energy, kT. In this case, only particles in the range of energies, E, such that $|E-E_f| \lesssim kT$ play a role in the transport properties of the system, since only these particles can be thermally excited. The resulting quantum plasmas can exhibit many interesting and important phenomena. Another difference between gaseous and solid-state plasmas arises from the presence of the lattice in the solid. The interaction between the electrons and holes and the lattice is usually quite strong. Consequently, the collective modes are frequently heavily damped, and the plasma is nearly in equilibrium with the lattice even in the presence of external driving forces.

The collective nature of solid-state plasmas was first observed experimentally by Boyle, A. D. Brailsford, and J. K. Galt in 1958.[87] In studying the magneto-optical properties of bismuth at liquid-helium temperatures, they observed changes of the reflection coefficient of the solid. Reasoning by analogy with the case of a plasma in zero magnetic field, they interpreted these changes as evidence for the excitation of collective modes. In 1959, Galt and coworkers provided additional evidence that the regions of strong absorption between cyclotron harmonics could not be explained by the single-particle behavior of the charge carriers.[88] These features were interpreted in 1961 by Buchsbaum and Galt to be caused by the excitation of Alfvén waves.[89] They also pointed out that, because of the relatively high plasma densities achievable in solid state plasmas, the phase velocity of Alfvén waves is small compared to the speed of light; consequently, a sample of modest size can be many wavelengths across. Therefore, Alfvén waves could be studied more conveniently in solid state plasmas than in gas plasmas. G. A. Williams and G. E. Smith subsequently investigated in detail the propagation of Alfvén waves in bismuth.[90]

Another collective plasma mode is the helicon. This wave was first discovered in radio research, where it was called the *whistler wave,* named for the characteristic sounds that whistler waves (excited by lightning strokes) make when detected by a radio receiver. The helicon is a circularly polarized electromagnetic wave that can propagate at frequencies $\omega \ll \omega_{ce}$ through a plasma even when ω is smaller than the plasma frequency ω_{pe}. In this wave, the electric field vector rotates in the same direction in which the electrons spiral around the magnetic field lines. The transverse electron motion then produces an effective dielectric constant, which is of opposite sign to that of the dielectric constant without a magnetic field, and consequently, electromagnetic wave propagation is permitted. The existence of this mode in solid-state plasmas was pointed out by O. V. Konstantinov and V. I. Perel[91] and by P. Aigrain,[92] and it was first observed experimentally in metallic sodium by R. Bowers, C. Legendy, and F. Rose at Cornell University.[93]

At Bell Labs, helicons were studied experimentally in silver by C. C. Grimes, G. Adams, and P. H. Schmidt[94] and discussed theoretically by Buchsbaum and P. A. Wolff.[95] By varying the orientation of the magnetic field with respect to some crystal axis, they were able to pass from a regime of essentially single-particle behavior to propagating helicon waves, and finally to a nearly compensated situation (that is, equal numbers of electrons and holes), supporting rather heavily damped Alfvén waves. A unified analysis, tying together both the cyclotron resonances of the individual carriers and the plasma-like variations in the dielectric response of the solid near the plasma

hybrid resonances, was achieved for bismuth by Smith, L. C. Hebel, and Buchsbaum.[96] Later, Grimes and Buchsbaum studied the interaction between helicon waves and transverse sound waves in potassium.[97] The damping of helicon waves in metals can be used to study properties of the Fermi surface, since the condition for Landau damping involves the momentum associated with the Fermi energy. A. Libchaber and Grimes studied the damping of helicon waves in potassium.[98] [Fig. 6-11] D. J. Bartelink[99] and C. Nanney[100] discussed the

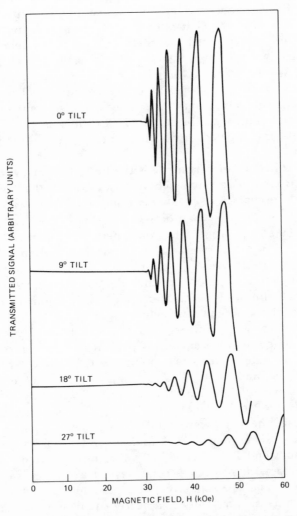

Fig. 6-11. Series of traces showing how Landau damping attenuates the transmitted signal as the angle between the field and the propagation direction increases. [Libchaber and Grimes, *Phys. Rev.* **178** (1969): 1150].

effects of electrical currents on Alfvén and helicon waves in solid state plasmas at current values below the threshold for instability.

In 1965, W. M. Walsh and Platzman discovered a set of linearly polarized waves propagating perpendicular to the applied magnetic field at frequencies between the electron cyclotron harmonics.[101] These waves are analogous to the Bernstein waves in gaseous plasmas[102] that had been observed in an inhomogeneous plasma by Buchsbaum and Hasegawa.[103] They have a short wavelength (as compared, for example, to Alfvén or helicon waves) and were shown in solid state plasmas to depend on correlations of electron motion.[104]

Platzman, Wolff, and N. Tzoar considered the scattering of light from collective modes (for example, Bernstein waves) in solid state plasmas.[105] C. K. N. Patel and R. E. Slusher studied these collective modes in plasmas in InAs[106] and GaAs.[107]

S. Schultz and G. Dunnifer at the University of California at La Jolla observed another plasma mode in sodium and potassium.[108] These data were first interpreted by Platzman and Wolff, who showed that the new mode arises both from the quantum nature of the plasma and from the exchange interaction between electron spins.[109] Study of this "spin wave" allowed a sensitive test of theories of interacting quantum liquids. T. M. Rice calculated parameters appropriate to sodium and potassium from Landau's theory of Fermi liquids and obtained excellent agreement with the experimental results.[110] These experiments and calculations for the spin waves in potassium and sodium provide a very important part of our understanding of charged quantum liquids.

2.3 Plasma Instabilities

2.3.1 Electron and Ion Beam Instabilities

In some plasma systems the available energy drives collective plasma modes to instability. One example is the traveling wave tube, (TWT) where energy in the electron beam drives a mode on the beam to large amplitudes while simultaneously coupling energy to an electromagnetic mode on the slow-wave structure surrounding the beam. However, in the late 1940s the traveling wave tubes had sufficiently poor vacuum so that there were always positive ions present, forming an electron-ion plasma and creating a source of noise. In studying this noise, J. R. Pierce discovered the electron-ion, two-stream instability.[111] In this instability, beam energy is used to excite ion-acoustic waves (that is, sound waves in the plasma) at frequencies below the ion-plasma frequency. In other areas of plasma physics this instability has turned out to be very useful. For example, when excited to high levels, the ion waves can scatter the electrons in the beam. This leads to a greatly enhanced electrical resistivity. Because of this effect, the electron-ion two-stream instability became recognized as an effective method of plasma heating.

Another geometry of the electron beam that Pierce considered in detail was the "double-stream amplifier" where two beams of electrons travel along the same axis (for example, a hollow beam surrounding a solid beam) with different beam velocities.[112] The function of the helical structure in the TWT is replaced by the second beam, which can also support a slow electromagnetic wave. This was the first consideration of the electron-electron two-stream instability, which is also recognized to be important in many situations in plasma physics. In Pierce's early work on electron beams in the presence of background ions, he discovered a very low-frequency instability that can limit the maximum electron-beam current.[113] This instability, which is known as the Pierce instability, has been recognized to be important in connection with nonlinear plasma excitations called double layers.[114]

Other aspects of beam instabilities, such as the effect of a finite-temperature electron beam and the interaction of the nearly resonant particles with a wave, were studied during this period. The latter is the situation that is now referred to as Landau damping, but was studied independently of Landau's work in the 1940s and early 1950s by Bell Labs scientists.

In 1951, S. Millman, in the course of developing an amplifier at a frequency of 50 gigahertz (GHz), identified a new wave in the TWT.[115] He observed spurious oscillations in the tube under certain operating conditions. Measuring the wavelength of these oscillations as a function of tube voltage, Millman showed that they were caused by waves traveling in the direction *opposite* to that of the electron beam. These *backward waves* on the electron beam were actually included in Pierce's analysis of the TWT but were not appreciated at the time. In 1952, Kompfner and N. T. Williams designed the voltage-tuneable backward-wave oscillator based on this collective mode of the electron beam.[116] The backward wave oscillator is a case of an "absolute instability," which grows simultaneously at all points in space. This is in contrast to the case of the TWT, which is an example of a "convective instability" (growing from a particular point in space). The distinction between convective and absolute instabilities is another important result that has had many applications in plasma physics. A detailed analysis of the problem of the electron beam coupled to a periodic structure with particular emphasis on the case of the backward wave oscillator was made by L. R. Walker at Bell Labs in 1953.[117]

Walker was also the first to write down the general condition for the stability of the collective modes of an arbitrary distribution of plasma particles.[118] This condition is frequently referred to as the "Penrose criterion," after O. Penrose who rederived it several years after Walker. [119] This analysis can be applied to an arbitrary velocity distribution to give qualitative insight into the problem without detailed calculations. For this reason it is useful in the analysis of a great number of plasma problems.

Work on electron beams continued at Bell Labs into the late 1950s. The quest for higher-power electron beams led to the discovery and study of instabilities in the important case of a magnetic field parallel to the direction of propagation of the beam. In the case of a mono-energetic ("zero temperature") electron beam, there exists a self-consistent steady-state solution that is referred to as Brillouin flow. Generalizations of Brillouin flow were discussed by Walker.[120] He also treated the problem of energy storage and power flow in electron beams.[121] Other electron-beam phenomena were discussed by C. C. Cutler,[122] W. W. Rigrod,[123] Rigrod and Pierce,[124] and A. Ashkin.[125]

The case of the three-dimensional ion-acoustic instability driven by the flow of electrons in a plasma was studied by Slusher, C. M. Surko, and D. R. Moler in collaboration with M. Porkolab at the Princeton Plasma Physics Laboratory.[126] [Fig. 6-12] They developed small-angle CO_2 laser scattering techniques to study the wave vector and frequency spectra of density fluctuation phenomena in plasmas.[127] They applied these techniques to measure the wave vector distribution of the ion-acoustic fluctuations as a function of electron current in order to understand the nonlinear mechanisms involved in determining the saturated state of the instability.

In addition to *electron* beams and currents, ion beams can also generate plasma instabilities. R. P. H. Chang[128] and H. Ikezi at Bell Labs, with collaborators from Princeton University, studied the excitation of the lower hybrid wave (having a frequency close to the ion plasma frequency) by an ion beam.[129] In a related set of experiments, R. A. Stern, in collaboration with scientists from the University of California at Irvine,[130] and Ikezi in collaboration with a group at Princeton University,[131] studied the excitation of the electrostatic ion cyclotron instability by an ion beam. Stern and J. A. Johnson at Rutgers University developed a diagnostic technique using a laser to resonantly excite the fluorescence of ions in a plasma.[132] The ion fluorescence radiation is spread in frequency by Doppler shifts caused by the ion motions and is therefore a measure of the ion velocity distribution. This technique was used to study the spatial distribution of ion heating caused by the ion-beam induced instability. These ion-beam instabilities may play important roles in heating fusion plasmas. In particular, there is evidence that these instabilities are created when "neutral beams" (that is, neutralized ion beams) are used to heat fusion plasmas.

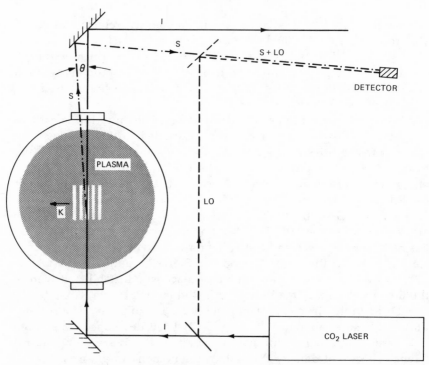

Fig. 6-12. Optical arrangement used by Slusher and Surko to study waves and fluctuations in plasmas. The waves of interest typically have wavelengths (λ) in the range of a few millimeters corresponding to wavevectors K ($K = 2\pi/\lambda$) near 20 cm^{-1}. The techniques used to study small scattering angles ($\theta \sim 0.1°$) permit the study of a wide range of wavelengths with only a small angular access to the plasma. The scattered radiation (S) is heterodyne-detected using a reference local oscillator beam (LO). This detection method permits the study of very small perturbations in plasma density ($\sim 10^7$ electrons/cm^3). These techniques were applied to a wide range of plasma problems (See references 126, 127 and 160).

2.3.2 *Parametric Decay*

The parametric process is a nonlinear coupling between three waves with frequencies f_1, f_2, and f_3 such that

$$f_1 = f_2 + f_3.$$

For example, by modulating an electron beam at frequency f_0, a wave at $f_0/2$ can be amplified with the power supplied at f_0. Shortly after H. Suhl proposed the first parametric amplifier using a ferromagnetic sample in a microwave cavity,[133] T. J. Bridges,[134] and W. H. Louisell and C. F. Quate[135] discussed the use of the modes on an electron beam to amplify microwave-frequency signals. Parametric processes have been found to be very important in plasma physics and have been studied in a wide range of situations. J. M. Manley and H. E. Rowe recorded the general relationships that govern parametric processes.[136] These equations, now known as the "Manley-Rowe relations," have had many applications to nonlinear plasma processes.

In 1966, Stern and Tzoar performed the first experiments to study parametric processes in a compensated plasma.[137] They injected microwaves into a plasma to excite an electron-plasma wave and an ion-acoustic wave. They also demonstrated that a plasma wave could be excited by two microwave signals whose frequency difference was that of the plasma wave.[138] In 1969, Stern studied another parametric process where a microwave signal decays into two lower-hybrid waves.[139]

Later, Chang at Bell Labs, in collaboration with Porkolab and M. Ono at the Princeton Plasma Physics Laboratory, studied the parametric decay of radiation near the ion cyclotron frequency in plasmas with more than one ion species.[140] They found that the electromagnetic radiation can decay into the ion-ion hybrid mode (which had been discovered previously by Buchsbaum), and a lower-frequency drift wave. This process may be important in situations where plasmas are heated using power near the ion-cyclotron frequency.

The parametric decay processes of modes *in* the plasma are also important. Chang and Porkolab showed that a lower-hybrid wave excited in the plasma can decay into another lower-hybrid wave and either an ion quasi-mode (an over-damped ion-acoustic acoustic wave) or a nonoscillatory mode near zero frequency.[141,142] They also observed heating of the particles in the plasma as a result of these parametric instabilities, which again may play an important role in the heating of fusion plasmas. The theory of plasma heating by nonlinear excitation of the lower-hybrid waves was studied by Hasegawa and Chen.[143] Hasegawa studied the decay of a plasma wave (that is, a Langmuir wave) into two electromagnetic waves,[144] and Hasegawa and Chen[145] showed that the decay of the kinetic Alfvén wave can be important in plasma heating.

Parametric decay processes are also important in the nonlinear development of plasma instabilities. Stern, J. F. Decker, and Platzman studied the decay of modes excited in a plasma by an ion beam.[146] Ikezi, Chang, and Stern studied the nonlinear wave interaction between electron-plasma waves (excited by an electron beam) and ion-acoustic waves.[147] They observed that the electron-plasma wave is trapped in a wave packet of ion-acoustic modes.

An important application of the parametric decay instabilities is the free electron laser that utilizes the stimulated Raman or Compton scattering from a relativistic electron beam to up-shift the radiation from a lower-frequency laser beam.[148] In this application, Hasegawa and coworkers showed theoretically that the limitation in the laser gain is caused by heating the electron beam by a large pump field, and they obtained the condition for the optimization of the gain.[149]

2.3.3 The Disruptive Instability in Tokamaks

The tokamak is a prototype fusion device that uses a toroidally shaped magnetic field configuration to contain a hot plasma. In the tokamak, a current induced in the plasma both stabilizes and heats the plasma. In general, this device has been quite successful in achieving hot, dense, well-contained plasmas. However, some regions of density and plasma current have been unachievable because of the appearance of an instability of the plasma called the "disruptive instability." This instability can cause the plasma to strike the wall of the containing vessel. H. Ikezi and K. F. Schwartzenegger at Bell Labs, in collaboration with S. Yoshikawa at Princeton University, have developed a new magnetic field design for the tokamak.[150] They invented a winding that looks like a zipper, which, when placed on the outer major radius side of the plasma, helps to stabilize and control it. This design appears to be particularly useful in studying and controlling the disruptive instability.

2.3.4 Instabilities in Solid-State Plasmas

Instabilities have also been created and studied in a number of solid-state plasmas where the collective modes are excited by electrical currents in the plasma. Buchsbaum, A. G. Chynoweth, and W. L. Feldmann observed the generation of microwave radiation when electric and magnetic fields were applied to a plasma in InSb.[151] Similar phenomena in BiSb alloys were later studied by C. A. Nanney at Bell Labs and E. V. George at M.I.T.[152] D. J. Bartelink studied instabilities created in bismuth plasmas, including those involving helicon and Alfvén waves.[153] He found that both "convective" instabilities (that is, growing in space) and "absolute" instabilities (growing in time at all points in space) could be generated in these plasmas.

2.4 Highly Nonlinear Plasma States

2.4.1 Plasma Turbulence

Plasma turbulence is a relatively common phenomenon that, in general, is not well understood. Several problems in plasma turbulence of practical significance have been considered at Bell Labs. Upon re-entering the atmosphere, satellites and missiles generate a turbulent plasma, an area studied as part of the National Defense research conducted in the 1960s. D. S. Bugnolo studied theoretically the turbulence in weakly ionized gases characteristic of the wakes of reentry vehicles.[154] He considered the nature of the fluctuations, the effect of velocity shear on these fluctuations, and the effects of anisotropies in the velocity distribution of the plasma particles. He also considered the problem of an electrical breakdown in a flowing gas.[155] V. L. Granatstein,[156] and Granatstein, Buchsbaum, and Bugnolo,[157] studied experimentally the resulting neutral and plasma density fluctuations when a plasma is present in a turbulent neutral gas flow. They found that if the plasma electrons are not in thermal equilibrium with the neutral gas, differences between the neutral fluid turbulence and the plasma turbulence can result. Finally, K. B. McAfee and R. M. Lum studied cesium plasmas in the wakes of spheres entering the earth's atmosphere.[158]

In a fully ionized plasma, C. N. Judice, J. F. Decker, and Stern studied theoretically and experimentally the highly nonlinear evolution of large-amplitude, ion-acoustic waves.[159] [Fig. 6-13] They found that the waves first steepen to form shock fronts at the leading edges of the waves. These shocks then drive ions ahead of the shock, which in turn generates short-wavelength, ion-acoustic wave turbulence through the ion-ion two-stream instability. As time progresses, the orderly motion of the ions in response to the potential of the long-wavelength, ion-acoustic wave is rapidly converted to very short-wavelength and highly turbulent fluctuations.

Using small-angle CO_2 laser scattering techniques, Surko and Slusher studied the turbulent low-frequency density fluctuations driven in tokamak plasmas by the energy associated with temperature and density gradients in the plasma.[160] The plasma in a tokamak is relatively stable and long-lived, and is therefore convenient for the study of many collective plasma phenomena, in addition to having considerable practical importance as a prototype fusion device. Surko and Slusher showed that the fluctuations in tokamaks form a nearly isotropic two-dimensional turbulence in the plane perpendicular to the toroidal magnetic field. This turbulence is thought to play an important role in particle and energy transport across the magnetic field (that is, out of the tokamak's "magnetic bottle"). Hasegawa and K. Mima considered this turbulence theoretically and pointed out important nonlinear terms that determine the spectra of the fluctuations.[161] The nonlinear equations that they used to describe the turbulence are now known as the Hasegawa-Mima equations and are closely related to those used to study atmospheric turbulence.

Later, Slusher and Surko developed a technique to study the spatial distribution of fluctuations in plasmas by correlating the forward scattering from two crossed CO_2 laser beams.[162] Using this technique, they showed that the fluctuations in tokamaks have a marked dependence on plasma density. The fluctuations are very large at the edge of high density tokamak plasmas, and may have physical consequences for transport and plasma heating.

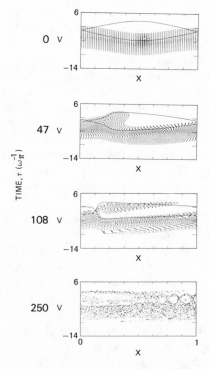

Fig. 6-13. The evolution of a one-dimensional plasma turbulence from a large-amplitude, coherent wave is studied using a computer simulation (see reference 159). The distribution of ions in position x and velocity v is shown at four different times τ (in units of ω_π^{-1}) in response to the potential of a long-wavelength, ion acoustic wave. At $\tau = 47$, a shock front begins to develop near $x=0.4$. Later, at $\tau = 108$, an ion beam can be seen near $v=3$, which was driven by the potential of the shock. Finally, this ion beam generates a short-wavelength, ion acoustic turbulence as shown in the figure at $\tau = 250$.

2.4.2 Solitons

A nonlinear interaction of waves in the plasma does not necessarily lead to plasma turbulence. In fact, it sometimes leads to a *coherent* nonlinear state. In 1965, N. J. Zabusky at Bell Labs and M. D. Kruskal at Princeton University showed that elastic waves with a cubic non-linearity form a set of isolated nonlinear waves that are stable even with respect to collisions among themselves.[163] Zabusky and Kruskal named these waves "solitons." The nonlinear properties of soliton propagation are characteristic of a wide range of phenomena including shallow water waves, waves in plasmas, and phonons in anharmonic crystals. [Fig. 6-14]

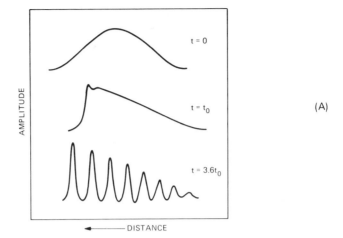

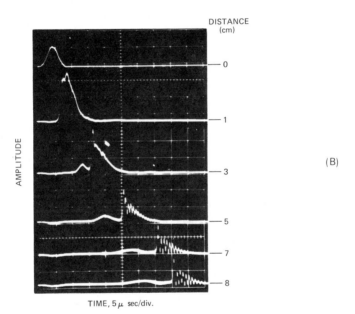

Fig. 6-14. (A) The evolution of a large-amplitude disturbance in a system with a non-linear coupling is shown as a function of distance and time, t (from the theoretical work of Zabusky and Kruskal, Reference 163). The pulse first steepens to form a shock front and then evolves into a train of solitons. Solitons, once formed, tend to propagate without distortion. In fact, Zabusky and Kruskal showed that solitons can actually propagate through one another (i.e., "collide") and still retain their identity. (B) The experimental evolution of an ion-acoustic disturbance in a plasma into a train of ion-acoustic soliton pulses is shown as a function of time at various distances from the source (from the work of Ikezi and collaborators, Reference 164). The agreement with the predictions of Zabusky and Kruskal is remarkably good. These experiments also verified that solitons maintain their identity after undergoing collisions with one another.

Ion-acoustic wave solitons were observed and studied in a double plasma (DP) device (consisting of two plasmas at different potentials separated by a grid) by H. Ikezi, R. J. Taylor, and D. R. Baker at the University of California at Los Angeles.[164] A similar DP machine was used at Bell Labs by Stern and Decker,[165] and by Judice, Decker, and Stern,[166] to study a wide variety of related nonlinear phenomena. In the case of the large-amplitude, ion-acoustic waves, solitons were observed to form behind the sharply steepened wavefronts.

Hasegawa and coworkers obtained solitary-wave solutions of the electron plasma wave in both two and three dimensions,[167] and Hasegawa and Mima showed that the kinetic Alfvén wave can form an exact solitary wave.[168]

In a nonlinear and strongly dispersive medium, the envelope of a continuous train of waves can also become a soliton. Such localized waves are often called envelope solitons. They can result from the modulational instability, which is an instability in the amplitude modulation of a plane wave in a nonlinear dispersive medium. Using theory and computer experiment, Hasegawa showed that a cyclotron wave propagating in the direction of a magnetic field develops a modulational instability.[169] Hasegawa and M. Kato demonstrated that the ion-acoustic wave is also modulationally unstable if (and only if) the modulation is applied in a direction oblique to the direction of the wave propagation.[170] The behavior of amplitude modulation on the ion-acoustic waves was studied experimentally by Ikezi, Schwartzenegger, and A. L. Simons of Bell Labs and coworkers at Nagoya University, Japan. The ion waves were found to be modulationally stable if the modulation is applied in the direction of the wave propagation.[171] In 1975, Hasegawa showed theoretically that an envelope of random phase waves can become a soliton, but unlike the case of an envelope of a single wave, it can have an arbitrary shape.[172]

III. MOLECULAR BIOPHYSICS

The emerging molecular approach to the study of fundamental biological processes showed that it might be possible for physicists to contribute to the understanding of some of these processes in a quantitative way. This possibility induced many physicists during the 1960s and 1970s to undertake research in the exciting new field of molecular biophysics. In the early 1960s several physicists at Bell Labs became interested in applying the approaches and techniques of solid state physics to studies of biological molecules. In these studies it was necessary to match the techniques to problems very carefully so that physical certainty was retained in the complicated biological systems.

The early interest in biological research was activated in 1961 by a report of an unexplained electron spin resonance (ESR) signal from deoxyribonucleic acid (DNA) at laboratories in the Soviet Union. After studying the ESR properties of DNA at Bell Labs, it was concluded that the signal was caused by a ferromagnetic resonance arising from an iron-oxide impurity, and that DNA itself was *not* ferromagnetic.[173]

3.1 Nuclear Magnetic Relaxation of Water Protons in DNA

It had been proposed that many biological processes produced unpaired electrons, or free radicals. W. E. Blumberg, who had been studying nuclear relaxation in solids, designed an apparatus to measure the spin lattice relaxation times of the nuclear spins of water protons in solutions of biological samples. Blumberg's purpose was to detect free radicals formed during biological processes such as cell division.[174] However, no effects that could be assigned to such free radicals were observed. The same apparatus was used in a subsequent series of experiments in which paramagnetic metal ions were introduced into water solutions of biological molecules, in particular DNA. The idea was to study the metal-ion binding because it was expected that binding to the DNA would shield the paramagnetic ion from the water molecules. If this occurred, the large magnetic moments of the paramagnetic electrons would not induce nuclear spin-flips of the water protons in DNA as efficiently as in water solution. Surprisingly, the paramagnetic ions were *more* effective in inducing transition of the water protons when the metal was bound to DNA. This "nuclear relaxation enhancement" was explained and developed at Bell Labs by J. Eisinger, R. G. Shulman, and Blumberg,[175] and later by others elsewhere,[176] as a useful probe of the structure of biological molecules.

By this time it was clear to the scientists involved that it was possible to make simple and interpretable physical measurements on large and complex biological molecules. The philosophy that soon developed among the Bell Labs workers was to use the biomolecules in experiments and to use simpler molecules only as models in experiments suggested by initial studies with the biomolecules. In this way the scientist is in a better position to devise methods and obtain data that are useful from the biological point of view.

3.2 Optical Studies of DNA and Other Molecules

Irradiation of DNA with ultraviolet light at low temperature was shown to result in the formation of a free radical.[177] Determination of the hyperfine interaction of the radical from its ESR spectrum eventually led to its identification by Eisinger, Shulman, and their collabora-

tors as the hydrogen atom adduct of thymine.[178] [Fig. 6-15] In order
to understand the path by which the radiation produced the free radical, an investigation of the electronically excited states of DNA and
its constituents was initiated, first at low temperatures and afterward
at room temperature.[179] A first-order picture of electronic relaxation,
energy transfer, and the mechanisms of the photochemical processes
emerged. On the basis of these studies it was realized that it was possible to introduce electronic excitation selectively into the thymine
bases by a sensitization technique.[180] [Sensitization means that the
energy ($h\nu$) absorbed by a sensitizer molecule is passed on to another
molecule, which then may fluoresce or undergo photochemical reaction.] The consequence of this is the formation of a single stable photoproduct in the DNA, a dimer formed by two adjacent thymines.
Subsequent chemical studies on the thymine dimer showed that it
could be formed with 100-percent quantum efficiency by light at
2800Å and broken with 100-percent efficiency by light at 2400Å.[181]
These two different states of the thymine dimer had different absorption spectra, which could be identified by the difference in the
dispersion of light in the visible region. This led to the suggestion
that analogous photodimers could be used as materials for optical
memory devices.[182]

Fig. 6-15. R. G. Shulman (left) and J. Eisinger discuss damage centers in DNA induced
by ultraviolet radiation. They are standing in front of a model of the DNA double helix.

In a biological application of the sensitization technique, a way to sensitize DNA in a bacteriophage was developed.[183] It was shown that the thymine dimer is virtually the only stable photoproduct formed in a bacteriophage under these conditions. This made it possible to study the lethal and mutagenic effects of a particular change in the DNA introduced by radiation with light and helped to sort out the effects of the several other changes introduced by direct irradiation of the DNA.[184]

In addition to the use of the most advanced physical techniques developed elsewhere, new approaches and techniques for studying biomolecules were developed at Bell Labs. One useful technique for determining distances between certain groups in biological molecules involved the measurement of the efficiency of electronic energy transfer between absorbing and emitting centers. In the 1970s, such an energy transfer approach was combined with fluorescence polarization measurements. A complete mathematical analysis demonstrated that the combined approach allows much more accurate determination of the molecular distances.[185]

3.3 Physical Transport of Biomolecules

Biochemists had been using electrophoresis for many years to separate electrically charged biomolecules on the basis of their different mobilities in an electric field. Eisinger and Blumberg realized that these molecules would obey the differential equations of motion, including interactions between molecules of different kinds, just as the various carriers in a semiconductor would drift and interact. They showed that the interactions among the molecules could be determined if the concentration profiles of the various molecules present were measured at time zero and after a known time under an electric field.[186] This technique has been used to measure interactions among many different types of biomolecules—for example, the transfer ribonucleic acids (RNAs), one kind of molecule participating in protein synthesis.[187]

3.4 Nuclear Magnetic Resonance

3.4.1 Nuclear Magnetic Resonance of Proteins and Nucleic Acids

In the late 1960s, emphasis in magnetic resonance studies shifted to high-resolution nuclear magnetic resonance (NMR) studies of protons and ^{13}C in large biological molecules. The motions of most proteins are rapid enough so that it is possible to get reasonably narrow, resolved lines in their NMR spectra at the high magnetic fields available from superconducting solenoids. Fourier transform techniques resulted in increased sensitivity, so that with the current NMR equipment resonances from single nuclei in large molecules (molecular weight up to 65,000) could be observed, resolved, and identified. At the time of this writing, the emphasis of the NMR work has been on the structure of biological molecules in solution under conditions where they are functional. In this way the clearest picture of the relationship between structure and function can be achieved.

D. J. Patel pointed out that certain hydrogen-bonded protons could be easily and selectively studied by NMR because a hydrogen bond shifts the proton resonance to lower fields, resolving it from the resonances caused by the majority of the protons. Furthermore, the slow exchange rate in and out of the hydrogen bond enables the resonances to be distinguished from those of the solvent and to be identified by exchanging them with deuterons in D_2O.[188] Hydrogen bonding makes a major contribution to the three-dimensional structure of biomolecules, especially nucleic acids, and the NMR method has revealed the kinetics of molecular motion.[189]

The NMR spectrum of a large macromolecule such as DNA in solution is very complex and unresolved because molecular tumbling is so slow that motional narrowing is not achieved as it is for the relatively small molecules found in drugs. Patel exploited this difference to study the binding of drugs to DNA.[190] In this way, he was able to explain the mechanism of action of a number of antibiotic and carcinostatic drugs that inhibit DNA transcription.[191]

Considerable attention has been paid to hemoglobin, where NMR and kinetic experiments have been combined to determine the mechanism responsible for the cooperative oxygenation in that molecule. In these experiments the NMR spectra were used to characterize the three-dimensional state of the molecules in solution. The kinetics of oxygen binding showed that when the state changed so did the oxygen affinity. The hypothesis of the so-called two-state allosteric mechanism was shown to be a good approximation of the behavior of the biomolecule. The extensive literature on hemoglobin was analyzed and shown to be consistent with this hypothesis.[192] The idea that one hypothesis could explain data from diverse sources, familiar to physicists, had been a novelty in biochemistry.

3.4.2 Nuclear Magnetic Resonance of Biomolecules in Vivo

The advent of spectrometers with high sensitivity and large sample volumes made it possible to detect continuously resonances from a variety of low molecular weight intracellular metabolites in suspension of living cells and perfused intact organs. Previously, measurements of metabolite concentrations required destruction of the cells. The earlier studies by J. M. Salhany and coworkers concentrated on ^{31}P, with a nuclear spin of ½, a 100-percent natural molecule of considerable biological importance.[193] They studied correlations between the state of energization of bacterial cells, as reflected in the levels of adenosine tri-phosphate (ATP), which could be clearly seen in the ^{31}P NMR spectra, and the difference in pH between the inside and the outside of the cell that could be obtained from the pH dependence of the chemical shift of inorganic phosphate. This correlation is the basis of biological energy use, because in many cases ATP is derived from the proton gradient across the cell.

Building on this earlier work, T. R. Brown and coworkers used the techniques of double-resonance NMR to measure enzymatic rates *in vivo*. These techniques rely on the fact that a nuclear spin will "remember" a perturbation for a time on the order of its spin-lattice relaxation time. Thus, if the spin states of a particular species are saturated while they are also chemically exchanging with another species, the second species will show a reduced magnetization if the chemical exchange rate is comparable to the spin-lattice relaxation rate. The exchange rate can be obtained by measuring the magnetization reduction and the spin-lattice relaxation time. Applying these techniques to a suspension of the bacterium *Escherichia coli*, Brown, K. Ugurbil, and Shulman were able to measure the synthesis rate of ATP in *E. coli* while the cells were respiring. This was the first time that a unidirectional enzymatic rate had been measured in a living system. In the late 1970s, Brown and collaborators at Oxford University used these techniques to study enzymatic rates in perfused muscles and hearts.[194] These experiments revealed that the function and activity of the enzyme creatine phosphokinase in these systems was considerably more complex than previously thought.

In addition to the NMR work with ^{31}P, Bell Labs scientists pioneered in the use of compounds in which ^{13}C has been incorporated at known locations to study *in vivo* metabolism of cells and organs. Realizing that inserting a chemical label into a molecule, which would later be catabolized by the cell, would provide a vast amount of information on the rate processes that occur *in vivo*, Ugurbil and coworkers studied the uptake and metabolism of ^{13}C-labelled glucose in *E. coli*.[195] [Fig. 6-16] They were able to measure the reaction rates of several enzymes caused by the movement of the ^{13}C label in the glucose that had been fed to the cells but which was observed at the C6 position in several intermediate metabolites. Additional studies on rat liver cells,[196] yeast,[197] and on whole perfused mouse liver,[198] have demonstrated the large amounts of information on metabolic rates and pathways that can be acquired by this technique in short periods of time.

3.5 Paramagnetic Resonance in Metalloenzymes

In a parallel fashion, Blumberg and J. Peisach advanced EPR studies of the paramagnetic ions such as copper and iron in metalloenzymes to the point where the data could be interpreted in terms of the electronic state of the ion, and translated into the chemical structure at

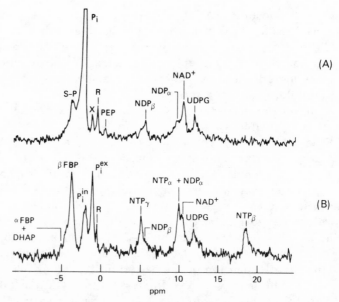

Fig. 6-16. Phosphorus-31 NMR spectra at 145.7 MH$_z$ of an anaerobic *E. coli* suspension containing approximately 5×10^{11} cells per milliliter (A) before and (B) 4 to 6 minutes after glucose addition. ppm is the departure, in parts-per-million, from the true value of the nuclear magnetic moment of ^{31}P. Each spectrum was the sum of 400 scans with a repetition time of 0.34 second and a 45-degree radio-frequency pulse. Abbreviations: $S-P$, sugar phosphates; P_i, inorganic phosphate; P_i^{ex}, P_i^{in}, external and internal P_i, respectively; *PEP*, phosphoenolpyruvate; *NOP*, nucleotide diphosphate; NAD^+, nicotinamide adenine dinucleotide; *UDPG*, uridine diphosphate glucose; *FBP*, fructose 1,6-biphosphate; *DHAP*, dihydroxyacetone phosphate; *NTP*, nucleotide triphosphate. *R* is the reference signal from 0.1 percent orthophosphoric acid in 0.1-mole HCl; *X* is unassigned. [Shulman et al., *Science* **205** (1979): 161; adapted from Ugurbil et al., *Proc. Natl. Acad. Sci. U.S.A.* **75** (1978): 2244].

the ion site. The systematics of the approach have elucidated the relationships between structure around the iron proteins.[199] Using a method of classification of the EPR spectra of copper developed by Peisach and Blumberg,[200] unknown metal-ligand atoms can sometimes be identified in copper-containing proteins.

3.6 Translation of the Genetic Code

One of the most puzzling questions in biological information retrieval has been the mechanisms by which the genetic code is translated from the DNA to proteins. J. J. Hopfield proposed a kinetic proofreading mechanism that uses the energy obtained by splitting adenosine triphosphate (ATP), a small molecule commonly used for biological energy storage, to enable the protein synthesis enzymes to read the amino acid selected for a second time. Essentially, this uses the free energy obtained from splitting ATP to reduce the entropy of the system. This would give a rejection ratio for the incorrect amino acid approaching the initial rejection ratio squared. T. Yamane and Hopfield tested this hypothesis on several systems, and the results strongly support the proposed mechanism.[201] It is important to note that this hypothesis, which has generally been accepted, postulates a novel role for the high-energy bond of ATP, in that it is no longer split just to create another unstable bond in a coupled reaction. In addition it points out that nature's way of retrieving information stored in the gene is novel, rapid, and efficient.

3.7 Extended X-Ray Absorption Spectroscopy in Biomolecules

In the mid-1970s Shulman and Blumberg became interested in applying the newly developed technique of extended X-ray absorption spectroscopy (see section 2.3 of Chapter 8) to biological molecules such as rubredoxin and hemoglobin. G. S. Brown and P. Eisenberger, together with a group from the University of California at Berkeley, developed the fluorescence detection approach and applied it to absorption spectroscopy.[202] By the end of 1975, a whole new apparatus had been constructed for this detection approach. With this development, the technique of absorption spectroscopy could be applied to dilute biological systems. Work on rubredoxin by Shulman, Eisenberger, and Blumberg initially started by using the transmission detection approach.[203] The technique was extended to greater accuracy with the help of Brown, B. M. Kincaid, and B. K. Teo, and the utilization of the fluorescence detection approach.[204] It was found that contrary to proposed explanation by early X-ray crystallography, no short iron-sulfur bond in rubredoxin exists. Subsequent X-ray crystallography work confirmed the X-ray absorption results.

Eisenberger and coworkers studied the cooperative process of oxygen binding in blood.[205] They found that the change in oxygen affinity responsible for the cooperative oxygen binding process was not due solely to local structural changes around the iron porphyrin site. They suggested that the mechanism for the cooperative process was more complicated and delocalized than was thought to be the case on the basis of previous work.

L. Powers, Eisenberger, and J. Stamatoff used the focused X-ray beam line, together with a newly developed focusing X-ray fluorescence detector, to study very dilute biological systems.[206] Their measurements of calcium proteins and calcium ions in membranes indicated changes in coordination and bond length as the concentration of ions was varied.

3.8 Fluorometric Screening Test for Lead Poisoning

The development of an instrument that permits rapid screening of populations at risk for lead poisoning parallels the long-standing interest at Bell Labs in ways to inhibit photodegradation and oxidation of polymers in telephone-cable sheathing. (For more on this topic, see Chapter 14, section 3.1.) Research scientists became interested in how living organisms are protected from sunlight damage. This led them to investigate the heightened sunlight sensitivity associated with protoporphyria, one variety of a family of human genetic diseases.

Heme iron complex of protoporphyrin is a constituent of many important proteins and enzymes found in the body. For example, heme is the key constituent of hemoglobin, the oxygen-carrying red-colored component of blood, and provides the center of reaction of molecular oxygen in all higher organisms. In patients with protoporphyria there is a deficiency in the activity of the enzyme that catalyzes the insertion of iron into protoporphyrin and protoporphyrin accumulates in the red cells in excessive amounts.[207] This free protoporphyrin leaks from the red cells, and some of it diffuses to the skin and causes photosensitivity in the patients by allowing oxygen to react in an uncontrolled way. It can be observed in the blood because it is strongly fluorescent. Heme, because of the iron, is neither fluorescent nor is it a photosensitizer.

It was reported that patients with severe lead poisoning have as much protoporphyrin in their blood as do patients with protoporphyria.[208] But intriguingly, there is no photosensitivity associated with lead poisoning. Investigation of the nature of fluorescence exhibited by porphyrins in the blood of porphyrics and of lead-intoxicated patients led A. A. Lamola and Yamane to discover that the porphyrin accumulating in the blood of a lead-poisoned person was, in fact, zinc protoporphyrin and not metal-free porphyrin.[209] In contrast to free protoporphyrin, the zinc protoporphyrin persists in the red cells for their entire life span, about four months.[210] It does not diffuse to the skin and, therefore, does not lead to photosensitivity. Zinc protoporphyrin, unlike heme, fluoresces in the red region of the spectrum when excited by blue light. This permits fluorometry, with its inherent high sensitivity, to be used as a measure of the concentration of zinc protoporphyrin in the blood. It was quickly demonstrated that the blood-zinc protoporphyrin level was well correlated with the lead level in a population of children.[211]

Optical emission spectroscopy in the laboratory has been an extremely useful tool in uncovering the differences between the porphyrins and their binding sites in red blood cells. However, commercial fluorometers generally require that the blood be diluted until a negligible fraction of the exciting light is absorbed in the sample. In order to avoid this dilution step, which is difficult to perform accurately in a non-laboratory situation, Lamola, Eisinger, and Blumberg decided to excite a drop of whole blood placed on a thin glass slide from underneath and to measure the red fluorescence emitted from the same side of the slide—a technique known as frontface fluorescence. [Fig. 6-17] An automated instrument called the hematofluorometer was developed by Blumberg, Eisinger, Lamola, and D. M. Zuckerman using this technique.[212] The instrument is relatively inexpensive, requires only one small drop of untreated blood, and is readily portable. Its operation is very simple, and it presents the answer in any desired units, such as micrograms of zinc protoporphyrin per gram of hemoglobin.

Although a way to assay blood protoporphyrin in small samples had been worked out in New York City by S. Piomelli,[213] the method developed by the Bell Labs group was even more specific, simpler,

Fig. 6-17. A. A. Lamola operating the original hematofluorometer used to detect lead poisoning by examination of a drop of blood.

and less expensive, since it required no chemical manipulation of the sample. The simple and portable instrument for on-the-spot testing obviates the need for expensive and inefficient follow-up procedures. [Fig. 6-18]

The hematofluorometer has been recommended by the Department of Health, Education, and Welfare for use in childhood lead poisoning screening programs and in the Early and Periodic Screening, Diagnostic, and Treatment Program.[214] The hematofluorometer has also been approved by the Occupational Safety and Health Administration for monitoring undue lead absorption in workers occupationally exposed to lead.[215] As of the summer of 1980, more than 800 hematofluorometers were in use in public health agencies, hospital clinics, and industrial hygiene departments. These instruments were manufactured by several instrument companies licensed by the Bell System at no cost. Bell Labs provided technical information and assistance to these companies in the public interest.

Using the hematofluorometer, the Bell Labs group took part in epidemiological studies of lead intoxication in occupationally exposed groups carried out with the Environmental Sciences Laboratory of the Mount Sinai School of Medicine in New York. It was established that the concentration of zinc protoporphyrin in blood is a much better indicator of chronic lead intoxication than is the concentration of lead

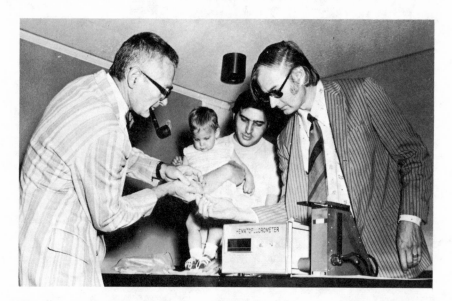

Fig. 6-18. The portable testing device for lead poisoning developed by Bell Labs scientists, shown being demonstrated at a Massachusetts Governor's Conference on childhood lead paint poisoning. Dr. R. Klein, left, director of the state's childhood lead poisoning prevention program, tests an infant while her father and Bell Labs' W. E. Blumberg, right, one of the developers of the testing equipment, look on.

in the blood.[216] Thus, the hematofluorometer test is directly related to the actual health of a patient. Ominously, the epidemiological study also demonstrated that the central nervous system is affected by lead intoxication at levels not very much higher than the average level attained by city dwellers in the U.S.[217]

At the time of this writing, the hematofluorometer is in use within the Bell System, where more than 40,000 employees work with lead—for example, in soldering and in replacing and reclaiming old lead-sheathed cable. Because of the accuracy of the hematofluorometer even at low zinc protoporphyrin levels, it was shown that the average lead absorption by solderers in a Western Electric plant was no higher than a control group of nonsolderers and lower than the average city dweller, a testimony to the effective industrial hygiene practices of the Bell System.[218]

3.8.1 Application to Management of Neonatal Jaundice

A hematofluorometer based on the principles discussed in the previous section and capable of assessing the status of newborn infants with neonatal jaundice was in the final stages of successful clinical testing in the early 1980s.

Bilirubin, the natural breakdown product of heme, is a potent central nervous system poison. In adults, it is transported to the liver where it is detoxified and prepared for excretion into the bile. Not present in the fetus, this detoxifying system is induced after birth. Because of either or both a delay in the induction of detoxification and an excessive production of bilirubin due, for example, to Rh factor difficulties, there is often a transient rise in the serum. This leads to a yellow coloration of the skin known as jaundice. If enough bilirubin enters the central nervous system, irreversible brain damage occurs. Neonatal jaundice is the most common problem encountered in the newborn nursery, the main concern being the proper assessment of risk for brain damage so that appropriate preventive therapy can be applied. Because the risk for bilirubin-associated brain damage is not simply related to the serum bilirubin level, therapeutic indication in neonatal jaundice is often complicated.[219]

In a series of papers, Lamola and coworkers demonstrated that some relatively simple fluorimetric measurements made on very small specimens of whole blood reveal much information concerning the risk for bilirubin-associated brain damage in a neonate.[220-223] Blumberg, Lamola, and Zuckerman developed a microprocessor-controlled hematofluorometer for simple automated testing of blood specimens from neonates. Using this instrument, less than 0.2 cc of whole blood and a few minutes of operator time is required, making the protocol useful directly in the intensive care nursery around the clock. While other approaches to blood tests aimed at assessing brain damage risk have been developed over the years none has been adopted for routine use because all of them are technically complicated or require large volumes of blood.

The technology for the bilirubin hematofluorometer was made available to instrument manufacturers so that the medical benefit of this advance could be expedited.

REFERENCES

1. W. E. Lamb, Jr. and R. C. Retherford, "Fine Structure of the Hydrogen Atom, Part I," *Phys. Rev.* **79** (August 1950), pp. 549-572.

2. M. Leventhal and P. E. Havey, "Precision Lamb-Shift Measurement in the $n = 2$ State of $^6Li^{2+}$," *Phys. Rev. Lett.* **32** (April 15, 1974), pp. 808-811.

3. D. E. Murnick, M. Leventhal, and H. W. Kugel, "Determination of the Hydrogenic-Carbon Lamb Shift via $2S_{1/2}$ Metastable Quenching," *Phys. Rev. Lett.* **27** (December 13, 1971), pp. 1625-1628.

4. H. W. Kugel, M. Leventhal, D. E. Murnick, C. K. N. Patel, and O. R. Wood, "Infrared-X-Ray Double Resonance Study of $2P_{3/2}-2S_{1/2}$ Splitting in Hydrogenic Flourine," *Phys. Rev. Lett.* **35** (September 8, 1975), pp. 647-650.

5. O. R. Wood, C. K. N. Patel, D. E. Murnick, E. T. Nelson, M. Leventhal, H. W. Kugel, and Y. Niv, "Lamb Shift Studies of Cl^{16+}," *Laser Spectroscopy V*, ed. A. R. W. McKeller, T. Oka, B. F. Stoicheff (Berlin: Springer-Verlag, 1981), pp. 45-48.

6. H. G. Dehmelt and K. B. Jefferts, "Alignment of the H_2^+ Molecular Ion by Selective Photodissociation. I," *Phys. Rev.* **125** (February 1962), pp. 1318-1322.

7. K. B. Jefferts, "Hyperfine Structure in the Molecular Ion H_2^+," *Phys. Rev. Lett.* **23** (December 29, 1969), pp. 1476-1478.

8. A. Kastler, "Some Suggestions Concerning the Production and Detection by Optical Means of Inequalities in the Populations of Levels of Spatial Quantization in Atoms. Application to the Stern and Gerlach and Magnetic Resonance Experiments," *J. Phys. Radium* **11** (June 1950), pp. 255-265.

9. H. M. Gibbs, B. Chang, and R. C. Greenhow, "Optical Orientation of the $^3P_0$ Ground State of Pb^{207}," *Phys. Rev. Lett.* **22** (February 17, 1969), pp. 270-272; idem, "Polarization of Pb Vapor. I. Orientation of the $^3P_0$ Ground State of Pb^{207}," *Phys. Rev.* **188** (December 1969), pp. 172-179; H. M. Gibbs and C. M. White, "Polarization of Pb Vapor. II. Disorientation of the Pb^{207} Ground State and $\mu_I(Pb^{207})/\mu_I$ (Hg^{199})," *Phys. Rev.* **188** (December 1969), pp. 180-187.

10. N. H. Tolk, C. W. White, S. H. Dworetsky, and L. A. Farrow, "Quantum-Mechanical Phase-Interference Effects in Low-Energy He^+Ne and Ne^+-He Inelastic Collisions," *Phys. Rev. Lett.* **25** (November 2, 1970), pp. 1251-1254.

11. J. B. Hasted, *Physics of Atomic Collisions* (London: Butterworth's Scientific Publications, Ltd., 1964), pp. 420-423.

12. N. H. Tolk, C. W. White, S. H. Neff, and W. Lichten, "Strong Optical Polarization Effects in Radiation from Low-Energy Na^+-Ne Collisions," *Phys. Rev. Lett.* **31** (September 10, 1973), pp. 671-674.

13. N. H. Tolk, J. C. Tully, C. W. White, J. Kraus, A. A. Monge, D. L. Simms, M. F. Robbins, S. H. Neff, and W. Lichten, "Quantum-Mechanical Phase Interference and Optical Polarization in Low-Energy Na^+-Ne Inelastic Collisions," *Phys. Rev.* **A13** (March 1976), pp. 969-984.

14. T. A. Miller and R. S. Freund, "Singlet-Triplet Anticrossings in H_2," *J. Chem. Phys.* **61** (September 1, 1974), pp. 2160-2162; idem, "Magnetic Resonance Induced by Electrons: Studies of the Simplest Atomic and Molecular Systems," *Advances in Magnetic Resonance* **9** (New York: Academic Press, 1977), pp. 49-187.

15. C. K. N. Patel, "Determination of Atomic Temperature and Doppler Broadening in Gaseous Discharge with Population Inversion," *Phys. Rev.* (August 1963), pp. 1582-1584.

16. P. W. Smith and T. Hänsch, "Cross Relaxation Effects in the Saturation of the 6328-Å Neon-Laser Line," *Phys. Rev. Lett.* **26** (March 29, 1971), pp. 740-743.

17. P. F. Liao, J. E. Bjorkholm, and P. R. Berman, "Effects of Velocity-Changing Collisions on Two-Photon and Stepwise Absorption Spectroscopic Line Shapes," *Phys. Rev.* **A21** (June 1980), pp. 1927-1938.

18. M. S. Sorem and A. L. Schawlow, "Saturation Spectroscopy in Molecular Iodine by Intermodulated Fluorescence," *Opt. Comm.* **5** (June 1972), pp. 148-151.

19. R. R. Freeman, P. F. Liao, R. Panock, and L. M. Humphrey, "Isotope Shift of the 2^3P-3^3D Transition in Helium," *Phys. Rev.* **A22** (October 1980), pp. 1510-1516; P. F. Liao, R. R. Freeman, R. Panock, and L. M. Humphrey, "Hyperfine-Induced Singlet-Triplet Mixing in ^{3}He," *Opt. Comm.* **34** (August 1980), pp. 195-198.

20. P. F. Liao and J. E. Bjorkholm, "Measurement of the Fine-Structure Splitting of the 4 F State in Atomic Sodium Using Two-Photon Spectroscopy with a Resonant Intermediate State," *Phys. Rev. Lett.* **36** (June 28, 1976), pp. 1543-1545.

21. R. R. Freeman and G. C. Bjorklund, "Effects of Electric Fields upon Autoionizing States of Sr," *Phys. Rev. Lett.* **40** (January 9, 1978), pp. 118-121.

22. R. R. Freeman and N. P. Economou, "Electric Field Dependence of the Photoionization Cross Section of Rb," *Phys. Rev.* **A20** (December 1979), pp. 2356-2363; N. P. Economou, R. R. Freeman, and P. F. Liao, "Diamagnetic Structure of Rb in Intense Magnetic Fields," *Phys. Rev.* **A18** (December 1978), pp. 2506-2509.

23. C. V. Shank and E. P. Ippen, "Subpicosecond Kilowatt Pulses from a Mode-Locked CW Dye Laser," *Appl. Phys. Lett.* **24** (April 15, 1974), pp. 373-375; E. P. Ippen and C. V. Shank, "Picosecond Response of a High-Repetition-Rate CS_2 Optical Kerr," *Appl. Phys. Lett.* **26** (February 1, 1975), pp. 92-93.

24. R. L. Fork, B. I. Greene, and C. V. Shank, "Picosecond Nonequilibrium Carrier Transport in GaAs," *Appl. Phys. Lett.* **38** (February 1, 1981), pp. 104-105.

25. E. P. Ippen and C. V. Shank, "Sub-Picosecond Spectroscopy," *Physics Today* (May 1978), pp. 41-47; P. M. Rentzepis, "Direct Measurements of Radiationless Transitions in Liquids," *Chem. Phys. Lett.* **2** (June 1978), pp. 117-120; E. P. Ippen, C. V. Shank, and R. L. Woerner, "Picosecond Dynamics of Azulene," *Chem. Phys. Lett.* **46** (February 15, 1977), pp. 20-23.

26. L. B. Kreuzer and C. K. N. Patel, "Nitric Oxide Air Pollution: Detection by Optoacoustic Spectroscopy," *Science* **173** (July 2, 1971), pp. 45-47.

27. A. G. Bell, *Proc. Am. Assoc. Adv. Sci.* **29** (1880), p. 115.

28. J. Tyndall, "Action of Intermittent Beam of Radiant Heat upon Gaseous Matter," *Proc. Royal Soc.* **31** (January 13, 1881), pp. 307-317.

29. W. C. Roentgen, "On Tones Produced by the Intermittent Irradiation of a Gas," *Phil. Mag.* **11** (January/June 1881), pp. 308-311.

30. C. K. N. Patel and R. J. Kerl, "A New Optoacoustic Cell with Improved Performance," *Appl. Phys. Lett.* **30** (June 1, 1977), pp. 578-579.

31. C. K. N. Patel, "Laser Detection of Pollution," *Science* **202** (October 13, 1978), pp. 157-173.

32. C. K. N. Patel, E. G. Burkhardt, and C. A. Lambert, "Spectroscopic Measurements of Stratospheric Nitric Oxide and Water Vapor," *Science* **184** (June 4, 1974), pp. 1173-1176; E. G. Burkhardt, C. A. Lambert, and C. K. N. Patel, "Stratospheric Nitric Oxide: Measurements During Daytime and Sunset," *Science* **188** (June 13, 1975), pp. 1111-1113; C. K. N. Patel, "Spectroscopic Measurements of the Stratosphere Using Tunable Infrared Lasers," *Opt. Quant. Electron.* **8** (March 1976), pp. 145-154.

33. R. J. H. Voorhoeve, C. K. N. Patel, L. E. Trimble, and R. J. Kerl, "Hydrogen Cyanide Production During Reduction of Nitric Oxide over Platinum Catalysts," *Science* **190** (October 10, 1975), pp. 149-151.

34. K. K. Darrow, "Some Contemporary Advances in Physics—V. Electrical Phenomena in Gases," *Bell System Tech. J.* **4** (January 1925), pp. 112-151.

35. K. K. Darrow, "Contemporary Advances in Physics—XXIV. High-Frequency Phenomena in Gases, First Part," *Bell System Tech. J.* **11** (October 1932), pp. 576-

607; idem, "Contemporary Advances in Physics—XXV. High-Frequency Phenomena in Gases, Second Part," *Bell System Tech. J.* **12** (January 1933), pp. 91-118.

36. S. B. Ingram, "Cold-Cathode Gas-Filled Tubes as Circuit Elements," *Trans. Am. Inst. Elec. Eng.* **58** (July 1939), pp. 342-346.

37. W. A. Depp and W. H. T. Holden, "Circuits for Cold-Cathode Glow Tubes," *Elec. Manufacturing* **44** (July 1, 1949), pp. 92-97.

38. M. A. Townsend and W. A. Depp, "Cold-Cathode Tubes for Transmission of Audio Frequency Signals," *Bell System Tech. J.* **32** (November 1953), pp. 1371-1391; M. A. Townsend, "Cold-Cathode Gas Tubes for Telephone Switching Systems," *Bell System Tech. J.* **36** (May 1957), pp. 755-768.

39. A. D. White, "New Hollow Cathode Glow Discharge," *J. Appl. Phys.* **30** (May 1959), pp. 711-719.

40. A. E. Joel, Jr., "An Experimental Switching System Using New Electronic Techniques," *Bell System Tech. J.* **37** (September 1958), pp. 1091-1124.

41. W. H. C. Higgins, "A Survey of Bell System Progress in Electronic Switching," *Bell System Tech. J.* **44** (July/August 1965), pp. 937-997.

42. R. W. Engstrom and W. S. Huxford, "Time-Lag Analysis of the Townsend Discharge in Argon with Activated Caesium Electrodes," *Phys. Rev.* **58** (July 1940), pp. 67-77.

43. L. B. Loeb, *Basic Processes of Gaseous Electronics*, 2nd ed. (Berkeley, CA: Univ. of California Press, 1960).

44. R. R. Newton, "Transients in Townsend Discharges," *Phys. Rev.* **73** (March 1948), pp. 570-583.

45. J. A. Hornbeck, "Microsecond Transient Currents in the Pulsed Townsend Discharge," *Phys. Rev.* **83** (July 1951), pp. 374-379.

46. J. P. Molnar, "Form of Transient Currents in Townsend Discharges with Metastables," *Phys. Rev.* **83** (September 1951), pp. 933-940.

47. J. A. Hornbeck, "The Drift Velocities of Molecular and Atomic Ions in Helium, Neon, and Argon," *Phys. Rev.* **84** (November 1951), pp. 615-620.

48. G. H. Wannier, "Motion of Gaseous Ions in a Strong Electric Field. II," *Phys. Rev.* **87** (September 1952), pp. 795-798; idem, "Motion of Gaseous Ions in Strong Electric Fields," *Bell System Tech. J.* **32** (January 1953), pp. 170-254.

49. J. A. Hornbeck and J. P. Molnar, "Mass Spectrometric Studies of Molecular Ions in the Noble Gases," *Phys. Rev.* **84** (November 15, 1951), pp. 621-625.

50. R. N. Varney, "Drift Velocities of Ions in Krypton and Xenon," *Phys. Rev.* **88** (October 1952), pp. 362-364; idem, "Drift Velocity of Ions in Oxygen, Nitrogen, and Carbon Monoxide," *Phys. Rev.* **89** (February 1953), pp. 708-711; idem, "Liberation of Electrons by Positive-Ion Impact on the Cathode of a Pulsed Townsend Discharge Tube," *Phys. Rev.* **93** (March 1954), pp. 1156-1160.

51. K. B. McAfee, Jr., "Pulse Technique for Measurement of the Probability of Formation and Mobility of Negative Ions," *J. Chem. Phys.* **23** (August 1955), pp. 1435-1440.

52. A. J. Ahearn and N. B. Hannay, "The Formation of Negative Ions of Sulphur Hexaflouride," *J. Chem. Phys.* **21** (January 1953), pp. 119-124.

53. K. B. McAfee, Jr., and D. Edelson, "Drift Velocities of Atomic and Molecular Ions in Nitrogen," *Proc. Sixth International Symposium on Ionization Phenomena in Gases* (Paris: 1963); K. B. McAfee, Jr., D. Sipler, and D. Edelson, "Mobilities and Reactions of Ions in Argon," *Phys. Rev.* **160** (August 1967), pp. 130-135; D. Edelson, J. A. Morrison, and K. B. McAfee, Jr., "Ion Distributions in a Pulsed Townsend Discharge," *J. Appl. Phys.* **35** (June 1964), pp. 1682-1690.

54. L. H. Germer and F. E. Haworth, "A Low Voltage Discharge Between Very Close Electrodes," *Phys. Rev.* **73** (March 1948), p. 1121.

55. R. R. Newton, "Ejection of Electrons by Ions at High Fields," *Phys. Rev.* **73** (March 1948), pp. 1122.

56. J. J. Lander and L. H. Germer, "The Bridge Erosion of Electrical Contacts. Part I.," *J. Appl. Phys.* **19** (October 1948), pp. 910-928.

57. W. S. Boyle and P. P. Kisliuk, "Departure from Paschen's Law of Breakdown in Gases," *Phys. Rev.* **97** (January 1955), pp. 255-259.

58. W. S. Boyle and F. E. Haworth, "Glow-to-Arc Transition," *Phys. Rev.* **101** (February 1956), pp. 935-938.

59. L. H. Germer and W. S. Boyle, "Two Distinct Types of Short Arcs," *J. Appl. Phys.* **27** (January 1956), pp. 32-39.

60. L. H. Germer, "Electrical Breakdown Between Close Electrodes in Air," *J. Appl. Phys.* **30** (January 1959), pp. 46-51.

61. P. P. Kisliuk, "Electron Emission at High Fields Due to Positive Ions," *J. Appl. Phys.* **30** (January 1959), pp. 51-55.

62. D. J. Rose and S. C. Brown, "Microwave Gas Discharge Breakdown in Air, Nitrogen, and Oxygen," *J. Appl. Phys.* **28** (May 1957), pp. 561-563.

63. I. Langmuir, "Scattering of Electrons in Ionized Gases," *Phys. Rev.* **26** (November 1925), pp. 585-613.

64. L. Tonks and I. Langmuir, "Oscillations in Ionized Gases," *Phys. Rev.* **33** (February 1929), pp. 195-210.

65. G. L. Pearson, "Fluctuation Noise in Vacuum Tubes," *Bell System Tech. J.* **13** (October 1934), pp. 634-653.

66. A. J. Rack, "Effect of Space Charge and Transit Time on the Shot Noise in Diodes," *Bell System Tech. J.* **17** (October 1938), pp. 592-619.

67. F. B. Llewellyn and A. E. Bowen, "The Production of Ultra-High-Frequency Oscillations by Means of Diodes," *Bell System Tech. J.* **18** (April 1939), pp. 280-291.

68. J. R. Pierce, "Limiting Current Densities in Electron Beams," *J. Appl. Phys.* **10** (October 1939), pp. 715-724.

69. F. B. Llewellyn and L. C. Peterson, "Vacuum Tube Networks," *Proc. IRE* **32** (1944), pp. 144-166.

70. R. Kompfner, "Traveling Wave Valve—New Amplifier for Centimeter Wavelengths," *Wireless World* **52** (November 1946), pp. 369-372.

71. J. R. Pierce, *Traveling Wave Tubes* (New York: D. Van Nostrand Co., Inc., 1950).

72. J. R. Pierce, "Critical Points in the Theory of Electron-Beam Devices," *J. Nuclear Energy* **2** (January 1961), pp. 73-80.

73. R. Kompfner and N. T. Williams, "Backward-Wave Tubes," *Proc. IRE* **41** (1953), pp. 1602-1611.

74. J. R. Pierce, "Possible Fluctuations in Electron Streams Due to Ions," *J. Appl. Phys.* **19** (March 1948), pp. 231-236.

75. J. R. Pierce and W. B. Hebenstreit, "A New Type of High-Frequency Amplifier," *Bell System Tech. J.* **28** (January 1949), pp. 33-51.

76. See reference 71.

77. S. J. Buchsbaum, "Resonance in a Plasma with Two Ion Species," *Phys. Fluids* **3** (May/June 1960), pp. 418-420.

78. S. J. Buchsbaum and A. Hasegawa, "Longitudinal Plasma Oscillations Near Electron Cyclotron Harmonics," *Phys. Rev.* **143** (March 1966), pp. 303-309.

79. I. B. Bernstein, "Waves in a Plasma in a Magnetic Field," *Phys. Rev.* **109** (January 1958), pp. 10-21.

80. A. Hasegawa and L. Chen, "Kinetic Process of Plasma Heating Due to Alfvén Wave Excitation," *Phys. Rev. Lett.* **35** (August 11, 1975), pp. 370-373.

81. H. Alfvén, "Existence of Electromagnetic-Hydrodynamic Waves," *Nature* **150** (October 3, 1942), pp. 405-406.

82. A. Hasegawa and L. Chen, "Plasma Heating by Alfvén-Wave Phase Mixing," *Phys. Rev. Lett.* **32** (March 4, 1974), pp. 454-456.

83. L. D. Landau, "On the Vibrations of the Electronic Plasma," *J. Phys. (U.S.S.R.)* **10**, No. 1 (1946), pp. 25-34.

84. P. M. Platzman and S. J. Buchsbaum, "Effect of Collisions on the Landau Damping of Plasma Oscillations," *Phys. Fluids* **4** (October 1961), pp. 1288-1292.
85. G. M. Sessler, "Velocity and Attenuation of Longitudinal Ion Waves in a Weakly Ionized Gas Plasma," *Phys. Lett.* **16** (June 1965), pp. 277-278; G. M. Sessler and G. A. Pearson, "Propagation of Ion Waves in Weakly Ionized Gases," *Phys. Rev.* **162** (October 5, 1967), pp. 108-116.
86. T. Huang, L. Chen, and A. Hasegawa, "Collisional Effects on Ion-Acoustic Waves in a Nonequilibrium Plasma," *Phys. Fluids* **17** (September 1974), pp. 1744-1748.
87. W. S. Boyle, A. D. Brailsford, and J. K. Galt, "Dielectric Anomalies and Cyclotron Absorption in the Infrared: Observations on Bismuth," *Phys. Rev.* **109** (February 15, 1958), pp. 1396-1398.
88. J. K. Galt, W. A. Yager, F. R. Merritt, B. B. Cetlin, and A. D. Brailsford, "Cyclotron Absorption in Metallic Bismuth and Its Alloys," *Phys. Rev.* **114** (June 15, 1959), pp. 1396-1413.
89. S. J. Buchsbaum and J. K. Galt, "Alfvén Waves in Solid-State Plasmas," *Phys. Fluids* **4** (December 1961), pp. 1514-1516.
90. G. A. Williams and G. E. Smith, "Alfvén Wave Propagation in Bismuth: Quantum Oscillations of the Fermi Surface," *IBM J. Res. Develop.* **8** (July 1964), pp. 276-283.
91. O. V. Konstantinov and V. I. Perel, "Possible Transmission of Electromagnetic Waves Through a Metal in a Strong Magnetic Field," *Sov. Phys. JETP* **11** (July 1960), pp. 117-119.
92. P. Aigrain, "Les Helicons dans les Semiconducteurs," in *Proceedings of the International Conference on Semiconductor Physics* (Prague: Czechoslovak Academy of Sciences, 1961), pp. 224-226.
93. R. Bowers, C. Legendy, and F. Rose, "Oscillatory Galvanomagnetic Effect in Metallic Sodium," *Phys. Rev. Lett.* **7** (November 1, 1961), pp. 339-341.
94. C. C. Grimes, G. Adams, and P. H. Schmidt, "Observation of the Effect of Open Orbits on Helicon-Wave Propagation," *Phys. Rev. Lett.* **15** (August 30, 1965), pp. 409-412.
95. S. J. Buchsbaum and P. A. Wolff, "Effect of Open Orbits on Helicon and Alfvén-Wave Propagation in Solid-State Plasmas," *Phys. Rev. Lett.* **15** (August 30, 1965), pp. 406-409.
96. G. E. Smith, L. C. Hebel, and S. J. Buchsbaum, "Hybrid Resonance and 'Tilted-Orbit' Cyclotron Resonance in Bismuth," *Phys. Rev.* **129** (January 1963), pp. 154-168.
97. C. C. Grimes and S. J. Buchsbaum, "Interaction Between Helicon Waves and Sound Waves in Potassium," *Phys. Rev. Lett.* **12** (March 30, 1964), pp. 357-360.
98. A. Libchaber and C. C. Grimes, "Resonant Damping of Helicon Waves in Potassium," *Phys. Rev.* **178** (February 1969), pp. 1145-1155.
99. D. J. Bartelink, "Interaction of a Drift Current with Transverse Waves in a Solid State Plasma," *Phys. Rev. Lett.* **12** (April 27, 1964), pp. 479-482.
100. C. Nanney, "Helicon-Drift-Current Interaction in a Solid-State Plasma Waveguide," *Phys. Rev.* **138** (May 1965), pp. A1484-A1489.
101. W. M. Walsh, Jr. and P. M. Platzman, "Excitation of Plasma Waves Near Cyclotron Resonance in Potassium," *Phys. Rev. Lett.* **15** (November 15, 1965), pp. 784-786.
102. See reference 78.
103. See reference 77.
104. P. M. Platzman, W. M. Walsh, Jr., and E-Ni Foo, "Fermi-Liquid Effects on High-Frequency Wave Propagation in Simple Metals," *Phys. Rev.* **172** (1968), pp. 689-699; W. M. Walsh, Jr., "Magnetic Resonances and Waves in Simple Metals," *Science* **171** (January 8, 1971), pp. 36-42.
105. P. M. Platzman, P. A. Wolff, and N. Tzoar, "Light Scattering from a Plasma in a Magnetic Field," *Phys. Rev.* **174** (October 1968), pp. 489-494.
106. C. K. N. Patel and R. E. Slusher, "Light Scattering by Plasmons and Landau Levels of the Electron Gas in InAs," *Phys. Rev.* **167** (March 1968), pp. 413-415.

107. C. K. N. Patel and R. E. Slusher, "Light Scattering from Electron Plasmas in a Magnetic Field," *Phys. Rev. Lett.* **21** (December 1968), pp. 1563-1565.

108. S. Schultz and G. Dunnifer, "Observation of Spin Waves in Sodium and Potassium," *Phys. Rev. Lett.* **18** (February 20, 1967), pp. 283-287.

109. P. M. Platzman and P. A. Wolff, "Spin-Wave Excitation in Nonferromagnetic Metals," *Phys. Rev. Lett.* **18** (February 20, 1967), pp. 280-283; idem, *Waves and Interactions in Solid-State Plasmas* (New York: Academic Press, 1973).

110. T. M. Rice, "Landau Fermi-Liquid Parameters in Na and K," *Phys. Rev.* **175** (November 1968), pp. 858-867.

111. C. C. Cutler, "Spurious Modulation of Electron Beams," *Proc. IRE* **44** (January 1956), pp. 61-64.

112. See reference 75.

113. J. R. Pierce, "Limiting Stable Current in Electron Beams in the Presence of Ions," *J. Appl. Phys.* **15** (October 1944), pp. 721-726.

114. S. Iizuki, K. Saeki, N. Sato, and Y. Hatta, "Buneman Instability, Pierce Instability, and Double Layer Formation in a Collisionless Plasma," *Phys. Rev. Lett.* **43** (November 5, 1979), pp. 1404-1407.

115. S. Millman, "A Spatial Harmonic Traveling-Wave Amplifier for Six Millimeters Wavelength," *Proc. IRE* **39** (1951), pp. 1035-1043.

116. See reference 73.

117. L. R. Walker, "Starting Currents in the Backward Wave Oscillator," *J. Appl. Phys.* **24** (July 1953), pp. 854-859.

118. L. R. Walker, "The Dispersion Formula for Plasma Waves," *J. Appl. Phys.* **25** (January 1954), pp. 131-132.

119. O. Penrose, "Electrostatic Instabilities of a Uniform Non-Maxwellian Plasma," *Phys. Fluids* **3** (March-April 1960), pp. 258-265.

120. L. R. Walker, "Generalizations of Brillouin Flow," *J. Appl. Phys.* **26** (June 1955), pp. 780-781.

121. L. R. Walker, "Stored Energy and Power Flow in Electron Beams," *J. Appl. Phys.* **25** (May 1954), pp. 615-618.

122. C. C. Cutler, "Instability in Hollow and Strip Electron Beams," *J. Appl. Phys.* **27** (September 1956), pp. 1028-1029.

123. W. W. Rigrod, "Noise Spectrum of Electron Beam in Longitudinal Magnetic Field, Part I—The Growing Noise Phenomenon," *Bell System Tech. J.* **36** (July 1957), pp. 831-853; W. W. Rigrod, "Noise Spectrum of Electron Beam in Longitudinal Magnetic Field, Part II—The UHF Noise Spectrum," *Bell System Tech. J.* **36** (July 1957), pp. 855-878.

124. W. W. Rigrod and J. R. Pierce, "Space-Charge Wave Excitation in Solid-Cylindrical Brillouin Beams," *Bell System Tech. J.* **38** (January 1959), pp. 99-118.

125. A. Ashkin, "Dynamics of Electron Beams from Magnetically Shielded Guns," *J. Appl. Phys.* **29** (November 1958), pp. 1594-1604.

126. R. E. Slusher, C. M. Surko, D. R. Moler, and M. Porkolab, "Study of the Current-Driven Ion-Acoustic Instability Using CO_2—Laser Scattering," *Phys. Rev. Lett.* **36** (March 22, 1976), pp. 674-677.

127. C. M. Surko, R. E. Slusher, D. R. Moler, and M. Porkolab, "10.6 μm Laser Scattering from Cyclotron-Harmonic Waves in a Plasma," *Phys. Rev. Lett.* **29** (July 10, 1972), pp. 81-84.

128. R. P. H. Chang, "Lower-Hybrid Beam-Plasma Instability," *Phys. Rev. Lett.* **35** (August 4, 1975), pp. 285-288.

129. S. Seiler, M. Yamada, and H. Ikezi, "Lower Hybrid Instability Driven by a Spiraling Ion Beam," *Phys. Rev. Lett.* **37** (September 13, 1976), pp. 700-703.

130. R. A. Stern, D. L. Correll, H. Böhmer, and N. Rynn, "Nonlocal Effects in the Electrostatic Ion-Cyclotron Instability," *Phys. Rev. Lett.* **37** (September 27, 1976), pp. 833-836.

131. M. Yamada, S. Seiler, H. W. Hendel, and H. Ikezi, "Electrostatic Ion Cyclotron Instabilities Driven by Parallel Ion Beam Injection," *Phys. Fluids* **20** (March 1977), pp. 450-458.

132. R. A. Stern and J. A. Johnson, III, "Plasma Ion Diagnostics Using Resonant Fluorescence," *Phys. Rev. Lett.* **34** (June 23, 1975), pp. 1548-1551.

133. H. Suhl, "Proposal for a Ferromagnetic Amplifier in the Microwave Range," *Phys. Rev.* **106** (April 1957), pp. 384-385.

134. T. J. Bridges, "A Parametric Electron Beam Amplifier," *Proc. IRE* **46** (1958), pp. 494-495.

135. W. H. Louisell and C. F. Quate, "Parametric Amplification of Space Charge Waves," *Proc. IRE* **46** (1958), pp. 707-716.

136. J. M. Manley and H. E. Rowe, "General Energy Relations in Nonlinear Reactances," *Proc. IRE* **47** (1959), pp. 2115-2116.

137. R. A. Stern and N. Tzoar, "Parametric Coupling Between Electron-Plasma and Ion-Acoustic Oscillations," *Phys. Rev. Lett.* **17** (October 24, 1966), pp. 903-905.

138. R. A. Stern and N. Tzoar, "Resonant Excitation of Plasma Oscillations by Transverse Electromagnetic Waves," *Phys. Rev. Lett.* **16** (May 2, 1966), pp. 785-787.

139. R. A. Stern, "Radiation-Induced Decay Instability of Bernstein Modes," *Phys. Rev. Lett.* **2** (April 14, 1969), pp. 767-770.

140. M. Ono, R. P. H. Chang, and M. Porkolab, "Parametric Excitation of Electrostatic Ion Cyclotron Waves in a Multi-Ion-Species Plasma," *Phys. Rev. Lett* **38** (April 25, 1977), pp. 962-966.

141. R. P. H. Chang and M. Porkolab, "Experimental Observation of the Nonoscillatory Parametric Instability at the Lower Hybrid Frequency," *Phys. Rev. Lett.* **31** (November 12, 1973), pp. 1241-1244.

142. R. P. H. Chang and M. Porkolab, "Parametrically Induced Nonlinear Wave-Particle Scattering and Plasma Heating near the Lower Hybrid Frequency," *Phys. Rev. Lett.* **32** (June 3, 1974), pp. 1227-1231.

143. A. Hasegawa and L. Chen, "Theory of Plasma Heating by Nonlinear Excitation of Lower Hybrid Resonance," *Phys. Fluids* **18** (October 1975), pp. 1321-1326.

144. A. Hasegawa, "Decay of a Plasmon into Two Electromagnetic Waves," *Phys. Rev. Lett.* **32** (April 15, 1974), pp. 817-820.

145. A. Hasegawa and L. Chen, "Parametric Decay of 'Kinetic Alfvén Wave' and Its Application to Plasma Heating," *Phys. Rev. Lett.* **36** (June 7, 1976), pp. 1362-1365.

146. R. A. Stern, J. F. Decker, and P. M. Platzman, "Decay Instability of the Ion-Beam Mode," *Phys. Rev. Lett.* **32** (February 18, 1974), pp. 357-362.

147. H. Ikezi, R. P. H. Chang, and R. A. Stern, "Nonlinear Evolution of the Electron-Beam-Plasma Instability," *Phys. Rev. Lett.* **36** (April 26, 1976), pp. 1047-1051.

148. A. Hasegawa, "Free Electron Laser," *Bell System Tech. J.* **57** (October 1978), pp. 3069-3089.

149. A. Hasegawa, K. Mima, P. Sprangle, H. H. Szu, and V. L. Granatstein, "Limitation in Growth Time of Stimulated Compton Scattering in X-ray Regime," *Appl. Phys. Lett.* **29** (November 1, 1976), pp. 542-544.

150. H. Ikezi, K. F. Schwartzenegger, and S. Yoshikawa, "A Tokamak with Stellarator Windings on the Large-Major-Radius Side," *Bull. Am. Phys. Soc.* **23** (September 1978), p. 899.

151. A. G. Chynoweth, S. J. Buchsbaum, and W. L. Feldmann, "Low Field Microwave Emission from Indium Antimonide," *J. Appl. Phys.* **37** (June 1966), pp. 2922-2924.

152. C. A. Nanney and E. V. George, "Coherent Microwave Radiation from BiSb Alloys," *Phys. Rev. Lett.* **22** (May 19, 1969), pp. 1062-1065.

153. D. J. Bartelink, "Propagation and Instability of Transverse Waves in Current-Carrying Electron-Hole Plasmas," *Phys. Rev.* **158** (June 1967), pp. 400-414.

154. D. S. Bugnolo, "Effects of a 'Mixing-In-Gradient' on the Spectrum of the Electron Density in a Turbulent Weakly Ionized Gas," *J. Geophys. Res.* **70** (August 1, 1965), pp. 3725-3734.

155. D. S. Bugnolo, "Some Effects of Laminar and Turbulent Flow on Breakdown in Gases," *Bell System Tech. J.* **44** (December 1965), pp. 2393-2408.

156. V. L. Granatstein, "Structure of Wind-Driven Plasma Turbulence as Resolved by Continuum Ion Probes," *Phys. Fluids* **10** (June 1967), pp. 1236-1244.

157. V. L. Granatstein, S. J. Buchsbaum, and D. S. Bugnolo, "Fluctuation Spectrum of a Plasma Additive in a Turbulent Gas," *Phys. Rev. Lett.* **16** (March 21, 1966), pp. 504-507.

158. K. B. McAfee, Jr., and R. M. Lum, "Diffusion and Deionization Near the Stratopause from a Meteorlike Reentry," *J. Geophys. Res.* **81** (September 1, 1976), pp. 4685-4695.

159. C. N. Judice, J. F. Decker, and R. A. Stern, "Breaking and Turbulent Transition in Ion-Acoustic Waves," *Phys. Rev. Lett.* **30** (February 12, 1973), pp. 267-270.

160. C. M. Surko and R. E. Slusher, "Study of the Density Fluctuations in the Adiabatic Toroidal Compressor Scattering Tokamak Using CO_2 Laser," *Phys. Rev. Lett.* **37** (December 27, 1976), pp. 1747-1750.

161. A. Hasegawa and K. Mima, "Stationary Spectrum of Strong Turbulence in Magnetized Nonuniform Plasma," *Phys. Rev. Lett.* **39** (July 25, 1977), pp. 205-208; idem, "Pseudo-Three-Dimensional Turbulence in Magnetized Nonuniform Plasma," *Phys. Fluids* **21** (January 1978),,pp. 87-92.

162. R. E. Slusher and C. M. Surko, "Study of Density Fluctuations in the Alcator Tokamak Using CO_2 Laser Scattering," *Phys. Rev. Lett.* **40** (February 6, 1978), pp. 400-403.

163. N. J. Zabusky and M. D. Kruskal, "Interaction of 'Solitons' in a Collisionless Plasma and the Recurrence of Initial States," *Phys. Rev. Lett.* **15** (August 9, 1965), pp. 240-243.

164. H. Ikezi, R. J. Taylor, and D. R. Baker, "Formation and Interaction of Ion-Acoustic Solitons," *Phys. Rev. Lett.* **25** (July 6, 1970), pp. 11-14.

165. R. A. Stern and J. F. Decker, "Nonlocal Instability of Finite-Amplitude Ion Waves," *Phys. Rev. Lett.* **27** (November 8, 1970), pp. 1266-1270.

166. See reference 155.

167. P. K. Kaw, K. Nishikawa, Y. Yoshida, and A. Hasegawa, "Two-Dimensional and Three-Dimensional Envelope Solitons," *Phys. Rev. Lett.* **35** (July 14, 1975), pp. 88-91.

168. A. Hasegawa and K. Mima, "Exact Solitary Alfvén Wave," *Phys. Rev. Lett.* **37** (September 13, 1976), pp. 690-693.

169. A. Hasegawa, "Theory and Computer Experiment on Self-Trapping Instability of Plasma Cyclotron Waves," *Phys. Fluids* **15** (May 1972), pp. 870-881.

170. M. Kato and A. Hasegawa, "Stability of Oblique Modulation on an Ion-Acoustic Wave," *Phys. Fluids* **19** (December 1976), pp. 1967-1969.

171. H. Ikezi, K. Schwartznegger, A. L. Simons, Y. Ohsawa, and T. Kamimura, "Nonlinear Self-Modulation of Ion-Acoustic Waves," *Phys. Fluids* **21** (February 1978), pp. 239-248.

172. A. Hasegawa, "Dynamics of an Ensemble of Plane Waves in Nonlinear Dispersive Media," *Phys. Fluids* **18** (January 1975), pp. 77-79.

173. W. M. Walsh, R. G. Shulman, and R. D. Heidenreich, "Ferromagnetic Inclusions in Nucleic Acid Samples," *Nature* **192** (December 16, 1961), pp. 1041-1043.

174. W. E. Blumberg, "Nuclear Spin-Lattice Relaxation Caused by Paramagnetic Impurities," *Phys. Rev.* **119** (July 1960), pp. 79-84; idem, "Spin Relaxation of *F*-Center Electrons," *Phys. Rev.* **119** (September 1960), pp. 1842-1850.

175. J. Eisinger, R. G. Shulman, and W. E. Blumberg, "Relaxation Enhancement by Paramagnetic Ion Binding in Deoxyribonucleic Acid Solutions," *Nature* **192** (December 9, 1961), pp. 963-964.

176. R. A. Dwek, *Nuclear Magnetic Resonance in Biochemistry, Applications to Enzyme Systems* (Oxford: Clarendon Press, 1973).

177. R. Salovey, R. G. Shulman, and W. M. Walsh, Jr., "Electron Spin Resonance of Irradiated DNA," *J. Chem. Phys.* **39** (August 1963), pp. 839-840.

178. P. S. Pershan, R. G. Shulman, B. J. Wyluda, and J. Eisinger, "Electron Spin Resonance of Irradiated DNA," *Science* **148** (April 16, 1965), pp. 378-380.

179. A. A. Lamola, M. Güeron, T. Yamane, J. Eisinger, and R. G. Shulman, "Triplet State of DNA," *J. Chem. Phys.* **47** (October 1, 1967), pp. 2210-2217; M. Gúeron, J. Eisinger, and A. A. Lamola, *Basic Principles in Nucleic Acids Chemistry*, Vol. 1, ed. P.O.P. (New York: Academic Press, 1974), pp. 312-394.

180. A. A. Lamola and T. Yamane, "Sensitized Photodimerization of Thymine in DNA," *Proc. Nat'l. Acad. Sci.* **58** (August 15, 1967), pp. 443-446.

181. A. A. Lamola and J. Eisinger, "On the Mechanism of Thymine Photodimerization," *Proc. Nat'l. Acad. Sci.* **59** (January 15, 1968), pp. 46-51.

182. W. J. Tomlinson, E. A. Chandross, R. L. Fork, C. A. Pryde, and A. A. Lamola, "Reversible Photodimerization: A New Type of Photochromism," *Applied Optics* **11** (March 1972), pp. 533-548.

183. M. L. Meistrich and A. A. Lamola, "Triplet-State Sensitization of Thymine Photodimerization in Bacteriophage T4," *J. Mol. Biol.* **66** (April 28, 1972), pp. 83-95.

184. M. L. Meistrich and R. G. Shulman, "Mutagenic Effect of Sensitized Irradiation of Bacteriophage T4," *J. Mol. Biol.* **46** (November 28, 1969), pp. 157-167.

185. R. E. Dale and J. Eisinger, "Intramolecular Distances Determined by Energy Transfer. Dependence on Orientational Freedom of Donor and Acceptor," *Biopolymers* **13** (1974), pp. 1573-1605.

186. J. Eisinger and W. E. Blumberg, "Binding Constants from Zone Transport of Interacting Molecules," *Biochemistry* **12** (September 11, 1973), pp. 3648-3662.

187. J. Eisinger and N. Gross, "The Anticodon-Anticodon Complex," *J. Mol. Biol.* **88** (September 5, 1974), pp. 165-174.

188. D. R. Kearns, D. J. Patel, and R. G. Shulman, "High Resolution Nuclear Magnetic Resonance Studies of Hydrogen-Bonded Protons of TRNA in Water," *Nature* **229** (January 29, 1971), pp. 338-339.

189. D. J. Patel, "High-Resolution NMR Studies of the Structure and Dynamics of TRNA Solution," *Ann. Rev. Phys. Chem.* **29** (1978), pp. 337-362.

190. D. J. Patel, "Peptide Antibiotic-Dinucleotide Interactions. Nuclear Magnetic Resonance Investigations of Complex Formation Between Actinomycin D and d-pGpC in Aqueous Solution," *Biochemistry* **13** (May 21, 1974), pp. 2388-2395; idem, "Proton and Phosphorus NMR Studies of d-CpG(pCpG)n Duplexes in Solution. Helix-Coil Transition and Complex Formation with Actinomycin-D," *Biopolymers* **15** (1976), pp. 533-558.

191. D. J. Patel, "Nuclear Magnetic Resonance Studies of Drug-Nuclei Acid Interactions at the Synthetic DNA Level in Solution,"*Act. Chem. Res.* **12** (1979), pp. 118-125.

192. R. G. Shulman, J. J. Hopfield, and S. Ogawa, *Quart. Rev. Biophys.* **8** (July 1975), pp. 325-420.

193. J. M. Salhany, T. Yamane, R. G. Shulman, and S. Ogawa, "High Resolution ^{31}P Nuclear Magnetic Resonance Studies of Intact Yeast Cells," *Proc. Nat'l. Acad. Sci.* **72** (December 1975), pp. 4966-4970; G. Navon, S. Ogawa, R. G. Shulman, and T. Yamane, "^{31}P Nuclear Magnetic Resonance Studies of Ehrlich Ascites Tumor Cells," *Proc. Nat'l. Acad. Sci.* **74** (January 1977), pp. 87-91.

194. T. R. Brown, K. Ugurbil, and R. G. Shulman, "^{31}P Nuclear Magnetic Resonance of ATPase Kinetics in Aerobic *Escherichia Coli* Cells," *Proc. Nat'l. Acad. Sci.* **74** (December 1977), pp. 5551-5553; T. R. Brown, D. G. Badian, P. B. Garlick, G. K. Radda, P. J. Seeley, and P. Styles, in *Frontiers in Biological Energetics*, ed. P. L. Duttou, J. Leigh, and A. Scarpa (New York: Academic Press, 1978), p. 1341.

195. K. Ugurbil, T. R. Brown, J. A. den Hollander, P. Glynn, and R. G. Shulman, in *Frontiers in Biological Energetics*, ed. P. L. Duttou, J. Leigh, and A. Scarpa (New York: Academic Press, 1978), p. 3742.

196. S. M. Cohen, S. Ogawa, and R. G. Shulman, "^{13}C NMR Studies of Gluconeogenesis in Rat Liver Cells: Utilization of Labeled Glycerol by Cells from Euthyroid and Hyperthyroid Rats," *Proc. Nat'l. Acad. Sci.* **76** (April 1979), pp. 1603-1607.

197. J. A. den Hollander, T. R. Brown, R. G. Shulman, and K. Ugurbil, "^{13}C Nuclear Magnetic Resonance Studies of Anaerobic Glycolysis in Suspension of Yeast Cells," *Proc. Nat'l. Acad. Sci.* **76** (December 1979), pp. 6096-6100.

198. S. M. Cohen, R. G. Shulman, and A. C. McLaughlin, "Effects of Ethanol on Alanine Metabolism in Perfused Mouse Liver Studied by ^{13}C NMR," *Proc. Nat'l. Acad. Sci.* **76** (October 1979), pp. 4808-4812.

199. J. Peisach and W. E. Blumberg, "Structural Implications Derived from the Analysis of Electron Paramagnetic Resonance Spectra of Natural and Artificial Copper Proteins," *Arch. Biochem. Biophys.* **165** (1974), pp. 691-708; W. E. Blumberg and J. Peisach, "Low-Spin Compounds of Heme Proteins," *Bioinorganic Chemistry, Advances in Chemistry Series* **100** (Washington, D.C.: American Chemical Society Publications, 1971), pp. 271-291; idem, "Measurement of Zero-Field Splitting and Determination of Ligand Composition in Mononuclear Nonheme Iron Proteins," *Ann. N.Y. Acad. Sci.* **222** (December 1973), pp. 539-560.

200. See reference 199.

201. J. J. Hopfield, "Kinetic Proofreading: A New Mechanism for Reducing Errors in Biosynthetic Processes Requiring High Specificity," *Proc. Nat'l. Acad. Sci.* **71** (October 1974), pp. 4135-4139; T. Yamane and J. J. Hopfield, "Experimental Evidence for Kinetic Proofreading in the Aminoacylation of TRNA by Synthetase," *Proc. Nat'l. Acad. Sci.* **74** (June 1977), pp. 2246-2250.

202. J. Jaklevic, J. A. Kirby, M. P. Klein, A. J. Robertson, G. S. Brown, and P. Eisenberger, "Fluorescence Detection of EXAFS Sensitivity Enhancement for Dilute Species and Thin Films," *Sol. State Comm.* **23** (1977), p. 679.

203. R. G. Shulman, P. Eisenberger, W. E. Blumberg, and N. A. Stombaugh, "Determination of the Iron-Sulfur Distances in Rubredoxin by X-Ray Absorption Spectroscopy," *Proc. Nat'l. Acad. Sci.* **72** (October 1975), pp. 4003-4007.

204. R. G. Shulman, P. Eisenberger, B. K. Teo, P. M. Kincaid, and G. S. Brown, "Fluorescence X-Ray Absorption Studies of Rubredoxin and its Model Compounds," *J. Mol. Biol.* **124** (1978), p. 305.

205. P. Eisenberger, R. G. Shulman, G. S. Brown, and S. Ogawa, "Structure-Function Relations in Hemoglobin as Determined by X-Ray Absorption Spectroscopy," *Proc. Nat'l. Acad. Sci.* **73** (February 1976), pp. 491-495.

206. L. Powers, P. Eisenberger, and J. Stamatoff, "Investigation of Structural Organization of Calcium in Biological Molecules by Extended X-Ray Absorption," *Ann. N.Y. Acad. Sci.* **307** (April 1978), pp. 113-124.

207. U. A. Meyer and R. Schmid, in *The Metabolic Basis of Inherited Disease*, ed. J. B. Stanbury, J. B. Wyngaarden, and D. S. Fredrickson (New York: McGraw-Hill, 1978), pp. 1167-1220.

208. A. A. H. Van den Bergh and W. Grotepass, "Porphyrinamie ohne Porphyrinurie," *Klin. Wochenschr.* **12** (1933), p. 586.

209. A. A. Lamola and T. Yamane, "Zinc Protoporphyrin in the Erythrocytes of Patients with Lead Intoxication and Iron Deficiency Anemia," *Science* **186** (December 6, 1974),pp. 936-938.

210. S. Piomelli, A. A. Lamola, M. B. Poh-Fitzpatrick, C. Seaman, and L. C. Harber, "Erythropoietic Protoporphyria and Pb Intoxication: The Molecular Basis for Difference in Cutaneous Photosensitivity. I. Different Rates of Diffusion of Protoporphyrin from the Erythrocytes, Both in vivo and in vitro," *J. Clin. Invest.* **56** (1975), pp. 1519-1527.

211. A. A. Lamola, M. Joselow, and T. Yamane, "Zinc Protoporphyrin (ZPP): A Simple, Sensitive, Fluorometric Screening Test for Lead Poisoning," *Clin. Chem.* **21** (1975), pp. 93-97.

212. W. E. Blumberg, J. Eisinger, A. A. Lamola, and D. M. Zuckerman, "Zinc Protopor-phyrin Level in Blood Determined by a Portable Hematofluorometer: A Screening Device for Lead Poisoning," *J. Lab. Clin. Med.* **84** (1977), pp. 712-723.

213. S. Piomelli, "A Micromethod for Free Erythrocyte Porphyrins: The FEP Test," *J. Lab. Clin. Med.* **81** (1972), pp. 932-937.

214. "Preventing Lead Poisoning in Young Children—A Statement by the CDC," U. S. Dept. of Health, Education and Welfare, Public Health Service, Center for Disease Control (U. S. Government Printing Office), April 1978.

215. "Occupational Exposure to Lead," *Federal Register* **43**, No. 220 (1978), pp. 52952-53014.

216. J. Eisinger, W. E. Blumberg, A. Fischbein, R. Lilis, and I. J. Selikoff, "Zinc Proto-porphyrin in Blood as a Biological Indicator of Chronic Lead Disease," *J. Environ. Path. Toxicol.* **1** (1978), pp. 897-910.

217. J. A. Valciukas, R. Lilis, A. Fischbein, I. J. Selikoff, J. Eisinger, and W. E. Blum-berg, "Central Nervous System Dysfunction Due to Lead Exposure," *Science* **201** (August 4, 1978), pp. 465-467.

218. C. D. Barrett and H. C. Belk, "Blood Lead Study of Long-Term Hand Soldering Operators," *J. Occup. Med.* **12** (1977), pp. 791-794.

219. M. H. Klaus and A. V. Fanoroff, *Care of the High Risk Neonate* (Philadelphia: W. B. Saunders Co., 1979), pp. 243-266.

220. A. A. Lamola, J. Eisinger, W. E. Blumberg, S. C. Patel, and J. Flores, "Fluorometric Study of the Partition of Bilirubin Among Blood Components: Basis for Rapid Microassays of Bilirubin and Bilirubin Binding Capacity in Whole Blood," *Anal. Biochem.* **100** (1979), pp. 25-42.

221. W. E. Blumberg, J. Eisinger, J. Flores, A. A. Lamola, S. Patel, and D. M. Zucker-man, "Rapid Fluorometric Determination of Bilirubin Levels and Bilirubin Reserve Binding Capacity in Blood of Neonates," *Fed. Proc.* **37**, No. 6 (1978), p. 1517.

222. A. K. Brown, J. Eisinger, W. E. Blumberg, J. Flores, G. Boyle, and A. A. Lamola, "A Rapid Fluorometric Method for Determining Bilirubin Levels and Binding in the Blood of Neonates: Comparisons with a Diazo Method and with 2-4'-Hydroxybenzeneazobenzoic Acid Dye Binding," *Pediatrics* **65** (1980), pp. 767-776.

223. W. J. Cashore, W. Oh, W. E. Blumberg, J. Eisinger, and A. A. Lamola, "Rapid Fluorometric Assay of Bilirubin and Bilirubin Binding Capacity in Blood of Jaun-diced Neonates: Comparisons with Other Methods," *Pediatrics* **66** (1980), pp. 411-416.

Chapter 7

Astrophysics and Magnetospheric Physics — Cosmic Background Radiation

The interest of Bell Labs scientists in both astrophysics and the physics of the magnetosphere stems from a desire to understand the factors affecting electromagnetic propagation in the earth's atmosphere. The contributions to astrophysics began in the early 1930s, soon after sensitive antennas were built to gather data on radio propagation. Serious studies of the earth's magnetosphere did not begin until three decades later when Bell Labs launched the first Telstar communications satellite. K. G. Jansky's investigation of the source of noise affecting transatlantic radio propagation gave rise to the birth of the astrophysics field of radio astronomy. The research of A. A. Penzias and R. W. Wilson in the 1960s on microwave background radiation had strong impact on modern cosmology. Other research contributions by Bell Labs scientists to astrophysics include the development and use of highly sensitive detectors, which led to the discovery of many molecules in the intergalactic space as well as to gamma-ray astronomy and the search for gravity waves.

The studies of the magnetosphere dealt with the earth's radiation environment produced by energetic electrons and protons trapped in distinct belts around the earth and how these are affected by solar flares. Satellite investigations are complemented by magnetic data on ultra-low-frequency variations in the earth's magnetic field, obtained from magnetometers placed in experimental stations in Antartica and at high northern latitudes.

I. ASTROPHYSICS

Studies in astrophysics at Bell Laboratories were motivated by the need to understand sources of interference in radio communication. In the 1920s and early 1930s interest was focused in the 10^5 to 10^8

Principal authors: L. J. Lanzerotti, R. A. Linke, and R. W. Wilson

hertz (Hz) region of the electromagnetic spectrum, covering the range of AM and FM radio-frequency bands. With the development of radio-relay microwave applications to cross-country communication in the 1940s and the beginning of exploration of electromagnetic propagation in the circular waveguide, interest shifted to the study of possible sources of interference in the microwave and millimeter wavelength (10^9 Hz to 10^{12} Hz) regions. The two major fields of astrophysics in which Bell Labs scientists played leading roles—radio astronomy and the experimental confirmation of the "Big Bang" theory of the origin of the universe—can be traced directly to the Bell System's involvement in communications in these two broad regions of the electromagnetic spectrum.

1.1 Radio Astronomy – Early Observation of Galactic Radio Noise

The science of radio astronomy was initiated in 1932 by K. G. Jansky, who had been studying the sources of noise on high-frequency—20 megahertz (MHz)—transatlantic radio circuits. He had built a large, highly directive antenna on a turntable that rotated three times per hour, in order to resolve the angle of arrival of the noise. [Fig. 7-1] The received signal strength was recorded on a chart recorder. Jansky also listened to determine the character of the noise, and discovered that there were three major sources of noise: the familiar crackling noise from nearby thunderstorms, distant thunderstorms, and a continuous hiss-like noise whose intensity varied in a pattern that almost exactly repeated from one day to the next.[1] In further investigation of the continuous hiss component, Jansky discovered that its maximum occurred four minutes earlier each day and after a year had shifted by a full twenty-four hours. A. M. Skellett of Bell Laboratories, a Ph.D. astronomy student at Princeton University, showed him that this is what would be expected from a source associated with the fixed stars.[2] In a later paper, Jansky showed that the hiss-type static came from the plane of the Milky Way and that the maximum came from the direction of its center.[3] This first radio-astronomical observation was published and publicized, but astronomers of the day did not fully appreciate its significance. Part of the problem was that the astronomers did not understand that the strength of the hiss that Jansky reported in microvolts/meter actually corresponded to a thermal temperature many times greater than the value of 10,000K that they would have expected from ionized hydrogen regions.[4] It was only after World War II, when the radar developers took an interest, that the science of radio astronomy began to blossom.

Fig. 7-1. K. G. Jansky in front of the antenna he used to discover radio waves coming from space.

1.2 Microwave Background Noise Studies — Impact on Cosmology

The cosmic microwave background radiation, considered a relic of the explosive beginning of the universe, was discovered in 1965 by A. A. Penzias and R. W. Wilson [Fig. 7-2] at Bell Labs' Crawford Hill, New Jersey, site.[5,6] Penzias and Wilson received the Nobel Prize in physics in 1978 for their work in this area. The discovery was made with a uniquely sensitive microwave receiving system, originally built for receiving signals bounced from the Echo balloon—the world's first communications satellite. Two developments formed the key components in the Echo receiving system. The first was a traveling-wave maser amplifier with an intrinsic noise temperature of only a few degrees kelvin.[7] The other was the 20-foot horn reflector antenna,[8] whose most important property in this application was its very effective rejection of radiation from the backward direction, which reduced the pickup of ground radiation to negligible levels (approximately 0.1K). [Fig. 7-3]

In 1963, when the Echo receiving system was no longer needed for satellite work, preparations were made to use the 20-foot horn reflector for radio astronomy. At that time a maser amplifier from project Telstar, operating at a microwave wavelength of 7.35 centime-

Fig. 7-2. R. W. Wilson (left) and A. A. Penzias, discoverers of cosmic background radiation, direct evidence for the "Big Bang" theory of cosmology.

Fig. 7-3. The 20-foot horn-reflector antenna used in the discovery of microwave background radiation.

ters (cm), was installed and an accurate measurement of its sensitivity was underway.[9] A radio astronomy receiver (radiometer) incorporating the maser was designed to make accurate measurements. It contained two additional unique features: a liquid-helium-cooled reference noise source whose equivalent noise temperature (a convenient measure of its output power) was 5K and could be accurately calculated;[10] and a waveguide switch that allowed very accurate comparisons of the intensity of the radiation from the antenna and the reference noise source. The first radio astronomy project used the measured gain of the 20-foot horn reflector to make precise measurements of the intensities of several bright radio sources that had traditionally been used as radio-astronomical calibrators.[11,12] The results of this work also provided the data for a convenient and widely used method of measuring the sensitivity of satellite earth stations.

When the radiometer was put into operation, the first measurements showed that the equivalent antenna temperature was about 7K—hotter than the reference noise source by about 2K. The antenna temperature should have been only 3.3K—the sum of the atmospheric contribution (2.3K) and the radiation from the walls of the antenna and ground (1K). This would have been 1.7K less than the cold load. During the period when accurate source measurements were being made (almost a year), the excess antenna temperature was found to be constant, independent of direction in the sky, polarization, and season. At the end of that period an intensive effort to find the physical origin of excess temperature was undertaken.

Success came in an unexpected way when contact was made with R. H. Dicke and his group at Princeton University. Although not the first to do so, Dicke predicted the existence of such all-pervasive radiation as a result of a postulated "Big Bang" origin of the universe. (A review of early theories of the "Big Bang"-type universe appears in a paper by Penzias.[13]) Dicke also suggested that the radiation would be observable, and his group set out to make a measurement. However, measurements by Penzias and Wilson gave a value of the temperature of the microwave background and suggested that the expected radiation from the early universe was present. Subsequent measurements have borne this out.[14]

The discovery of cosmic microwave background radiation has had a dramatic effect on the science of cosmology. Not only has it provided direct evidence for a "Big Bang" type of cosmology, it serves as a probe of conditions in very early stages of the universe.

In 1966, a second well-calibrated radiometer was built for the 20-foot horn reflector. The radiometer was capable of receiving the 21-cm microwave line of atomic hydrogen, the more important of the two then-known radio frequency lines. A background temperature measurement was made with this radiometer,[15] adding to the confirmation of the thermal spectrum of the background; it was then used for several additional measurements.[16] A new lower limit to the amount of intergalactic neutral hydrogen was obtained, confirming that neutral hydrogen does not make up a significant fraction of the mass of the universe. The high-velocity hydrogen emission in the neighborhood of the astronomical coordinates $l = 30°$, $b = 45°$ was extensively mapped and found to be one continuous cloud.[17] Another region near the south galactic pole was found to extend approximately 60° and to exhibit a continuous velocity shift along its length, suggestive of rigid motion.[18] Extensive measurements of hydrogen in the vicinity of the galactic center resulted in new kinematic models of the explosive events of that region.[19] Additional calibration measurements of interest to the radio-astronomy community were also made.[20]

1.3 Application of Sensitive Receivers to the Study of Molecules in Interstellar Space

In 1968, Penzias and Wilson made a low-noise, 4-millimeter wavelength receiver using components that had been developed at Crawford Hill for the circular electric-mode waveguide system. The most important advance in this receiver was the use of GaAs Schottky barrier diodes made by C. A. Burrus in the mixer.[21] This receiver was used with the new 36-foot diameter antenna for millimeter-wave radiation studies by the National Radio Astronomy Observatory (NRAO).

In 1970, K. B. Jefferts, Penzias, and Wilson started a revolution in the understanding of the interstellar medium by discovering an intense spectral line of carbon monoxide at 2.6 millimeter (mm) wavelength coming from the Orion Nebula.[22] They used a 90 to 140 gigahertz (GHz) spectral-line receiver that they had assembled for the 36-foot antenna in collaboration with S. Weinreb of the NRAO. This receiver used Burrus diodes for both the main mixer and for the harmonic mixer, which was used to phase-lock the local oscillator klystron. In the next year nine new molecular species were discovered by the Bell Labs group, including molecules containing the rare isotopes ^{13}C and ^{18}O. Other observers using a derivative of the 4-millimeter receiver discovered several other species. The advantage of millimeter-wave spectroscopy of rotational levels is that any molecule containing two or more elements heavier than hydrogen and having a dipole moment can be measured.

In the decade from 1970 to 1980, Bell Labs continued at the forefront of millimeter-wave spectral-line astronomy. The Crawford Hill

7-meter antenna, built for the Comstar Beacon experiment and radio astronomy,[23] has been the world's most sensitive millimeter-wave spectral-line radio telescope since its operation began in 1977. Much work has been directed to studying isotope ratios as an aid for understanding nucleosynthesis.[24] The discovery of deuterated molecules[25] has made it possible to obtain measurements that indicate that the expansion of the universe will continue forever, that is, that we live in an open universe.[26,27] In the 1970s, scientists at Bell Labs discovered 24 new molecular species, studied the chemistry and physics of dense molecular clouds, and demonstrated that carbon monoxide is an excellent tracer of the special activities present in spiral arms of galaxies.[28] [Fig. 7-4]

1.3.1 Instrumentation

In an effort to reach higher frequencies, as well as to detect weaker signals, scientists at Bell Labs have introduced a number of new de-

CARBON MONOSULFIDE	$^{12}C\,^{32}S$	SILICON MONOXIDE	$Si\,O$
	$^{13}C\,^{32}S$	SULFUR DIOXIDE	$^{34}SO_2$
	$^{12}C\,^{34}S$	METHYL CYANIDE	$CH_3\,CN$
	$^{13}C\,^{34}S$		$CH_3\,C^{15}N$
CARBON MONOXIDE	$^{12}C\,^{16}O$		$^{13}CH_3\,CN$
	$^{13}C\,^{16}O$		$CH_3\,^{13}CN$
	$^{12}C\,^{17}O$	HYDROCYANIC ACID	$HC^{15}N$
	$^{12}C\,^{18}O$		DCN
	$^{13}C\,^{18}O$	HYDROGEN SULFIDE	H_2S
PARAFORMALDEHYDE	H_2CO	FORMAL ION	$HC^{18}O^+$
	$HD\,CO$		$HC^{17}O^+$
THIOFORMALDEHYDE	$H_2\,^{13}CS$	THIOFORMAL ION	HCS^+
	$H_2\,C^{34}S$	METHYL MERCAPTAN	$CH_3\,SH$
CARBONYL SULFIDE	OCS	ISOTHIOCYANIC ACID	$HNCS$
	$O^{13}CS$		
	$OC^{34}S$		
	$OC^{33}S$		

ALSO:
261 NEW LINES OF KNOWN MOLECULES
117 AS YET UNIDENTIFIED LINES

Fig. 7-4. Molecules in interstellar space discovered by Bell Labs scientists.

vices and techniques. In 1970, T. G. Phillips and Jefferts developed a new type of radio receiver for millimeter and submillimeter waves.[29] The new receiver made use of the bulk properties of a single crystal of highly pure indium antimonide. The electrical resistance of this material provided a sensitive measure of the temperature change of the electron gas. This temperature rises above that of the lattice at liquid helium temperatures by the absorption of incident photons. This device, called the "hot electron bolometer," is sensitive at frequencies up to 500 GHz and was used to detect interstellar carbon atoms through a transition at 492 GHz.[30]

The sensitivity of the more conventional down-converter receivers was increased nearly fourfold when a mixer diode produced by molecular beam epitaxy (MBE) was operated at cryogenic temperatures.[31] (For more on this topic see Chapter 2, section IV.) M. V. Schneider, R. A. Linke, and A. Y. Cho demonstrated in 1977 that a millimeter-wave-mixer diode could be specifically tailored for cryogenic operation through MBE by depositing a very lightly doped active layer on the more heavily doped buffer layer.[32,33] Cryogenic receivers using MBE diodes and covering 70 GHz to 140 GHz were put into use on the offset Cassegrainian antenna at Bell Labs' Crawford Hill, N.J., site. They proved to be the most sensitive receivers available in this band for a number of years.

In 1978, G. J. Dolan, Phillips, and D. P. Woody demonstrated that the nonlinear properties of superconducting tunnel junctions could be used to make a mixer receiver at 115 GHz with extremely low noise.[34] The physical effect that is used in the device is photon-assisted tunneling between two superconducting films separated by an oxide barrier—an effect first observed in 1962 by A. H. Dayem and R. J. Martin.[35] (See Chapter 9, section 1.5.)

1.4 Statistical Study of Galaxies

Knowledge of the nature of the universe during the 15-billion year time span from the "Big Bang" to the present is sparse, but desireable for understanding the physics of the early universe and stellar evolution. Research into these questions through statistical studies of the thousands of faint images on photographic plates exposed on large telescopes had long been impractical. However, a technique for automated pattern recognition of faint images developed by J. A. Tyson and J. F. Jarvis in the late 1970s made possible an automated analysis of galaxies and resulted in the statistical study of galaxy evolution and cosmology.[36]

From this study, it appears that galaxies are apparently older than had been thought, substantially changing the picture of the early universe. In addition to new constraints on spiral galaxy star-formation rates, the resulting limits for the epoch of galaxy formation are a factor-of-five earlier than previously obtained.

1.5 Gravity Waves

In 1913, Albert Einstein saw that his new theory of gravity, the general theory of relativity, would predict the existence of gravitational waves that would be radiated when highly dense matter elastically deforms or accelerates.[37] These waves would travel at the speed of light and cause a small tidal force on a detector. The detection of such gravity waves would contribute significantly to astrophysics.

In 1969, J. Weber, using a prototype gravity antenna at the University of Maryland, claimed to have detected intense short bursts of gravitational waves.[38] This publication captured the interest of many in the astrophysical community, as the data implied an emitter consuming about 10^5 suns per year.

In 1970, Tyson constructed a larger detector with more than 100 times the sensitivity of the University of Maryland system, but Weber's claimed bursts were not detected.[39] In order to improve the signal-to-noise ratio, in 1973 Tyson arranged to have two detectors in joint operation, one at Bell Labs, Murray Hill, and the other at the University of Rochester (which was funded in part by the National Science Foundation). By 1974, the sensitivity was nearly 2,000 times that of Weber's original detector, but even this did not lead to detection of any gravity waves.[40] In a collaborative experiment, a group of German scientists also obtained null results, in disagreement with Weber's claims.[41] Toward the end of the 1970s the large detector at Bell Labs had become sensitive enough to see any small burst of gravitational waves at the center of our galaxy (30,000 light years distance) corresponding to the gravitational radiation resulting from consumption of one seventh of a sun's mass per year.

1.6 Gamma-Ray Line Astronomy

A new subfield of astrophysics, in which a Bell Labs/Sandia Laboratories group led by M. Leventhal has played a pioneering role since 1973, is gamma-ray line astronomy.[42] The gamma-ray lines, in the range of 0.05 MeV to 20 MeV, arise from transitions that occur between the nuclear energy levels of atoms and molecules immediately following radioactive decay, inelastic nuclear collisions, or neutron capture. One byproduct of many high-energy astrophysical processes occurring between ordinary matter and photons is the production of anti-electrons, that is, positrons. The annihilation of electrons and positrons usually results in two photons, each carrying 0.511 MeV of energy. The other gamma-ray line process is the synchrotron emission arising from the motion of electrons in the enormous magnetic fields of neutron stars or pulsars.

Since gamma rays are highly absorbed in the earth's atmosphere, large balloons were used to lift the telescope and its related instruments. The telescope itself was built around a large-volume, hyperpure germanium diode detector operated at liquid-nitrogen temperature as the central element. Considerable amounts of data were obtained when the apparatus was aimed in the direction of two recent nova explosions and at the Crab Nebula.[43] Evidence for a line feature at 400 keV was obtained, leading to the suggestion that this may be due to positron annihilation on the surface of a neutron star being gravitationally redshifted from 511 keV.

Two flights of the system took place over Alice Springs, Australia, on NASA-supported balloons in November 1977 and April 1979. The principal observation target on both flights was the galactic-center region, from which evidence for a line at 0.511 MeV was obtained.[44] The intensity of this line corresponds to the annihilation of about 10^{43} positrons-per-second in the galactic-center region. This is the radiation equivalent of about 10,000 suns. It is not yet known what is generating all these positrons.

1.7 The Indium Solar Neutrino Spectrometer

The generation of energy in the interior of the sun is believed to be accomplished by the conversion of four protons into an alpha particle with a net release of 25 MeV of energy. This conversion takes place through a series of nuclear reactions. Various steps of this nuclear reaction chain result in the formation of neutrinos. These very weakly interacting, stable particles provide a unique probe of the core of the sun because they are the only particles that can escape practically unimpeded by the sun's mass.

In 1976, R. S. Raghavan proposed a neutrino spectrometer that offers the unique possibility of measuring the energy spectrum of solar neutrinos.[45] This will allow separation of neutrinos produced in different branches of the nuclear reaction chain, and in addition will give direct indications of neutrino time variations (bursts) if they occur. The detector is based on the inverse beta reaction $^{115}\mathrm{In}(\nu,e)^{115}\mathrm{Sn}^*$. The electron (produced immediately upon neutrino capture) is followed by two gamma rays with a few microseconds delay. This triple signature identifies a neutrino capture and distinguishes it from background. The incoming neutrino energy is measured by the energy of the electron.

Raghavan's detection scheme is very different from that used in the only experiment on solar neutrinos reported previously by R. Davis at Brookhaven National Laboratory.[46] It promises to resolve ambiguities in the solar models raised by the Davis experiment.

II. THE MAGNETOSPHERE

Records of the interest in the nature of the space around the earth, as manifested in particular by auroral phenomena, go far back into history.[47] Beginning in the early part of this century with the observations and analyses of K. Birkeland[48] and C. Stormer,[49] the associations between solar activity and geomagnetic and auroral disturbances were placed on a more solid theoretical footing through the insights of a number of investigators, especially S. Chapman and V. C. A. Ferraro,[50] and Alfvén.[51] The launching by the United States and the Soviet Union of the first artificial earth satellites, with their instrumentation for measuring charged particles and magnetic fields, provided the first opportunities for measuring the space environment in the vicinity of the earth. The discovery of the trapped radiation belts around the earth by J. A. Van Allen and his colleagues,[52] and by S. N. Vernov and his associates,[53] opened an entire new chapter in the exploration and understanding of the earth's upper-atmosphere environment.

2.1 Study of Electrons and Protons in the Van Allen Belts with Detectors in the Telstar Satellite

Bell Labs entry into the field of *in-situ* study of the earth's radiation environment and magnetosphere began with the launching of the first Telstar experimental communications satellite on July 10, 1962. Telstar was equipped with a complement of solid state radiation detectors that were designed by W. L. Brown and coworkers to measure the distribution in energy, position, and time of the electrons and protons trapped in the Van Allen belts in the earth's magnetic field.[54] Telstar I was launched one day after an American high-altitude nuclear explosion injected large numbers of additional electrons and protons into the radiation belts. Thus, the measurements by Brown and J. D. Gabbe, using the radiation sensors on Telstar, played an important role in defining the characteristics of the nuclear-explosion radiation at high altitudes,[55] as well as in determining the time dependence of the radiation as dynamical processes in the magnetosphere produced losses of the trapped particles.[56] A nuclear explosion by the Soviet Union in October 1962 produced a very narrow (in altitude) belt of trapped electrons. Measurements of this narrow electron belt made with the use of particle detectors on Telstar (see Chapter 8, sections 1.1 and 1.1.1) and on the National Aeronautics and Space Administration (NASA) Explorer-15 satellite provided the first significant data on the simultaneous magnetosphere processes of particle loss along magnetic field lines into the atmosphere and particle loss by diffusion across magnetic field lines to lower and higher altitudes.[57,58]

The radiation-belt electron measurements with Bell Laboratories instruments on the Telstar and Explorer-15 satellites provided evidence that the trapped electrons (both natural and artificial) were being lost faster than would be predicted theoretically by considerations of simple Coulomb scattering with ionospheric constituents. It had been suggested that very low-frequency (VLF) waves in the magnetosphere might resonate with the individual electron's cyclotron frequency, producing a pitch-angle scattering of the particles into the atmospheric-loss cone.[59] However, C. S. Roberts, in a pioneering work, demonstrated that this mechanism was totally insufficient to produce the observed electron losses because the cyclotron resonance mechanism is very inefficient for scattering particles with pitch angles close to 90°.[60] He suggested instead that wide-band electromagnetic noise in the magnetosphere should be the primary source of a pitch-angle scattering mechanism. In a later study, Roberts and M. Schulz demonstrated that magnetospheric waves with frequencies comparable to a particle's bounce frequency along a magnetic-field line would be very efficient for scattering particles with such pitch angles.[61] They envisioned a two-stage loss process for magnetospheric particles with pitch angles close to 90°: first, bounce resonance scattering to change the particle pitch angle to an off-equatorial value, and then cyclotron resonance scattering into the atmosphere.

2.1.1 Radiation Belt Instability and Magnetic Storms

As space exploration of the magnetosphere continued into the middle and late 1960s, investigations into the natural sources of the trapped particle populations became of fundamental scientific importance. A team of scientists responsible for charged-particle and magnetic-field instruments on the Explorer-26 satellite reported the first evidence of *in-situ* electron energization in the radiation belts during a magnetic storm.[62] Later theoretical work by A. Hasegawa and his colleagues established for the first time the importance of a plasma instability for particle accelerations within the radiation belts during a magnetic storm.[63] Another study of the effects of magnetic storms on radiation-belt electrons, using data from Bell Labs' instruments on Explorer 26, established the occurrence of electron accelerations internal to the radiation belts during all large magnetic storms.[64] This study also suggested that the electron energization occurred outside the plasmapause, a cold-plasma feature in the magnetosphere that had been discovered earlier by D. L. Carpenter of Stanford University.[65]

2.2 Outer Zone Studies with Synchronous Altitude Satellites

The first experimental communications satellite at synchronous altitude, Applications Technology Satellite 1 (ATS-1), was launched by

NASA in December 1966. Bell Labs semiconductor detector apparatus on this satellite was used to acquire proton, alpha particle, and electron data in the outer radiation zone of the magnetosphere until it was turned off in September 1970. The data from this instrument have contributed to a number of important discoveries and studies. These include contributions made by L. J. Lanzerotti, Brown, and Roberts to an understanding of severe magnetic storm conditions when the magnetospheric boundary is pushed inside the synchronous orbit altitude.[66] Other studies include collaborative observations of the geomagnetic substorm acceleration and particle loss processes,[67] and the relationships between substorm-produced electrons in the magnetosphere and in the magneto tail.[68] Hasegawa proposed theoretical explanations for possible radiation-belt electron accelerations at the plasmapause and by a driftwave instability in the vicinity of a magnetosphere-plasma-density gradient.[69]

One of the discoveries that resulted from the experiment on ATS-1 was the identification of periodic oscillations, dependent upon particle energy, in the trapped electron fluxes.[70] These "drift echoes" were attributed to sudden changes in the magnetosphere configuration induced by changes in the solar wind dynamic pressure.[71] They provided crucial evidence of the importance of such magnetospheric field changes on the redistribution of trapped particles by the process of radical diffusion.[72] Subsequently, trapped proton flux data from ATS-1 as analyzed by Lanzerotti, C. G. Maclennan, and M. F. Robbins, provided the first evidence of drift echoes in the fluxes of these particles.[73] [Fig. 7-5]

2.3 Effect of Solar Flares on Particles in Interplanetary Space

In May 1967 and June 1969, Bell Laboratories particle instruments were launched on the Explorer-34 and Explorer-41 spacecraft, respectively. The instruments were designed to study the electron, proton, and alpha particle fluxes from solar flares in interplanetary space. The instruments on both spacecraft functioned well until each satellite burned up upon re-entry into the atmosphere; Explorer-34 in May 1969, and Explorer-41 in December 1972. The data acquired by both of these spacecraft and interpreted by Lanzerotti and coworkers provided important new information on the intensities, composition, and time dependence of low-energy, solar-flare particles. These data provided the first detailed time-intensity profiles of low-energy, solar-flare alpha particle fluxes and established that the propagation of the low-energy (few MeV and less energy) protons and alpha particles did not obey the classical theory of diffusive particle propagation from the flare region to the earth.[74] The solar cosmic-ray data from the Explorer-34 experiment also provided the first evidence of the *in-situ* acceleration of low-energy particles by interplanetary shock waves.[75] Later work, using electron data, provided an important link

Fig. 7-5. L. J. Lanzerotti pioneered in fundamental
investigations of the earth's magnetosphere.

between the time-dependence of the particle fluxes and the fluctuations of the interplanetary field that produces the particle diffusion between the sun and the earth.[76]

The simultaneous acquisition of data with the instruments on both ATS-1 and Explorer-34 led to the important discovery of the rapid access of solar-flare particles deep into the magnetosphere under most conditions of geomagnetic activity.[77] This discovery, which was studied extensively, led to the new concept of the importance of a diffusive, particle-scattering mechanism that acts to move solar particles rapidly into trapped orbits in the magnetosphere.[78] During the same time period an important theoretical work was published by A. Eviatar and R. A. Wolff on the stability of the magnetopause and small-amplitude wave disturbances at the magnetopause.[79]

2.4 Ground-Based Magnetometers in Antarctica and at High Northern Latitudes

The decline in the national space program at the end of the 1960s, together with a growing realization that single (or even dual) satellite measurements were not sufficient for a complete spatial understanding of the magnetospheric wave propagation that modulated the energetic particle fluxes detected on spacecraft in the magnetosphere, led to the planning and design of a ground-based magnetometer array by Lanzerotti and his associates. The array, consisting initially of three, and later of four, fluxgate magnetometers and the associated digital data acquisition systems, was spaced in latitude at a fixed longitude in the northern hemisphere to be close to the nominal plasmapause field-line intercept with the ionosphere. Another magnetometer instrument was located at the National Science Foundation Siple Station in Antarctica. The Antarctic instrument is located at the southern end of a magnetic field line that also passes through one of the northern stations.

At the time of this writing, data from this array have been exceedingly important in elucidating the nature of the low-amplitude [about $(1-10) \times 10^{-5}$ gauss] ultra-low-frequency (about 2 mHz to 50 mHz) variations in the earth's magnetic field. The data from the array provided the discovery that ULF fluctuations can be highly localized in latitude, near the plasmapause, within the magnetosphere.[80,81] The discovery of the localization of the ULF phenomena led to the understanding that these fluctuations can be characterized predominantly as odd-mode standing Alfvén (shear) waves along a field line.[82] An important implication of this discovery is that the amplitudes of the fluctuations near the equator on a field line should nearly vanish; this hypothesis was found to hold in the only extensive comparison between satellite and ground data made to date.[83] Theoretical calculations by L. Chen and Hasegawa provided the first detailed predictions of magnetospheric ULF phenomena that can be rigorously compared with observations.[84] These calculations made possible the explanation of much of the ULF wave phenomena observed near the plasmapause, as well as the prediction of features of the exciting source that are amenable to further experimental investigations.

In addition to the wave studies, new methods of data acquisition and analysis have permitted detailed spectral-analysis studies of the more noise-like geomagnetic field fluctuations. In the 1970s, these analyses were used to propose a more quantitative measure of geomagnetic activity than that previously used worldwide[85] and to study the temporal changes in the radial diffusion coefficient for radiation-belt electrons under the influence of the geomagnetic field fluctuations.[86] The results of this latter study were found to agree with the results previously obtained using radiation-belt particles measured by the Bell Laboratories instrument on Explorer 15.[87]

REFERENCES

1. K. G. Jansky, "Directional Studies of Atmospherics at High Frequencies," *Proc. IRE* **20** (December 1932), pp. 1920-1932.
2. K. G. Jansky, "Electrical Disturbances Apparently of Extraterrestrial Origin," *Proc. IRE* **21** (October 1933), pp. 1387-1398.
3. K. G. Jansky, "A Note on the Source of Interstellar Interference," *Proc. IRE* **23** (October 1935), pp. 1158-1163.
4. J. K. Greenstein, private communication.
5. A. A. Penzias and R. W. Wilson, "A Measurement of Excess Antenna Temperature at 4080 Mc/s," *Astrophys. J.* **142** (July 1965), pp. 419-421.
6. R. W. Wilson, "The Cosmic Microwave Background Radiation," *Rev. Mod. Phys.* **51,** (July 1979), pp. 433-445.
7. R. W. De Grasse, J. J. Kostelnick, and H. E. D. Scovil, "The Dual Channel 2390-mc Traveling-Wave Maser," *Bell System Tech. J.* **40** (July 1961), pp. 1117-1127.
8. A. B. Crawford, D. C. Hogg, and L. E. Hunt, "A Horn Reflector Antenna for Space Communication," *Bell System Tech. J.* **40** (July 1961), pp. 1095-1116.
9. D. C. Hogg and R. W. Wilson, "A Precise Measurement of the Gain of a Large Horn-Reflector Antenna," *Bell System Tech. J.* **44** (July-August 1965), pp. 1019-1030.
10. R. W. Wilson and A. A. Penzias, "The Flux Density of Six Radio Sources at 4.08 GHz," *Astrophys. J.* **146** (October 1966), pp. 286-287.
11. A. A. Penzias and R. W. Wilson, "Measurement of the Flux Density of CAS A at 4080 Mc/s," *Astrophys. J.* **142** (October 1965), pp. 1149-1155.
12. A. A. Penzias, "Helium-Cooled Reference Noise Source in a 4-kMc Waveguide," *Rev. Sci. Instr.* **36** (January 1965), pp. 68-70.
13. R. H. Dicke, P. J. E. Peebles, P. G. Roll, and D. T. Wilkenson, "Cosmic Black-Body Radiation," *Astrophys. J.* **142** (1965), pp. 414-419; see also reference 5; and A. A. Penzias, "The Origin of the Elements," *Science* **205** (August 1979), pp. 549-554.
14. See reference 6.
15. A. A. Penzias and R. W. Wilson, "Background Temperature Measurement at 1415 MHz," *Appl. J.* **72** (1967), p. 315.
16. A. A. Penzias and E. H. Scott, III, "Intergalactic HI Absorption at 21 Centimeters," *Astrophys. J.* **153** (July 1968), pp. L7-L9; A. A. Penzias and R. W. Wilson, "Intergalactic HI Emission at 21 Centimeters," *Astrophys. J.* **156** (June 1969), pp. 799-802; A. A. Penzias, R. W. Wilson, and P. J. Encrenaz, "Measurements of 21 cm Line Calibration Regions," *Astron. J.* **75** (March 1970), pp. 141-143; P. J. Encrenaz, A. A. Penzias, and R. W. Wilson, "Flux of Cassiopeia at 1415 MHz," *Astrophys. J.* **160** (June 1970), pp. 1185-1186.
17. P. J. Encrenaz, A. A. Penzias, J. R. Gott, G. T. Wrixon, and R. W. Wilson, "The High Velocity Complex Around l^{II}=130° b^{II}=45°: A Single Cloud?," *Astron. Astrophys.* **12** (April 1971), pp. 16-20.
18. P. G. Wannier and G. T. Wrixon, "An Unusual High-Velocity Hydrogen Feature," *Astrophys. J.* **173** (May 1972), pp. L119-L123.
19. R. H. Sanders, G. T. Wrixon, and A. A. Penzias, "Further Evidence of Explosive Events in the Galactic Nucleus," *Astron. Astrophys.* **16** (January 1972), pp. 322-326; R. H. Sanders and G. T. Wrixon, "An Expanding and Rotating Ring of Gas 2.4 kpc from the Galactic Center," *Astron. Astrophys.* **18** (1972), pp. 92-96; R. H. Sanders and G. T. Wrixon, "High Velocity Hydrogen Apparently Associated with Continuum Jets Near the Galactic Center," *Astron. Astrophys.* **18** (1972), pp. 467-470.
20. A. A. Penzias, R. W. Wilson, and P. J. Encrenaz, "Measurements of 21 cm Line Calibration Regions," *Astron. J.* **75** (March 1970), pp. 141-143; G. T. Wrixon and C.

Heiles, "Baseline Determination for 21-cm Hydrogen Line Astronomy," *Astron. Astrophys.* **18** (1972), pp. 444-449; P. J. Encrenaz, A. A. Penzias, and R. W. Wilson, "Attenuation of Radio Waves by the Atmosphere at the Frequency 1415 MHz," *Astron. Astrophys.* **9** (1970), pp. 51-52.

21. A. A. Penzias and C. A. Burrus, "Millimeter-Wavelength Radio-Astronomy Techniques," *Annual Review of Astronomy and Astrophysics* **11** (1973), pp. 31-72.

22. R. W. Wilson, K. B. Jefferts, and A. A. Penzias, "Carbon Monoxide in the Orion Nebula," *Astrophys. J.* **161** (July 1970), pp. L43-L44.

23. T. S. Chu, R. W. Wilson, R. W. England, D. A. Gray, and W. E. Legg, "The Crawford Hill 7-Meter Millimeter Wave Antenna," *Bell System Tech. J.* **57** (May-June 1978), pp. 1257-1288.

24. A. A. Penzias, "Nuclear Processing and Isotopes in the Galaxy," *Science* **208** (May 1980), pp. 663-669.

25. K. B. Jefferts, A. A. Penzias, and R. W. Wilson, "Deuterium in the Orion Nebula," *Astrophys. J.* **179** (January 1973), pp. L57-L59.

26. A. A. Penzias, "Interstellar HCN, HCO^+ , and the Galactic Deuterium Gradient," *Astrophys. J.* **228** (March 1979), pp. 430-434.

27. A. A. Penzias, "The Riddle of Cosmic Deuterium," *American Scientist* **66** (May-June 1978), pp. 291-297.

28. A. A. Stark, "Galactic Kinematics of Molecular Clouds," Princeton University Thesis, 1979.

29. T. G. Phillips and K. B. Jefferts, "A Low Temperature Bolometer Heterodyne Receiver for Millimeter Wave Astronomy," *Rev. Sci. Instrum.* **44** (August 1973), pp. 1009-1014.

30. T. G. Phillips, P. J. Huggins, T. B. H. Kuiper, and R. E. Miller, "Detection of the 610 Micron (492 GHz) Line of Interstellar Atomic Carbon," *Astrophys. J.* **238** (June 1980), pp. L103-L106.

31. A. Y. Cho and J. R. Arthur, "Molecular Beam Epitaxy," *Progress in Solid-State Chemistry* **10,** ed. G. Somorjai and J. McCaldin (New York: Pergamon Press, 1976), pp. 157-191.

32. M. V. Schneider, R. A. Linke, and A. Y. Cho, "Low-Noise Millimeter-Wave Mixer Diodes Prepared by Molecular Beam Epitaxy (MBE)," *Appl. Phys. Lett.* **31** (August 1977), pp. 219-221.

33. R. A. Linke, M. V. Schneider, and A. Y. Cho, "Cryogenic Millimeter-Wave Receiver Using Molecular Beam Epitaxy Diodes," *IEEE Trans. Microwave Theory Tech.* **MTT-26** (December 1978), pp. 935-938.

34. G. J. Dolan, T. G. Phillips, and D. P. Woody, "Low-Noise 115-GHz Mixing in Superconducting Oxide Barrier Tunnel Junctions," *Appl. Phys. Lett.* **34** (March 1979), pp. 347-349.

35. A. H. Dayem and R. J. Martin, "Quantum Interaction of Microwave Radiation with Tunneling Between Superconductors," *Phys. Rev. Lett.* **8** (March 1962), pp. 246-248.

36. J. A. Tyson and J. F. Jarvis, "Evolution of Galaxies: Automated Faint Object Counts to 24th Magnitude," *Astrophys. J.* (June 1979), pp. L153-L156.

37. A. Einstein, "Zum Gegenwartigen Stande des Gravitationsproblems," *Phys. Z.* **14** (December 1913), pp. 1249-1266.

38. J. Weber, "Evidence for Discovery of Gravitational Radiation," *Phys. Rev. Lett.* **22** (June 1969), pp. 1320-1325.

39. J. A. Tyson, "Detection of Gravitational Radiation," *Ann. N. Y. Acad. Sci.* **224** (1973) pp. 74-92.

40. D. H. Douglass, R. Q. Gram, J. A. Tyson, and R. W. Lee, "Two-Detector-Coincidence Search for Bursts of Gravitational Radiation," *Phys. Rev. Lett.* **35** (August 1975), pp. 480-483.

41. H. Billing, P. Kafka, K. Maischberger, F. Meyer, and W. Winkler, "Results of the Munich-Frascati Gravitational-Wave Experiment," *Lett. Nuovo Cimento* 12 (January 1975), pp. 111-116.

42. M. Leventhal and C. J. MacCallum, "Gamma-Ray-Line Astronomy," *Scientific American* 243 (July 1980), pp. 50-58.

43. M. Leventhal, C. J. MacCallum, and A. C. Watts, "A Search for Gamma-Ray Lines from Nova Cygni 1975, Nova Serpentis 1970, and the Crab Nebula," *Astrophys. J.* 216 (September 1977), pp. 491-502.

44. M. Leventhal, C. J. MacCallum, and P. D. Stang, "Detection of 511 keV Positron Annihilation Radiation from the Galactic Center Direction," *Astrophys. J.* 225 (October 1978), pp. L11-L14.

45. R. S. Raghavan, "Inverse b Decay of $^{115}In^{115}Sn^*$: A New Possibility for Detecting Solar Neutrinos from the Proton-Proton Reaction," *Phys. Rev. Lett.* 37 (August 1976), pp. 259-262.

46. J. N. Bahcall and R. Davis, Jr., "Solar Neutrinos: A Scientific Puzzle," *Science* 191 (January 1976), pp. 264-267.

47. S. Chapman, *Physics of Geomagnetic Phenomena, Vol. I,* ed. S. Matsushita and W. H. Campbell (New York: Academic Press, Inc., 1967), pp. 3-24.

48. K. Birkeland, *The Norwegian Aurora Polaris Expedition 1902-1903* (Christiania: 1908).

49. C. Stormer, *The Polar Aurora* (Oxford: C. Clarendon Press, 1955).

50. S. Chapman and V. C. A. Ferraro, "A New Theory of Magnetic Storms, Part I - The Initial Phase," *Terrest. Magn. Atmosph. Elec.* 36 (June 1931), pp. 77-98.

51. H. Alfvén, "A Theory of Magnetic Storms and of the Aurorae," *Kgl. Svenska Vetenskapsakad, Handl.* 18, No. 1 (1939).

52. J. A. Van Allen, G. H. Ludwig, E. C. Ray, and C. E. McIlwain, "Observation of High Intensity Radiation by Satellites 1958 Alpha and Gamma," *Jet Propulsion* 28 (September 1958), pp. 588-592.

53. S. N. Vernov, A. E. Chudakov, E. V. Garchakov, J. L. Logachev, and P. V. Vakulov, "Study of the Cosmic-Ray Soft Component by the 3rd Soviet Earth Satellite," *Planet. Space Sci.* 1, No. 86 (April 1959), pp. 86-93.

54. W. L. Brown, T. M. Buck, L. V. Medford, E. W. Thomas, H. K. Gummel, G. L. Miller, and F. M. Smits, "The Spacecraft Radiation Experiments," *Bell System Tech. J.* 42 (July 1963), pp. 899-941.

55. W. L. Brown and J. D. Gabbe, "The Electron Distribution in the Earth's Radiation Belts During July 1962 as Measured by Telstar," *J. Geophys. Res.* 68 (February 1963), pp. 607-618.

56. W. L. Brown, "Observations of the Transient Behavior of Electrons in the Artificial Radiation Belts," ed. B. M. McCormac (New York: D. Reidel Publishing Co., 1966), pp. 610-633.

57. J. W. Dungey, "Loss of Van Allen Electrons Due to Whistlers," *Planet. Space Sci.* 11 (June 1963), pp. 591-595.

58. J. M. Cornwall, "Scattering of Energetic Trapped Electrons by Very-Low Frequency Waves," *J. Geophys. Res.* 69 (April 1964), pp. 1251-1258.

59. See references 57 and 58.

60. C. S. Roberts, "Electron Loss from the Radiation Trapped in the Earth's Magnetic Field," ed. B. M. McCormac (New York: D. Reidel Publishing Co., 1966), pp. 403-421.

61. C. S. Roberts and M. Schulz, "Bounce Resonant Scattering of Particles Trapped in the Earth's Magnetic Field," *J. Geophys. Res.* 73 (December 1968), pp. 7361-7376.

62. W. L. Brown, L. J. Cahill, L. R. Davis, C. E. McIlwain, and C. S. Roberts, "Acceleration of Trapped Particles During a Magnetic Storm on April 18, 1965," *J. Geophys. Res.* 73 (January 1968), pp. 153-161.

63. A. Hasegawa, "Drift Mirror Instability in the Magnetosphere," *Phys. Fluids* 12 (December 1969), pp. 2642-2650; L. J. Lanzerotti, A. Hasegawa, and C. G. Maclen-

nan, "Drift Mirror Instability in the Magnetosphere: Particle and Field Oscillations and Electron Heating," *J. Geophys. Res.* **74** (November 1969), pp. 5565-5578.

64. D. J. Williams, J. F. Arens, and L. J. Lanzerotti, "Observations of Trapped Electrons at Low and High Altitudes," *J. Geophys. Res.* **73** (September 1968), pp. 5673-5696.

65. D. L. Carpenter, "Whistler Evidence of a 'Knee' in the Magnetospheric Ionization Density Profile," *J. Geophys. Res.* **68** (March 1963), pp. 1675-1682.

66. L. J. Lanzerotti, W. L. Brown, and C. S. Roberts, "Energetic Electrons at 6.6 R during the January 13-14, 1967, Geomagnetic Storm," *J. Geophys. Res.* **73** (September 1968), pp. 5751-5760.

67. E. W. Hones, S. Singer, L. J. Lanzerotti, D. Pierson, and T. J. Rosenberg, "Magnetospheric Substorms of August 25-26, 1967," *J. Geophys. Res.* **76** (May 1971), pp. 2977-3009.

68. E. W. Hones, Jr., R. Karas, L. J. Lanzerotti, and S. I. Akasofu, "Magnetospheric Substorms on September 14, 1968," *J. Geophys. Res.* **76** (October 1971), pp. 6765-6780.

69. A. Hasegawa, "Heating of the Magnetospheric Plasma by Electromagnetic Waves Generated in the Magnetosheath," *J. Geophys. Res.* **74** (April 1969), pp. 1763-1771; idem, "Drift-Wave Instability at the Plasmapause," *J. Geophys. Res.* **76** (August 1971), pp. 5361-5364.

70. L. J. Lanzerotti, C. S. Roberts, and W. L. Brown, "Temporal Variations in the Electron Flux at Synchronous Altitudes," *J. Geophys. Res.* **72** (December 1967), pp. 5893-5902; W. L. Brown, "Energetic Outer Belt Electrons at Synchronous Altitudes," *Earth's Particles and Fields*, ed. B. M. McCormac (New York: Reinhold Book Corporation, 1968), pp. 33-44.

71. H. R. Brewer, M. Schulz, and A. Eviatar, "Origin of Draft-Periodic Echoes in Outer Zone Electron Flux," *J. Geophys. Res.* **74** (January 1969), pp. 159-167.

72. M. Schulz and L. J. Lanzerotti, *Particle Diffusion in the Radiation Belts* (New York: Springer-Verlag, 1974).

73. L. J. Lanzerotti, C. G. Maclennan, and M. F. Robbins, "Proton Drift Echoes in the Magnetosphere," *J. Geophys. Res.* **76** (January 1971), pp. 259-263.

74. L. J. Lanzerotti, "Low-Energy Solar Protons and Alphas as Probes of the Interplanetary Medium: The May 28, 1967, Solar Event," *J. Geophys. Res.* **74** (June 1969), pp. 2851-2868.

75. L. J. Lanzerotti and M. F. Robbins, "Solar Flare Alpha to Proton Ratio Changes Following Interplanetary Disturbances," *Solar Phys.* **10** (November 1969), pp. 212-218.

76. L. J. Lanzerotti, D. Venkatesan, and G. Wibberenz, "Rise Time to Maximum Flux of Relativistic Solar Electron Events and its Relation to the High-Frequency Component of the Interplanetary Field Power Spectrum," *J. Geophys. Res.* **78** (December 1973), pp. 7986-7995.

77. L. J. Lanzerotti, "Penetration of Solar Protons and Alphas to the Geomagnetic Equator," *Phys. Rev. Lett.* **21** (September 1968), pp. 929-933.

78. L. J. Lanzerotti, "Access of Solar Particles to Synchronous Altitude," *Intercorrelated Satellite Observations Related to Solar Events*, ed. V. Manno and D. E. Page (Holland: D. Reidel, 1970), pp. 205-228.

79. A. Eviatar and R. A. Wolff, "Transfer Processes in the Magnetopause," *J. Geophys. Res.* **73** (September 1968), pp. 5561-5576.

80. L. J. Lanzerotti, H. Fukunishi, A. Hasegawa, and L. Chen, "Excitation of the Plasmapause at Ultralow Frequencies," *Phys. Rev. Lett.* **31** (September 1973), pp. 624-628.

81. H. Fukunishi and L. J. Lanzerotti, "ULF Pulsation Evidence of the Plasmapause 1. Spectral Studies of Pc 3 and Pc 4 Pulsations Near L=4," *J. Geophys. Res.* **79** (January 1974), pp. 142-158; ibid, **79** (November 1974), pp. 4632-4647.

82. L. J. Lanzerotti, A. Hasegawa, and N. A. Tartaglia, "Morphology and Interpretation of Magnetospheric Plasma Waves at Conjugate Points During December Solstice," *J. Geophys. Res.* **77** (December 1972), pp. 6731-6745; L. J. Lanzerotti and H. Fukunishi, "Modes of Magnetospheric Alfven Waves," *Rev. Geophys. Space Phys.* **12** (December 1974), p. 724.

83. L. J. Lanzerotti, C. G. Maclennan, H. Fukunishi, J. K. Walker, and D. J. Williams, "Latitude and Longitude Dependence of Storm Time Pc 5 Type Plasma-Wave," *J. Geophys. Res.* **80** (March 1975), pp. 1014-1018.

84. L. Chen and A. Hasegawa, "A Theory of Long-Period Magnetic Pulsations. 1. Steady State Excitation of Field Line Resonance," *J. Geophys. Res.* **79** (March 1974), pp. 1024-1032; idem, **79** (March 1974), pp. 1033-1037.

85. L. J. Lanzerotti and A. J. Surkan, "ULF Geomagnetic Power Near L=4. 4. Relationship to the Fredericksburg K Index," *J. Geophys. Res.* **79** (June 1974), pp. 2413-2419.

86. L. J. Lanzerotti and C. G. Morgan, "ULF Geomagnetic Power near L=4. 2. Temporal Variation of the Radian Diffusion Coefficient for Relativistic Electrons," *J. Geophys. Res.* **78** (August 1973), pp. 4600-4610.

87. L. J. Lanzerotti, C. G. Maclennan, and M. Schulz, "Radial Diffusion of Outer-Zone Electrons: An Empirical Approach to Third-Invariant Violation," *J. Geophys. Res.* **75** (October 1970), pp. 5351-5371.

Chapter 8

Ion Beams, X-Rays, Electrons, and Neutrons in Solids— Channeling and Ion Implantation

The interaction of particles or photons obtained from relatively high energy sources (10^4 eV to 10^7 eV) with solids has been an area of intensive study at Bell Laboratories. A program initiated by Bell Labs scientists, initially through the application of semiconductor particle detectors, in collaboration with researchers at Brookhaven National Laboratory and Rutgers University, led to the discovery of particle channeling and the invention of ion implantation. Particle channeling proved to be a very useful technique for the study of such problems as the location of impurity sites in semiconductors and for measuring ultrashort lifetimes in nuclei. Ion implantation came to be a necessary technique for impurity doping in electronic devices. Various aspects of X-ray spectroscopy have also been investigated at Bell Labs, including X-ray diffraction as well as inelastic scattering applied to the measurement of electron momentum transfer in solids, to photoabsorption, to ionic and covalent bonding, and to surface studies. Neutron scattering has been developed for the study of phase transitions and the electronic structure of magnetic systems.

I. PARTICLE DETECTORS, NUCLEAR PHYSICS, AND ION BEAM RESEARCH

The initiation of a research program in the field of nuclear physics resulted from a policy decision by the research administration. This

Principal authors: W. L. Brown, P. Eisenberger, L. C. Feldman, W. M. Gibson, P. M. Platzman, G. K. Wertheim, and E. A. Wood

289

decision was made on the recommendation of A. H. White,[1] who was, in the late 1950s, the executive director of the physical sciences division of Bell Laboratories. In late 1958 and early 1959 the first staff members were hired specifically to carry out nuclear physics research. (There were many ex-nuclear physicists already on the staff, working in other fields of physics, some of whom played a significant role in advising the administration in its decision to initiate such a program.)

Their first task was to evaluate specific ways in which Bell Labs could make an impact in the field. In a technical memorandum P. F. Donovan and W. M. Gibson, together with J. Hensel, outlined the importance of the then new tandem Van de Graaff accelerator to nuclear physics studies and proposed that Bell Labs acquire an accelerator. Indeed, as predicted in that memo, nuclear physics was about to embark on a new period of growth, spurred by three technological developments: the tandem accelerators, semiconductor diode particle detectors, and on-line digital computers. The small nuclear physics group at Bell Labs, with its ready access to solid state technology, was in a very good position to make an impact in this field. Within a period of five years the group became widely respected because of its significant contribution to the development of particle detectors and the use of on-line computers for nuclear physics experiments.

In the absence of an experimental nuclear facility, Bell Labs collaborated with other laboratories, especially Brookhaven National Laboratory in Upton, New York. In the context of these collaborations, the first Bell Labs nuclear physics papers centered on nuclear reaction mechanisms in light elements and the spectroscopy of light nuclei by Donovan and collaborators,[2,3] and on the nuclear fission mechanisms by Gibson and coworkers.[4]

1.1 Semiconductor Particle Detectors

Virtually from the beginning, it was recognized that semiconductor detectors represented a potentially powerful tool in nuclear physics research and a possible entry for the small Bell Labs group into the established nuclear physics community. Indeed, it was at Bell Labs that semiconductor particle detectors had previously been invented by K. G. McKay,[5,6] following the intensive investigation into the properties of so-called "crystal detectors" by D. E. Wooldridge, A. J. Ahearn, and J. A. Burton.[7] Outside Bell Labs, there had been contributions by R. Hofstadter and others.[8] However, the new detectors did not catch on and had for the most part been dropped, except at Purdue University, where J. W. Mayer was working as a graduate student in 1958 demonstrating some of the possibilities.

Soon thereafter, Donovan began producing "state-of-the-art" semiconductor detectors. It was not long before scores of visitors from nuclear laboratories all over the world began making Bell Labs a port of call and carrying away a "recipe," small vials of p-type and n-type "paint," and even samples of filter paper, laboratory wipes, and wooden sticks used by Donovan to perform his "magic art." The techniques were gradually modified and improved, largely by T. C. Madden and Gibson, to include oxide passivation, controlled diffusion, and improved contacting and mounting procedures.

One outcome of this work was an invention for improved phosphorus and boron diffusion procedures that became widely adopted throughout the semiconductor industry. Two important contributors to the developments during this period were G. L. Miller and W. L. Brown. Miller began collaborating with the Bell Labs nuclear physics group while he was still at Brookhaven National Laboratory. He was later recruited to Bell Labs. In the period of development of semiconductor detectors, Brown provided the basis for defining and quantifying the physics underlying these devices. [Fig. 8-1]

1.1.1 Effect of Radiation Damage on Transistors and Telstar Malfunction

It was largely the involvement of Brown and Miller that resulted in the first major spin-off from the nuclear physics program. In early 1961, as plans for the Telstar communications research satellite were being formulated, important questions arose about the effects of radiation from the newly discovered Van Allen Belt. The detector development effort (with its associated electronics development) prompted Brown and Miller to propose a series of experiments to be included on Telstar to measure the amount, type, and energy spectrum of radiation encountered by the satellite. T. M. Buck, H. E. Kern, J. W. Rodgers, L. V. Medford, H. P. Lie, E. W. Thomas, and others were recruited to help with the intensive design and testing effort. The highly successful experiments were continued on Telstar I, Telstar II, and other satellites, and resulted in the Bell Labs magnetospheric research program, which is described in Chapter 7 of this volume.

During 1961, Gibson and Miller, together with T. D. Thomas of Brookhaven Laboratory and G. Safford of Columbia University, carried out a series of studies of the mechanism of thermal-neutron-induced fission of uranium and plutonium. This experiment involved placing semiconductor detectors and associated preamplifiers in a high-radiation region of the Brookhaven graphite research reactor. After troublesome reliability problems with commercial transistors in the preamplifiers, they succeeded in obtaining a few of the exten-

Fig. 8-1. W. L. Brown, who has led the Bell Labs research effort in the use of energetic ions, in one of the two Van de Graaff accelerator laboratories at the Murray Hill, New Jersey, location of Bell Labs. This accelerator is used as a source of high-energy positive ions (up to 3 MeV) for ion implantation, modification of the properties of solids, and ion beam analysis of the composition and lattice perfection of solids.

sively tested transistors specially selected for use in Telstar. To their surprise, it was found that even with these transistors the preamplifiers rapidly became inoperative in the reactor radiation environment even though they were fine elsewhere. The implications for Telstar were immediately evident and an intensive investigation traced the failure to ions produced by the incident radiation in the gas surrounding the encapsulated transistor chip. When operating voltages were applied to the device in the presence of radiation, the ions were attracted to the silicon surface near the p-n junction of the transistor, producing surface inversion layers and resulting in catastrophic failure. It was also found that the transistors showed a very large variability in sensitivity to this newly discovered radiation effect. The discovery of this effect in late 1961, just months before the scheduled Telstar launch, made it impractical to carry out the investigations and design changes necessary to substitute some other kind of transistor not subject to this surface ionization problem. Consequently, a massive program was carried out to test thousands of transistors, and a new satellite electronics system was built containing less sensitive components.

In spite of all of these precautions, radiation damage terminated the life of Telstar I and posed its central problem in reliability. After more than four months of successful performance, the satellite command system began to cause difficulty. This led to suspicion that certain transistors in the command decoder circuit, which were protected by enough aluminum to stop electrons of energy less than about 1.5 million electronvolts, were probably damaged by more energetic electrons. Before the satellite was launched, it was believed that there were very few electrons as energetic as this in the inner Van Allen Belt. However, the Telstar radiation measurements of flux and energy indicated a substantial fraction of electrons with energies about 1.5 MeV (the observed flux was about 1,000 times that expected), probably the result of a high-altitude nuclear explosion that occurred the day before the satellite was launched. A replica of the suspected circuit was similarly bombarded with electrons in the laboratory, and it also failed, confirming the postulated cause for the failure of the Telstar circuits. [Fig. 8-2]

Because the Brookhaven experiments had shown that in the absence of applied voltage the transistors recovered, even in the presence of radiation, an ingenious "trick" was played on the satellite to get it to turn off its batteries during a period when the satellite was eclipsed by the earth's shadow. This turned off the power from the solar panels and resulted in the celebrated "repair in space" that prolonged the useful life of the satellite for some weeks more. This accidental discovery in the Brookhaven experiments provided a possible explanation of previous satellite and missile malfunctions.

1.1.2 *Instrumentation of Nuclear Physics Experiments*

The reconsideration of the technology of nuclear physics measurement was also a feature of much of the effort in the Bell Labs program as well as at other laboratories during the decade of the 1960s. This led to the development of low-noise, charge-sensitive amplifiers by Miller and E. A. Gere in association with the Brookhaven Laboratory Instrumentation Division. Charge-sensitive amplifiers became of major importance in optical communication systems, in applications involving charge-coupled devices (CCDs), and in other advanced design instruments. The effort also led to the work of Miller, J. V. Kane, Gere, Lie, and J. F. Mollenauer who, among others, pioneered the coupling of experimental measurements directly with small, dedicated computers. In particular, the Bell Labs group, together with E. H. Cook-Yarborough, visiting for a year from the Atomic Energy Research Establishment at Harwell, England, initiated the data bus approach (a common pathway for back-and-forth transmission among the subunits of the computer and associated experiments) to computer-experiment and computer-output equipment interfaces.

Pulse-counting techniques, largely developed in nuclear laboratories, became increasingly important to communications technology and other non-nuclear areas of scientific research, and the small nuclear instrumentation group continued to play a role in making developments available.

A major outcome of the early years that was somewhat unusual for Bell Labs (or any industrial laboratory) was the establishment of a joint Bell Laboratories-Rutgers University nuclear physics research program and facility.

1.2 The Rutgers University-Bell Laboratories Accelerator Laboratory

In late 1959, it became evident that the effective involvement of Bell Labs in nuclear physics required a facility closer to home and more under our control than those being used at Brookhaven Laboratory, at Oak Ridge National Laboratory in Tennessee, at the University of California at Berkeley, and other places.

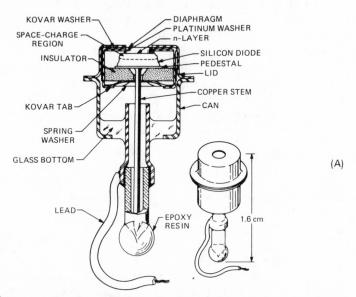

(A)

Fig. 8-2. (A) Drawing of a silicon diffused junction diode particle detector used as the sensitive element in the particle detector experiments flown on Telstar I and II. The diode was specially designed and fabricated for operational reliability. It is totally enclosed in a vacuum-sealed can with a 0.008 cm-thick Kovar window to permit even low-energy particles to reach the detector. For diode stability and sensitivity it is formed by high-temperature diffusion of phosphorous into high-resistivity p-type silicon. For low contact resistance it has a gold-alloy back contact and a platinum-ring front contact. This design was based on experience with detectors used in nuclear physics experiments combined with experience with high-vacuum techniques of

Through the efforts of Brown and Burton of Bell Labs, and H. C. Torrey, then physics department chairman at Rutgers University, an arrangement was established to provide a program of joint use of nuclear facilities. At that same time an order was placed with High Voltage Engineering Corporation in Massachusetts for a tandem Van de Graaff accelerator. This was the first of a new higher-energy series of "King" tandems designed to accelerate protons in two stages up to 16 MeV. A joint Bell Labs-Rutgers University committee was established to make major decisions about the design and operation of the facility.

In 1963, G. M. Temmer [Fig. 8-3] was recruited to be director of the Nuclear Physics Laboratory and chairman of the joint accelerator committee. The building was completed in the spring of 1964 and the accelerator installation completed in mid-1965. During the installation period and the first ten years of operation of the accelerator facility, Bell Labs received international recognition for contributions to physics, as well as technology, arising from this program. For example, during the design of the accelerator laboratory, Miller and Gibson, together with Gere, did a careful study of the optimum of

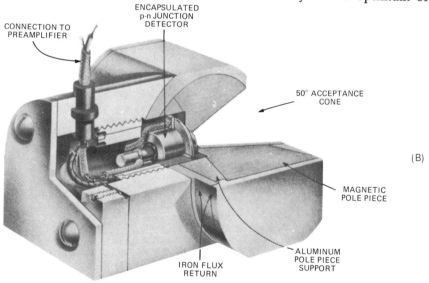

encapsulation. (B) A cutaway view of one of the detector assemblies flown on Telstar I and Telstar II. There were four detectors on each satellite measuring different particles and energy ranges. This detector is mounted in a special housing to enable the measurement of electrons with energies above 230 keV. Because Telstar I was launched one day after a high-altitude nuclear test explosion, a large region of space was filled with an unexpectedly high concentration of energetic electrons, and this detector played a critical role in helping to understand their distribution and their origin.

Fig. 8-3. G. M. Temmer (right), director of the Nuclear Physics Laboratory
at Rutgers University, and G. L. Miller of Bell Laboratories standing in front
of the Rutgers-Bell Labs tandem accelerator. The accelerator facility has
been used collaboratively since its installation in the mid-1960s. Miller and
coworkers at Bell Labs were involved in the design, construction, and
implementation of the nuclear instrumentation and accelerator control systems.

cabling, ground system, power system, and so on for handling and
transmitting low-level pulses. This has served as the guide for many
of the nuclear accelerator facilities built in the United States and elsewhere since that time. The impressive physics output from the
Rutgers University-Bell Labs Accelerator Laboratory reflects the close
collaboration of Bell Labs scientists with Rutgers faculty, visitors, and
students. In fact, the extent of the interaction with graduate student
research has represented a unique feature of this program as compared to other research programs at Bell Labs. Since its inception, 12
student Ph.D. research programs and 2 Masters degree programs have
been directed either wholly or in part by Bell Labs scientists. Many of
these students have continued to play an important role in Bell Labs
work subsequent to their graduation.

The flavor and evolution of nuclear physics research at Bell Laboratories during its initial period can be conveyed by outlining some of
the major achievements.

1.2.1 Nuclear Reactions, Nuclear Structure, and Magnetic Moments

In the first years, studies of two-body and three-body final states utilizing coincidence measurements of reaction products with the newly developed solid state detectors was perhaps the best known and most scientifically important result of the program. D. Donovan was the spokesman of a group that included Kane and Mollenauer, D. Wilkinson of Oxford University, D. Alberger from Brookhaven Laboratory, and other visitors and collaborators. This group gained new insights into neutron, proton, and light nuclei bonding and interactions.[9] Studies of mechanisms and properties of nuclear fission by Gibson, Miller, and collaborators also characterized the early years.[10] At the time of this writing, nuclear reaction studies have been dominated by applications of a new blocking lifetime technique, which utilizes the particle channeling effect discussed in section 1.3 of this chapter. In this technique, charged particles, emerging from a nuclear reaction, have an angular distribution that is influenced by neighboring atoms in rows and planes in the crystal. These serve to *block* transmission in certain directions. If the radiative emission has a long *lifetime*, so that the nucleus emits radiation after it has recoiled from its lattice position, then blocking is reduced. The technique, first developed at Rutgers University by Gibson and K. A. Nielsen from Aarhus University in Denmark, has evolved into a valuable tool for studying nuclear reactions.[11] This work has been carried on in collaboration with Temmer, who was at Rutgers University at the time, together with a host of visitors and postdoctoral associates and students from Australia, Japan, Canada, Denmark, and the United States. The short decay times that can be measured (approximately 10^{-18} seconds) represent a new time frame for studies that might be called nuclear kinetics.

As in the reaction studies, nuclear spectroscopic studies were dominated in the first years by the coincidence work of Donovan, Kane, Mollenauer, and collaborators. Structure and excited states of ^{12}C and the discovery of excited states of ^{4}He were the highlights of the period.[12] The middle period was characterized principally by the systematic studies of transition rates in ^{58}Ni and ^{56}Fe, and the extensive study of the spectroscopic and decay properties of ^{40}Ca by J. R. Mac-Donald who had joined the group from Oxford University.[13] Doppler-shift attenuation measurements of gamma rays were a primary tool in these studies, which were carried out together with N. Koller from Rutgers University and a number of visitors and students. Following this lead, new techniques based on solid state effects became more and more a part of the program. Nuclear moments in a variety of nuclei were studied by using perturbation of angular correlations of emitted radiation from nuclei imbedded, usually by implantation, in a magnetic matrix. This research was the work of D. E. Murnick who joined the nuclear physics group at Bell Labs from M.I.T. in 1967.[14] E. N. Kaufmann, and R. S. Raghavan and P. Raghavan have also made major contributions to this field of hyperfine interactions in crystals applied to studies of fundamental nuclear properties.[15,16]

1.2.2 *Application to Other Physics Problems*

Bell Labs nuclear physics program has had a very strong dependence on solid state physics techniques. Simultaneously, solid state or atomic physics studies have made strong and effective use of the techniques and tools of nuclear physics. Particle channeling studies were the first, and continue to be an example of the interaction between solid state and nuclear physics. This is discussed in more detail below. In the mid-1970s, studies of hyperfine fields led by Murnick, Kaufmann, R. S. Raghavan, and P. Raghavan addressed an impressive variety of questions concerning magnetic and quadrupole interactions,[17] transient field strengths experienced by moving ions, and temperature dependence of hyperfine fields.[18] In some cases these have been combined with channeling studies to define the details of specific magnetic environments inside crystals. Other activities in the 1970s centered on studies of basic quantum electrodynamics by Murnick, M. Leventhal, C. K. N. Patel, and O. R. Wood, together with H. W. Kugel of Rutgers University. In their work, the Lamb shifts of very high energy beams of hydrogenic (one-electron) carbon, oxygen, and fluorine ions were measured after excitation in passing through thin foils or gas targets. (See Chapter 6, section 1.1.) In the fluorine case the measurement involved a pioneering achievement in the use of an HBr laser to resonantly examine the excited states produced.[19] A CO_2 laser was used for the ionized chlorine studies.

1.3 Particle Channeling

It may be of interest to relate briefly one series of events that may be considered to represent a self-contained microcosm of the whole research story—how unexpected results in one field can lead to important applications in another, which may, in turn, provide new opportunities in the first field again. In 1962, Gibson and Madden began to develop a very thin [approximately 10 to 20 micrometer (μm)] semiconductor detector through which particles are transmitted.

This detector would be used to determine the atomic number and mass of low-mass particles (protons, deuterons, helium ions, and so on) that might be emitted during nuclear fission of heavy elements. H. E. Wegner of Brookhaven National Laboratory and others had attempted to take advantage of the intrinsically improved statistics (and hence, better resolution) of semiconductor detectors as compared with other detectors. The expected improvement had not been observed, and the problem had been ascribed to thickness variations in the thin silicon detector. Modifying a planar etching technique developed by other people at Bell Labs, Madden and Gibson produced detectors that could be shown to be uniform in thickness to ±5 percent and were thinner (15 μm) than any previously produced. However, measurements with monoenergetic, 5 MeV helium ions showed detector response variations even larger than had been obtained previously. It was soon discovered that the detector response depended on small variations in the detector orientation relative to the direction of the incident particles. It was recognized that this was a manifestation, at high particle energy, of a particle channeling effect—the steering of particles through the crystal lattice by rows or planes of lattice atoms that had previously been demonstrated at very much lower particle energy (10 to 30 keV) in a number of laboratories in the United States, Canada, England, and Germany. [Fig. 8-4]

Interest in this new phenomenon led to an intensive series of studies at Brookhaven Laboratory, Columbia University, and on the Bell Labs-Rutgers University accelerator. These studies, which concentrated on measurements of particles transmitted through thin crystals, played an important role in the understanding of particle channeling. Over the next few years, increasing numbers of people became involved in the channeling studies and in related particle-solid interaction studies. Brown was involved from the beginning; B. R. Appleton, L. C. Feldman, M. R. Altman, and J. K. Hirvonen were all involved initially as Rutgers University graduate students. Appleton and Feldman continued at Bell Labs following their completion of graduate studies at Rutgers and helped to establish a small accelerator program at Murray Hill. The increased understanding of energetic particle interactions with crystals and the general interest generated by this work led to the development of an ion implantation program at Bell Labs. This is perhaps the most significant spin-off to date from the nuclear physics program. It is interesting that just as in the case of particle detectors, the general advantages and principles of ion implantation were recognized and patented at Bell Labs in the early 1950s, but the development awaited establishment of supporting technology (such as nuclear accelerators) and related background knowledge.

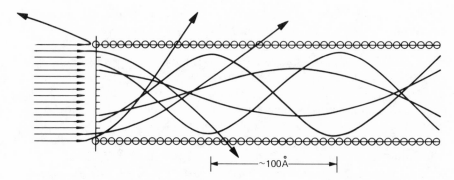

Fig. 8-4. Channeling of ions in a crystal. This schematic is a greatly distorted view of two rows of atoms in a crystal and the trajectories of ions between them. The spacing between the two rows has been enlarged for clarity by a factor of 30 compared with the spacing between atoms in the rows. A beam of particles arrives from the left moving parallel to the rows. The beam particles encounter the two rows at all possible impact distances. The trajectories are deflected by the mutual repulsion between the positive cores of the ions and the atoms. Ions that happen to have close encounters with the two surface atoms (the end atom in each row) are strongly deflected. Ions having more distant encounters are less strongly deflected and may take up oscillating trajectories between the two rows. Such ions are channeled. They are deflected by gentle repulsive collisions with several atoms at each turning point and do not have hard collisions with any individual nucleus. Channeled ions thus penetrate much more deeply into a crystalline solid. If the incident ion beam is not nearly parallel to the atom rows channeling cannot take place. For 1-MeV He$^+$ ions in silicon the critical angle within which the beam must be aligned to a <110> axis in order to channel is ~0.3°.

When an energetic ion is incident on a single crystal within a certain critical angle of a major symmetry direction, the strings of atoms form channels for the beam, steering the beam by successive small-angle coulomb collisions. The most direct result of this trajectory guiding is that projectile-atom distances cannot become very small, so that those violent atomic collisions that require very small impact distances do not occur. All nuclear reactions, including Rutherford scattering, depend on violent collisions. It is this modified nuclear encounter probability that has given rise to so many of the channeling applications described below. In channeling trajectories, ions also encounter lower-than-average electron densities. Since an energetic ion loses energy primarily by collisions with electrons, the low electronic encounter probability gives rise to reduced energy loss processes. It was this energy loss reduction that Gibson and Madden first observed.

1.3.1 *Ion Transmission Through Thin Crystals*

The energy loss of projectiles through thin crystals was the major emphasis of the early Bell Labs channeling program. In a series of classic experiments on the Bell Labs-Rutgers University tandem Van de Graaff accelerator, Gibson, in collaboration with C. Erginsoy and Wegner of Brookhaven Laboratory and Appleton, a Rutgers graduate student at the time, explored the orientation dependence of energy loss and multiple scattering (beam spreading effects) for MeV protons channeled through silicon and germanium.[20-25] They demonstrated the importance of trajectory steering by planes of atoms, provided precise measurements and models of the channeling energy loss, and measured the dramatic narrowing of the emergent-beam angular distribution for channeled ions. Transmission experiments continued into the mid-1970s to refine the understanding of the channeled ion trajectories and the flux distribution of channeled ions. Gibson's collaborators in this effort included Feldman, Altman, and J. A. Golovchenko as well as those mentioned above.[26-29] The work with Golovchenko is of particular note. Using very thin silicon crystals (1000Å), transmission angular distributions were analyzed to determine the effective channeling atomic potential and the breakdown of statistical equilibrium, a fundamental tenet of channeling theory.[30]

In order to coordinate the transmission results with the reduction in nuclear scattering in channeling, Gibson enlisted Feldman, another Rutgers graduate student, to initiate a study of scattering under channeling conditions.[31] They examined the effect of atomic arrangement on the angular distribution of ions emerging from a crystal after a nuclear collision. Such ions are "blocked" by these neighbors in symmetry densities. [Fig. 8-5]

Feldman was among the first to compare his measurements with computer simulations of the channeling process, including lattice vibrational changes in atomic position. In later years, such calculations became the standard for experimental comparison. Working with Feldman during a one-year visit to Bell Laboratories, J. U. Andersen of Aarhus University in Denmark made detailed comparisons between these computer simulations and an analytical approach originated at Aarhus.[32] Other work on the channeling process in the 1967-1970 period included electron and positron channeling done by W. M. Augustyniak and Andersen in order to obtain more insight into the importance of quantum effects in channeling descriptions;[33-35] de-channeling studies by Feldman, Brown, and Appleton that considered the various multiple scattering mechanisms that give rise to the escape of particles from channels;[36,37] and "double alignment" studies of Appleton and Feldman that explored the simultaneous use of channeling and blocking.[38-40]

1.3.2 Impurity Sites Location

Possibilities for the applications of channeling processes were recognized early in the development of the field. Two of the most

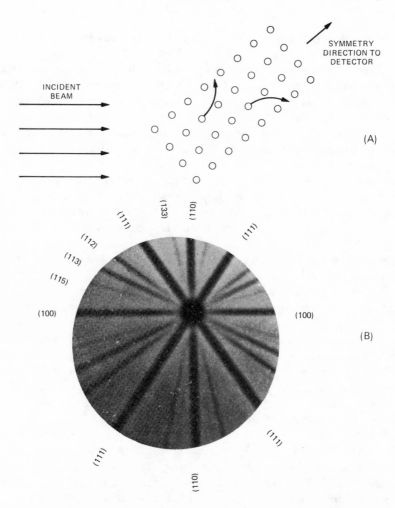

Fig. 8-5. (A) Illustration of the blocking phenomenon in a single crystal of silicon. An ion beam, not aligned with an axis or a plane in the crystal, enters the solid. After a collision between an incident particle and a nucleus in the crystal, it may be scattered and headed toward some other atom. It is blocked from continuing in that direction and will be deflected away. Since the scattered particle starts from a nuclear position, it is blocked by other nuclei from emerging in axial or planar directions. The blocking is thus the inverse of channeling; that is, whereas a channeling ion does not interact strongly with an atom in a row or plane, the strongly scattered ion cannot enter a channeling direction. (B) The blocking pattern of protons from a single crystal of silicon near the <110> axis. The dark lines, corresponding to the absence of particles, are blocked planes around the <110> axis in silicon. If the crystal contains atoms out of place (not in the normal rows or planes), scattering from them can occur in axial or planar directions, and the blocking pattern becomes measurably less distinct. [Brown, in *Radiation Effects in Semiconductors*: 378, 379].

useful applications were the determination of the lattice site of impurities in single crystals and indications of the crystalline damage in the surface region of a solid. These two applications were rather finely honed because they were strongly coupled to the understanding of ion implantation, a method of impurity doping that was being developed at the time. [Fig. 8-6]

The lattice location technique is based on the trajectory of channeled ions, namely, that channeled ions do not undergo close-encounter processes with atoms on regular crystal sites. As a result, channeled ions cannot scatter from substitutional impurities. However, they can interact with interstitial impurities—hence, there is a discrimination between impurities on different lattice sites. The process is sufficiently well understood for it to be a quantitative tool for lattice site determination in many instances.

Sensitivity to crystalline damage is a result of the fact that channeling requires an ordered arrangement of atoms, and imperfections in that arrangement disrupt the channeling process. In the limit, an amorphous or random arrangement of atoms displays no channeling effects whatsoever. Compared to other damage probes, channeling is relatively insensitive; however, it is ideal for measuring the rather massive damage that accompanies ion implantation into most semiconductors.

In 1968, W. M. Gibson spent a year at Aarhus University and carried out some of the first channeling measurements on implanted systems in silicon.[41,42] In the same year, Brown supervised the installation of a 2 MeV Van de Graaff at Bell Labs' Murray Hill, N.J., site that became the workhorse for all the channeling applications to follow. As expected, 1-MeV to 2-MeV helium appeared to be the best probe for many of the channeling applications, and the majority of the channeling programs moved from Rutgers, with its high energy tandem Van de Graaff accelerator useful for transmission studies, to the Bell Labs facility. Measurements of the impurity lattice location type were carried out in a number of general areas involving implantation into semiconductors, atomic systems of interest to the field of hyperfine physics, and implantation formation of alloys in metals.

Studies of internal hyperfine fields at the sites of impurity ions implanted into metallic hosts were carried out in the early 1970s. Those studies coordinated the internal electromagnetic field of an impurity with its lattice location. Measurements were made by Feldman, Kaufmann, MacDonald, Murnick, and J. M. Poate in a variety of atomic systems.[43-47] As a result of these measurements, a variety of anomalous results in the systematics of the hyperfine measurements were interpreted.

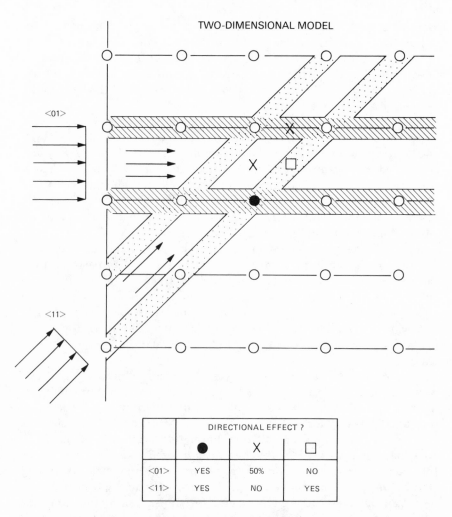

Fig. 8-6. Lattice site location of impurity atoms in a crystal using channeling. Three different impurity positions are illustrated in the figure: a substitutional position ● (atom in a normal lattice site) and two interstitial positions X, □. An ion beam channeling in the <01> direction passes between the rows of atoms of the crystal marked with diagonal shading. Such a beam does not interact strongly (as required for a nuclear reaction or for backscattering) with the ● or one of the X's because they are in the atomic rows that guide the channeling motion. The other half of the X's and the □ are "visible" to the beam and may strongly interact with it. From the standpoint of a beam channeling in the <11> direction, the situation is much different. The ● is still "invisible" to the channeling beam, as is also the □. However, both X's are now out in the channeled beam path and susceptible to strong interaction. In this way, it is possible to triangulate on the location of an impurity and locate it with respect to the position of atoms of the lattice.

The work in metals led to more general interest in the study of metals and the possibilities of forming alloys by implantation. Lattice location measurements again played a significant role in those studies. In the very dilute regime, the systems of carbon in iron,[48] and boron in iron and tungsten, were explored—both clear cases of interstitial impurities. In the high-dose regime, systems such as tungsten in copper and gold in nickel were measured and channeling measurements indicated that a new metastable, substitutional phase was formed.[49,50] This basic work in metals continued beyond the period covered in this chapter.

1.3.3 *Ultrashort Lifetime of Excited Nuclei*

One interesting postscript to this story was the use of the channeling effect to measure the lifetime for proton-induced fission of uranium by Gibson and Nielsen at the Bell Labs-Rutgers University accelerator in 1969. The channeling effect technique has resulted in the shortest direct determinations of the lifetime of excited nuclei ever reported (less than 10^{-18} seconds) and has developed into a powerful new tool in nuclear physics studies. In addition, applications of particle channeling have been extended to single-crystal studies of the positions of impurity ions, radiation damage, and interatomic potential distributions. The technique has even been extended to ultrahigh energies of several billion electronvolts, where other new applications may be anticipated.

1.4 Ion Implantation

Ion implantation is the process of injecting (implanting) charged atoms (ions) into a solid. The materials research scientist may use the implantation process to alter the electrical, optical, chemical, magnetic, or mechanical properties of a solid. In general, such modifications may come about by the interactions of the ion-solid system as the projectile slows down and by its presence after it comes to rest. The internal electromagnetic fields in solids can provide large perturbations to a variety of fundamental processes. Thus implantation is a broadly applied technique and an area of active research.[51]

It is apparent why the implantation process has such appeal. The electronic properties of materials are often governed chiefly by their impurities and defects. A more conventional method of introducing impurities, prior to the introduction of ion implantation, was through thermal diffusion. By contrast, in the implantation scheme, impurity atoms are "fired" into the material in a highly directed injection process. A solid must accept the impurity, and implantations of any solid with any impurity are possible at any temperature. In addition, since the impurities are in the form of an ion beam, great control is possible in terms of measuring the implanted dose, in reproducibility, and in terms of the spatial extent of the implanted region.

The implantation process found its first applications in the semiconductor field. The development of semiconductors and their application in the nuclear energy field stimulated studies of the effects of nuclear radiation on such devices. The effects were invariably considered as detrimental processes. It required imagination on the part of R. S. Ohl who, in 1952, reported perhaps the first ion bombardment experiment that *improved* device characteristics.[52]

The modern era of ion implantation in science and technology began in the mid-1960s and was stimulated by interest and technical progress in a number of areas having to do with ion beams and solids. Of paramount importance in this development were Gibson's studies of the phenomenon of ion channeling on the Rutgers-Bell tandem Van de Graaff accelerator.[53] Not only was the channeling effect of interest in the field of particle-solid interactions, but its application played an important role in the further development of ion implantation. [Fig. 8-7]

1.4.1 Semiconductor Doping

Stimulated by the development of the channeling technique, ion implantation as a doping technique began to be studied in detail. In 1968, Gibson reported a number of studies on the modification of semiconductors by ion implantation.[54] A. U. MacRae and T. E. Seidel formed some of the first devices made by implantation at Bell Labs.[55] (For more on this topic see section 3.2 of Chapter 19.)

The importance of ion implantation as a research tool and potential technological applications was quickly realized by Brown and Burton at Bell Labs. [Fig. 8-8] They arranged to have the Murray Hill laboratory equipped with proper ion beam accelerators, which are relatively large and expensive pieces of equipment that are normally found in nuclear physics establishments. Bell Labs' interest in particle-solid interaction studies and applications increased to the point that as of 1981 a total of ten accelerators, or ion implantation machines, were in operation at Murray Hill and an even larger number at branch laboratories and Western Electric installations.

The first reports of implantation studies in semiconductors from the Murray Hill 2-MeV facility appeared in 1969. Feldman and Rodgers

Fig. 8-7. W. M. Gibson adjusting apparatus at the Rutgers University-Bell Laboratories tandem Van de Graaff accelerator. Gibson is particularly noted for his pioneering studies of ion channeling in crystalline solids and ion implantation for doping semiconductors and for modifying other properties of solids.

studied the depth profile of the lattice disorder accompanying ion implantation into silicon,[56] and J. C. North and Gibson studied boron implantation into silicon.[57] In the following years, there were extensive studies of the bismuth in gallium phosphide system by J. L. Merz and Feldman.[58] Other studies included bismuth in silicon by Brown, S. T. Picraux, and Gibson,[59] and heavy ion damage studies in silicon by Brown, Gibson, P. M. Glotin (a visitor from France), and Hirvonen.[60,61]

1.4.2 Device Applications

Beginning in 1969, the publication of papers having to do with ion implantation increased markedly. Of particular note is the work of Feldman, Merz, and Augustyniak, who studied the formation of photoluminescence centers in ZnTe by implantation of ^{16}O and ^{18}O.[62] These authors also did an extensive study of the implantation of bismuth into the compound semiconductor GaP. The bismuth isoelectronic trap corresponds to the substitutional replacement of phosphorus with bismuth and is observed as a characteristic line in

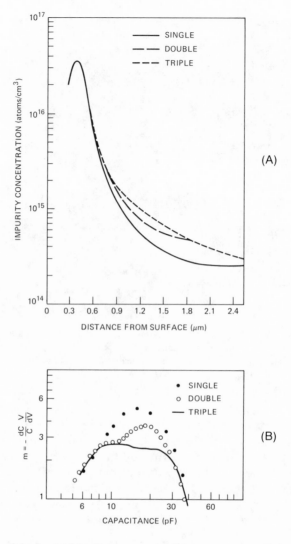

Fig. 8-8. Ion implantation has permitted the very precise tailoring of doping distributions to achieve unique device parameters. Varactor diodes (voltage variable capacitors) are an example. In the work of Moline and Foxhall, implantation of phosphorous ions into silicon was carried out (1) singly — 10^{12} 300 keV P/cm^2, 7° off the <111> axis; (2) doubly — (1) plus 4×10^{10} 600 keV P/cm^2, parallel to <111>; (3) triply (1) + (2) plus 6×10^{10} 300 keV P/cm^2 parallel to <111>. The impurity distributions for these three cases are shown in part (A) of the figure. The subtle differences among them are evident. Part (B) of the figure shows the sensitivity of the varactor diodes, dC/C/dV/V, with capacitance. A high and uniform value is desirable for some applications, the result achieved with the triple implant. Achieving such subtle distributions with reproducibility is impractical without the control of both dose and depth that implantation provides.

the luminescence spectrum. Using channeling and photoluminescence techniques, the optimum implantation and annealing conditions were determined for maximum light emission.

The important system of boron implanted into silicon was studied by North and Gibson.[63] Correlating channeling measurements to determine the substitutionality of the boron with electrical measurements of the donor concentration, they studied the proper conditions for efficient implantation. D. F. Daly and K. A. Picker studied implantation damage using electron paramagnetic resonance techniques.[64] The widespread scientific applicability of implantation was also brought forth by the work of Murnick and coworkers, in which nuclear excited atoms were recoil implanted into ferromagnetic hosts.[65] In these measurements either the internal electromagnetic fields or the nuclear properties of the excited atom were deduced.

The rapid progress in ion implantation and ion beam techniques continued through the early 1970s. Motivated by the implantation experiments in ferromagnets, fundamental research into implantation in metals was begun. Seeking to correlate the results of the internal field measurements with the lattice position of the implanted ion, a number of channeling-lattice location experiments were carried out in metals by Feldman, Kaufmann, and Poate.[66] High-dose implantations were investigated in metals as the bridge between impurity injection and alloy formation was crossed. The classic system of carbon implanted into iron was explored.

The studies of implantation into silicon continued with increasing sophistication. Using channeling techniques, Feldman, Brown, and Gibson made contributions to the efforts being carried on in many laboratories around the world to understanding the implantation process in silicon.[67] These studies yielded very successful prescriptions for the use of ion implantation in the production of semiconductor devices.

Ion bombardment techniques were also applied to superconductors, in this case to create defects in a controlled way in order to understand their effect. The implantation of radioactive species into hexagonal crystals, combined with channeling techniques by Kaufmann, R. S. Raghavan, and P. Raghavan, led to new insights into the origins of the electric field gradients in non-cubic metals.[68] Implantation was still a growing technique beyond the end of the period described herein and continued to provide new developments in science and technology into the 1980s.

1.4.3 *Implantation in Insulators and Metals*

While semiconductors have dominated the development of ion implantation because of their technological importance, some research has also been carried out with insulators and metals. In insulators, the principal interest in 1972-1974 was in the alteration of the index of refraction of transparent solids (amorphous SiO_2 in particular) by ion implantation with the idea of being able to form optical waveguides of small dimensions in patterns that might be useful in optical circuits. It was found by R. D. Standley and coworkers that a wide variety of ions were effective, the major effect being caused by structural changes, rather than by the presence of a specific impurity.[69] Studies with light ions by H. M. Presby and Brown showed that both electronic excitation in SiO_2 and elastic collisions of ions with nuclei of the solid caused changes in the refractive index.[70] In these early studies, the optical loss in guides formed by implantation was relatively high.

There has been a continuing interest in ion implantation into metals. The studies in the late 1960s and early 1970s were primarily concerned with determining the lattice site locations of implanted impurities in ferromagnetic hosts (iron and nickel) in order to aid in the interpretation of hyperfine interaction measurements.[71] In 1973, J. M. Poate and his colleagues started a series of experiments to investigate the metallurgy of the implantation process.[72] They studied copper binary alloys with implantation concentrations up to approximately 30 percent and observed the formation of equilibrium solid solutions, metastable solid solutions, and amorphous alloys. These studies have demonstrated the strong similarities between implantation and the more conventional rapid quenching techniques.

A major step in ion implantation metallurgy was taken by E. N. Kaufmann and collaborators in work starting in 1973.[73] They chose beryllium as the host lattice for implantation studies because of the very low probability of dynamic replacement collisions and low defect densities. The final impurity should therefore represent the metallurgical or chemical propensities of the species involved. They implanted over 25 metallic elements into beryllium to form unique metastable substitutional and interstitial configurations, and in collaboration with the theorists J. R. Chelikowsky and J. C. Phillips, were able to correlate these configurations using an extension of the existing theory of metallic alloying.

These studies have shown implantation to be a unique tool for producing surface alloys, with much interest at Bell Laboratories and elsewhere in evaluating other properties of these surface alloys such as corrosion resistance and hardness.[74]

1.5 Ion Scattering

1.5.1 *Medium Energy Ion Scattering*

In 1968, T. M. Buck initiated ion scattering research using ions in the energy range of 100 keV to 300 keV to analyze surface composition and, possibly, surface structure. He was motivated by the need for improved surface analytical techniques in semiconductor technology (Auger electron spectroscopy was not yet widely used), by the simple kinematic relationships that prevail in the scattering technique, by the available data on the Rutherford scattering cross sections, and by the recently discovered channeling effect.

Buck and coworkers used 100 keV He^+ and H^+ beams to analyze trace impurities on silicon and graphite surfaces and thin oxide films on silicon, with detection sensitivity of 0.001 to 0.01 monolayer, depending on the atomic number of the target atoms.[75] The channeling effect was also used to study abrasion and polishing damage on silicon.

Electrostatic energy analysis was used because it offered better energy and depth resolution than could be achieved with a silicon surface barrier detector. However, the use of an electrostatic analyzer meant that ions that were neutralized as they scattered from a surface would not be counted. Information on neutralization probabilities was needed to correct for this, which led to experiments by Buck and coworkers that revealed that for H^+ and He^+ neutralization depended primarily on exit velocity independent of the particle path inside the solid.[76,77] There was some dependence on target material and cleanliness, but there was no evidence of neutralization occurring inside the solid.

1.5.2 Low-Energy Ion Scattering and Neutralization

Ion scattering experiments at lower energies were started in 1970. These were stimulated by the results obtained by D. P. Smith at 0.5 keV to 3 keV that indicated extreme surface selectivity.[78] At Bell Labs, D. J. Ball and coworkers studied the transition from medium energy to low-energy, scattered-ion behavior for He^+ and Ar^+.[79] They observed dramatic changes in the scattered-ion energy spectra, which were believed to arise from the neutralization of low energy ions that penetrate beyond the surface being backscattered, in sharp contrast to the medium energy behavior.

Semiquantitative surface composition analysis was demonstrated to have trace impurity detection limits of 0.005 monolayer for heavy elements and 0.1 to 0.01 for light elements.[80] The technique has proven to be ideally suited to study equilibrium surface segregation in alloys—for example, in the copper-nickel system. Working with H. H. Brongersma at Philips Research Laboratories in the Netherlands, Buck showed strong copper segregation.[81] This was in fair agreement with calculations based on bond energies—the element with weaker bonds going to the surface where bonds are missing.

Low-energy ion scattering has also been applied at Bell Labs to a wide variety of technological materials, for example, electroplated platinum and stainless steel by D. L. Malm.[82]

Beginning in 1973, work was started to develop a time-of-flight technique to allow studies of scattered neutrals as well as ions.[83] The technique also provided a large reduction in the beam required for measurement (and thus in the damage it caused) by allowing scattered particles of all energies to be measured at once. With this technique, Buck and coworkers found that in addition to the strong neutralization effects mentioned above, the large scattering cross sections for low-energy projectiles depleted the ion beam and further reduced scattering from deeper lying layers.[84]

Stimulated by the observations of R. L. Erickson and Smith,[85] N. H. Tolk and coworkers measured the dependence on scattering angle and target orientation of the dramatic oscillatory structure in the energy-dependent yield of He^+ ions scattered from surfaces.[86] Behavior of this kind was quickly observed in several laboratories, including the Philips Research Laboratories, where Buck was working with Brongersma.[87]

It was recognized that this phenomenon was very similar to biparticle collision-induced oscillatory behavior of optical emission previously studied.[88] These angular-dependent experiments yielded important information about the ion-surface interaction at low energies (0.1 keV to 5 keV) and supported the view that the oscillatory behavior arises from quantum mechanical phase interference between near-resonant ionic and neutral levels.[89]

1.5.3 Rutherford Backscattering from Thin Films

Thin films play an important role in science and technology, especially in the all-pervasive technology of integrated circuits. An essential criterion of the thin-film structures in these applications is that they maintain structural integrity on the submicron scale. However, it is generally observed that pronounced interdiffusion or phase formation can occur at quite low temperatures.

Rutherford backscattering is a powerful, and undoubtedly the most quantitative, technique for studying the composition of thin films. Although the principles and practices of this technique have been understood for many decades, it was only in the early 1970s that backscattering was applied to the study of thin films at several laboratories in the United States. In 1971, Poate initiated a program at Bell Labs for the systematic study of thin-film reactions and other composition-related phenomena using the 2-MeV Van de Graaff accelerator.

An ion impinging on a solid interacts with the atoms and electrons by means of the coulomb force. At MeV energies, the elastic or Rutherford scattering cross sections from the atomic cores are small and the ion interacts predominantly with the electrons in the solid. These inelastic electronic interactions, while not imparting sufficient momentum to deflect the ion, cause an overall energy loss. The measurement of the loss can be used to deduce the thickness of material traversed. The ion moves essentially on an undeviated trajectory, losing energy to the electrons until, by chance, it undergoes a large-angle elastic scattering collision with an atomic core. The fraction of the projectile energy lost in this elastic collision can be derived from the conservation laws and is a simple function of mass and scattering angle. Measurement of a backscattered energy spectrum can therefore be used to obtain depth and composition information.

Rutherford backscattering for thin-film analysis is such a quantitative technique because the physical processes are so well understood. The Rutherford cross sections are known to better than 5 percent absolute accuracy, and electronic energy losses, from which depth scales are calculated, are usually known to better than 10 percent. Thin films or near-surface layers typically 5000Å thick can be probed with MeV ion beams with a depth resolution of 200Å using silicon surface barrier particle detectors. Buck and his colleagues were the first to use this technique to study the gettering of iron, cobalt, nickel, copper, and gold impurities in an ion-damaged surface layer in silicon by measuring the backscattering of 2-MeV ^{4}He ions.[90]

Many thin-film phenomena were subsequently investigated using MeV He$^+$ scattering. A principal objective was to understand and characterize low-temperature interdiffusion between thin metal films. Gold was chosen as a major material of interest because gold films have been well characterized and because of its importance to the Bell System.[91] Backscattering measurements demonstrated the large amount of mass transport occurring at low temperatures and the concomitant importance of grain boundary diffusion.[92] However, the high concentrations of interdiffused materials in the soluble systems such as Au-Ag and Au-Pd could not be explained by simple grain-boundary and bulk diffusion. Experiments on thin self-supporting single crystal and polycrystalline couples of Ag-Au showed that the large mass transport was accomplished during grain growth, solute being dumped from the grain boundaries into the interior of the grains.[93]

The reactions between metal films and semiconductors is another area where large-scale mass transport occurs at low temperatures. For example, contacts of remarkable lateral uniformity can be formed when platinum is reacted with silicon at low temperatures. This contact metallurgy was developed by M. P. Lepselter and is one of the most widely used contacts in integrated circuits.[94] Backscattering studies showed that the reaction proceeded by the formation and growth of well-defined, laterally uniform silicide layers; the first phase to grow was Pt_2Si followed by Pt Si.[95] The kinetics and activation energies for the growth of these silicides were determined. The reaction of metal films with compound semiconductors is much more complicated than the metal-silicon reactions.[96] But backscattering studies, for example, did reveal some similarities between Pt-Si and Pt-GaAs reactions with a stable, well-defined layer of $PtAs_2$ being formed at the GaAs interface. [Fig. 8-9]

Backscattering was also used to measure the composition of many different insulating films of importance to the Bell System: GaP and GaAs oxides,[97,98] Ta-Si and Ta-Ti oxides,[99,100] and silicon nitrides.[101] These amorphous films were interesting because compositions could be widely varied and backscattering permitted accurate determination of their composition. Because of the closeness in mass of the gallium and the arsenic, it was difficult to measure their depth profiles in the oxides from Rutherford backscattering. However, differentiation between the two elements was feasible by observing the ^1H or ^4He ion-induced X-rays using a technique developed at Bell Labs by Feldman. This technique was then used to characterize plasma-grown oxides on GaAs.

The MeV ion-beam techniques were also applied to the study of the $A15$ superconductors with the A_3B configuration. Materials with this configuration possess particularly high superconducting transition temperatures, T_c; the sputter-deposited Nb_3Ge films of L. R. Testardi and coworkers exhibited the highest measured T_c.[102] The compositions of many of these sputtered Nb-Ge films were measured and correlated with the superconducting transition temperature.[103] The exact proportion of Nb and Ge did not turn out to be a critical variable for maximum T_c. It appeared, instead, that high T_c was attained by the elimination of disorder in the film, as was demonstrated by deliberately damaging high-T_c films with the ^4He beams from the accelerator.[104]

Following ^4He damage, the use of channeling on single-crystal V_3Si, and X-ray diffraction from polycrystalline Nb_3Sn films gave strong clues as to the nature of the disorder.[105,106] It was concluded that the reduction in T_c was associated with substantial displacements of the A atoms from their equilibrium sites; this was envisaged as a buckling of the tightly compressed A chains.

1.6 Sputtering

Sputtering is the ejection of atoms from a solid as a result of a cascade of collisions initiated by an incident energetic particle striking

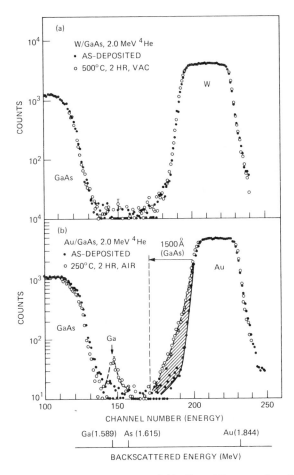

Fig. 8-9. Rutherford backscattering studies of thin films. The scattering of 2 MeV He⁺ ions from solids provides a nondestructive way of measuring the composition profile. These two examples were important in the investigation by Sinha and Poate of the stability of metallic contacts on GaAs. In each of the backscattering spectra, energy of the backscattered helium ions is the abscissa as represented by channel numbers. The number of events per unit energy is the ordinate. Scattering from tungsten is distinct from scattering from GaAs because of the large mass difference of the two and since, in a collision, the helium ion loses much less energy when scattered off from a heavy nucleus than from a light one. The flat-topped part of the spectrum identified as tungsten is due to the full thickness of the tungsten film, with the higher energies due to ions scattered from the outer surface. Scattering from deeper inside provides lower energies because the helium ions lose energy going in and coming out. The fall-off at the low energy edge of the tungsten mesa signifies scattering from the inside surface of the tungsten layer. Part (a) shows that tungsten is a highly stable contact to GaAs since, even when heated in vacuum to 500°C for 2 hrs, the spectrum remains essentially unchanged. Part (b) shows the case for gold on GaAs, where the spectra are substantially altered by heat treatment in air at 250°C. The small peak marked Ga corresponds to gallium atoms that have diffused through the gold layer and oxidized on the surface. The low-energy side of the gold mesa is also changed, reflecting diffusion of gold into the GaAs, to a depth of about 1500 Å. [Sinha and Poate, *Appl. Phys. Lett.* **23** (December 15, 1973): 667].

the solid surface. The rudiments of these phenomena were understood very early and it was recognized that the process could be used either to erode a solid or to deposit the eroded material on another substrate. Sputtering has played an important role in Bell System technology from very early times. The application of sputtering to sample preparation is discussed in Chapter 19 of this volume.

1.6.1 Optical Radiation from Sputtered Particles

As a direct result of the Bell Laboratories studies of low-energy, ion-atom collisions, in 1970 Tolk and C. W. White discovered that significant amounts of visible, ultraviolet, and infrared radiation are produced when a beam of low-energy ions (30 eV to a few tens of keV) or neutral heavy particles impinge on a surface.[107] It is interesting to note that this discovery evolved as a result of intensive experimental study of an apparently undesirable optical radiation background that ultimately was found to arise from stray ions colliding with nearby surfaces. This background from ion-surface collisions came to be as important an area of experimental and theoretical study as the research area from which it arose.

Ultimately, three kinds of low-energy, collision-induced radiation were identified.[108] The first of these is the sputtering of surface atoms, molecules, and ions in excited states caused by ion or neutral beam bombardment. The excited particles then decay and give rise to optical line radiation that is characteristic of surface constituents. The second kind of radiation observed has a similar nature but arises from backscattering of excited beam particles. The third type of radiation is a broad continuum of radiation that comes from the solid surface itself.

The first two kinds of radiation phenomena have proved important in understanding ion-surface biparticle collision processes and sputtering cascade interactions, as well as in providing insight into experimentally derived parameters for the radiationless de-excitation processes experienced by an excited surface atom or molecule near a surface.[109] In 1971, the first kind of radiation phenomena also provided the basis for the invention by White, D. L. Simms, and Tolk of a new and sensitive method for the analysis of surface composition called SCANIIR (surface composition by analysis of neutral and ion impact radiation).[110,111] This technique recognizes the characteristic optical line radiation emitted by sputtered surface constituents, including contaminants, with a detection sensitivity as great as 1 part in 10^7.

1.6.2 Alloy Sputtering

Although satisfactory quantitative agreement with sputtering theory for elemental solids had been attained in the 1960s, no such agreement prevailed for alloys or compounds. The question of possible preferential sputtering in multicomponent solids was addressed in a series of experiments by Poate and Brown in collaboration with J. W. Mayer from the California Institute of Technology.[112] They found a very general preference for sputtering of the lighter atomic species with a consequent buildup of the composition of the heavier species near the surface. The composition was found to be modified to depths comparable to the range of the incident particle that produces the sputtering. The results are important for sputtering used as a tool in analysis of the depth distribution of the composition of solids by secondary ion mass spectrometry or by sputter-Auger techniques, and in the cleaning of solid surfaces before ultrahigh vacuum surface studies or during device processing.

1.6.3 Sputtering of Condensed Gas Films

A lunchroom conversation concerning the effects of energetic particles in the solar system on frozen gases on planetary surfaces led to a series of experiments by Brown, L. J. Lanzerotti, and Poate starting in 1976.[113] Frost layers of water, carbon dioxide, ammonia, and methane, thought to exist on many of the outer planets and their moons, were found to have orders-of-magnitude larger erosion rates under high-energy nuclear particle (protons and helium ions) bombardment than would be explained by established sputtering theory. The phenomenon is limited to insulators and is caused by electronic excitation of the solids that cannot subsequently distribute the excitation by electronic conduction as in metals or semiconductors. The large erosion rates have broad implications for planetary atmospheres and surfaces.

II. X-RAY SCATTERING AND SPECTROSCOPY

A decade after M. von Laue and coworkers in Germany had first shown that X-rays can be diffracted by the regular array of atoms in a crystal,[114] the techniques of X-ray diffraction were introduced at Bell Laboratories by L. W. McKeehan for the determination of the crystal structure of iron-nickel alloys.[115] These techniques, which found wide application to many classes of solid state materials including ferroelectrics, superconductors, and semiconductors, made use of the *elastic* scattering of a beam of X-rays from the atoms in the crystal. Since the mid-1960s, scientists at Bell Labs have also become interested in the *inelastic* scattering of X-rays as a tool for the study of the electronic structure of the atoms in crystals.

2.1 X-Ray Diffraction

Some applications of X-ray diffraction were made before and during World War II. Using a double-crystal spectrometer, R. M. Bozorth and F. E. Haworth measured the perfection of quartz and other crystals.[116] Bozorth's apparatus was also used for the orientation of the nickel crystals in the Davisson-Germer experiment and for orienting quartz plates for frequency control of radio communications. W. L. Bond designed a number of specialized instruments for determining the orientation and perfection of quartz. He designed a double-crystal X-ray goniometer,[117] a single-crystal automatic diffractometer,[118] a simple high-temperature powder camera, and an instrument for measuring lattice constants with unprecedented accuracy.[119] This last instrument made possible the determination that the oxygen in silicon was interstitial, rather than substitutional,[120] and allowed the measurement of X-ray wavelengths with greater accuracy than had ever before been attained.[121]

In the 1950s and 1960s, single crystals became key elements in Bell Labs experimental research in ferroelectricity, semiconductivity, lasers, magnetism, and superconductivity. The crystallographer E. A. Wood collaborated on many experiments, using the appropriate X-ray diffraction techniques to determine the crystal structure of the materials under study. This helped to develop an understanding of the relationship between physical properties and crystal structure and made possible the synthesis of many new substances with predictable properties. Substituent atoms could be introduced into a known structure in a controlled way, and the relationship between properties and the substituents at known sites could be quantitatively determined.[122-124] The effect of an applied field in actually changing the structure of the crystal sodium niobate was demonstrated with X-ray diffraction studies.[125]

The role of S. Geller's X-ray diffraction techniques in determining the structure of magnetic oxides, leading to the discovery of the magnetic garnets, is described in some detail in Chapters 1 and 12 of this volume.

2.1.1 X-Ray Standing Waves

While X-ray diffraction patterns provided the main "fingerprints" for determining the atomic scale and geometrical structure of materials, the years following the development of diffraction techniques saw the development of new ways of probing crystals with this extremely short wavelength radiation. This progress was made possible by the extraordinarily high crystalline perfection obtained in semiconductor materials (that is, silicon and germanium). A Bragg-diffracted X-ray beam from such a crystal can have the same intensity as the beam incident on the crystal. Both within the diffracting crystal and in the region just outside its surface, where the incident and diffracted beams overlap, there will be a strong X-ray standing wave excited by interference between these two beams. These standing waves have the direction and periodicity of the planes responsible for the diffraction. The phase between the atomic planes and the standing waves may even be adjusted by making small changes in the X-ray incidence angle about the Bragg condition. Angular changes of a few seconds of arc sweep the standing wave antinodes from lying between the diffracting planes to lying on top of them. This fine control over the standing wave position provides an atomic-scale probe of the positions of impurity atoms on the surface or in the near-surface region of the crystal.

Collaborative work of Bell Labs and Cornell University scientists in 1974 isolated the standing wave effect and identified the position of arsenic atoms in silicon.[126] The study was subsequently refined to the point where the standing wave "fringe shifts" of a few hundredths of an angstrom could be detected. In 1979, the standing waves were detected just outside the surface of a silicon crystal and the detailed information gained about standing wave motion was used to determine the position of bromine atoms. In addition, the experiments showed that impurities at crystal-liquid interfaces as well as at crystal-vacuum interfaces could be investigated because of the high penetrability of both exciting and scattered X-rays.[127]

2.2 Inelastic X-Ray Spectroscopy

When X-rays are weakly scattered inelastically from condensed matter, the scattering cross section is characterized by the momentum and energy transfer to the system. X-rays allow the experimentalist to probe a very interesting and heretofore inaccessible region in this energy momentum plane. Typical lengths in condensed matter systems are of the order of 1Å, and X-rays have the right wavelengths to probe this distance or momentum scale. However, the electronic excitation energy, and hence the energy loss in the scattering experiment for almost all circumstances, is about 1 eV or less. Because typical X-ray energies are about 10,000 eV, very high resolution is required for most experiments. With modern X-ray sources and high-resolution spectrometers such experiments became feasible for the first time in 1968.

2.2.1 Large Electron-Momentum Transfers

Almost all of the experimental work at Bell Labs in inelastic X-ray scattering was carried out during the 1970s.[128-134] The impetus for the work on high-momentum-transfer, inelastic X-ray scattering came from the 1965 theoretical paper by P. M. Platzman and N. Tzoar.[135] They showed that at large momentum transfers the X-ray scattering would be a direct measure of the momentum distribution of electrons in the solid. For the first time this gave experimentalists a way of making accurate direct measurements of wave functions describing such distributions. In 1929, J. W. H. DuMond at the California Institute of Technology in Pasadena had suggested that such a possibility existed and even did a preliminary experiment on graphite using old X-ray tubes and a film detector.[136] This singular experiment took many months of exposure time and gave very fragmentary information. The theory showed that better experiments could give, at least in principle, very important information. The analysis also showed that at these large momentum transfers the resolution required to obtain accurate wave-function information was not very prohibitive. Some preliminary experiments verifying these ideas were done by several groups, including R. J. Weiss and W. C. Phillips at the Watertown Arsenal in the United States,[137] and N. Cooper and J. A. Leaker in England.[138]

In 1968, P. Eisenberger set up a 60-kilowatt continuous-output X-ray source for doing inelastic X-ray scattering experiments. This source was almost 100 times more intense than other conventional sources in use. Thus experiments that took one month to do could be done in less than one day with comparable signal-to-noise ratio. The existence of this powerful source of high-intensity, short-wavelength X-rays made possible a broad range of inelastic scattering studies. Eisenberger, in collaboration with Platzman, W. C. Marra, and others began to investigate the large momentum regime (the so-called Compton regime) and explored many of the properties of wave functions in a variety of low atomic number materials. Atomic helium, molecular hydrogen, oxygen, and nitrogen, and metallic lithium and sodium were all probed with this source. The investigators were able to show quite systematically how various wave-function calculations compared with the experimental measurement of these wave functions to an accuracy of about 1 percent. In 1971, Eisenberger and Marra performed experiments on simple hydrocarbon compounds and were able to show, for the first time microscopically, that the concept of a localized transferable bond was a realistic picture of bonding in the hydrocarbons and that in some sense it could be extended to resonant structures like benzene.[139] [Fig. 8-10] In addition, many of the qualitative features of bonding that had been theoretically predicted were for the first time easily measured. The studies of hydrocarbon bonding were extended by W. A. Reed, Eisenberger, and L. C. Snyder, using gamma-ray Compton scattering.[140]

The large electron-momentum transfer inelastic scattering studies were extended to a higher momentum transfer regime using nuclear gamma-rays as a source of high-energy photons. This work was pioneered at Bell Labs by Reed and Eisenberger[141] and has been actively pursued by at least a dozen groups throughout the world. The advantage of the gamma-ray technique, with its very high energy (a few 100 KeV) photons, is that it enables wave functions of systems containing atoms from the whole Periodic Table to be examined. This is made possible by the availability of solid state detectors (developed at Bell Labs and now available commercially) and by the fact that the momentum spectrum is explored over an ever-increasing energy range as the primary energy range of the gamma-ray is increased. Using these techniques the wave-function properties of a whole host of materials including such elemental materials as silicon

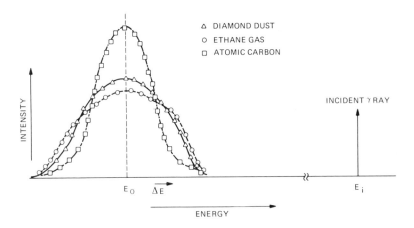

NOTE: BREAK INDICATES THAT THE INTENSITY SCALES
IN THE TWO PARTS ARE NOT RELATED.

Fig. 8-10. Scattering of high-energy photons (γ-rays) from carbon valence electrons for three different environments of the carbon atom. The incoming γ-ray is monochromatic, and the scattering angle is the same in each case. The abscissa is the energy loss, and e is proportional to the projection of the momentum distribution of the electrons in the carbon atom along the scattering direction. The energy loss, E_o, at the center of the dashed line corresponds to Compton scattering from a free electron at rest. The effect of bonding on the carbon atom is dramatically revealed. The Compton profile for atomic carbon is obviously narrower than the profile for the C-C bond in ethane gas, which has the same length as the C-C bond in diamond. The differences between the molecule and the crystal are smaller but quite evident—the valence electrons are somewhat more tightly bound in the molecule than in the crystal.

and germanium have been examined. The anisotropic Compton technique has focused on the solid state properties of the outer electrons by utilizing the difference between Compton profiles measured in different directions. The experiments require extremely good statistics and the highest quality resolution available.

2.2.2 Intermediate Electron-Momentum Transfer in Light Metals

The inelastic X-ray scattering techniques have also been applied to smaller momentum transfers, where the collective properties of the condensed matter systems begin to play an important role. The experiments by W. A. Reed and coworkers in 1974 focused on the long wavelength or plasmon properties of the simple light metals lithium, beryllium, sodium, and so on.[142] At this level, the experiments made contact with the work of C. J. Powell, reported in 1960, in which electron beams were used as a probe.[143]

At intermediate momentum transfers the inelastic X-ray scattering from simple metals was an unexplored field of great interest. Theories of the electron gas were based on weak-coupling or mean-field approaches which, when parametrized properly, gave a good description of both the long wavelength and short wavelength limits of the inelastic X-ray scattering results. At intermediate momentum transfers the intrinsic, strong, or intermediate coupling character of the electron gas began to show up. The experiments revealed a variety of phenomena that seemed to be characteristic of liquids in general and that have not yet been explained in any satisfactory way.[144] [Fig. 8-11] Because the electron gas, or the electron liquid, is one of the fundamental systems in solid state physics, these experiments stimulated new theoretical effort.

2.2.3 Electron Energy Loss Spectroscopy and Photoabsorption Spectroscopy

The use of electron scattering as a probe of the properties of matter has a long history at Bell Labs. In the 1970s, the trend was toward higher electron energies, since the problems of multiple scattering were reduced and penetrating power was increased. In 1973, G. S. Brown and A. E. Meixner built a high-energy electron spectrometer with very high energy resolution suitable for studying elementary excitations in solids. High-energy electrons (about 300 keV) would be necessary to penetrate reasonably thick samples (up to a few thousand angstroms) without suffering appreciable multiple scattering, and high-energy resolution (about 0.1 eV) would be necessary to observe details about characteristic excitations such as plasmons and valence band structure in solids. Brown used a clever

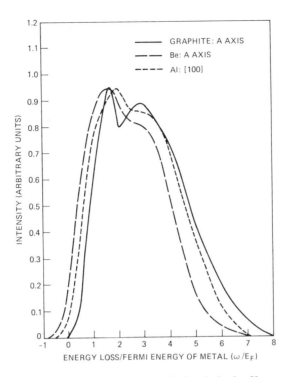

Fig. 8-11. Composite plot of the inelastic X-ray scattering from three very different metallic materials. These profiles have been normalized in terms of the free electron parameters of the substances (that is, the Fermi energy E_F). The two distinctive features of the plots are (1) they fall roughly on a universal curve, indicating that these spectra have a common origin, that is, interaction of X-rays with an electron gas; and (2) the plots have a double-humped structure, in contrast to prediction of theories that prevailed prior to the performance of the experiment. The theories predicted a broad single-humped curve that did not include the narrower peaked features at $\omega/E_F \sim 1$. It is now believed that this peak arises from the liquid-like behavior of the interacting electron gas in solids due to the short-range order that exists in this liquid. This experiment, for the first time, demonstrated the need for considering such short-range correlations for the electrons in free electron-like solids.

scheme, first used by S. E. Schnatterly and coworkers at Princeton University,[145] which involved accelerating the electrons up to high energy, doing the inelastic scattering at the high energy, and then decelerating back down to lower energy for a spectral analysis. By using a single power supply for both acceleration and deceleration, very high resolution (about one part in 10^6) could be achieved without using an extremely stable power source, since drift and ripple cancel to first order. A series of measurements were made with the use of such an apparatus by Brown, Meixner, and others on the momentum transfer dependence of the K-edge threshold in beryllium and on the M edge of nickel.[146] The nickel work involved using thin, single-crystal material that had been epitaxially grown on salt and then floated off in water to make a free-standing film 600Å thick. The use of single crystals reduced thermal diffuse background scattering and made it possible to observe the breakdown of the dipole approximation as momentum transfer increased.

At the end of 1977, B. M. Kincaid realized that there was a very close correspondence between electron energy loss spectroscopy and photoabsorption spectroscopy. The only source of photons covering the range of excitation energies that could be studied using electron energy loss was synchrotron radiation, at that time a rather rare commodity, involving travel to distant laboratories and difficult working conditions. Kincaid, Meixner, and Platzman showed that better data for the carbon K edge at 284 eV could be produced using the Bell Labs, energy loss machine than could be obtained using synchrotron radiation.[147] The study of the electron loss fine structure (ELFS) on the carbon edge extended the use of absorption loss structure studies from the then limited range in the conventional X-ray (EXAFS) part of the spectrum down to the soft X-ray and ultraviolet regions. The K edges of beryllium, carbon, oxygen, magnesium, aluminum, and silicon have been studied at Bell Labs, along with the L edges of aluminum, silicon, titanium, nickel, and copper. M, N, and O edges of higher Z elements have also been studied. Energy loss fine structure has been observed on all these edges, and has been quantitatively analyzed and compared with theory using analysis techniques developed by Kincaid for the cases of carbon in graphite and titanium in titanium metal.[148] The electron energy loss method provided reasonable signal rates in regions of the spectrum where synchrotron radiation sources were, at least before 1980, very difficult if not impossible to use.

At the time of this writing, improvements in the electron energy loss method involving higher beam current, parallel detection of energy loss events rather than the present sequential method, and increased angular acceptance in the electron detection system are expected to yield improvement of at least a factor of 10^5 in signal rate for the electron technique. This will open the prospect of measuring electronic and structural properties of dilute impurities, surface monolayers, and interfaces in a short time, as well as ELFS for K

edges of the first row elements and *L*, *M*, and *N* edges of other elements, all with synchrotron radiation-like intensities but with a small lab-sized electron energy loss machine.

2.3 Extended X-Ray Absorption Fine-Structure Spectroscopy

Since the 1930s, it has been known that X-ray absorption spectra have complex oscillatory structures near the absorption threshold and extending out as far as 1 keV above threshold. The near-edge structure was generally understood to be caused by transitions to low-lying, unoccupied bound states and therefore could be useful in understanding the electronic environment surrounding the absorbing atom. Many speculations existed concerning the extended structure. In the late 1960s and early 1970s, using more modern techniques, D. E. Sayers and E. A. Stern at the University of Washington and F. W. Lytle at the Boeing Aerospace Company began to reinvestigate the extended structure.[149] By early 1970, there was a semiquantitative understanding that the extended absorption reflected the local geometry around the absorbing atom. Some information had also been obtained on the coordination number, the atomic character, and the thermal motion of the neighboring atoms. The power of the technique is that it can be applied to a material in any state and that the reference atom may be selected by choosing the energy region to investigate that corresponds to the characteristic absorption energy threshold region of the chosen atom.

2.3.1 *High-Intensity Synchrotron Radiation and the Measurement of Inter-atomic Distances*

In 1973, Eisenberger and Marra used a high-powered 60-kilowatt X-ray tube to make high-resolution measurements of the absorption spectra of copper and silver. At that time Eisenberger became interested in the synchrotron radiation facility at Stanford University and collaborated with Kincaid (who at the time was a graduate student at Stanford) to conduct measurements using this new source of high-energy photons. The attraction of this facility was its promise of increases in photon flux by a factor of 10^4 to 10^6. This increase could drastically reduce the time of the measurement from weeks to minutes and could considerably extend the application of the technique from concentrated systems such as copper to very dilute systems.

In January 1974, Kincaid and Eisenberger designed an apparatus, the most critical feature of which was the utilization of a channel-cut crystal spectrometer, to convert the broad spectrum radiation from the synchrotron into a tuneable monochromatic source. The first spectrum obtained with this apparatus was that of copper. As hoped, 10^5 more flux was available with this facility with the result that the first spectrum of copper was measured in ten minutes and had ten times higher signal-to-noise ratio than the spectrum of copper obtained using the X-ray tubes, which had taken two weeks to obtain.

In the short period between May and July of 1974, Eisenberger and Kincaid measured over 100 spectra.[150] One significant result came from the measurements of the simple molecules Br_2 and $GeCl_4$. These measurements, combined with theoretical calculations made by Kincaid for his Ph.D. thesis, quantitatively demonstrated that the extended X-ray structure reflected the local geometry and that interatomic distances could be obtained to an accuracy of 0.1Å. The relatively large uncertainty arose from the approximations made in calculating the energy-dependent scattering phase shift that alters the extended structure and which consequently affects the distance determined from the measurement.

Some early experiments were also made on ions in dilute aqueous solutions and metalloproteins (see section 3.7 of Chapter 6). These demonstrated the power of the technique for determining local structural information in disordered systems that could not otherwise be obtained. However, it soon became clear that if the technique was to have an impact on understanding the function of the systems studied, better than 0.1Å accuracy would be required. Toward this end, Eisenberger and Kincaid were joined by P. H. Citrin in early 1975, and measurements were made on a large series of simple molecules in an attempt to experimentally determine the energy-dependent phase shifts. Since the energy-dependent phase shifts originated from scattering from the core electrons, it was thought that the phase shift would be the same for any absorbing and neighboring atom pair independent of their chemical environment. This concept of chemical transferability was experimentally verified.[151] Accurate determination of the phase shifts, together with data analysis techniques developed by Kincaid, enabled an accuracy of 0.01Å to be obtained on a whole range of simple molecules. Shortly thereafter, P. A. Lee and G. Beni improved the theoretical calculations of the phase shifts and demonstrated that their results agreed with the experimentally determined values and thus could be used to obtain distance information to 0.01Å accuracy.[152]

In 1976, the applications of the technique to chemistry were seriously pursued by J. Reed and B. Teo, in collaboration with Eisenberger and Kincaid.[153] Reed and coworkers were able to determine the structural changes associated with binding catalysts to polymers for the first time. The significant structural changes observed were related to the previously observed changes in catalytic activity. Teo and collaborators investigated a series of metal complexes in which the degree of metal-metal binding was related to the degree of oxidation of the metal atom. The degree of metal-metal binding was determined and the nature of the changes in the chemical bonding with oxidation was explained.

2.3.2 *Application to Superconducting Thin Films*

Two of the more significant EXAFS experiments in solid state physics were the study of zinc single crystals by G. S. Brown and Eisenberger[154] and the study of Nb_3Ge superconducting thin films by Brown and coworkers.[155] The zinc single-crystal studies showed that the local geometry as well as the distance information could be determined. The anisotropic mean-squared relative displacement caused by the thermal motion of the atoms was also determined and compared to theoretical calculations of Beni and Platzman.[156] This study strongly suggested that valuable information could be obtained about interatomic forces. The thin-film work by Brown and coworkers attempted to relate the observed structural changes on Nb_3Ge films with deposition conditions and their superconducting transition temperature. Significant variations were observed and interpreted.

2.3.3 *Application to Adsorbed Atoms on Surfaces*

In the fall of 1976, a major innovation was successfully implemented. A focusing mirror was included as part of a new and improved experimental station that was assembled by Kincaid and Eisenberger, together with J. Hastings from Stanford University. Measurements showed that the new geometry (beam line) had 50 times the flux and 500 times the intensity of the earlier experimental apparatus. This new development further extended the range of possible experiments.

The most innovative of these experiments was the application of absorption spectroscopy to the study of adsorbed atoms on surfaces. Following an initial suggestion of Lee,[157] Citrin, Eisenberger, and R. C. Hewitt assembled a new experiment based upon the detection of the Auger electrons emitted following the absorption of the X-ray photon.[158] The new high-vacuum apparatus, together with the new beam line, were successfully used to measure the structure of an absorbed monolayer of iodine on silver and nickel single-crystal surfaces. The distances to the neighboring atoms and the site geometry of the iodine on various symmetry crystal faces were determined. Thus, a badly needed analytic tool for surface science was demonstrated. In fact, this experiment was a measurement on only 10^{12}

atoms, compared with the 10^{21} atoms that were originally measured in 1973.

III. X-RAY PHOTOELECTRON SPECTROSCOPY

Research in X-ray photoelectron spectroscopy at Bell Laboratories was started in 1970. At that time the technique had been well established through the efforts of K. Siegbahn at Uppsala University in Sweden,[159] but its promise was only delineated. The basic approach was to measure the kinetic energy of electrons emitted from solids by the photoelectric absorption of highly monochromatic, low-energy X-rays. The K_α radiation of aluminum or magnesium at 1486.6 or 1253.6 eV was typically employed. The aluminum K_α radiation was monochromatized by Bragg reflection to achieve a total resolution of approximately 0.5 eV, and the electron kinetic energy was measured in a hemispherical electrostatic analyzer. The binding energy of the electron was obtained by subtracting the kinetic energy and spectrometer work function from the X-ray photon energy.

3.1 Ionic and Covalent Bonding

The electron binding energies are characteristic of an element but are subject to small ($\leqslant 5$ eV) chemical perturbations. Detailed theoretical discussions of the factors that determined these binding energies were an integral part of the early years of X-ray photoelectron spectroscopy and continue as additional sophistication is brought to bear. The early point of view was highly chemical. Elemental analysis and determination of bonding character appeared to be the primary applications, motivating the acronym ESCA, electron spectroscopy for chemical analysis.

The initial work undertaken at Bell Labs by G. K. Wertheim fell into this general pattern. The chemical shifts associated with the ionic and covalently bonded iron in the ferric-ferrocyanide known as Prussian Blue were established.[160] Another experiment dealt with a mixed-valence compound, $K_x FeF_3$, in which iron exists in both divalent and trivalent states in a ratio that depends on the potassium content. Two discrete iron-states were found in ESCA as well as in the Mössbauer effect, indicating that the charge hopping was slow.[161] The study of other mixed-valence compounds was later to cover an extensive period.

Subsequent work revealed a wealth of phenomena, basically of atomic physics character. This is not unexpected since core electrons, which largely retain their atomic character, are readily studied by this technique. One of the most interesting early discoveries by Wertheim and A. Rosenzwaig was the final-state, configuration-interaction satellites in alkali halides.[162] It was deduced that multielectron final states would be excited directly in the photoemission process, even though the photon couples to only one electron. A detailed study was then made of the so-called s electron multiplet splitting in the rare earth trifluorides, which represents the exchange coupling between the 4f and the s electrons.[163] It was found that electron correlation effects greatly modify the multiplet splitting within the shell that contains the open subshell, a phenomenon closely related to the configuration-interaction phenomenon.

3.2 Core Electron and Conduction Electron Spectroscopy

Aspects of solid state physics began to enter the research when attention shifted to the valence and conduction electron of metals and alloys. S. Hüfner and coworkers obtained the band structures of noble and transition metals and of CuNi and AgPd alloys. The data on the noble metals were found to be in very good agreement with the details of band structure calculations, those of transition metals less so. The significance of the small width of the d band of nickel remained a puzzle for many years, and was accepted as a real manifestation of the bulk band structure only after angle-resolved photoemission later revealed the details of the nickel bands.[164] The data on the two alloy systems showed that the coherent potential approximation provides the best description of noble-transition metal alloys; that is, the d bands remain separated, charge transfer is minimal, and all the bands narrow with dilution.[165] In the dilute palladium limit the AgPd alloys exhibit the Friedel-Anderson virtual bound state, that is, the palladium d electron resonance superimposed on the silver s conduction band. The extension of this work to metallic oxides, especially ReO_3, demonstrated the importance of the covalent mixing of metal d states into the anion p valence band.[166] The d component is directly revealed in this experiment by virtue of the much larger photoelectric cross section of the d states.

The conduction electrons of a metal manifest themselves even in core-electron spectroscopy because they react to screen the core hole produced by photoemission. There are two aspects to this phenomenon. The first concerns the binding energy of the core electron, which may be thought of equivalently as the energy of the screened final-hole state. This was studied in a definitive experiment by Citrin and D. R. Hamann on gas atoms implanted into the noble metal.[167] It gave a direct measure of this relaxation energy. The second aspect concerns the spectrum of the electron-hole pair excitations that produce the screening process. Theoretical calculations by G. D. Mahan,[168] and by P. Noziéres and C. T. DeDominicis,[169] predicted a long-tailed, asymmetric line shape and other spectral characteristics. The manifestations of this phenomenon were found in the spectra of alkali, noble, transition, and s-p metals and gave the first unambiguous experimental demonstration of the many-body screening phenomenon.[170] A quantitative study, extending over a number of years, was ultimately instrumental in establishing the role of this same phenomenon in X-ray emission and absorption edges.[171]

3.3 Rare Earth Ion Spectroscopy

The $4f$ electrons of rare earth ions have a unique character. On the one hand, they are core-like, of small radial extent, and well shielded from the neighboring ions; on the other, they are valence-like, have small binding energies, and exist in fractionally occupied shells. The photoionization of an incomplete shell gives rise to a spectrum of final states that are eigenstates of the hole-state atom. This phenomenon was first observed in the study of the rare earth trifluorides where the attainable resolution is limited by phonon broadening.[172] Subsequent work by E. Bucher and M. Campagna on the rare earth antimonides displayed the final-state multiplets in great detail. The intensities of the multiplets are compatible with fractional parentage calculations and their energies are compatible with the optical spectra of the element of next lower atomic number.[173] With detailed spectra available for each $4f^n$ configuration, Wertheim was able to study the rare earth interconfiguration fluctuation phenomenon that occurs in homogeneous systems like TmSe,[174] SmS,[175] and SmB$_6$.[176] This work, in collaboration with Campagna and J. N. Chazalviel, clearly showed the multiplets of two discrete final states separated by the Coulomb correlation energy, a quantity not previously directly measured. It also put limits on the time scale of the fluctuations.

3.4 Application to Surface Studies

Another aspect of X-ray photoemission spectroscopy is its surface sensitivity, predicated on the small (15Å) mean-free path of low energy electrons in solids. On the one hand, this means that careful surface preparation in vacuum is required for bulk studies; on the other, it makes the technique particularly useful for surface studies. This aspect was used by R. F. Roberts to elucidate the mechanism by which certain organic materials, for example, benzotriazole, passivate the surface of copper.[177] A dip into an aqueous solution of this compound has been used extensively by Western Electric to prevent the oxidation of copper on circuit boards. Another technologically important material, tin-nickel electroplate, spontaneously grows a passivating layer with good electrical conductivity when exposed to air. The chemical nature of this 25Å oxide film has been thoroughly investigated by ESCA by J. H. Thomas and S. P. Sharma at Bell Labs' Columbus, Ohio, laboratory,[178] with some additional work on the time evolution of the film by H. G. Tompkins and Wertheim.[179] The general finding is that the film is initially a hydrated oxide of tin which eventually, over a period of months, incorporates divalent nickel in the form of nickel stannate. In the late 1970's the thrust of work shifted toward studies of surfaces; X-rays from a conventional tube were expected to be replaced by synchrotron radiation as the form of excitation; and the general trend continued toward greater use of this technique to solve technological problems.

IV. NEUTRON SCATTERING

Neutron scattering is an important probe of the static and dynamic structure of condensed matter systems. Typically, thermal neutrons coming from a nuclear reactor have a wavelength in the range 1Å to 5Å, which is well matched to the atomic spacing in solids and liquids. This characteristic combines with the fact that neutrons scatter both from the nuclei of atoms and from the magnetic electrons surrounding them to permit neutron-diffraction study of crystal structures and magnetic structures. Furthermore, neutrons in this wavelength range have energies in the range of 0.1 eV to 0.005 eV, which is characteristic of many types of dynamical excitations that occur in condensed matter systems. Because of their large mass, neutrons couple to phonons—the collective motion of the nuclei in a solid. Because neutrons have a magnetic moment, they couple to the collective motion of the magnetic moments of the electrons in a solid, the spin excitations, and to local magnetic excitations such as crystal field levels.

Neutron scattering experiments by Bell Laboratories scientists began in the mid-1950s at Brookhaven National Laboratory. The early work by E. Prince, and S. C. Abrahams concentrated on determining magnetic structures.[180,181] The major emphasis in the late 1960s and early 1970s centered on the physics of phase transitions. As discussed in Chapter 9 of this volume, major advances have been made in the understanding of the evolution of one phase into another with changes in thermodynamic variables such as temperature and pressure.

Neutron scattering has been used to study the divergence of the correlation length near second-order transitions in magnetic systems and to measure the spontaneous magnetization. The form of the divergence of these properties was thought to depend fundamentally on the dimensionality of the magnetic system. In a classic series of experiments, R. J. Birgeneau and coworkers studied a model two-dimensional magnetic system, K_2MnF_4, and clearly established the two-dimensional behavior of the critical properties of the phase transition and verified many of the theoretical predictions.[182] These experiments were followed by a pioneering series of studies, beginning with work by R. Dingle and Birgeneau, that elucidated the role of idealized one-dimensional effects in three-dimensional materials.[183] [Fig. 8-12] Quasielastic and inelastic measurements were reported on two model one-dimensional systems, $(CD_3)_4NMnCl_3$ and $CuCl_2-2NC_5D_5$. The former is composed of effectively isolated one-dimensional $MnCl_3$ chains—which simulate *classical* one-dimensional isotropic spin systems—while in the latter, the isolated $CnCl_2N$ chains are an excellent representation of the $S = \frac{1}{2}$ isotropic chain—a *quantum mechanical* system of considerable interest to mathematical physicists. Both of these mathematical models exhibit exact solutions for the static correlations and for the dynamics—a rare accomplishment in the many-body problem. The neutron scattering systems confirmed these exact solutions and showed that they were not just mathematical curiosities but, indeed, were pertinent to real materials. Further, they elucidated a whole new range of previously unpredicted finite temperature properties.

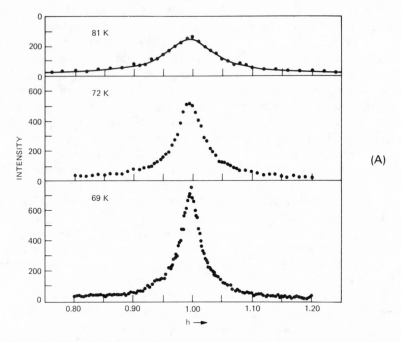

Fig. 8-12. The structure of certain antiferromagnetic spin systems, of which K_2NiF_4 and Rb_2MnF_4 are examples, allows only those spins that lie in parallel crystal planes to interact. These two-dimensional magnetic systems also have the property that the magnetic sites may be occupied by two different types of ions in a completely random way. These two properties made these materials invaluable for studying the effects of dimensionality and disorder on critical phenomena and spin dynamics. (A) shows the intensity of scattered neutrons from the momentum transfer, h, system $Rb_2Mn_{0.5}Ni_{0.5}F_4$, in which the manganese and nickel ions are randomly distributed, as a function of neutron for various temperatures above the antiferromagnetic transition, $T_N = 68.7K$. The peak in the intensity occurs in each case at $h = 1$, which

4.1 Phase Transition in Magnetic Systems

In addition to the understanding of the divergence of many physical properties at some phase transitions, the use of neutron scattering has made progress toward elucidating the driving force behind a number of structural phase transitions. The structural phase transition in the high-temperature superconductor V_3Si is driven by a softening of a phonon mode; the nature of this softening was studied by Birgeneau and coworkers.[184] A series of phase transitions in $PrAlO_3$ was shown to be driven by a coupling of the phonons to the magnetic exciton arising from the $4f$ electrons of the praseodymium ions.

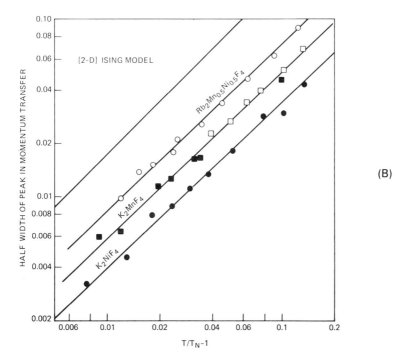

(B)

corresponds to a neutron wavelength characteristic of the ordered structure. It becomes narrower and more intense as the transition is approached, as it would in a uniform system, showing that the site disorder does not affect the sharpness of the critical transition phenomena. [J. Als-Nielsen et al., *Phys. Rev.* **B12** (1975): 4977]. (B) is a log-log plot of the variation in the resonance half widths of curves similar to those shown in (A) as a function of temperature near the transition, T_N, for both uniform and random systems. Both exhibit the same behavior which, in form, agrees with the theoretical prediction for a two-dimensional system. [J. Als-Nielsen et al., *Sol. State Phys.* **9** (1976): L124].

4.2 Electronic Structure of Magnetic Systems

Another class of phase transitions arises in some metals from an instability in the coupled electron-phonon system. Many of these transitions are to a state that exhibits a distortion of the charge density with a periodicity that is not related to the lattice periodicity. The existence of such incommensurate periodicities means that these materials are no longer crystals in the traditional sense, and many properties of the compounds reflect this fundamental difference. At a lower temperature, the coupling between the lattice and the charge density wave may drive a second transition in which the charge density wave becomes commensurate with the lattice periodicity. Both of these phenomena were established in the $2H$ polytypes of the layer compounds $NbSe_2$ and $TaSe_2$ using neutron scattering by D. E. Moncton and coworkers. (Moncton was then a graduate student at M.I.T.).[185] After joining Bell Laboratories, Moncton went on to study the role of impurities in pinning the charge density waves and thereby destroying long-range, three-dimensional order in the $1T$ phase of $TaSe_2$.[186] In another polytype $4Hb-TaSe_2$, two independent charge density waves were found to coexist.[187]

Neutron scattering is a unique probe of local magnetic excitations in metallic systems. It is well known from light scattering experiments that the degeneracy of the electronic configuration of the $4f$ electrons in rare earth ions in insulators is lifted by the crystalline electric field generated by the surrounding ligands. In metallic systems, similar effects were inferred from measurements of the magnetic susceptibility and heat capacity. The crystal field levels were determined directly by neutron scattering in a systematic study of the rare earth metallic compounds by Birgeneau and Bucher of Bell Labs, in collaboration with K. C. Turberfield and L. Passell of Brookhaven National Laboratory.[188] They found that the effective point charge model could be used to describe the crystal field splittings across a large part of the rare earth series, which implied that the conduction electrons did not modify the effective field in a fundamental fashion.[189] However, an experiment by D. B. McWhan, E. I. Blount, and coworkers measured the change in the crystal field levels as a function of pressure in PrSb and demonstrated that the microscopic physics is more complicated than the initial experiments seemed to indicate. In particular, the shifts predicted by the model are of the wrong sign, so that the interaction with the conduction electrons undoubtedly plays a central role.[190] Subsequently, neutron scattering has been used to probe the interplay between superconductivity and magnetism in several ternary rare earth systems such as $ErRh_4B_4$ and in the Chevrel phases such as Mo_6S_8.[191]

Thus, neutron scattering emerged as a powerful tool for investigating magnetic structure, phase transitions, and other magnetic properties of solids.

REFERENCES

1. A. H. White, "Basic Research in Industry," *Proceedings of Inaugural Meeting of European Industrial Research Management Association*, 1966.

2. P. F. Donovan, J. V. Kane, R. E. Pixley, and D. H. Wilkinson, "States of Be^{11}, B^{11}, and C^{11}," *Phys. Rev.* **123** (July 1961), pp. 589-597.

3. P. F. Donovan, J. V. Kane, Če. Zupančeiče, C. P. Baker, and J. F. Mollenauer, "Angular and Energy Correlations in the Reaction $O^{16}(\alpha,2\alpha)C^{12}$ g.s. at 40-MeV Incident Alpha-Particle Energy," *Phys. Rev.* **135** (July 1964), pp. B61-B75.

4. W. M. Gibson, T. D. Thomas, and G. L. Miller, "Structure in the Kinetic Energy Spectrum of Fragments from Thermal-Neutron-Induced Fission of U^{235}," *Phys. Rev. Lett.* **7** (July 15, 1961), pp. 65-66.

5. K. G. McKay, "A Germanium Counter," *Phys. Rev.* **76** (November 1949), p. 1537.

6. K. G. McKay, "The Crystal Conduction Counter," *Physics Today* **6** (May 1953), pp. 10-13.

7. D. E. Wooldridge, A. J. Ahearn, and J. A. Burton, "Conductivity Pulses Induced in Diamond by Alpha-Particles," *Phys. Rev.* **71** (June 1947), p. 913.

8. R. Hofstadter, "Crystal Counters, Part I," *Nucleonic* **4** (April 1949), pp. 2-27; idem, "Crystal Counters, Part II," *Nucleonic* **4** (May 1949), pp. 29-43.

9. D. E. Alburger, R. E. Pixley, D. H. Wilkinson, and P. Donovan, "β-Decay of ^{16}N: Conservation of Spin and Parity in ^{16}O," *Phil. Mag.* **6** (January 1961), pp. 171-174.

10. See reference 4; also, R. A. Atneosen, T. D. Thomas, W. M. Gibson, and M. L. Perlman, "X Rays and Electrons Emitted in Coincidence with the Fission of Cf^{252}," *Phys. Rev.* **148** (August 1966), pp. 1206-1220; T. D. Thomas, W. M. Gibson, and G. Safford, "Thermal-Neutron-Induced Fission of ^{235}U, ^{233}U, and ^{239}Pu," *Proceedings of the Symposium on Physics and Chemistry of Fission*, Vol. 1 (1965), pp. 467-479.

11. W. M. Gibson and K. A. Nielsen, "Use of Angular-Distribution Measurements of Fission Fragments Emitted from Single Crystals for Determining the Lifetimes of Excited Compound Nuclei," *Proc. of the 2nd IAEA Symposium on Physics and Chemistry of Fission* (1969), pp. 861-878; idem, "Direct Determination of the Lifetime of Excited Compound Nuclei by Angular Distribution Measurements of Fission Fragments Emitted from Single Crystals," *Phys. Rev. Lett.* **24** (January 19, 1970), pp. 114-117.

12. D. E. Alburger and P. F. Donovan, "Studies of Alpha-Particle Emitting States of C^{12} Observed in the Reactions $B^{10}(He^3,p)C^{12}(a)Be^8$ and $C^{13}(He^3,a)C^{12}(a)Be^8$," *Rev. Mod. Phys.* **37** (July 1965), pp. 448-450; P. D. Parker, P. F. Donovan, J. V. Kane, and J. F. Mollenauer, "Energy Levels of He^4," *Phys. Rev. Lett.* **14** (January 4, 1965), pp. 15-18.

13. J. R. MacDonald, N. Benczer-Koller, J. Tape, L. Guthman, and P. Goode, "Measurement of the Mean Life of the 4.49-MeV(5^-) State of ^{40}Ca. Effects of Deformed Components on the Lifetimes of the Odd-Parity States," *Phys. Rev. Lett.* **23** (September 15, 1969), pp. 594-597; E. Beardsworth, R. Hensler, J. W. Tape, N. Benczer-Koller, W. Darcey, and J. R. MacDonald, "Double Gamma Decay in ^{40}Ca," *Phys. Rev.* **C8** (July 1973), pp. 216-229.

14. G. M. Heestand, R. R. Borchers, B. Herskind, L. Grodzins, R. Kalish, and D. E. Murnick, "g-Factors for 2^+ States of Doubly Even Nuclei (Ge, Se, Mo, Ru, Pd, Cd, and Te)," *Nucl. Phys.* **A133** (August 18, 1969), pp. 310-320; G. K. Hubler, H. W.

Kugel, and D. E. Murnick, "Magnetic Moment of the 1.409-MeV 2^+ State of ^{54}Fe," *Phys. Rev. Lett.* **29** (September 4, 1972), pp. 662-665.

15. E. N. Kaufmann, H. P. Lie, and D. E. Murnick, "Implantation Perturbed Angular Correlation Studies of ^{238}U in Iron," *Proceedings of International Conference on Nuclear Reactions Induced by Heavy Ions* (Amsterdam: North Holland Publishing Co., 1970), pp. 424-430.

16. R. S. Raghavan, P. Raghavan, E. N. Kaufman, K. Krien, and R. A. Naumann, "Time Differential-Perturbed-Angular-Correlation Measurement of the Hyperfine Field at Hg in Iron," *Phys. Rev.* **B7** (May 1973), pp. 4132-4137.

17. R. S. Raghavan, E. N. Kaufmann, and P. Raghavan, "Universal Correlation of Electronic and Ionic Field Gradients in Noncubic Metals," *Phys. Rev. Lett.* **34** (May 19, 1975), pp. 1280-1283.

18. H. W. Kugel, L. Eytel, G. Hubler, and D. E. Murnick, "Temperature Dependence of Hyperfine Fields at Rare-Earth Nuclei in Iron and Nickel," *Phys. Rev.* **B13** (May 1976), pp. 3697-3708.

19. H. W. Kugel, M. Leventhal, D. E. Murnick, C. K. N. Patel, and O. R. Wood, II, "Infrared-X-Ray Double-Resonance Study of $2P_{3/2}$ -$2S_{1/2}$ Splitting in Hydrogenic Fluorine," *Phys. Rev. Lett.* **35** (September 8, 1975), pp. 647-650.

20. C. Erginsoy, H. E. Wegner, and W. M. Gibson, "Anisotropic Energy Loss of Light Particles of MeV Energies in Thin Silicon Single Crystals," *Phys. Rev. Lett.* **13** (October 26, 1964), pp. 530-534.

21. W. M. Gibson, C. Erginsoy, H. E. Wegner, and B. R. Appleton, "Direction and Energy Distribution of Charged Particles Transmitted Through Single Crystals," *Phys. Rev. Lett.* **15** (August 23, 1965), pp. 357-360.

22. C. Erginsoy, "Anisotropic Effects in Interactions of Energetic Charged Particles in a Crystal Lattice," *Phys. Rev. Lett.* **15** (August 23, 1965), pp. 360-364.

23. B. R. Appleton, C. Erginsoy, H. E. Wegner, and W. M. Gibson, "Axial and Planar Effects in the Energy Loss of Protons in Silicon Single Crystals," *Phys. Lett.* **19** (1965), pp. 185-186.

24. B. R. Appleton, C. Erginsoy, and W. M. Gibson, "Channeling Effects in the Energy Loss of 3-11-MeV Protons in Silicon and Germanium Single Crystals," *Phys. Rev.* **161** (September 1967), pp. 330-349.

25. B. R. Appleton, "Channeling of Charged Particles in Single Crystals," PhD. Thesis, Rutgers University, New Brunswick, N. J., 1966 (unpublished).

26. B. R. Appleton, C. Erginsoy, and W. M. Gibson, "Channeling Effects in the Energy Loss of 3-11-MeV Protons in Silicon and Germanium Single Crystals," *Phys. Rev.* **161** (September 1967), pp. 330-349.

27. M. R. Altman, "Thermal Effects in the Passage of Charged Particles Through Single Crystals," PhD. Thesis, Rutgers University, New Brunswick, N. J., June 1969 (unpublished).

28. M. R. Altman, L. C. Feldman, and W. M. Gibson, "Dechanneling of 5 MeV Protons from Planar Channels in Silicon and Its Temperature Dependence," *Rad. Effects* **18** (April 1973), pp. 171-180.

29. D. D. Armstrong, W. M. Gibson, A. Goland, J. A. Golovchenko, R. A. Levesque, R. L. Meek, and H. E. Wegner, "A Qualitative Description of the Transverse Motion of Axial Channeled Particles in Thin Crystals," *Rad. Effects* **12** (February 1972), pp. 143-147.

30. W. M. Gibson and J. A. Golovchenko, "Deduction of Continuum Potentials from Planar Channeling," *Phys. Rev. Lett.* **28** (May 15, 1972), pp. 1301-1304; J. A. Golovchenko, "Channeling in Very Thin Crystals," PhD. Thesis, Rensselaer Poly. Inst., Troy, N. Y., 1972 (unpublished).

31. L. C. Feldman, "Large Angle Elastic Scattering of Energetic Protons in Silicon Single Crystals," PhD. Thesis, Rutgers University, New Brunswick, N. J., 1967 (unpublished).

32. J. U. Andersen and L. C. Feldman, "Comparison of Average-Potential Models and Binary-Collision Models of Axial Channeling and Blocking," *Phys. Rev.* **B1** (March 1970), pp. 2063-2069.

33. J. U. Andersen, W. M. Augustyniak, and E. Uggerhoj, "Channeling of Positrons," *Phys. Rev.* **B3** (February 1971), pp. 705-711.

34. M. J. Pederson, J. U. Andersen, and W. M. Augustyniak, "Channeling of Positrons," *Rad. Effects* **12** (January 1972), pp. 47-52.

35. J. U. Andersen, S. K. Andersen, and W. M. Augustyniak, "Channeling of Electrons and Positrons Correspondence Between Classical and Quantal Descriptions," *Mat.-Fys. Medd. Dan. Vidensk. Selsk.* **39** (1977), pp. 1-58.

36. B. R. Appleton, L. C. Feldman, and W. L. Brown, in "Solid State Physics Research with Accelerators," Brookhaven National Laboratory Report No. BNL-50083 (1968), p. 153.

37. L. C. Feldman and B. R. Appleton, "Multiple Scattering and Planar Dechanneling in Silicon and Germanium," *Phys. Rev.* **B8** (August 1973), pp. 935-951.

38. L. C. Feldman and B. R. Appleton, "Unidirectional Channeling and Blocking: A New Technique for Defect Studies," *Appl. Phys. Lett.* **15** (November 1, 1969), pp. 305-307.

39. B. R. Appleton and L. C. Feldman, "Uni-directional Channeling and Blocking," *Atomic Collision Phenomena in Solids*, ed. D. W. Palmer, M. W. Thompson, and P. D. Townsend (Amsterdam: North Holland Publishing Co, 1970), pp. 417-433.

40. B. R. Appleton and L. C. Feldman, "Investigation of Interstitial Zn Concentrations in Additively Colored ZnO Using the Uni-Directional Channeling and Blocking Technique," *J. Phys. Chem. Solids* **33** (February 1972), pp. 507-517.

41. J. U. Andersen, W. M. Gibson, and E. Uggerhoj, "Channeling of Swift Charged Particles and Various Applications of Particles Channeling," *Proceedings of the International Conf. on Appl. of Ion Beams to Semiconductor Technology*, Grenoble, France, May 1967, ed. P. Glotin (Gap, France: Editions Ophrys, 1968), p. 153-178.

42. W. M. Gibson, F. W. Martin, R. Stensgaard, F. Palmgren Jensen, N. I. Meyer, G. Galster, A. Johansen, and J. S. Olsen, "Electrical and Physical Measurements on Silicon Implanted with Channeled and Nonchanneled Dopant Ions," *Can. J. Phys.* **46** (March 15, 1968), pp. 675-688.

43. L. C. Feldman and D. E. Murnick, "Channeling in Iron and Lattice Location of Implanted Xenon," *Phys. Rev.* **B5** (January 1972), pp. 1-6.

44. L. C. Feldman, E. N. Kaufmann, D. W. Mingay, and W. M. Augustyniak, "Lattice-Location Studies on Tl, Pb, and Bi in Iron, and the Hyperfine Field at Pb in Iron," *Phys. Rev. Lett.* **27** (October 25, 1971), pp. 1145-1148.

45. E. N. Kaufmann, J. M. Poate, and W. M. Augustyniak, "Lattice-Location Study of Hf Implanted in Ni," *Phys. Rev.* **B7** (February 1973), pp. 951-955.

46. H. deWaard and L. C. Feldman, "Lattice Location of Impurities Implanted into Metals," in *Applications of Ion Beams to Metals*, ed. S. T. Picraux, E. P. EerNisse, and F. L. Vook (New York: Plenum Press, 1974), pp. 317-352.

47. J. R. MacDonald, R. A. Boie, W. Darcey, and R. Hensler, "Lattice-Location Studies of Argon, Potassium, and Calcium in Iron," *Phys. Rev.* **B12** (September 1975), pp. 1633-1637.

48. L. C. Feldman, E. N. Kaufmann, J. M. Poate, and W. M. Augustyniak, "The Lattice Site Location of Carbon Implanted into Iron," in *Ion Implantation in Semiconductors and Other Materials*, ed. B. L. Crowder (New York: Plenum Press, 1973), pp. 491-502.

49. J. A. Borders and J. M. Poate, "Lattice-Site Location of Ion-Implanted Impurities in Copper and Other FCC Metals," *Phys. Rev.* **B13** (February 1976), pp. 969-979.

50. J. M. Poate, W. J. DeBonte, W. M. Augustyniak, and J. A. Borders, "Formation of Substitutional Alloys by Ion Implantation in Metals," *Appl. Phys. Lett.* **25** (December 15, 1974), pp. 698-701.

51. G. Dearnaley, J. H. Freeman, R. S. Nelson, and J. Stephen, *Ion Implantation* (Amsterdam: North Holland Publishing Co., 1973).

52. R. S. Ohl, "Properties of Ionic Bombarded Silicon," *Bell System Tech. J.* **31** (January 1952), pp. 104-121.

53. See references 20 and 21.

54. See reference 42; also, E. Laegsgaard, F. W. Martin, and W. M. Gibson, "Position Sensitive Detectors Made by Ion Implantation in Silicon," *Nuclear Instru. & Methods* **60** (March 1968), pp. 24-26.

55. T. E. Seidel and A. U. MacRae, "Some Properties of Ion-Implanted Boron in Silicon," *TMS-AIME* **245** (March 1969), pp. 491-498; R. A. Moline and G. F. Foxhall, "Ion-Implanted Hyperabrupt Junction Voltage Variable Capacitors," *IEEE Trans. Elec. Dev.*, **ED-19** (February 1972), pp. 267-273.

56. L. C. Feldman and J. W. Rodgers, "Depth Profiles of the Lattice Disorder Resulting from Ion Bombardment of Silicon Single Crystals," *J. Appl. Phys.* **41** (August 1970), pp. 3776-3782.

57. J. C. North and W. M. Gibson, "Channeling Study of Boron-Implanted Silicon," *Appl. Phys. Lett.* **16** (February 1, 1970), pp. 126-129; idem, "Channeling Study of Boron-Implanted Silicon: Liquid Nitrogen Temperature Implantation," *Rad. Effects* **6** (December 1970), pp. 199-203.

58. J. L. Merz, L. C. Feldman, and E. A. Sadowski, "Ion Implantation of Bismuth into GaP. I. Photoluminescence," *Rad. Effects* **6** (December 1970), pp. 285-291; L. C. Feldman, W. M. Augustyniak, and J. L. Merz, "Implantation of Bi into GaP. II. Channeling Studies," *Rad. Effects* **6** (December 1970), pp. 293-299; J. L. Merz, L. C. Feldman, D. W. Mingay, and W. M. Augustyniak, "Implantation of Bismuth into Gallium Phosphide III. Hot-Implant Behavior," *Proc. of the II Int'l. Conf. on Ion Implantation in Semiconductors*, ed. I. Ruge and J. Graul (Berlin: Springer-Verlag, 1971), pp. 182-192.

59. S. T. Picraux, W. L. Brown, and W. M. Gibson, "Lattice Location by Channeling Angular Distributions: Bi Implanted in Si," *Phys. Rev.* **B6** (August 1972), pp. 1382-1394.

60. J. K. Hirvonen, W. L. Brown, and P. M. Glotin, "Structural Differences in Light and Heavy Ion Disorder in Silicon Studied by Single and Double Alignment Channeling Techniques," *Proceedings of the II Int'l Conf. on Ion Implantation in Semiconductors*, ed. I. Ruge and J. Graul (Berlin: Springer-Verlag, 1971), pp. 8-16.

61. J. K. Hirvonen, "Investigations of Ion Implantation in Silicon Using Particle Channeling," PhD. Thesis, Rutgers University, New Brunswick, N. J., 1971 (unpublished).

62. See reference 58.

63. J. C. North and W. M. Gibson, "Channeling Study of Boron-Implanted Silicon," *Appl. Phys. Lett.* **16** (February 1, 1970), pp. 126-129.

64. D. F. Daly and K. A. Picker, "Electron Paramagnetic Resonance in Ion-Implanted Silicon," *Appl. Phys. Lett.* **15** (October 15, 1969), pp. 267-269.

65. D. E. Murnick, "Implantation Perturbed Angular Correlation Techniques in Ferromagnetic and Nonferromagnetic Materials," *Proceedings of the Int'l Conference on Angular Correlations in Nuclear Disintegration*, ed. H. van Krugten and B. van Nooijen (Rotterdam: Rotterdam University Press, 1971), pp. 455-486; see also reference 49.

66. L. C. Feldman, E. N. Kaufmann, J. M. Poate, and W. M. Augustyniak, "The Lattice Site Location of C Implanted into Fe," *Ion Implantation in Semiconductors and Other Materials*, ed. B. L. Crowder (New York: Plenum Press, 1973), pp. 491-502.

67. L. C. Feldman and J. W. Rodgers, "Depth Profiles of the Lattice Disorder Resulting from Ion Bombardment of Silicon Single Crystals," *J. Appl. Phys.* **41** (August 1970), pp. 3776-3782; S. T. Picraux, W. L. Brown, and W. M. Gibson, "Lattice Location by Channeling Angular Distributions: Bi Implanted in Si," *Phys. Rev.* **B6** (August 1972), pp. 1382-1394; see also reference 60.

68. E. N. Kaufmann, P. Raghavan, R. S. Raghavan, K. Krien, E. J. Ansaldo, and R. A. Naumann, "Determination of Unique Site Population in Various Implanted Non-Cubic Metals Using Angular Correlations and the Nuclear Electric Quadrupole Interaction," *Applications of Ion Beams to Metals*, ed. S. T. Picraux, E. P. Eernisse, and F. L. Vook (New York: Plenum Press, 1974), p. 379; P. Raghavan, E. N. Kaufmann, R. S. Raghavan, E. J. Ansaldo, and R. A. Naumann, "Sign and Magnitude of the Quadrupole Interaction of ^{111}Cd in Non-Cubic Metals: Universal Correlation of Ionic and Electronic Field Gradients," *Phys. Rev.* **B13** (April 1976), pp. 2835-2847.

69. R. D. Standley, W. M. Gibson, and J. W. Rodgers, "Properties of Ion Bombarded Fused Quartz for Integrated Optics," *Appl. Phys. Lett.* **11**, (June 1972), pp. 1313-1316.

70. H. M. Presby and W. L. Brown, "Refractive Index Variations in Proton Bombarded Fused Silica," *Appl. Phys. Lett.* **24**, (May 15, 1974), pp. 511-513.

71. H. de Waard and L. C. Feldman, "Lattice Location of Impurities Implanted into Metals," *Applications of Ion Beams to Metals*, ed. S. T. Picraux, E. P. Eernisse, and F. L. Vook (New York: Plenum Press, 1974), pp. 317-352.

72. J. M. Poate, W. J. DeBonte, W. M. Augustyniak, and J. A. Borders, "Formation of Substitutional Alloys by Ion Implantation in Metals," *Appl. Phys. Lett.* **25** (December 15, 1974), pp. 698-701; A. G. Cullis, J. M. Poate, and J. A. Borders, "The Physical State of Implanted Tungsten in Copper," *Appl. Phys. Lett.* **28** (March 15, 1976), pp. 314-316; J. M. Poate, J. A. Borders, A. G. Cullis, and J. K. Hirvonen, "Ion Implantation as an Ultrafast Quenching Technique for Metastable Alloy Production: The Ag-Cu System," *Appl. Phys. Lett.* **30** (April 15, 1977), pp. 365-368.

73. E. N. Kaufmann, R. Vianden, J. R. Chelikowsky, and J. C. Phillips, "Extension of Equilibrium Formation Criteria to Metastable Microalloys," *Phys. Rev. Lett.* **39** (December 26, 1977), pp. 1671-1675; R. Vianden, E. N. Kaufmann, and J. W. Rodgers, "Impurity Lattice Location in Ion-Implanted Beryllium: Measurements and Systematics," *Phys. Rev.* **22** (July 1980), pp. 63-79.

74. *Ion Implantation Metallurgy*, ed. C. M. Preece and J. K. Hirvonen (Metallurgical Soc. AIME, 1980).

75. T. M. Buck and R. L. Meek, "Crystallographic Damage to Silicon by Typical Slicing, Lapping, and Polishing Operations," in *Silicon Device Processing*, Nat'l Bureau Standards Spec. Publ. 337, ed. C. P. Marsden (U.S. Dept. of Commerce, 1970), pp. 419-430; T. M. Buck and G. H. Wheatley, "Studies of Solid Surfaces with 100 keV Singly Ionized Helium and Hydrogen Ion Beams," *Surface Sci.* **33** (October 1972), pp. 35-55.

76. T. M. Buck, G. H. Wheatley, and L. C. Feldman, "Charge States of 25-150 keV H and ^4He Backscattered from Solid Surfaces," *Surface Sci.* **35** (March 1973), pp. 345-361.

77. T. M. Buck, L. C. Feldman, and G. H. Wheatley, "Charge Neutralization of Medium Energy H and ^4He Ions Backscattered from Solid Surfaces. Effects of Surface Cleaning," *Atomic Collisions in Solids*, ed. S. Datz, B. R. Appleton, and C. D. Moak (New York: Plenum Press, 1975), pp. 331-340.

78. D. P. Smith, "Scattering of Low-Energy Noble Gas Ions from Metal Surfaces," *J. Appl. Phys.* **38** (January 1967), pp. 340-347.

79. D. J. Ball, T. M. Buck, D. MacNair, and G. H. Wheatley, "Investigation of Low-Energy Ion Scattering as a Surface Analytical Technique," *Surface Sci.* **30** (March 1972), pp. 69-90.

80. H. H. Brongersma and T. M. Buck, "Selected Topics in Low-Energy Ion Scattering: Surface Segregation in. Cu/Ni Alloys and Ion Neutralization," *Surface Sci.* **53** (December 1975), pp. 649-658.

81. H. H. Brongersma, M. J. Sparnaay, and T. M. Buck, "Surface Segregation in Cu-Ni and Cu-Pt Alloys: A Comparison of Low-Energy Ion-Scattering Results with Theory," *Surface Sci.* **71** (February 1978), pp. 657-678.

82. D. L. Malm and M. J. Vasile, "A Study of Contamination on Electroplated Gold, Copper, Platinum, and Palladium," *J. Electrochem. Soc.* **120** (November 1973), pp. 1484-1487; R. P. Frankenthal and D. L. Malm, "Analysis of the Air-Formed Oxide Film on a Series of Iron-Chromium Alloys by Ion-Scattering Spectrometry," *J. Electrochem. Soc.* **123** (February 1976), pp. 186-191.

83. Y. S. Chen, G. L. Miller, D. A. H. Robinson, G. H. Wheatley, and T. M. Buck, "Energy and Mass Spectra of Neutral and Charged Particles Scattered and Desorbed from Gold Surfaces," *Surface Sci.* **62** (January 1977), pp. 133-147.

84. T. M. Buck, Y. S. Chen, G. H. Wheatley, and W. F. Van der Weg, "Energy Spectra of 6-32 keV Neutral and Ionized Ar and He Scattered from Au Targets; Ionized Fractions as Functions of Energy," *Surface Sci.* **47** (January 1975), pp. 244-255.

85. R. L. Erickson and D. P. Smith, "Oscillatory Cross Sections in Low-Energy Ion Scattering from Surfaces," *Phys. Rev. Lett.* **34** (February 10, 1975), pp. 297-299.

86. N. H. Tolk, J. C. Tully, J. Kraus, C. W. White, and S. H. Neff, "Angular Dependence of Oscillatory Structure in Low-Energy Ion-Surface Scattering," *Phys. Rev. Lett.* **36** (March 29, 1976), pp. 747-750.

87. H. H. Brongersma and T. M. Buck, "Neutralization Behavior in Scattering of Low Energy Ions from Solid Surfaces," *Nucl. Instrum. & Methods* **132** (Jan./Feb. 1976), pp. 559-564.

88. N. H. Tolk, J. C. Tully, C. W. White, J. Kraus, A. A. Monge, D. L. Simms, M. F. Robbins, S. H. Neff, and W. Lichten, "Quantum-Mechanical Phase Interference and Optical Polarization in Low Energy Na$^+$-Ne Inelastic Collisions," *Phys. Rev.* **A13** (March 1976), pp. 969-984.

89. J. C. Tully and N. H. Tolk, "Nonadiabatic Neutralization at Surfaces: Oscillatory Ion Scattering Intensities," in *Inelastic Ion-Surface Collisions*, ed. N. H. Tolk, J. C. Tully, W. Heiland, and C. W. White (New York: Academic Press, 1977), p. 105.

90. T. M. Buck, J. M. Poate, K. A. Pickar, and C-M. Hsieh, "A Rutherford Scattering Study of the Diffusion of Heavy Metal Impurities in Silicon to Ion-Damaged Surface Layers," *Surface Sci.* **35** (March 1973), pp. 362-379.

91. M. P. Lepselter, "Beam-Lead Technology," *Bell System Tech. J.* **45** (February 1966), pp. 233-253.

92. J. M. Poate, P. A. Turner, W. J. DeBonte, and J. Yahalom, "Thin-Film Interdiffusion. I. Au-Pd, Pd-Au, Ti-Pd, Ti-Au, Ti-Pd-Au, and Ti-Au-Pd," *J. Appl. Phys.* **46** (October 1975), pp. 4275-4283.

93. R. G. Kirsch, J. M. Poate, and M. Eibschutz, "Interdiffusion Mechanisms in Ag-Au Thin-Film Couples," *Appl. Phys. Lett.* **29** (December 15, 1976), pp. 772-774.

94. See reference 91.

95. J. M. Poate and T. C. Tisone, "Kinetics and Mechanism of Platinum Silicide Formation on Silicon," *Appl. Phys. Lett.* **24** (April 15, 1974), pp. 391-393.

96. A. K. Sinha and J. M. Poate, "Effect of Alloying Behavior on the Electrical Characteristics of *n*-GaAs Schottky Diodes Metallized with W, Au, and Pt," *Appl. Phys. Lett.* **23** (December 15, 1973), pp. 666-668.

97. J. M. Poate, P. J. Silverman, and J. Yahalom, "The Growth and Composition of Anodic Films on GaP," *J. Phys. Chem. Solids* **34** (November 1973), pp. 1847-1857.

98. L. C. Feldman, J. M. Poate, F. Ermanis, and B. Schwartz, "The Combined Use of He Back-Scattering and He-Induced X-rays in the Study of Anodically Grown Oxide Films on GaAs," *Thin Solid Films* **19** (December 3, 1973), pp. 81-89.

99. P. J. Silverman and N. Schwartz, "A Rutherford Scattering Analysis of Anodic Tantalum-Silicon Oxides," *J. Electrochem. Soc.* **121** (April 1974), pp. 550-555.

100. R. L. Ruth and N. Schwartz, "A Rutherford Backscattering Analysis of Anodic Tantalum-Titanium Oxides," *J. Electrochem. Soc.* **123** (December 1976), pp. 1860-1867.

101. C. J. Mogab and E. Lugujjo, "Backscattering Analysis of the Composition of Silicon-Nitride Films Deposited by RF Reactive Sputtering," *J. Appl. Phys.* **47** (April 1976), pp. 1302-1309.

102. L. R. Testardi, J. H. Wernick, and W. A. Royer, "Superconductivity with Onset Above 23°K in Nb-Ge Sputtered Films," *Solid State Commun.* **15** (July 1, 1974), pp. 1-4.

103. L. R. Testardi, R. L. Meek, J. M. Poate, W. A. Royer, A. R. Storm, and J. H. Wernick, "Preparation and Analysis of Superconducting Nb-Ge Films," *Phys. Rev.* **B11** (June 1975), pp. 4304-4317.

104. J. M. Poate, L. R. Testardi, A. R. Storm, and W. M. Augustyniak, "^{4}He-Induced Damage in Superconducting Nb-Ge Films," *Phys. Rev. Lett.* **35** (November 10, 1975), pp. 1290-1293.

105. L. R. Testardi, J. M. Poate, W. Weber, W. M. Augustyniak, and J. H. Barrett, "Channeling in V_3Si: Atomic Displacements and Electron-Phonon/Defect Interactions," *Phys. Rev. Lett.* **39** (September 12, 1977), pp. 716-719.

106. R. D. Burbank, R. C. Dynes, and J. M. Poate, "X-ray Study of Atomic Displacements in Nb_3Sn Induced by Radiation Damage," *J. Low Temp. Phys.* **36** (1979), pp. 573-585.

107. C. W. White and N. H. Tolk, "Optical Radiation from Low-Energy Ion-Surface Collisions," *Phys. Rev. Lett.* **26** (March 1, 1971), pp. 486-489.

108. N. H. Tolk, D. L. Simms, E. B. Foley, and C. W. White, "Photon Emission from Low-Energy Ion and Neutral Bombardment of Solids," *Rad. Effects* **18** (April 1973), pp. 221-229.

109. See reference 108.

110. C. W. White, D. L. Simms, and N. H. Tolk, "Surface Composition Determined by Analysis of Impact Radiation," *Science* **177** (August 11, 1972), pp. 481-486.

111. N. H. Tolk, I. S. T. Tsong, and C. W. White, "In Situ Spectrochemical Analysis of Solid Surfaces by Ion Beam Sputtering," *Anal. Chem.* **49** (January 1977), pp. 16A-30A.

112. J. M. Poate, W. L. Brown, R. Homer, W. M. Augustyniak, J. W. Mayer, K. N. Tu, and W. F. Van der Weg, "The Sputtering of PtSi and NiSi," *Nucl. Instrum. & Methods* **132** (January/February 1976), pp. 345-349.

113. W. L. Brown, L. J. Lanzerotti, J. M. Poate, and W. M. Augustyniak, "'Sputtering' of Ice by MeV Light Ions," *Phys. Rev. Lett.* **40** (April 10, 1978), pp. 1027-1030.

114. W. Friedrich, P. Knipping, and M. von Laue, "Interference Phenomena with Röntgen Rays," *Sitzungberichte der (Kgl) Bayerische Academie der Wissenschaften* (1912), pp. 303-322.

115. L. W. McKeehan, "The Crystal Structure of Silver-Palladium and Silver-Gold Alloys," *Phys. Rev.* **19** (May 1922), pp. 537-538.

116. R. M. Bozorth and F. E. Haworth, "The Perfection of Quartz and Other Crystals and Its Relation to Surface Treatment," *Phys. Rev.* **45** (June 1934), pp. 821-826.

117. W. L. Bond, "A Double-Crystal X-Ray Goniometer for Accurate Orientation Determination," *Proc. IRE* **38** (August 1950), pp. 886-889.

118. W. L. Bond, "A Single-Crystal Automatic Diffractometer. I," *Acta Cryst.* **8** (1955), pp. 741-746.

119. W. L. Bond, "Precision Lattice Constant Determination," *Acta Cryst.* **13** (October 10, 1960), pp. 814-818.

120. W. L. Bond and W. Kaiser, "Interstitial Versus Substitutional Oxygen in Silicon," *Phys. Chem. Solids* **16** (November 1960), pp. 44-45.

121. A. S. Cooper, "The Mo Kα_1/Cu Kα_1 Wavelength Ratio," *Acta Cryst.* **18** (June 1965), pp. 1078-1080.

122. B. T. Matthias, E. A. Wood, and A. N. Holden, "New Ferroelectric Crystals," *Phys. Rev.* **76** (July 1949), p. 175.

123. E. A. Wood, "Polymorphism in Potassium Niobate, Sodium Niobate, and Other ABO_3 Compounds," *Acta. Cryst.* **4** (1951), pp. 353-362; idem, "Detwinning Ferroelectric Crystals," *Bell System Tech. J.* **30** (October 1951), pp. 945-955.

124. B. T. Matthias, E. A. Wood, E. Corenzwit, and V. B. Bala, "Superconductivity and Electron Concentration," *Phys. Chem. Solids* **1** (November 1956), pp. 188-190.

125. E. A. Wood, R. C. Miller, and J. P. Remeika, "The Field-Induced Ferroelectric Phase of Sodium Niobate," *Acta. Cryst.* **15** (December 1962), pp. 1273-1279.

126. J. A. Golovchenko, B. W. Batterman, and W. L. Brown, "Observation of Internal X-Ray Wave Fields During Bragg Diffraction with an Application to Impurity Lattice Location," *Phys. Rev.* **B10** (November 1974), pp. 4239-4243.

127. P. L. Cowan, J. A. Golovchenko, and M. F. Robbins, "X-Ray Standing Waves at Crystal Surfaces," *Phys. Rev. Lett.* **44** (June 23, 1980), pp. 1680-1683.

128. P. Eisenberger and P. M. Platzman, "Compton Scattering of X-Rays from Bound Electrons," *Phys. Rev.* **A2** (August 1970), pp. 415-423; P. Eisenberger, "Electron Momentum Density of He and H_2; Compton X-Ray Scattering," *Phys. Rev.* **A2** (November 1970), pp. 1678-1686.

129. P. Eisenberger, W. H. Henneker, and P. E. Cade, "Compton Scattering of X-Rays from Ne, N_2, and O_2: A Comparison of Theory and Experiment," *J. Chem. Phys.* **56** (February 1, 1972), pp. 1207-1209.

130. P. Eisenberger and W. C. Marra, "Identification of Localized Bonds in the Hydrocarbons," *Phys. Rev. Lett.* **27** (November 22, 1971), pp. 1413-1416.

131. P. Eisenberger and W. A. Reed, "Gamma-Ray Compton Scattering: Experimental Compton Profiles for He, N_2, Ar, and Kr," *Phys. Rev.* **A5** (May 1972), pp. 2085-2094.

132. P. Eisenberger, L. Lam, P. M. Platzman, and P. Schmidt, "X-Ray Compton Profiles of Li and Na: Theory and Experiments," *Phys. Rev.* **B6** (November 1972), pp. 3671-3681.

133. P. Eisenberger, P. M. Platzman, and K. C. Pandy, "Investigation of X-Ray Plasmon Scattering in Single-Crystal Beryllium," *Phys. Rev. Lett.* **31** (July 30, 1973), pp. 311-314.

134. P. M. Platzman and P. Eisenberger, "Presence of an Incipient Wigner Electron Lattice in Solid-State Electron Gases," *Phys. Rev. Lett.* **33** (July 15, 1974), pp. 152-154.

135. P. M. Platzman and N. Tzoar, "X-Ray Scattering from an Electron Gas," *Phys. Rev.* **139** (July 1965), pp. A410-A413.

136. J. W. M. DuMond, "Compton Modified Line Structure and its Relation to the Electron Theory of Solid Bodies," *Phys. Rev.* **33** (May 1929), pp. 643-658.

137. W. C. Phillips and R. J. Weiss, "X-Ray Determination of Electron Momenta in Li, Be, B, Na, Mg, Al, and LiF," *Phys. Rev.* **171** (July 1968), pp. 790-800.

138. N. Cooper and J. A. Leaker, "The Compton Profiles of Graphite and Diamond," *Phil. Mag.* **15** (June 1967), pp. 1201-1212.

139. See reference 130.

140. W. A. Reed, P. Eisenberger, K. C. Pandey, and L. C. Snyder, "Electron Momentum Distribution in Graphite and Diamond and Carbon-Carbon Bonding," *Phys. Rev.* **B15** (August 1974), pp. 1507-1515; W. A. Reed, L. C. Snyder, P. Eisenberger, X. J. Pinder, T. Weber, and Z. Wasserman, "The Spherical Compton Profile of Neopentane and the Carbon-Carbon Single Bond of Diamond," *J. Chem. Phys.* **67** (July 1977), pp. 143-146; W. A. Reed, L. C. Snyder, H. J. Guggenheim, T. A. Weber, and Z. R. Wasserman, "The Compton Profile of Urea," *J. Chem. Phys.* **69** (July 1978), pp. 284-296.

141. W. A. Reed and P. Eisenberger, "Gamma-Ray Compton Profiles of Diamond, Silicon, and Germanium," *Phys. Rev.* **B6** (December 1972), pp. 4596-4604; P. Eisenberger and W. A. Reed, "Gamma-Ray Compton Profiles of Copper and Nickel," *Phys. Rev.* **B9** (April 1974), pp. 3242-3247.

142. See the first two entries in reference 140.

143. C. J. Powell, "The Origin of the Characteristic Electron Energy Losses in Ten Elements," *Proc. Phys. Soc., London,* **76** (November 1, 1960), pp. 593-610.

144. See reference 134.

145. P. C. Gibbons, J. J. Ritsko, and S. E. Schnatterly, "Inelastic Electron Scattering Spectrometer," *Rev. Sci. Instr.* **46** (November 1975), pp. 1546-1554.

146. A. E. Meixner, M. Schlüter, P. M. Platzman, and G. S. Brown, "Inelastic Electron Scattering near the *K* Edge in Be," *Phys. Rev.* **B17** (January 1978), pp. 686-689; A. E. Meixner, R. E. Dietz, G. S. Brown, and P. M. Platzman, "Inelastic Electron Scattering in Nickel," *Solid State Comm.* **27** (September 1978), pp. 1255-1257; "Inelastic Electron Scattering in Nickel," talk presented at *International Conference on the Physics of Transition Metals,* Toronto, Canada, August 15-19, 1977.

147. B. M. Kincaid, A. E. Meixner, and P. M. Platzman, "Carbon *K* Edge in Graphite Measured Using Electron-Energy-Loss Spectroscopy," *Phys. Rev. Lett.* **40** (May 8, 1978), pp. 1296-1299.

148. P. Eisenberger and B. M. Kincaid, "EXAFS: New Horizons in Structure Determinations," *Science* **200** (June 30, 1978), pp. 1441-1447.

149. D. E. Sayers, F. W. Lytle, and E. A. Stern, "Point Scattering Theory of X-Ray K-Absorption Fine Structure," *Adv. X-Ray Anal.* **13** (New York: Plenum Press, 1970), pp. 248-271.

150. B. M. Kincaid and P. Eisenberger, "Synchrotron Radiation Studies of the *K*-Edge Photoabsorption Spectra of Kr, Br_2, and $GeCl_4$: A Comparison of Theory and Experiment," *Phys. Rev. Lett.* **34** (June 2, 1975), pp. 1361-1364; P. Eisenberger and B. M. Kincaid, "Synchrotron Radiation Studies of X-Ray Absorption Spectra of Ions in Aqueous Solutions," *Chem. Phys. Lett.* **36** (October 15, 1975), pp. 134-136; B. M. Kincaid, P. Eisenberger, K. O. Hodgson, and S. Doniach, "X-Ray Absorption Spectroscopy Using Synchrotron Radiation for Structural Investigation of Organometallic Molecules of Biological Interest," *Proc. Nat. Acad. Sci. USA* **72** No. 6 (June 1975), pp. 2340-2342.

151. P. H. Citrin, P. Eisenberger, and B. M. Kincaid, "Transferability of Phase Shifts in Extended X-Ray Absorption Fine Structure," *Phys. Rev. Lett.* **36** (May 31, 1976), pp. 1346-1349.

152. P. A. Lee and G. Beni, "New Method for the Calculation of Atomic Phase Shifts: Application to Extended X-ray Absorption Fine Structure (EXAFS) in Molecules and Crystals," *Phys. Rev.,* **B15** (March 1977), pp. 2862-2883; P. A. Lee, P. H. Citrin, P. Eisenberger, and B. M. Kincaid, "Extended X-ray Absorption Fine Structure—Its Strengths and Limitations as a Structural Tool," *Rev. Mod. Phys.* **53** (October 1981), pp. 769-806.

153. J. Reed, P. Eisenberger, B. K. Teo, and B. M. Kincaid, "Structure of the Catalytic Site of Polymer-Bound Wilkinson's Catalyst by X-ray Absorption Studies," *J. Am. Chem. Soc.,* **99** (July 1977), pp. 5217-5218.

154. G. S. Brown, P. Eisenberger, and P. Schmidt, "Extended X-Ray Absorption Fine Structure Studies of Oriented Single Crystals," *Solid State Comm.* **24** (October 1977), pp. 201-203.

155. G. S. Brown, L. R. Testardi, J. H. Wernick, A. B. Hallack, and T. H. Geballe, "EXAFS Measurements on Nb_3Ge Thin Films," *Solid State Comm.* **23** (1977), pp. 875-878.

156. G. Beni and P. M. Platzman, "Temperature and Polarization Dependence of Extended X-Ray Absorption Fine-Structure Spectra," *Phys. Rev.* **B14** (August 1976), pp. 1514-1518.

157. P. A. Lee, "Possibility of Adsorbate Position Determination Using Final-State Interference Effects," *Phys. Rev.* **B13** (June 1976), pp. 5261-5270; U. Landman and D. L. Adams, "Extended X-Ray-Absorption Fine Structure-Auger Process for Surface Structure Analysis: Theoretical Considerations of a Proposed Experiment," *Proc. Natl. Acad. Sci. USA* **73** (August 1976), pp. 2550-2553.

158. P. H. Citrin, P. Eisenberger, and R. C. Hewitt, "Extended X-Ray-Absorption Fine Structure of Surface Atoms on Single-Crystal Substrates: Iodine Adsorbed on Ag(111)," *Phys. Rev. Lett.* **41** (July 31, 1978), pp. 309-312.

159. K. Siegbahn, *ESCA, Atomic, Molecular and Solid State Structure Studied by Means of Electron Spectroscopy* (Uppsala: Almqvist and Wiksells, 1967).

160. G. K. Wertheim and A. Rosenzwaig, "Characterization of Inequivalent Iron Sites

in Prussian Blue by Photoelectron Spectroscopy," *J. Chem. Phys.* **54** (April 1, 1971), pp. 3235-3237.

161. D. N. E. Buchanan, M. Robbins, H. J. Guggenheim, G. K. Wertheim, and V. G. Lambrecht, Jr., "Mössbauer Effect and ESCA Shifts in the Mixed Valence Compound K_xFeF_3," *Solid State Comm.* **9** (May 1, 1971), pp. 583-586.

162. G. K. Wertheim and A. Rosenzwaig, "Configuration Interaction in the X-Ray Photoelectron Spectra of Alkali Halides," *Phys. Rev. Lett.* **26** (May 10, 1971), pp. 1179-1182.

163. R. L. Cohen, G. K. Wertheim, A. Rosencwaig, and H. J. Guggenheim, "Multiplet Splitting of the 4s and 5s Electrons of the Rare Earths," *Phys. Rev.* **B5** (February 1972), pp. 1037-1039.

164. S. Hüfner, G. K. Wertheim, N. V. Smith, and M. M. Traum, "XPS Density of States of Copper, Silver, and Nickel," *Solid State Comm.* **11** (July 15, 1972), pp. 323-326.

165. S. Hüfner, G. K. Wertheim, R. L. Cohen, and J. H. Wernick, "Density of States in CuNi Alloys," *Phys. Rev. Lett.* **28** (February 21, 1972), pp. 488-490; S. Hüfner, G. K. Wertheim, J. H. Wernick, and A. Melera, "The AgPd System: Density of States and Interpretation," *Solid State Comm.* **11** (July 1, 1972), pp. 259-262.

166. G. K. Wertheim, L. F. Mattheiss, M. Campagna, and T. P. Pearsall, "Transition Probabilities and Overlap-Covalency Effects in the X-ray Photoemission Spectra of Transition-Metal Compounds: ReO_3," *Phys. Rev. Lett.* **32** (May 6, 1974), pp. 997-999.

167. P. H. Citrin and D. R. Hamann, "X-Ray Photoelectron Spectroscopy of Implanted Rare Gases in Noble Metals: Polarization and Potential Effects," *Chem. Phys. Lett.* **22** (October 1, 1973), pp. 301-304.

168. G. D. Mahan, "Excitons in Metals: Infinite Hole Mass," *Phys. Rev.* **163** (November 1967), pp. 612-617.

169. P. Noziéres and C. T. de Dominicis, "Singularities in the X-Ray Absorption and Emission of Metals. III. One-Body Theory Exact Solution," *Phys. Rev.* **178** (February 1969), pp. 1097-1107.

170. S. Hüfner, G. K. Wertheim, D. N. E. Buchanan, and K. W. West, "Core Line Asymmetries in XPS-Spectra of Metals," *Phys. Lett.* **A46** (January 28, 1974), pp. 420-421; P. H. Citrin, G. K. Wertheim, and Y. Baer, "Many Electron Effects in Core-Level X-Ray and Electron Spectroscopies from Na, Mg, and Al," *Phys. Rev. Lett.* **35** (September 29, 1975), pp. 885-888.

171. Y. Baer, P. H. Citrin, and G. K. Wertheim, "X-Ray Photoemission from Lithium: An Explanation of Its X-Ray Edge," *Phys. Rev. Lett.* **37** (July 5, 1976), pp. 49-52.

172. G. K. Wertheim, A. Rosencwaig, R. L. Cohen, and H. J. Guggenheim, "Exchange Splitting in the 4f Photoelectron Spectra of the Rare Earths," *Phys. Rev. Lett.* **27** (August 23, 1971), pp. 505-507.

173. M. Campagna, G. K. Wertheim, and E. Bucher, "Spectroscopy or Homogeneous Mixed Valence Rare Earth Compounds," *Structure and Bonding* Vol. 30, ed. J. D. Dunitz et al. (Berlin: Springer-Verlag, 1976), pp. 99-140.

174. M. Campagna, E. Bucher, G. K. Wertheim, D. N. E. Buchanan, and L. D. Longinotti, "Spontaneous Interconfiguration Fluctuations in the Tm Monochalcogenides," *Phys. Rev. Lett.* **32** (April 22, 1974), pp. 885-889.

175. M. Campagna, E. Bucher, G. K. Wertheim, and L. D. Longinotti, "Valence Mixing and Semiconductor-Metal Transition in the Sm Monochalcogenides," *Phys. Rev. Lett.* **33** (July 15, 1974), pp. 165-168.

176. J. -N. Chazalviel, M. Campagna, G. K. Wertheim, and P. H. Schmidt, "Study of Valence Mixing in SmB_6 by X-Ray Photoelectron Spectroscopy," *Phys. Rev.* **B14** (November 1976), pp. 4586-4592.

177. R. F. Roberts, "X-Ray Photoelectron Spectroscopic Characterization of Copper Oxide Surfaces Treated with Benzotriazole," *J. Elec. Spect.* **4** (October 1974), pp. 273-291; R. F. Roberts and C. M. Truesdale, "ESCA Studies of Metal·Corrosion

Inhibition II. Nature of Films Formed on Copper by Benzotriazole and Some Related Azoles," *Electrochem. Soc. Extended Abstracts* **75-2** (1975), pp. 204-205; N. D. Hobbins and R. F. Roberts, "An Ellipsometric Study of Thin Films Formed on Copper by Aqueous Benzotriazole and Benzimidazole," *Surf. Technol.* **9** (October 1979), pp. 235-239.

178. J. H. Thomas, III, and S. P. Sharma, "ESCA Study of the Passive Layer on Sn-Ni Alloy," *J. Vac. Sci. Technol.* **14** (Sept./Oct. 1977), pp. 1168-1172.

179. H. G. Tompkins, G. K. Wertheim, and S. P. Sharma, "Time Dependence of the Chemical Composition of the Surface Film on the Metastable Tin-Nickel Alloy Studied with X-Ray Photoelectron Spectroscopy," *J. Vac. Sci. Technol.* **15** (Jan./Feb. 1978), pp. 20-23.

180. E. Prince, "Crystal and Magnetic Structure of Copper Chromate," *Acta Cryst.* **10** (September 1957), pp. 554-556.

181. S. C. Abrahams, "Crystal and Magnetic Structure of Cupric Fluoride Dihydrate at $4.2°K$," *J. Chem. Phys.* **36** (January 1, 1962), pp. 56-61.

182. R. J. Birgeneau, H. J. Guggenheim, and G. Shirane, "Neutron Scattering from K_2NiF_4: A Two-Dimensional Heisenberg Antiferromagnet," *Phys. Rev. Lett.* **22** (April 7, 1969), pp. 720-723; J. Als-Nielsen, R. J. Birgeneau, and G. Shirane, "Spin Dynamics and Critical Fluctuations in a Two-dimensional Random Antiferromagnet," *Phys. Rev.* **B12** (December 1975), pp. 4963-4979; idem, "Critical Behavior of a Two-dimensional Random Antiferromagnet: $Rb_2Mn_{0.5}Ni_{0.5}F_4$," *J. Phys.* **C9** (1976), pp. L121-L125.

183. R. J. Birgeneau, R. Dingle, M. T. Hutchings, G. Shirane, and S. L. Holt, "Spin Correlations in a One-Dimensional Heisenberg Antiferromagnet," *Phys. Rev. Lett.* **26** (March 22, 1971), pp. 718-721; M. T. Hutchings, G. Shirane, R. J. Birgeneau, and S. L. Holt, "Spin Dynamics in the One-Dimensional Antiferromagnet $(CD_3)_4 NMnCl_3$," *Phys. Rev.* **B5** (March 1972), pp. 1999-2014.

184. G. Shirane, J. D. Axe, and R. J. Birgeneau, "Neutron Scattering Study of the Lattice Dynamical Phase Transition in V_3Si," *Solid State Comm.* **9** (April 1, 1971), pp. 397-400; R. J. Birgeneau, J. K. Kjems, G. Shirane, and L. G. Van Uitert, "Cooperative Jahn-Teller Phase Transition in $PrAlO_3$," *Phys. Rev.* **B10** (September 1974), pp. 2512-2534.

185. D. E. Moncton, J. D. Axe, and F. J. DiSalvo, "Study of Superlattice Formation in $2H$-$NbSe_2$ and $2H$-$TaSe_2$ by Neutron Scattering," *Phys. Rev. Lett.* **34** (March 24, 1975), pp. 734-737.

186. D. E. Moncton, F. J. DiSalvo, J. D. Axe, L. J. Sham, and B. R. Patton, "Charge-Density Wave Stacking Order in $1T$-$Ta_{1-x}Zr_xSe_2$: Interlayer Interactions and Impurity (Zr) Effects," *Phys. Rev.* **B14** (October 1976), pp. 3432-3437.

187. F. J. DiSalvo, D. E. Moncton, J. A. Wilson, and S. Mahajan, "Coexistence of Two Charge-Density Waves of Different Symmetry in $4Hb$—$TaSe_2$," *Phys. Rev.* **B14** (August 1976), pp. 1543-1546.

188. K. C. Turberfield, L. Passell, R. J. Birgeneau, and E. Bucher, "Neutron Crystal-Field Spectroscopy in Rare-Earth Metallic Compounds," *J. Appl. Phys.* **42** (March 15, 1971), pp. 1746-1754.

189. R. J. Birgeneau, E. Bucher, J. P. Maita, L. Passell, and K. C. Turberfield, "Crystal Fields and the Effective-Point-Charge Model in the Rare-Earth Pnictides," *Phys. Rev.* **B8** (December 1973), pp. 5345-5347.

190. C. Vettier, D. B. McWhan, E. I. Blount, and G. Shirane, "Pressure Dependence of Magnetic Excitations in PrSb," *Phys. Rev. Lett.* **39** (October 17, 1977), pp. 1028-1031.

191. D. E. Moncton, D. B. McWhan, J. Eckert, G. Shirane, and W. Thomlinson, "Neutron Scattering Study of Magnetic Ordering in the Reentrant Superconductor $ErRh_4B_4$," *Phys. Rev. Lett.* **39** (October 31, 1977), pp. 1164-1166.

Chapter 9

Ordered Phases of Matter and Phase Transitions

The ordered arrangement of atoms or molecules in some lattice structure, whether it is a crystalline solid or a liquid, is a common feature of several fields of physics studied at Bell Laboratories. Research in two areas—superconductivity and ferroelectricity—began in the early 1950s. Contributions to the fundamental theory of superconductivity were stimulated by experimental programs such as the demonstration of the absence of the isotope effect in ruthenium on the superconducting transition temperature, and studies of Josephson junctions and quantized flux lines. In ferroelectricity, the physics of domain formation and domain motion in the well-known ferroelectric barium titanate was studied, along with a search that led to the discovery of many new ferroelectrics for potential memory devices. Liquid crystals, requiring negligible power for operation, turned out to be more practical for applications such as display devices.

The buildup of a capability in liquid helium techniques stimulated other research activities in low-temperature physics, such as the work on the superfluidity of the lighter isotope of helium, ^{3}He, and high pressure experiments at low temperatures, with the phase changes involved in metal-insulator transitions. Related fundamental studies on phase transitions and critical phenomena have also been carried out.

I. SUPERCONDUCTIVITY – SUPERCONDUCTIVE TUNNELING

From 1948 to 1978, superconductivity advanced from a research novelty to a physical property of great technological usefulness. A theory was developed that explains the enormous variety of superconducting phenomena including, even in important cases, the onset temperature, T_c. Bell Laboratories scientists have made important

Principal authors: R. C. Dynes, P. A. Fleury, C. C. Grimes, P. C. Hohenberg, D. B. McWhan, S. Meiboom, R. C. Miller, and J. M. Rowell contributions to both theoretical and experimental developments, as well as to the applied aspects of superconductivity.

1.1 Contributions to Fundamental Theory

The earliest theoretical work was that of J. Bardeen. Prior to joining Bell Labs he had examined the effect of lattice distortions on the energy of electrons as a possible explanation of superconductivity. In 1950, while he was at Bell Labs, Bardeen returned to the subject of the electron-phonon interaction when he learned of the discovery that T_c of mercury depended on isotopic mass.[1] However, the idea that electrons could be bound together in pairs through this interaction was not realized until later when Bardeen, L. Cooper, and J. R. Schrieffer, at the University of Illinois, developed a self-consistent theory of superconductivity, which became generally referred to as the BCS theory. At Bell Labs, P. W. Anderson was one of the first to appreciate the full significance of the BCS theory. Using his concept of broken symmetry,* Anderson was able to meet the criticism advanced by G. Wentzel, a visitor at Bell Labs physical research department, that the BCS theory lacked gauge invariance.

A limitation on the strength of the magnetic field in which a material can retain its superconductivity was pointed out by A. M. Clogston.[2] He noted that the upper critical field, H_{c2}, could become so large that the Pauli spin paramagnetic energy of the normal electrons becomes comparable to the condensation energy. This sets an upper limit on H_{c2}. Subsequently, successful quantitative predictions of H_{c2}, including spin orbit scattering of the electrons, were made by N. R. Werthamer, E. Helfand, and P. C. Hohenberg.[3]

High-field superconductivity was only one of the puzzles posed for the theorists during this period. For example, the question of why materials remain superconducting even when very impure was answered by Anderson in his "Theory of Dirty Superconductors."[4] However, magnetic impurities, which were excluded in Anderson's theory, were shown experimentally by B. T. Matthias, H. Suhl, and E. Corenzwit to have a very strong effect in reducing T_c.[5] This was explained quantitatively by A. A. Abrikosov and L. P. Gorkov in the Soviet Union.[6] Superconductivity was discovered in elemental molybdenum when it was realized that as little as 100 parts per million of iron could suppress the T_c.[7]

---

* The theory of "broken symmetry" is based on the observation that, although no stationary state of a system can be asymmetric, most systems from the scale of molecules on up are in a metastable asymmetric state (which may last as long as the universe itself), thus breaking the law of symmetry.

1.2 Quantized Flux Lines

The high-current capacity of Nb_3Sn in high fields, at first thought to be due to a filamentary superconducting structure, was explained about 1962 when the significance of the work of V. L. Ginzburg,[8] and especially Abrikosov,[9] was finally appreciated. According to these ideas, if the coherence length is short compared with the penetration depth, the magnetic field can penetrate the superconductor as a lattice of quantized flux lines. Each line has a phase rotation of 360 degrees, but the material everywhere away from the lines is superconducting, as observed in the heat capacity measurements of F. J. Morin and coworkers.[10]

The Abrikosov theory did not mention flux line motion. From his work on the Josephson effect, Anderson predicted that as a result of the motion of the flux lines these materials might show resistance even in the superconducting state. In their study of critical currents in superconductors, Y. B. Kim, C. F. Hempstead, and A. R. Strnad observed a very slow motion of the flux and a small resistance.[11] This was explained by Anderson as a flux-creep process in which bundles of flux are thermally activated away from pinning centers.[12] Thus, increased numbers of pinning centers led to high critical currents, in agreement with the earlier realization of J. R. Kunzler and coworkers that cold-working of wires increased the current-carrying capacity. Thus the term "hard superconductivity" has the literal meaning that the mechanisms of superconductivity and mechanical hardness are very similar. Shortly thereafter, Kim also demonstrated the process he called flux flow, the unimpeded motion of the line structure, leading to normal-like resistance and the Hall effect, which Anderson and Kim called the resistive state of superconductors.[13]

1.3 Strong Coupling Theory

A direct challenge to the BCS theory came from the measurement in 1961 by T. H. Geballe and Matthias, [Fig. 9-1] which showed that there is essentially no dependence of T_c on the isotopic mass of ruthenium, whereas the theory predicted $T_c \propto (mass)^{-1/2}$.[14] The solution to this problem, provided by P. Morel and Anderson, pointed out that the interaction between electrons in superconductors consists of an instantaneous Coulomb repulsion plus the "retarded" (in time) electron-phonon-electron interaction, with only the phonon part depending on isotopic mass.[15] This paper also hinted that the detailed form of the material's phonon spectrum might be important in determining superconducting properties, but the fact that the details of this spectrum might be available from studies of superconductors was not anticipated. However, in 1960, I. Giaever at the

Fig. 9-1. B. T. Matthias (right) and T. H. Geballe (left), collaborators on many experiments on superconductivity, with J. P. Remeika, who has synthesized a large number of new superconducting compounds.

General Electric Company discovered that electron tunneling through thin insulators into superconductors measures the electronic density of states.[16] This led to determinations of the phonon density of states. In 1963, J. M. Rowell, Anderson, and D. E. Thomas showed that fine details of the phonon spectra of lead and tin are reflected directly in the current-voltage characteristic of such tunnel junctions.[17] To turn these measurements into a spectroscopic tool required a computer program, written by W. L. McMillan, which matched solutions of the BCS theory (in a form developed by Eliashberg) to the data using an iterative procedure. In 1964, McMillan and Rowell used these techniques to calculate the lead phonon spectrum, taking into account the electron-phonon coupling strength.[18] Since that time the computer program has been widely used. The technique has been applied to many elements, alloys, and compounds by R. C. Dynes and Rowell, and by L. Y. L. Shen.[19] Such studies demonstrated the accuracy of the BCS-Eliashberg theory and also made it clear that the electron-phonon mechanism is responsible for superconductivity in all materials studied, including tantalum and $Nb_3 Sn$.

A significant step forward in elucidating the complexity of the high-temperature superconductors was reported in 1964 when B. W. Batterman and C. S. Barrett observed that the crystal structure of V_3Si transformed from cubic to tetragonal when the temperature was reduced to about 21K.[20] Subsequent measurements by L. R. Testardi of the velocity of ultrasound in V_3Si indicated a softening of the lattice as the temperature was lowered and a near vanishing at the transformation temperature of the restoring force for a certain direction of shear.[21] These results indicated an instability of the lattice in high-T_c materials and, thus, the importance of the phonon spectrum in determining T_c. Related insights into the BCS-Eliashberg theory were provided in 1968 by McMillan, who produced a simple equation linking T_c with an electron-phonon coupling strength and an average phonon frequency of the lattice, showing that in certain transition metals changes in this frequency dominate changes in T_c.[22] P. B. Allen and Dynes extended the calculations of McMillan in the strong electron-phonon coupling regime and showed that the maximum T_c was, in principle, limited only by the strength of the electron-phonon coupling, λ.[23]

1.4 The Proximity Effect

P. G. deGennes and Werthamer proposed a theory that calculated the superconducting transition temperature, T_c, of superimposed superconducting-normal films in terms of their individual electronic properties.[24] J. J. Hauser, H. C. Theuerer, and Werthamer verified this theory in a study of Pb-Au and Pb-Pt "sandwiches" and further showed the detailed validity of the theory by studying a sandwich composed of two superconductors (lead and aluminum).[25] They also conducted experiments on the proximity effect between superconducting and magnetic films and established the surprising result that superconductivity disappeared below a certain critical film thickness of the superconductor (this would not occur in a bare superconducting film).[26] This result implied that the superconducting order parameter vanishes at the superconducting-ferromagnetic interface.[27]

By tunneling into the silver side of an Ag/Pb proximity effect sandwich, Rowell and McMillan observed the superconducting energy gap induced in the silver film and, at higher energies, a series of oscillations in the electronic density of states.[28] [Fig. 9-2] These were explained by McMillan and Anderson as an interference between electron-like and hole-like excitations in the superconducting film.[29]

1.5 The Josephson Effect and Tunnel Junctions

In 1962, Anderson was spending a year at Cambridge University when a student, B. D. Josephson, looking for a way to give experimental meaning to Anderson's ideas on broken symmetry, predicted that pairs of electrons should tunnel through a thin oxide layer between two superconductors and that the magnitude of this pair current would depend on the relative phase of the superconducting wave functions on the two sides. Returning to Bell Labs, Anderson encouraged a search for this effect. Early in 1963, suitable junctions of tin-tin oxide-lead were successfully made by Rowell and the

Fig. 9-2. J. M. Rowell (right) and W. L. McMillan (center) contributed to the understanding of superconducting energy gaps. Rowell, in collaboration with P. W. Anderson, was the first to observe tunneling supercurrents in Josephson junctions. G. Ahlers (left) performed precision calorimetric measurements on the superfluid transition in ^{4}He (see section 6.1 in this chapter). This photograph was taken at the occasion of the awarding of the Fritz London Memorial prize to Ahlers, McMillan, and Rowell in 1978.

predicted tunneling supercurrent was observed by Anderson and Rowell.[30] The magnetic field sensitivity of this current was first demonstrated as Anderson moved about the laboratory with a bar magnet. Later, a more quantitative measurement of this "Fraunhofer diffraction pattern" dependence was made by sliding the magnet along a table toward the junction. In his work following these observations Anderson made many advances in the theory, described in a set of lecture notes of May 1963 that was the first full paper written on the "Josephson effect."[31]

That Josephson effects can be observed in a narrow superconducting constriction linking two bulk superconductors was shown in 1964 by Anderson and A. H. Dayem during studies of the interaction of microwaves with the supercurrent.[32] This configuration was chosen to optimize interactions with radiation. In 1966, C. C. Grimes, P. L. Richards, and S. Shapiro were among the first to demonstrate the use of one such geometry as a sensitive radiation detector, an application that has attracted much interest, especially in astronomy.[33] The commercial Superconducting Quantum Interface Devices (SQUID) also use this geometry.

The potential importance of the Josephson junction as a digital logic element was recognized by Rowell and Anderson almost immediately following their first experimental observations. In the late 1960s, the development of these circuits was pursued by workers at other laboratories. In 1966, J. Matisoo at IBM demonstrated experimental switching speeds of less than 1 nanosecond.[34] Some years later, T. Gheewala measured this speed to be less than 13 picoseconds.[35] The theoretically predicted speed is less than 5 picoseconds. D. J. Herrell has demonstrated a one-bit adder and a four-bit multiplier in this technology.[36] In the IBM work, the magnetic field of a control current induces the switching.

At Bell Labs, the approach of current-switched logic in which the bias and control currents are summed together to induce switching has been pursued. Using this approach, T. A. Fulton, J. H. Magerlein, and L. N. Dunkleberger demonstrated an ac-powered one-bit full adder in 1976.[37] Both field and current switching methods are described in Rowell's original patent. In 1978, an improved version of the adder with subhundred picosecond delays per gate was demonstrated by Magerlein, Dunkleberger, and Fulton,[38] and a dc-powered flip-flop possessing subhundred picosecond switching speeds was reported by A. F. Hebard and coworkers.[39] Using a new current-switched gate design developed by Fulton, in 1979 S. S. Pei demonstrated a new "Josephson switch" that incorporates a 14-gate OR chain as a vehicle.[40]

In 1970, Anderson, Dynes, and Fulton proposed a novel memory device utilizing single quanta of magnetic flux in an oxide Josephson junction as "bits" of information.[41] An example of this type of structure was built and operated by Fulton in 1972.[42]

The effect of a microwave field on superconducting tunnel junctions was investigated by Dayem. In 1962, this study led to the discovery of the quantum interaction of microwave radiation with electrons tunneling between superconductors.[43,44] 1979 marked the beginning of renewed interest in such junctions as very high-frequency detectors, largely because the then-current photolithography techniques allowed them to be made with dimensions of approximately one micrometer. The interaction of phonons with electrons plays a crucial role in determining superconducting properties. Experimental evidence for this coupling was first obtained through ultrasonic measurements by H. E. Bömmel and W. P. Mason.[45] Their measurements showed a marked drop in the acoustic attenuation in lead as the temperature was lowered below the superconducting transition. These measurements were performed before the advent of the BCS theory. Later, more careful measurements by R. W. Morse and

H. V. Bohm at Brown University showed that the drop in attenuation could be quantitatively related to the decrease in the population of normal electrons in the superconducting state.[46] These measurements served as an important verification of the BCS theory and the existence of a superconduction energy gap.

A study of the behavior of quasiparticles injected into a superconductor was started in 1966. An experiment was designed by W. Eisenmenger and Dayem to detect the phonons emitted in the relaxation of injected quasiparticles using a sapphire single crystal with two parallel faces. On each face, a Sn-B-Sn tunnel junction was prepared, one to be used as a generator and the other as a detector. The experiment led to the invention of an ultrahigh-frequency phonon generator and detector.[47] Coherent sound waves of frequencies up to a few gigahertz had previously been generated in quartz by Bömmel and K. Dransteld in a microwave cavity by electromagnetic oscillations, using the piezoelectric properties of quartz.[48] Extensive study followed to determine the phonon spectrum emitted from an excited superconductor, in particular, the monochromatic recombination peak at energy equal to the superconducting energy gap. The phonon spectrum was then numerically calculated and showed to be in good agreement with all relevant experimental results.[49]

In 1971, V. Narayanamurti and Dynes showed that the broad frequency spectrum of a pulse of phonons is narrowed and cut off sharply at this gap frequency by transmission through a superconducting film.[50] The magnetic field tunability of this gap allowed them to make numerous studies of phonon propagation in both solid and liquid helium. In addition to using the relaxation processes in a superconductor as phonon generators and detectors at very high frequencies, this work led to fundamental questions regarding the response of superconductors when driven far from equilibrium, and became an area of very active research at Bell Laboratories.

II. FERROELECTRICITY

Ferroelectric crystals comprise a subclass of pyroelectric crystals that are, in turn, a subclass of piezoelectric crystals. In a piezoelectric crystal, the atom positions produce an acentric unit cell that develops a voltage when subjected to external mechanical stress. In a pyroelectric crystal, the acentric unit cell has, in addition, a permanent electric dipole moment caused by a displacement of the center of gravity of the positive charge with respect to that of the negative charge. The name pyroelectric reflects the temperature-dependence characteristic of the dipole moment. A pyroelectric crystal in which the direction of the dipole moment (spontaneous polarization P_S) can be reversed with an external electric field is called ferroelectric. Therefore, ferroelectric crystals are the dielectric analog of ferromagnets. As with ferromagnets, regions of uniform P_S are called domains and their interfaces are called domain walls. As in ferromagnets, domains can result from long-range electrostatic effects, since a domain terminating at a surface gives a net electrostatic surface charge that must either be compensated or must give rise to electrostatic energy. Domains can also result from strain relief. Sharp domain boundaries are energetically more favorable than perturbing the moment over a larger region.

The ferroelectric research effort at Bell Labs, which started in 1948, revolved around two aspects of ferroelectricity: the crystal chemistry of ferroelectric materials, leading to the discovery of new ferroelectrics; and the advancement of the understanding of the physics of ferroelectricity—formation of domains, the measurement of polarization as a function of temperature, and the utilization of reversible polarization. The materials effort was led by Matthias and J. P. Remeika with support from the crystallographers E. A. Wood and W. L. Bond, and from A. N. Holden. The physics research was initially carried out by W. J. Merz and J. R. Anderson, with theoretical support by J. R. Richardson and P. W. Anderson and later continued by A. G. Chynoweth and by R. C. Miller. Both groups were highly motivated by the possibility that ferroelectrics might be used for memory devices.

Initially the research effort centered on the ferroelectric $BaTiO_3$. Matthias brought some expertise in the growth of this crystal with him when he joined Bell Labs in 1949. Later interest was due in part to the availability of large, high-quality, single crystals grown by a method developed by Remeika,[51] the simple structure of this crystal, its amenable room-temperature ferroelectric parameters, and the possibility that $BaTiO_3$ might be useful for new devices utilizing the reversible polarization.

2.1 BaTiO$_3$ Experiments

W. J. Merz[52] and J. R. Anderson[53] studied many of the properties of $BaTiO_3$ including the three different phase changes that occur with temperature, the magnitude and temperature dependence of P_S, the highly anisotropic dielectric constants that are characteristic of ferroelectrics, and details of the thermodynamics of the ferroelectric to non-ferroelectric phase transition that occurs at 110°C. Merz also studied the electrical characteristics of ferroelectric switching. His studies showed for the first time that the polarizing current, i_{max}, is proportional to $e^{-\alpha/E}$ where α is the activation field (10^4 v/cm) and E is the electric field. [Fig. 9-3] Mason studied the aging of the elastic and dielectric properties of $BaTiO_3$ exposed to elevated temperatures

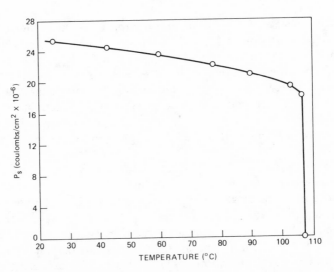

Fig. 9-3. The spontaneous dielectric polarization, P_s, of BaTiO$_3$ as a function of temperature. At 108°C this crystal goes through a very sharp transition from a tetragonal ferroelectric phase at temperatures below 108°C to a cubic nonferroelectric (paraelectric) phase at higher temperatures. [Merz, *Phys. Rev.* **91** (1953): 516].

caused by motion of the domain walls to improve the stabilization of device behavior.[54]

In 1959, R. C. Miller and A. Savage demonstrated the presence of antiparallel domains in unstrained BaTiO$_3$ using a polarizing microscope.[55] They found extensive, sidewise, 180° domain-wall motion over the range of electric fields studied (up to about 1,000 volts per centimeter). In some cases the entire electroded area (approximately 2.5 millimeters in diameter) could be reversed with a single growing domain expanding through sidewise 180° domain-wall motion.[55] The shapes of the expanding domains were size- and field-dependent. The smallest domains observed were circular in cross section (approximately 10^{-3} centimeters in diameter). The 180° domain-wall velocity v is given by $v = v_\infty e^{-\sigma E}$ with v_∞ and σ nearly field-independent over many decades of v. Experiments on other ferroelectrics were also carried out by Miller and collaborators.[56] [Fig. 9-4]

Miller and G. Weinreich, following a suggestion of P. W. Anderson, proposed a model that explained most of the domain-wall phenomena observed with BaTiO$_3$.[57] This model assumes that wall motion results from the repeated nucleation of steps along existing parent 180° domain walls, and that the nucleation rate is the controlling factor in the propagation of the wall. This model, which gives v proportional

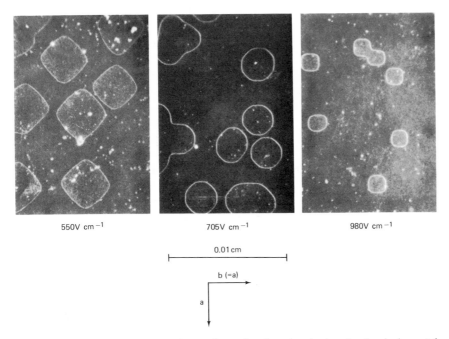

550V cm^{-1} 705V cm^{-1} 980V cm^{-1}

|— 0.01 cm —|

b (=a) →

a ↓

Fig. 9-4. The electric-field dependence of growing ferroelectric domains in single-crystal BaTiO$_3$. The spontaneous polarization of a single domain crystal, normal to the plane of the figure, is partially reversed with three different values of the electric field. [Miller, *Intro. Sol. State Phys.* (1971): 494].

to $e^{-\alpha E}$, explains many aspects of the data on domain dynamics for BaTiO$_3$.

2.2 Ferroelectric Domains in Triglycine Sulfate and Guanidine Aluminum Sulfate Hexahydrate

Triglycine sulfate (TGS) was discovered to be ferroelectric in 1956 by Matthias, Miller, and Remeika.[58] Investigations of domain patterns in TGS were carried out by A. G. Chynoweth and W. L. Feldman using water as an etchant to distinguish antiparallel domains.[59] The etch technique was first used in the study of ferroelectric domains by J. A. Hooton and W. J. Merz in 1955.[60] This technique, initially used on BaTiO$_3$, makes use of the fact that opposite dipole ends generally exhibit different etch rates.

Pearson and Feldman developed a powder technique involving colloidal suspensions of red lead oxide or sulfur to reveal antiparallel domains in guanidinium aluminum sulfate hexahydrate (GASH),[61] which was shown by A. N. Holden and coworkers to be ferroelectric.[62]

2.3 Lattice Dynamics and Ferroelectricity

One of the most interesting characteristics of ferroelectrics is the existence of ferroelectric-to-nonferroelectric phase transitions that occur, for example, at 110°C in barium titanate. Prior to about 1950, theories of the ferroelectric transition lacked a firm underlying microscopic basis and were largely couched in phenomenological terms. Expansions of the free energy as power series in the polarization were constructed and their properties investigated at the transition. It was not clear, however, whether ionic or electronic polarizabilities were responsible for the polarization or even whether there were permanent dipoles in each unit cell or only polarizable entities interacting via dipole fields. Mason and Matthias suggested the former in an early paper.[63] The evidence for the latter point of view, initially advanced by J. C. Slater and W. Shockley and also discussed in unpublished memoranda by Richardson, was summarized in 1951 by P. W. Anderson.[64]

In 1958, Anderson suggested that the ferroelectric transition was caused by an instability in an infrared-active, long-wavelength, optic phonon whose characteristic frequency approached zero as the transition temperature was approached.[65] In 1959, W. Cochran at Cambridge University also demonstrated the connection between the polarization catastrophe and the softening of a transverse, infrared-active, optic phonon at the ferroelectric transition.[66] The diverging susceptibility was therefore connected with a critical slowing down in the dynamic degree of freedom carrying the symmetry breaking that distinguished the ordered (ferroelectric) phase from the disordered phase.

This point of view, which came to be known as the soft-mode theory of displacive ferroelectric transitions, proved extremely helpful in providing a microscopic picture of the phase transition and in unifying the static and dynamic aspects of the ferroelectric transition. The first observation of a soft optical phonon was made in the 1940s by C. V. Raman in his investigation of the alpha-beta transition in quartz. However, neither the significance nor the microscopic implications of this observation were appreciated until more than two decades later. For the ferroelectric case, the first soft-mode studies were done using infrared reflection by A. S. Barker and M. Tinkham at the University of California, who investigated strontium titanate.[67] Their infrared experiments, and counterparts at Bell Labs by W. G. Spitzer and coworkers on rutile,[68] the ferroelectric $BaTiO_3$ and $SrTiO_3$, gave the correct behavior of the soft phonon qualitatively. However, as was shown in 1965 by the first scattering observation of ferroelectric soft modes, the quantitative values for the soft-mode frequency and linewidth inferred from the infrared experiments were incorrect.[69] The soft-mode concept was later shown to be applicable to a much broader class of structural phase changes that will be discussed in section 6.4 of this chapter.

III. LIQUID CRYSTALS

Liquid crystals—that is, liquids containing molecules with a preferred alignment—were recognized nearly a hundred years ago and were the object of active research during the first three decades of the 20th century.[70] Subsequently, interest in these materials declined and it was not until the early 1960s that dramatic revival began. One impetus to this renewed interest was the demonstration by G. H. Heilmeier and coworkers at RCA Laboratories that liquid crystals can provide a unique means for constructing alphanumeric displays requiring negligible power.[71] The use of liquid crystals in digital watches and calculators became widespread in the 1970s.

Traditionally, three different liquid crystalline phases were recognized: *nematic*, in which the molecules show orientational order, *smectic*, in which the molecules show some planar order, and *cholesteric*, in which the molecular orientation has a periodicity in the material.

3.1 The Nematic Phase

The first research at Bell Labs on the nematic phase was a follow-up of a discovery by A. Saupe and G. Englert, who showed that nematic liquid crystals used as a solvent in NMR spectroscopy produced a completely new kind of spectrum in which the direct dipolar interactions between nuclei are dominant.[72] It soon became apparent that these spectra provided a new tool for determining the geometry and conformation of molecules in solution. One formulation of the basic theory was worked out by L. C. Snyder.[73] The experimental techniques were developed by R. C. Hewitt and S. Meiboom, making them suitable, by the use of isotopic substitution and double irradiation, to increasingly complex molecules.[74] The technique was applied to determining the conformation of a variety of molecules, such as cyclooctane.[75]

3.2 The Smectic Phase

Around 1970, research in liquid crystals broadened; in particular, the interest in the smectic phases grew. It was soon shown that smectic, in fact, covers a whole series of phases, which were designated by the suffixes A through H. Some materials exhibit only a single liquid crystalline phase, but others show an amazing succession of thermodynamically stable phases with well-defined transitions. An important contribution to this subject was made by W. L. McMillan, who formulated a mean field theory for the smectic A phase, and using the Landau theory of critical fluctuations, made predictions about the character of the various transitions.[76] McMillan also used X-ray diffraction to study the phase transitions experimentally.[77]

As pointed out originally by P. G. deGennes at Orsay, France, there is a striking analogy between the nematic-smectic A transition and the normal superconducting transition in a metal.[78] Theoretical work by B. I. Halperin and T. Lubensky has shown that there is indeed a close analogy.[79] P. E. Cladis has studied experimentally a number of effects for which there are superconductor analogs.[80] She has shown that the nematic elastic constants of bend and twist, which correspond to the diamagnetic susceptibility of a superconductor, diverge as the nematic-smectic transition temperature is approached from above. Just as a superconductor expels magnetic flux, so does a smectic A expel bend and twist distortion. Other observed effects are the appearance of a periodic distortion in a bent nematic phase near the smectic transition,[81] and the appearance of the "re-entrant-nematic phase" in some bilayer liquid crystals, in which an apparently nematic phase appears both at higher and lower temperatures than the smectic A phase.[82] Finally, the solitary wave instability, observed in some flow experiments,[83] seems to be similar to the vortices created in superconducting tunnel junctions.[84]

Other work on the structure and properties of the smectic phases include NMR studies by Z. Luz, Hewitt, and Meiboom,[85] and studies of the rotational viscosity nematics and smectics by Meiboom and Hewitt.[86] These latter studies showed that the smectic C exhibits a strong viscous damping associated with the onset of another internal degree of freedom in the smectic D phase.

3.3 The Cholesteric Phase

The cholesteric phase is known to be a twisted nematic, occurring whenever the liquid crystal molecules lack a center of symmetry. When the pitch of the twist is comparable to the wavelength of visible light, cholesteric liquid crystals reflect light in brilliant colors. In 1970, D. W. Berreman and T. J. Scheffer developed a method to describe this optical phenomenon rigorously, and showed that the experiment indeed fits the theory in every detail.[87] This graphically illustrated that the cholesteric is locally uniaxial.

3.4 Liquid Crystal Display Devices

One of the striking properties of liquid crystals is that the molecules are aligned on the surface of the container in a specific way, their actual orientation depending on the nature and preparation of the surface. An advance in the understanding of the effects involved was made by Berreman in 1972, when he derived an approximate expression for the energy difference that yields preferred alignment parallel to grooves in a scribed surface.[88] This led to a better understanding of the art of aligning liquid crystals in display devices. Another important contribution of Berreman to the design of liquid crystal display (LCD) devices was made in 1974, when he developed a computer program that solved the complicated problem of electrohydrodynamic flow in a twist-cell LCD.[89] This program, and the one developed for the cholesteric liquid crystal, were combined into a rigorous simulation of the optical properties of a twist-cell LCD when the applied voltage is varied. Many laboratories have used these programs to help in the design of high-contrast LCDs.

A thermo-optic display of liquid crystal devices was first demonstrated at Bell Labs by H. Melchior and coworkers.[90] The writing is produced by the local heating from a laser beam to change a cholesteric liquid from an ordered to an isotropic phase, from which light is readily scattered. [Fig. 9-5] An improved light valve, based on the nematic-smectic *A* transition, was demonstrated by F. J. Kahn.[91] By combining thermal laser writing and high electric fields, he was able to obtain local erasure of previously written images.

One scheme for electro-optic liquid crystal displays uses pleochroic dyes dissolved in a liquid crystal. In 1972, D. L. White suggested such a scheme using a cholesteric host. By the use of a homeotropic orientation, and dyes with high order parameters, White and G. N. Taylor were able to demonstrate high-contrast displays.[92]

The twisted nematic liquid crystal display lacks memory. The smectic display demonstrated by Kahn (discussed previously) is thermally addressed. G. D. Boyd, J. Cheng, and P. D. T. Ngo demonstrated an electric, field-addressed, bistable nematic liquid crystal display using pleochroic dyes,[93] while Berreman and W. R. Heffner demonstrated a bistable cholesteric display.[94] The demonstration of bistability holds promise for large, flat-panel, liquid crystal displays.

IV. PHYSICS AT LOW TEMPERATURES

Studies of low-temperature physics began at Bell Laboratories in 1953 with the purchase of a Collins helium cryostat, which for many years was used primarily for superconductivity and resonance experi-

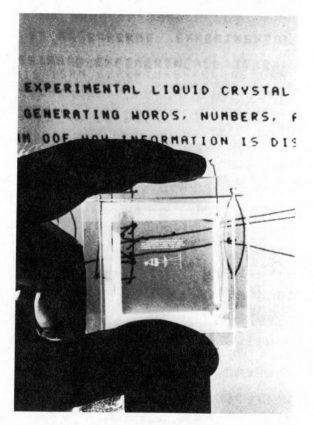

Fig. 9-5. Projection display using liquid crystal light valve. An infrared laser beam writes the information on the light valve, shown in the small sample being held. The background is a photograph of the projected image, which shows the clarity of the laser-written characters. [Maydan, *Proc. IEEE* **61** (July 1973)].

ments. Later, the liquid helium facilities provided low-temperature capabilities for experiments in specific branches of solid state physics. Some particularly interesting studies were resonance experiments by R. C. Fletcher and G. Feher on shallow energy levels in semiconductors (see Chapter 1, section 1.2.2), the early demonstrations of two-level and three-level maser action by Feher and coworkers (also discussed in Chapter 1), the work on phonon drag in semiconductors by T. H. Geballe and C. Herring discussed in Chapter 2, section 4.1, early tunneling studies of Chynoweth,[95] and J. R. Haynes' early work on exciton and impurity spectroscopy in semiconductors.[96] In all cases low temperatures led to vital simplifications of experimental situations because of the cessation of thermal agitation.

One of the first experiments at Bell Labs on liquid helium was an elegantly simple measurement by M. A. Woolf and G. W. Rayfield in 1965 of the energy required to inject an excess electron into liquid helium.[97] They measured the work function (the energy required to extract an electron from the surface of a solid) of a photocell first in vacuum and then again when it was immersed in liquid helium, and found that the work function increased by 1.1 electronvolt (eV). This energy is sufficiently large that an excess electron in liquid helium pushes the helium atoms away and forms a tiny cavity or bubble in which the electron resides.

Another experiment on liquid helium, proposed by Anderson and carried out in collaboration with P. L. Richards, was based on Anderson's ideas of broken symmetry and the analogy with the Josephson phenomenon in superconductivity, which leads to the presence of resistance in superconductors caused by flow and creep of quantized flux lines. He predicted that dissipation in superfluid helium would be accompanied by transverse motion of quantized vortices and by "phase slippage."[98] These ideas gained complete theoretical acceptance, but their practical experimental demonstration ran into serious problems. An attempt to observe ac Josephson "steps" of gravitational potential during the flow of helium through an orifice by Richards and Anderson[99] was criticized by D. L. Musinski and D. H. Douglass and others as involving acoustic resonance in the apparatus.[100] Some of the experiments were less vulnerable to this criticism, but none of them had clearly and reproducibly shown the effect.[101]

4.1 Vortex Rings in Superfluid Helium

The familiar phenomenon of smoke rings becomes a fascinating area to study in superfluid helium, where the analogous excitations are vortex rings. These are generated by accelerating ions that become bound to the cores of the vortex rings and move through the helium with the rings. At temperatures below 0.5K, vortex rings are long lived and can propagate several centimeters with little loss of energy. Experiments with such vortex rings at the University of California in Berkeley verified the prediction of early theoretical hydrodynamics that as a vortex ring gains in energy, its velocity of propagation decreases. At Bell Labs in 1969, G. Gamota and M. Barmatz measured the pressure exerted on a membrane by a beam of vortex rings in helium and showed that the impulse per ring, which is analogous to the momentum per particle in conventional mechanics, is proportional to the square of its energy.[102] Their experiment verified another of the predictions of classical hydrodynamics for the first time. Gamota, A. Hasegawa, and C. M. Varma also showed that a pulse of charged vortex rings tends to become bunched together as it propagates because of the interactions between rings, and that the bunching mechanism causes a steady beam of charged vortex rings to be unstable.[103]

4.2 Phonons in Helium

R. E. Slusher and C. M. Surko studied the scattering of laser light from liquid and solid ^{3}He and ^{4}He and obtained precise measurements for the frequencies of the transverse optic phonons in the hexagonal close-packed solid helium.[104] In general, the Raman spectra of the solids and liquids were surprisingly similar, which suggested that near the melting points solids are rather disordered and the motions of the atoms in the liquids are somewhat correlated.

K. Andres, Dynes, and V. Narayanamurti used heat pulses and superconducting devices to perform a series of measurements on the propagation of microwave frequency phonons in liquid helium.[105] These studies clearly revealed the transition from ballistic (noninteracting) phonon propagation to collective (second-sound) phonon propagation as the temperature was raised from below 0.5K to above 0.7K. They also observed for the first time that in superfluid helium under pressure at temperatures between 0.4K and 0.7K, a new type of collective sound wave appears, which has a low propagation velocity and is composed primarily of excitations called rotons. These measurements provide information on the lifetimes of the elementary excitations (phonons and rotons) in liquid helium. [Fig. 9-6] The measurements on roton second sound show that in nearly all collisions between rotons the total number of rotons is conserved. The lifetimes of high-frequency phonons were also shown to change markedly with pressure, consistent with the changes in shape of the dispersion curve (frequency versus wave vector relation) for phonons with pressure. These measurements provided a direct confirmation of the anomalous dispersion in the phonon branch of liquid helium at low pressures.

4.3 Surface Electrons on Superfluid Helium

It was noted earlier that liquid helium displays a repulsive barrier to penetration of an excess electron into the liquid. This barrier, together with the attractive image potential, causes helium to support novel surface states in which electrons are bound just outside the liquid surface but remain free to move parallel to the surface. The existence of such states was demonstrated in 1972 by T. R. Brown and Grimes.[106] Their experiments showed that when electrons are depo-

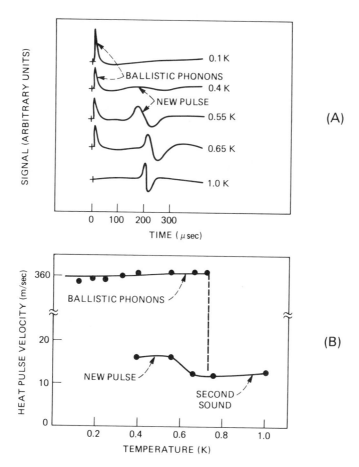

Fig. 9-6. (A) Experimental traces showing the arrival times of heat pulses that have propagated through 2.34 mm of superfluid ^{4}He at 24 bar (24 times atmospheric pressure). The new pulse, which has an anomalously low velocity, is composed mostly of propagating rotons. (B) Peak velocity of heat pulses at 24 bar, showing how ballistic phonons and the collective roton pulse merge into ordinary second sound at higher temperatures. [Dynes, Narayanamurti, and Andres, *Phys. Rev. Lett.* **30** (1973): 1129].

sited on the surface of liquid helium, the cyclotron precession frequency of the electrons depends only on the component of magnetic field perpendicular to the liquid surface. Other aspects of the potential that traps the electrons were studied by Grimes and coworkers using millimeter wavelength spectroscopy.[107] They confirmed theoretical predictions that the bound states have an energy spectrum that is very nearly hydrogenic.

A convenient feature of a layer of electrons on the surface of liquid helium is that the surface density can be varied continuously from about 10^5 to 10^9 electrons per square centimeter. This feature, together with the simplicity and cleanliness of the system, makes the electron layer a nearly ideal system in which to test ideas concerning collective effects caused by electron-electron interactions in two dimensions.[108] As the electron surface density is increased at low temperature, the properties of the electron layer are expected to change progressively from those of a gas to a liquid and finally to a solid. Theoretical considerations indicate that the solid should have a triangular crystal lattice.[109]

C. C. Grimes and G. Adams studied the collective mode, or plasmons, in the two-dimensional electron liquid formed by electrons on liquid helium.[110] They demonstrated that the square of the plasmon frequency was proportional to the electron areal density and inversely proportional to the plasmon wavelength, as theory had predicted. They also studied surface electron scattering at different temperatures by measuring the linewidths of plasmon standing-wave resonances, which was found to be proportional to the density of atoms in the helium vapor at temperatures above 0.75K. At lower temperatures the electrons are only weakly scattered by ripplons, which are microscopic ripples on the surface of the liquid helium, and have an electron mobility as high as 10^7 cm^2/(Vs).

C. L. Zipfel, Brown, and Grimes studied the linewidths of resonances corresponding to transitions between bound states when a magnetic field is applied parallel to the liquid helium surface.[111] They observed that at low electron surface densities the broadening is close to that expected for a classical electron gas, whereas at higher surface densities, where the electron motion is liquid-like, the broadening is much smaller. They attributed this smaller broadening to motional narrowing arising from an increase in the electron-electron scattering in the electron liquid.

The possibility that electrons can form a Coulomb crystal under appropriate conditions was first pointed out by E. P. Wigner in 1935.[112] The basic idea is that in an appropriate range of electron density, the Coulomb repulsive energy can be lowered if the electrons stay as far away from each other as possible by forming a regular crystalline array. Although the appropriate conditions have never been achieved in three dimensions, Grimes and Adams demonstrated the basic concept for the first time by showing that the electron layer on liquid helium does crystallize at high electron areal densities and low temperatures.[113] They measured the frequency dependence of the impedance of the electron layer, and observed the sudden appearance of a series of radio frequency (rf) resonances as the temperature was lowered below 0.46K at an electron density of about 4×10^8 cm^{-2}.

These rf resonances appeared when the electrons crystallized because the electron layer then possessed a new set of modes that could be resonantly excited. The new modes arose from coupling of the longitudinal phonons of the electron lattice to ripplons on the surface of the helium. The detailed spectrum of the coupled modes was calculated by D. S. Fisher, B. I. Halperin, and P. M. Platzman.[114] A study of the melting temperature of the electron crystal as a function of areal density tested the validity of computer simulations of the melting transition.

4.4 Superfluidity in ^{3}He

Soon after the development of the Bardeen, Cooper, Schrieffer (BCS) theory,[115] which explained the microscopic origins of superconductivity, physicists began to search for other systems of Fermi particles that might exhibit some physical properties similar to those exhibited by superconductors, such as superfluidity. Liquid ^{3}He became an obvious candidate, and experimental evidence of Fermi degeneracy in ^{3}He, coupled with L. D. Landau's successful Fermi liquid theory, increased theoretical interest in this system.[116]

Theoretical considerations indicated that if ^{3}He atoms were to form an analog to the Cooper pairs of the BCS theory, these atoms must be in a state of non-zero orbital angular momentum, $l > 0$.[117] This finite angular momentum greatly increased the complexity of the ordered state beyond that which is seen in superconductors, where $l = 0$.

Anderson and Morel at Bell Labs were the first to seriously consider this complexity. In 1961, they showed that for each l there existed many nonequivalent solutions to the BCS equations.[118] The state they predicted would possess the lowest free energy, and hence be stable, has become known as the Anderson-Morel state. One of the unusual features of this state is a unique axis along which all the angular momenta of the Cooper pairs would point, a phenomenon referred to as "orbital ferromagnetism."

In 1971, D. D. Osheroff, R. C. Richardson, and D. M. Lee at Cornell University discovered the phase transition leading to superfluidity in ^{3}He at about 0.00265K.[119] In 1972, the Cornell group showed the existence of two separate ordered phases of liquid ^{3}He.[120] They labeled the higher temperature phase ^{3}He A, and the lower temperature phase ^{3}He B. The A phase, in particular, showed unusual nuclear magnetic resonance (NMR) frequency shifts. This effect was almost immediately explained by A. J. Leggett at the University of Sussex, England, who considered the coupling between the spin and orbital components of odd-l BCS-like states as the possible superfluid states of liquid ^{3}He.[121] Leggett also predicted the existence of new magnetic resonance modes called longitudinal resonances, which should exist for many different BCS states but with frequencies that depended upon the specific orbital and spin structures.

Shortly after Leggett's results became known, Anderson and W. F. Brinkman at Bell Labs began to consider how particular interactions between ^{3}He atoms called spin fluctuations would affect the free energies of various $l = 1$ states.[122] They concluded that the formation of the condensate itself modified the nature of the spin fluctuations to a degree that depended upon the microscopic nature of the condensate wave function. This provided the key for understanding how two different BCS-like states with the same l-value could be stable over different temperature intervals. From a variety of considerations, Anderson and Brinkman tentatively identified ^{3}He A as a particular instance of the state originally studied by Anderson and Morel, which then became known as the ABM state. They identified ^{3}He B with another $l = 1$ state first considered by R. Balian and N. R. Werthamer in 1963, just prior to Werthamer's joining Bell Laboratories.[123] This was described as the B-W state.

Soon after Osheroff joined Bell Labs in 1973, he and Brinkman [Fig. 9-7] made the first observations of the new longitudinal reso-

Fig. 9-7. W. F. Brinkman (left) and D. D. Osheroff examine the experimental cell used to measure the nuclear magnetic resonance properties of superfluid ^{3}He. Data on the table and the equations on the blackboard were used to establish the microscopic identities of the A and B superfluid phases.

nance modes and verified the predictions of the Leggett theory.[124] In addition, they measured the magnetic susceptibility and NMR spectra of the *B* phase. Their results confirmed the hypothesis that ^{3}He *B* was a variation of the B-W state. More importantly, they interpreted subtle variations of the resonance lineshape as caused by spatial variations of the B-W anisotropy axis. Other aspects of Leggett's theory were also confirmed by Osheroff's NMR measurements in ^{3}He *B* and ^{3}He *A*.[125]

Bell Labs physicists also developed a theory of textures for ^{3}He *B*, which has been of key importance in interpreting NMR spectra in ^{3}He *B*,[126] and which has been used to predict and interpret the existence of spin wave modes in superfluid ^{3}He.[127]

It was known even before the original Cornell University NMR studies that if ^{3}He was cooled in the presence of a strong magnetic field, the superfluid transition temperature (then referred to as T_A) would split into two separate transitions. By 1974, this phenomenon was understood to arise from changes in the spin-up and spin-down nuclear spin populations caused by the magnetic field. The ordered fluid between the two transition temperatures, the A_1 phase, was thought to contain ordering in only one of the two spin populations.

In 1974, Osheroff and Anderson made an NMR study of the A_1 region that is obtained by cooling ^{3}He in a strong magnetic field.[128] They measured very small NMR frequency shifts in the A_1 phase, which they showed to be in excellent agreement with predictions by the spin fluctuation theory of Anderson and Brinkman,[129] and established that no longitudinal resonance mode existed in the A_1 region.

In late 1974, experiments and theoretical interpretations by Bell Labs physicists provided a direct measurement of the relative orientation of the spin and orbital structures in ^{3}He *B*.[130–132] Other experiments by Osheroff and coworkers confirmed the theory of textures in ^{3}He *B*,[133] and paved the way for the first observations of spin wave modes in superfluid ^{3}He, accomplished at Bell Labs in 1976.[134]

Additional contributions to understanding the superfluid phases of ^{3}He came from the realization by Anderson and Brinkman that certain textures in ^{3}He *A* have associated spontaneously orbital angular momentum.[135] This idea was further developed by Anderson and G. Toulouse in 1976 to show how the dissipation of flow can occur through the creation of singular textures possessing the type of deformation described in their paper.[136] Work by Osheroff and M. C. Cross led to the measurements and theoretical understanding of the surface energy associated with the interface between two macroscopic quantum condensates, and to a better understanding of the first-order phase transition between ^{3}He *A* and ^{3}He *B*.[137,138] In addition, measurements by L. R. Corruccini and Osheroff provided the first insights into spin recovery processes in both superfluid phases of ^{3}He.[139]

Although the superfluid properties of ^{3}He are not yet completely understood, it is worth noting that the knowledge gained about the microscopic nature of ^{3}He A and ^{3}He B in a few years compares favorably with that gained about the superfluidity of ^{4}He in a half-century.

V. PHYSICS AT HIGH PRESSURES

In the late 1950s, there was a rapid increase in the use of pressure as a variable, in addition to the traditional variables of temperature and chemical composition, in the study of condensed-matter physics. It became apparent that the electronic properties of many materials were sensitive functions of pressure and that many materials exhibited phase transitions at high pressure, with accompanying changes in crystal structure and electronic properties. In the early states of research at high pressure at Bell Labs, the phase diagrams in the temperature-pressure plane of a number of elements and simple compounds were determined.[140] Trends in the sequence of crystal structures or in the occurrence of superconductivity as a function of pressure and atomic number were delineated.[141] During this period Bell Labs scientists pioneered in the development of techniques for measuring transport properties,[142] nuclear magnetic resonance,[143] and inelastic neutron scattering down to liquid helium temperatures using pressures up to 50 to 100 kbar.[144] Of equal importance was the development of a simplified technique to obtain truly hydrostatic pressures of 50 kbar in volumes of several cubic centimeters.[145]

5.1 Phase Diagrams in Electronic Transitions

Strong attention was given to the discipline of many-body theory during the 1960s. (See Chapter 10 of this volume.) A number of electronic transitions that result from the correlated motions of large numbers of electrons were predicted. Bell Laboratories scientists contributed greatly to the search for and determination of the phase diagrams for some of these transitions using the pressure variable. In one class of transitions, the total electronic energy of the system can be lowered by introducing a periodic modulation of the spin density in momentum space. The transition to this state is a sensitive function of the geometry of the Fermi surface which, in turn, is a function of pressure. Chromium metal is a unique example of this phenomenon. The transition in chromium was first clearly established by M. E. Fine, E. S. Greiner, and W. C. Ellis in 1951.[146] A series of transport measurements at high pressure (done in conjunction with T. M. Rice, A. Jayaraman, and D. B. McWhan), optical measurements, and further theoretical developments confirmed a number of features of spin density waves.[147]

5.2 Metal-Insulator Transitions

Another class of transitions that occur under the application of increasing pressure involves a fundamental change in the electronic properties from an insulator in which the electrons are localized on the atoms to a metal in which the electrons form bands. This transition results from increasing electron-electron correlations in a narrow conduction band and was predicted by N. F. Mott to be discontinuous as a function of interatomic spacing.[148] Such a transition was known to occur in the oxides of vanadium. [Fig. 9-8] In a combination of experiments on mixed titanium-vanadium-chromium sesquioxides in

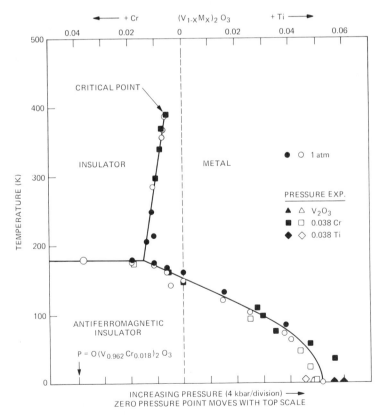

Fig. 9-8. Generalized phase diagram for metal-insulator transition in V_2O_3 as a function of composition (top scale) and pressure.

which both the composition and pressure were varied, McWhan and his colleagues established the general features of the phase diagram for the well-known Mott transition.[149,150] The addition of the pressure variable elucidated the relation between a number of seemingly isolated transitions observed in the mixed oxides at ambient pressure. Further measurements of the resistivity, nuclear magnetic resonance, and the heat capacity in the metallic phase at high pressure and low temperature established the highly correlated nature of the metallic phase near the Mott transition. Since these systems are too complicated to yield more than qualitative comparisons with theoretical models, the study of this transition shifted to the newly discovered condensation of excitons into an electron-hole liquid in several semiconductors at low temperatures. (See Chapter 2, section 5.6.)

5.3 Transitions in Mixed-Valence Compounds

Another class of materials in which pressure experiments at Bell Labs have played a pivotal role is the mixed-valence compounds. Electronic transitions were found as a function of pressure from the divalent toward the trivalent states in a number of normally divalent rare earth monochalcongenides, such as SmS.[151]

The high-pressure phase consists of a mixture of divalent and trivalent rare earth ions. The traditional models for the properties of rare earth ions with well-localized $4f$ electrons, with magnetic moments coupled together by the conduction electrons, are not adequate to explain the observed physical properties such as the absence of magnetic ordering at low temperatures.

VI. PHASE TRANSITIONS AND CRITICAL PHENOMENA

The most important manifestation of cooperative effects between atoms and molecules is the diversity of *phases* of matter that can occur in a single system. For example, the substance ^{3}He, composed of chemically inert atoms, is known to display the following bulk phases, which can be reached by varying temperature and pressure: gas, normal liquid, anisotropic superfluid (A phase), isotropic superfluid (B phase), nonmagnetic solid with face-centered cubic, body-centered cubic, hexagonal close-packed crystal structure, and two phases of antiferromagnetic solid. The precise understanding of the way in which one phase transforms into another at a well-defined value of temperature and pressure is one of the great challenges of condensed-matter physics and an area of considerable achievement in the last thirty years. An important class of transitions, the "continuous" or "second-order" transitions, were described in the 1930s by Landau's remarkably simple theory, which was supposed to apply to all such transitions. It is now known that the Landau theory is only approximately valid, and that the exact properties of continuous-phase transitions depend on such features as the symmetry of the ordered state and the dimensionality of space, but not on the details of the interatomic interactions. In the last 15 years, physicists have developed the phenomenological theories of scaling and universality and the mathematical technique of the renormalization group, which have enabled them to describe the exact behavior of substances near critical points. For example, thermodynamic functions such as the specific heat, the magnetic or dielectric susceptibility, or the bulk modulus, have singularities described by critical exponents that the theory seeks to calculate and classify.

6.1 Calorimetric Investigations

Bell Labs scientists have been at the forefront of many of these developments, both in carrying out accurate experiments on a variety of materials that illustrate and test the theories, and in formulating and refining these theories. One of the first theorists to question the accuracy of the Landau theory was G. H. Wannier, who had contributed to the solution of the two-dimensional Ising model and recognized its implications for the general theory of cooperative phenomena.[152] In 1967, G. Ahlers began a series of calorimetric measurements on the superfluid transition in ^{4}He, which were to set the standards of precision for experiments in the field of critical phenomena.[153] He improved considerably the accuracy of earlier determinations of the specific heat at constant volume C_p, and in collaboration with D. S. Greywall, he measured the precise variation of the superfluid density, ρ_s with temperatures at various pressures.[154] These experiments have permitted the most accurate verification to date of a scaling relation between critical exponents, and the accompanying universal amplitudes. Ahlers and coworkers also measured specific heats in solids undergoing magnetic transitions, and were able to observe unambiguously the effect of the symmetry of the ordered state on the critical exponents, thus verifying a key prediction of the theory.

6.2 The Effect of Dimensionality of Space

Another element of crucial importance in determining critical behavior is the dimensionality of space. Although real materials are all embedded in three-dimensional space, there exist magnetic systems, for instance, where interactions *within* a crystallographic plane are larger than interactions *between* planes by six or seven orders of magnitude. Such "two-dimensional" crystals were grown at Bell Labs by H. J. Guggenheim and led to striking illustrations of many features of the scaling theory. ("One-dimensional" crystals, where interactions along a line predominate, were also studied.) Neutron scattering provides a direct probe of the critical fluctuations of the appropriate magnetic order parameter, and in a series of experiments carried out at Brookhaven National Laboratory, R. J. Birgeneau (of Bell Labs) and coworkers studied many of these one-and-two-dimensional crystals.[155] Two examples of the crystals studied by Birgeneau are K_2MnF_4, a two-dimensional antiferromagnet, and $(CD_3)_4-NMnCl_3$, a classical one-dimensional antiferromagnet. Neutron scattering experiments on these and other systems confirmed the applicability of exact solutions of nontrivial many-body problems, and raised a number of important questions not previously considered by theorists.

6.3 Critical Dynamics

An important area of critical phenomena concerns *dynamic* behavior, that is, transport properties, or more generally, time-dependent correlation functions, as measured by inelastic scattering of neutrons or light. The generalization of the phenomenological scaling theory of critical phenomena to dynamic properties was formulated in a comprehensive way by B. I. Halperin and P. C. Hohenberg in 1967.[156] This theory, which focused on the conservation laws and nonlinear mode couplings obeyed by the order parameter, made predictions for essentially every class of continuous transition. The most dramatic confirmation of the theory was provided soon after its initial formulation by R. A. Ferrell and coworkers at the University of Virginia,[157] and in the measurements by Ahlers of the divergence of the thermal conductivity of ^4He at the superfluid transition.[158] Many other experiments, carried out at Bell Labs and elsewhere, showed that the dynamic scaling concepts gave a unified and accurate description of transport phenomena near critical points. [Fig. 9-9]

The theory of critical phenomena was placed on firmer mathematical and physical foundations in the 1970s by the renormalization group approach pioneered for static critical phenomena by K. G. Wilson of Cornell University; the generalization to dynamics was formulated by Halperin and coworkers.[159]

6.4 Structural Transitions

An area of critical phenomena where dynamics plays a crucial role is in structural phase transitions, where a *soft vibrational mode* describes the dynamics. Such soft modes can be observed either directly or indirectly. In addition to neutron diffraction, the inelastic

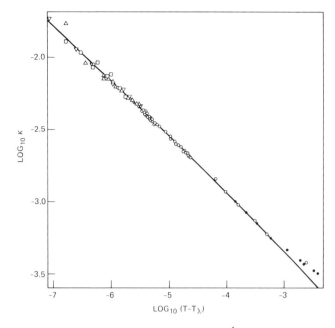

Fig. 9-9. Thermal conductivity, K, of liquid ^{4}He as a function of temperature above the phase transition temperature, T_λ, on log-log scales. The points are the data of Ahlers (see reference 153), and the line is the prediction of dynamic scaling theory (see references 156 and 157). The measurements extend to a distance $\Delta T = 10^{-7}\,K$ from the transition, which is still sharply defined on this scale. [Hohenberg and Halperin, *Rev. Mod. Phys.* **49** (1977): 463].

scattering of laser light has proved to be a valuable experimental tool in this area. The first light-scattering observations of a ferroelectric soft mode were made in SrTiO$_3$ and KTaO$_3$ by P. A. Fleury and J. M. Worlock.[160] This Raman study led to understanding the well-studied but puzzling transition in strontium titanate. The observation of a greatly increased number of lines in the Raman spectrum below T_c was attributed to the fact that the unit cell was doubled. In other words the transition was "antiferroelectric."

The experimental vindication of soft-mode viewpoint (discussed in section 2.3 of this chapter) gave rise to considerable theoretical and experimental activity during the decade of the 1970s. The inadequacy of the simple soft-mode picture was demonstrated in a series of experiments at Bell Labs and elsewhere addressed to anomalies in the low-frequency portion of the spectrum which had come to be called "central peak" phenomena. Attempts to explain these phenomena quantitatively led to increased understanding of anharmonic effects in the lattice dynamics of structural phase transitions and permitted structural transitions to be placed within the general context of critical phenomena.[161]

The concept of lattice instabilities also played an important role in the understanding of yet another class of structural transitions, the "incommensurate" transitions. These are caused by a phonon instability at some arbitrary point in the Brillouin zone, resulting in a new phase with a unit cell that is not an integral multiple of the parent unit cell. The existence of incommensurate order had been known for some time in magnetic systems, for example, in antiferromagnetic chromium. However, the discovery of incommensurate order in a structural phase transition was made only in 1970 by J. A. Wilson, F. J. DiSalvo, and S. Mahajan at Bell Labs.[162] This discovery led to an intense theoretical and experimental effort to understand not only the onset of incommensurate order but to explore the consequences of such order on the elementary excitations and transport properties. For example, many of these materials are metals or semimetals and undergo dramatic changes in their electrical resistivities and magnetic susceptibilities at the onset of incommensurate order.

Once the concept of incommensurate structures had been established within this family of transition metal dichalcogenides, a number of other incommensurate phase transitions in materials such as barium manganese fluoride, potassium selenate, and so on were discovered and explored. Whereas for the conducting compounds, the microscopic origin of the lattice instability is understood to be the electron-phonon interaction, the microscopic cause of incommensurability is less obvious for insulating incommensurate systems.

6.5 Impact on Other Fields

The advances made in the study of materials near critical points quickly found applications in such diverse areas of physics as crystal growth (see Chapter 19), liquid crystal films, discussed in section III of this chapter, surface physics (see Chapter 3), the theory of fundamental particles (quantum chromodynamics), and hydrodynamic instabilities. This last field especially experienced renewed activity in the late 1970s, as physicists sought to understand the transitions that occur between one mode of flow and another outside of thermal equilibrium. For example, Ahlers and coworkers were able to use the sophisticated thermometry techniques developed earlier to detect turbulent signals of small amplitude and low frequency immediately above the convective threshold, where the cellular flow was theretofore thought to be stable.[163]

REFERENCES

1. J. Bardeen, "Wave Functions for Superconducting Electrons," *Phys. Rev.* **80** (November 1950), pp. 567-574.

2. A. M. Clogston, "Upper Limit for the Critical Field in Hard Superconductors," *Phys. Rev. Lett.* **9** (September 15, 1962), pp. 266-267.

3. N. R. Werthamer, E. Helfand, and P. C. Hohenberg, "Temperature and Purity Dependence of the Superconducting Critical Field, H_{c2}. III. Electron Spin and Spin-Orbit Effects," *Phys. Rev.* **147** (July 1966), pp. 295-302.

4. P. W. Anderson, "Theory of Dirty Superconductors," *J. Phys. Chem. Solids* **11** (September 1959), pp. 26-30.

5. B. T. Matthias, H. Suhl, and E. Corenzwit, "Spin Exchange in Superconductors," *Phys. Rev. Lett.* **1** (August 1, 1958), pp. 92-94.

6. L. P. Gorkov, "The Critical Supercooling Field in Superconductivity Theory," *Sov. Phys. JETP* **10** (March 1960), pp. 593-599.

7. T. H. Geballe, B. T. Matthias, E. Corenzwit, and G. W. Hull, Jr., "Superconductivity in Molybdenum," *Phys. Rev. Lett.* **8** (April 15, 1962), pp. 313-315.

8. V. L. Ginzburg, *Nuovo Cimento* **2** (1955), p. 1234.

9. A. A. Abrikosov, "On the Magnetic Properties of Superconductors of the Second Group," *Sov. Phys. JETP* **5** (December 1957), pp. 1174-1182.

10. F. J. Morin, J. P. Maita, H. J. Williams, R. C. Sherwood, J. H. Wernick, and J. E. Kunzler, "Heat Capacity Evidence for a Large Degree of Superconductivity in V_3Ga in High Magnetic Fields," *Phys. Rev. Lett.* **8** (April 1, 1962), pp. 275-277.

11. Y. B. Kim, C. F. Hempstead, and A. R. Strnad, "Critical Persistent Currents in Hard Superconductors," *Phys. Rev. Lett.* **9** (October 1, 1962), pp. 306-309.

12. P. W. Anderson, "Theory of Flux Creep in Hard Superconductors," *Phys. Rev. Lett.* **9** (October 1, 1962), pp. 309-311.

13. P. W. Anderson and Y. B. Kim, "Hard Superconductivity: Theory of the Motion of Abrikosov Flux Lines," *Rev. Mod. Phys.* (January 1964), pp. 39-43.

14. T. H. Geballe, B. T. Matthias, G. W. Hull, Jr., and E. Corenzwit, "Absence of an Isotope Effect in Superconducting Ruthenium," *Phys. Rev. Lett.* **6** (March 15, 1961), pp. 275-277.

15. P. Morel and P. W. Anderson, "Calculation of the Superconducting State Parameters with Retarded Electron-Phonon Interaction," *Phys. Rev.* **125** (February 1962), pp. 1263-1271.

16. I. Giaever, "Electron Tunneling Between Two Superconductors," *Phys. Rev. Lett.* **5** (November 15, 1960), pp. 464-466.

17. J. M. Rowell, P. W. Anderson, and D. E. Thomas, "Image of the Phonon Spectrum in the Tunneling Characteristic Between Superconductors," *Phys. Rev. Lett.* **10** (April 15, 1963), pp. 334-336.

18. W. L. McMillan and J. M. Rowell, "Lead Phonon Spectrum Calculated from Superconducting Density of States," *Phys. Rev. Lett.* **14** (January 25, 1965), pp. 108-112.

19. R. C. Dynes and J. M. Rowell, "Influence of Electrons-per-Atom Ratio and Phonon Frequencies Under Superconducting Transition Temperature of Lead Alloys," *Phys. Rev.* **B11** (March 1975), pp. 1884-1894; L. Y. L. Shen, "Evidence for the Electron-Phonon Interaction in the Superconductivity of a Transition Metal—Tantalum," *Phys. Rev. Lett.* **24** (May 18, 1970), pp. 1104-1107.

20. B. W. Batterman and C. S. Barrett, "Crystal Structure of Superconducting V_3Si," *Phys. Rev. Lett.* **13** (September 28, 1964), pp. 390-392.

21. L. R. Testardi, T. B. Bateman, W. A. Reed, and V. G. Chirba, "Lattice Instability of

V_3Si at Low Temperatures," *Phys. Rev. Lett.* **15** (August 9, 1965), pp. 250-252.

22. W. L. McMillan, "Transition Temperature of Strong Coupled Superconductors," *Phys. Rev.* **167** (March 1968), pp. 331-344.

23. P. B. Allen and R. C. Dynes, "Transition Temperature of Strong-Coupled Superconductors Analyzed," *Phys. Rev.* **B12** (August 1975), pp. 905-922.

24. P. G. deGennes and E. Guyon, "Superconductivity in 'Normal' Metals," *Phys. Lett.* **3** (January 1, 1963), pp. 168-169; N. R. Werthamer, "Theory of the Superconducting Transition Temperature and Energy Gap Function of Superimposed Metal Films," *Phys. Rev.* **132** (December 1963), pp. 2440-2445.

25. J. J. Hauser, H. C. Theuerer, and N. R. Werthamer, "Superconductivity in Cu and Pt by Means of Superimposed Films with Lead," *Phys. Rev.* **136** (November 1964), pp. 637-641; J. J. Hauser and H. C. Theuerer, "Superconductivity in Pb-Al Superimposed Films," *Phys. Lett.* **14** (February 15, 1965), pp. 270-271.

26. J. J. Hauser, H. C. Theuerer, and N. R. Werthamer, "Proximity Effects Between Superconducting and Magnetic Films," *Phys. Rev.* **142** (February 1966), pp. 118-126.

27. J. J. Hauser, "Gapless Superconductivity Induced by the Proximity Effect," *Phys. Rev.* **164** (December 1967), pp. 558-565.

28. J. M. Rowell and W. L. McMillan, "Electron Interference in a Normal Metal Induced by Superconducting Contacts," *Phys. Rev. Lett.* **16** (March 14, 1966), pp. 453-456.

29. W. L. McMillan and P. W. Anderson, "Theory of Geometrical Resonances in the Tunneling Characteristics of Thick Films of Superconductors," *Phys. Rev. Lett.* **16** (January 17, 1966), pp. 85-87.

30. P. W. Anderson and J. M. Rowell, "Probable Observation of the Josephson Superconducting Tunneling Effect," *Phys. Rev. Lett.* **10** (March 15, 1963), pp. 230-232.

31. P. W. Anderson, *The Many-Body Problem*, Vol. II., ed. E. R. Caianello (New York: Academic Press, 1964).

32. P. W. Anderson and A. H. Dayem, "Radio-Frequency Effects in Superconducting Thin Film Bridges," *Phys. Rev. Lett.* **13** (August 10, 1964), pp. 195-197.

33. C. C. Grimes, P. L. Richards, and S. Shapiro, "Far Infrared Response of Point-Contact Josephson Junctions," *Phys. Rev. Lett.* **17** (August 22, 1966), pp. 431-433.

34. J. Matisoo, "The Tunneling Cryotron—A Superconductive Logic Element Based on Electron Tunneling," *Proc. IEEE* **55** (February 1967), pp. 172-180.

35. T. Gheewala, "30 Picosecond Josephson Current Injection Logic (CIL)," *IEEE J. Solid State Circuits* **14** (October 1979), pp. 787-793.

36. D. J. Herrell, "Femtojoule Josephson Tunneling Logic Gates," *IEEE J. S. S. C.* **SC-9** (October 1974), pp. 277-282; idem, "An Experimental Multiplier Circuit Based on Superconducting Josephson Devices," *IEEE J. S. S. C.* **SC-10** (October 1975), pp. 360-368.

37. J. H. Magerlein and L. N. Dunkleberger, "Direct-Coupled Josephson Full Adder," *IEEE Trans. Mag.* **MAG-13** (January 1977), pp. 585-588; T. A. Fulton, J. H. Magerlein, and L. N. Dunkleberger, "A Josephson Logic Design Employing Current-Switched Junctions," *IEEE Trans. Mag.* **MAG-13** (January 1977), pp. 56-58.

38. J. H. Magerlein, L. N. Dunkleberger, and T. A. Fulton, "A Current-Switched Full Adder Fabricated by Photolithographic Techniques," *AIP Conf. Proc.* **No. 44** (1978), pp. 459-464.

39. A. F. Hebard, S. S. Pei, L. N. Dunkleberger, and T. A. Fulton, "ADC-Powered Josephson Flip-Flop," *IEEE Trans. Mag.*, MAG-15, **408** (1979).

40. T. A. Fulton, S. S. Pei, and L. N. Dunkleberger, "A Simple High-Performance Current-Switched Josephson Gate," *Appl. Phys. Lett.* **34** (May 15, 1979), pp. 709-711.

41. P. W. Anderson, R. C. Dynes, and T. A. Fulton, "Josephson Flux Quantum Shuttles," *Bull. Am. Phys. Soc.* **16** (March 31, 1971), p. 399.

42. T. A. Fulton and L. N. Dunkleberger, "Experimental Flux Shuttle," *Appl. Phys. Lett.* **22** (March 1, 1973), pp. 232-233.

43. A. H. Dayem and R. J. Martin, "Quantum Interaction of Microwave Radiation with Tunneling Between Superconductors," *Phys. Rev. Lett.* **8** (March 15, 1962), pp. 246-248.

44. P. K. Tien and J. P. Gordon, "Multiphoton Process Observed in the Interaction of Microwave Fields with the Tunneling Between Superconductor Films," *Phys. Rev.* **129** (January 1963), pp. 647-651.

45. H. E. Bömmel, "Ultrasound Attenuation in Superconducting Lead," *Phys. Rev.* **96** (October 1954), pp. 220-221; W. P. Mason and H. E. Bömmel, "Ultrasonic Attenuation at Low Temperature for Metals in the Normal and Superconducting States," *J. Acoust. Soc. Am.* **28** (September 1956), pp. 930-943; W. P. Mason, "Ultrasonic Attenuation due to Lattice-Electron Interaction in Normal Conducting Metals," *Phys. Rev.* **97** (January 1955), pp. 557-558.

46. R. W. Morse and H. V. Bohm, "Superconducting Energy Gap from Ultrasonic Attenuation Measurements," *Phys. Rev.* **108** (September 1957), pp. 1094-1097.

47. W. Eisenmenger and A. H. Dayem, "Quantum Generation and Detection of Incoherent Phonons in Superconductors," *Phys. Rev. Lett.* **18** (January 1967), pp. 125-127.

48. H. E. Bömmel and K. Dransfeld, "Excitation of Very High Frequency Sound in Quartz," *Phys. Rev. Lett.* **1** (October 1, 1958), pp. 234-236.

49. A. H. Dayem and J. J. Wiegand, "Emitted Phonon Spectrum and Its Influence on the Detected Signal in Superconducting Sn Diodes," *Phys. Rev.* **B5** (June 1972), pp. 4390-4403.

50. V. Narayanamurti and R. C. Dynes, "Intense Tunable Phonon Fluorescence in Superconductors," *Phys. Rev. Lett.* **27** (August 16, 1971), pp. 410-413.

51. J. P. Remeika, "A Method for Growing Barium-Titanate Single Crystals," *J. Am. Chem. Soc.* **76** (February 5, 1954), pp. 940-941.

52. W. J. Merz, "The Electric and Optical Behavior of $BaTiO_3$ Single-Domain Crystals," *Phys. Rev.* **76** (October 1949), pp. 1221-1225; idem, "Double Hysteresis Loop of $BaTiO_3$ at the Curie Point," *Phys. Rev.* **91** (August 1953), pp. 513-517; idem, "Domain Formation and Domain Wall Motions in Ferroelectric $BaTiO_3$ Single Crystals," *Phys. Rev.* **95** (August 1954), pp. 690-698.

53. J. R. Anderson, G. W. Brady, W. J. Merz, and J. P. Remeika, "Effects of Ambient Atmosphere on the Stability of Barium Titanate," *J. Appl. Phys.* **26** (November 1955), pp. 1387-1388.

54. W. P. Mason, "Aging of the Properties of Borium Titanate and Related Ferroelectric Ceramics," *J. Acoust. Soc. Am.* **27** (January 1955), pp. 73-85.

55. R. C. Miller and A. Savage, "Direct Observation of Antiparallel Domains During Polarization Reversal in Single-Crystal Barium Titanate," *Phys. Rev. Lett.* **2** (April 1, 1959), pp. 294-296; idem, "Velocity of Sidewise 180° Domain-Wall Motion in $BaTiO_3$ as a Function of the Applied Electric Field," *Phys. Rev.* **112** (November 1958), pp. 755-762; idem, "Further Experiments on the Sidewise Motion of 180° Domain Walls in $BaTiO_3$," *Phys. Rev.* **115** (September 1959), pp. 1176-1180.

56. R. C. Miller, E. A. Wood, J. P. Remeika, and A. Savage, "$Na(Nb_{1-x}V_x)O_3$ System and 'Ferrielectricity,'" *J. Appl. Phys.* **33** (May 1962), pp. 1623-1630; E. A. Wood, R. C. Miller, and J. P. Remeika, "The Field-Induced Ferroelectric Phase of Sodium Niobate," *Acta. Crys.* **15** (December 1962), pp. 1273-1279.

57. R. C. Miller and G. Weinreich, "Mechanism for the Sidewise Motion of 180° Domain Walls in Barium Titanate," *Phys. Rev.* **117** (March 1960), pp. 1460-1466.

58. B. T. Matthias, C. E. Miller, and J. P. Remeika, "Ferroelectricity of Glycine Sulfate," Letters to the Editor, *Phys. Rev.* **104** (November 1, 1956), pp. 849-850.

59. A. G. Chynoweth and W. L. Feldman, "Ferroelectric Domain Delineation in Triglycine Sulphate and Domain Arrays Produced by Thermal Shocks," *J. Phys. Chem.*

Solids 15 (October 1960), pp. 225-233.

60. J. A. Hooton and W. J. Merz, "Etch Patterns and Ferroelectric Domains in BaTiO₃ Single Crystals," *Phys. Rev.* **98** (April 1955), pp. 409-413.

61. G. L. Pearson and W. L. Feldman, "Powder-Pattern Techniques for Delineating Ferroelectric Domain Structures," *J. Phys. Chem. Solids* **9** (January 1959), pp. 28-30.

62. A. N. Holden, W. J. Merz, J. P. Remeika, and B. T. Matthias, "Properties of Guanidine Aluminum Sulfate Hexahydrate and Some of Its Isomorphs," *Phys. Rev.* **101** (February 1956), pp. 962-966.

63. W. P. Mason and B. T. Matthias, "Theoretical Model for Explaining the Ferroelectric Effect in Barium Titanate," *Phys. Rev.* **74** (December 1948), pp. 1622-1636.

64. P. W. Anderson, "Theory of Ferroelectric Behavior of Barium Titanate," *Ceramic Age* **57** (April 1951), p. 29.

65. P. W. Anderson, "Qualitative Considerations in Phase Transition Statistics in BaTiO₃ Type Ferroelectrics," in *Fizika Dielektrikov, Proceedings of the 2nd All Union Conference on the Physics of Dielectrics, Leningrad, USSR, Nov. 1958*, ed. G. I. Skanavi (Moscow: Akademiya Nauk S.S.S.R., Fizichesk Inst. im. P. N. Lebedeva, 1960), pp. 290-296.

66. W. Cochran, "Crystal Stability and the Theory of Ferroelectricity," *Phys. Rev. Lett.* **3** (November 1, 1959), pp. 412-414.

67. A. S. Barker, Jr., and M. Tinkham, "Far-Infrared Ferroelectric Vibration Mode in SrTiO₃," *Phys. Rev.* **125** (March 1962), pp. 1527-1530.

68. W. G. Spitzer, R. C. Miller, D. A. Kleinman, and L. E. Howarth, "Far Infrared Dielectric Dispersion in BaTiO₃, SrTiO₃, and TiO₂," *Phys. Rev.* **126** (June 1962), pp. 1710-1721.

69. A. S. Barker, Jr., "Temperature Dependence of the Transverse and Longitudinal Optic Mode Frequencies and Charges in SrTiO₃ and BaTiO₃," *Phys. Rev.* **145** (May 1966), pp. 391-399.

70. For a short review of the earlier liquid crystal research, see W. H. Bragg, "Liquid Crystals," *Nature* **133** (March 24, 1934), pp. 445-456.

71. G. H. Heilmeier, L. A. Zanoni, and L. A. Barton, *Proc. IEEE* **56** (July 1968), pp. 1162-1171.

72. A. Saupe and G. Englert, "High-Resolution Nuclear Magnetic Resonance Spectra of Orientated Molecules," *Phys. Rev. Lett.* **11** (November 15, 1963), pp. 462-464.

73. L. C. Snyder, "Analysis of Nuclear Magnetic Resonance Spectra of Molecules in Liquid-Crystal Solvents," *J. Chem. Phys.* **43** (December 1965), pp. 4041-4050.

74. R. C. Hewitt, S. Meiboom, and L. C. Snyder, "Proton NMR in Nematic Liquid Crystalline Solvents: The Use of Deuterium Decoupling," *J. Chem. Phys.* **58** (June 1973), pp. 5089-5095; L. C. Snyder and S. Meiboom, "Theory of Proton NMR with Deuteron Decoupling in Nematic Liquid Crystalline Solvents," ibid, pp. 5096-5103.

75. The following papers are representative: E. Sackmann, S. Meiboom, and L. C. Snyder, "The Nuclear Magnetic Resonance Spectra of Enantiomers in Optically Active Liquid Crystals," *J. Am. Chem. Soc.* **90** (April 1968), pp. 2183-2184; S. Meiboom, R. C. Hewitt, and Z. Luz, "The Conformation of Cyclooctane: An Experimental Determination by NMR in an Oriented Solvent," *J. Chem. Phys.* **66** (May 1977), pp. 4041-4051.

76. W. L. McMillan, "Simple Molecular Model for the Smectic *A* Phase of Liquid Crystals," *Phys. Rev.* **A4** (September 1971), pp. 1238-1246; idem, "Measurement of Smectic *A*-Phase Order-Parameter Fluctuations near a Second-Order Smectic-*A*-Nematic-Phase Transition," *Phys. Rev.* **A7** (April 1973), pp. 1419-1422.

77. W. L. McMillan, "X-Ray Scattering from Liquid Crystals. I. Cholesteryl Nonanoate and Myristate," *Phys. Rev.* **A6** (September 1972), pp. 936-947.

78. P. G. deGennes, "An Analogy Between Superconductors and Smectics *A*," *Solid State Comm.* **10** (May 1972), pp. 753-756.

79. B. I. Halperin and T. C. Lubensky, "On the Analogy Between Smectic *A* Liquid Crystals and Superconductors," *Solid State Comm.* **14** (May 1974), pp. 997-1001.

80. P. E. Cladis, "Study of the Bend Elastic Constant Near a Smectic-*A*-Nematic Phase Transition," *Phys. Rev. Lett.* **31** (November 5, 1973), pp. 1200-1203.

81. P. E. Cladis and S. Torza, "Growth of a Smectic *A* from a Bent Nematic Phase and the Smectic Light Value," *J. Appl. Phys.* **46** (February 1975), pp. 584-599.

82. P. E. Cladis, "New Liquid-Crystal Phase Diagram," *Phys. Rev. Lett.* **35** (July 7, 1975), pp. 48-51.

83. P. E. Cladis and S. Torza, "Flow Instabilities in Couette Flow in Nematic Liquid Crystals," *Colloids and Interface Science*, Vol. IV, ed. M. Kerker (New York: Academic Press Inc., 1976), pp. 487-499.

84. T. A. Fulton, R. C. Dynes, and P. W. Anderson, "The Flux Shuttle-*A* Josephson Junction Shift Register Employing Single Flux Quanta," *Proc. IEEE* **61** (January 1973), pp. 28-35.

85. Z. Luz and S. Meiboom, "Nuclear Magnetic Resonance Studies of Smectic Liquid Crystals," *J. Chem. Phys.* **59** (July 1, 1973), pp. 275-295; Z. Luz, R. C. Hewitt, and S. Meiboom, "Deuterium Magnetic Resonance Study of a Smectic Liquid Crystal," *J. Chem. Phys.* **61** (September 1974), pp. 1758-1765.

86. S. Meiboom and R. C. Hewitt, "Measurements of the Rotational Viscosity Coefficient and the Shear-Alignment Angle in Nematic Liquid Crystals," *Phys. Rev. Lett.* **30** (February 12, 1973), pp. 261-263; idem, "Rotational Viscosity of a Smectic-C Liquid Crystalline Phase," *Phys. Rev. Lett.* **34** (May 5, 1975), pp. 1146-1149; idem, "Rational Viscosity in the Smectic Phases of Terephthal-Bis-Butylaniline (TBBA)," *Phys. Rev.* **A15** (June 1977), pp. 2444-2453.

87. D. W. Berreman and T. J. Scheffer, "Bragg Reflection of Light from Single-Domain Cholesteric Liquid-Crystal Films," *Phys. Rev. Lett.* **25** (August 31, 1970), pp. 577-581.

88. D. W. Berreman, "Solid Surface Shape and the Alignment of an Adjacent Nematic Liquid Crystal," *Phys. Rev. Lett.* **28** (June 26, 1972), pp. 1683-1686.

89. D. W. Berreman, "Electrical and Optical Properties of Twisted Nematic Structures," *Nonemissive Electro Optic Displays*, ed. A. R. Kmetz and F. K. von Willisen (New York: Plenum Press, 1976), pp. 9-24.

90. H. Melchior, F. J. Kahn, D. Maydan, and D. B. Fraser, "Thermally Addressed Electrically Erased High-Resolution Liquid-Crystal Light Values," *Appl. Phys. Lett.* **21** (October 15, 1972), pp. 392-394.

91. F. J. Kahn, "ir-Laser-Addressed Thermo-Optic Smectic Liquid-Crystal Storage Displays," *Appl. Phys. Lett.* **22** (February 1, 1973), pp. 111-113.

92. D. L. White and G. N. Taylor, "New Absorptive Mode Reflective Liquid-Crystal Display Device," *J. Appl. Phys.* **45** (November 1974), pp. 4718-4723.

93. G. D. Boyd, J. Cheng, and P. D. T. Ngo, "Liquid Crystal Orientational Bistability and Nematic Storage Effects," *Appl. Phys. Lett.* **36** (1980), pp. 556-558.

94. D. W. Berreman and W. R. Heffner, "New Bistable Cholesteric Liquid Crystal Display," *Appl. Phys. Lett.* **37** (1980), pp. 109-111.

95. A. G. Chynoweth, G. H. Wannier, R. A. Logan, and D. E. Thomas, "Observation of Stark Splitting of Energy Bands by Means of Tunnelling Transitions," *Phys. Rev. Lett.* **5** (July 15, 1960), pp. 57-58.

96. J. R. Haynes, "Experimental Proof of the Existence of a New Electronic Complex in Silicon," *Phys. Rev. Lett.* **4** (April 1, 1960), pp. 361-363; idem, "Experimental Observation of the Excitonic Molecule," *Phys. Rev. Lett.* **17** (October 17, 1966), pp. 860-862.

97. M. A. Woolf and G. W. Rayfield, "Energy of Negative Ions in Liquid Helium by Photoelectric Injection," *Phys. Rev. Lett.* **15** (August 9, 1965), pp. 235-237.

98. P. W. Anderson, "Considerations on the Flow of Superfluid Helium," *Rev. Mod. Phys.* **38** (April 1966), pp. 298-310.

99. P. L. Richards and P. W. Anderson, "Observation of the Analog of the ac Joseph-son Effect in Superfluid Helium," *Phys. Rev. Lett.* **14** (April 5, 1965), pp. 540-543.

100. D. L. Musinski and D. H. Douglass, "Search for the ac Josephson Effect in Liquid Helium," *Phys. Rev. Lett.* **29** (December 4, 1972), pp. 1541-1544; D. L. Musinski, "Experimental Status of the ac Josephson Effect in Liquid Helium," *J. Low Temp. Phys.* **13** (November 1973), pp. 287-311.

101. P. W. Anderson and P. L. Richards, "Comment on 'Search for the ac Josephson Effect in Liquid He,' " *Phys. Rev.* **B11** (April 1975), pp. 2702-2704.

102. G. Gamota and M. Barmatz, "Impulse of a Beam of Quantized Vortex Rings," *Phys. Rev. Lett.* **22** (April 28, 1969), pp. 874-876.

103. G. Gamota, A. Hasegawa, and C. M. Varma, "Evolution of a Pulse of Charged Vor-tex Rings in Superfluid Helium," *Phys. Rev. Lett.* **26** (April 19, 1971), pp. 960-963; A. Hasegawa and C. M. Varma, "Collective Modes in Streams of Charged Vortex Rings," *Phys. Rev. Lett.* **28** (June 26, 1972), pp. 1689-1691; G. Gamota, "Growing Collective Modes in Vortex Ring Beams in He II," *Phys. Rev. Lett.* **28** (June 26, 1972), pp. 1691-1693.

104. R. E. Slusher and C. M. Surko, "Raman Scattering from Condensed Phases of He^3 and He^4," *Phys. Rev. Lett.* **27** (December 20, 1971), pp. 1699-1702; C. M. Surko and R. E. Slusher, "Two-Roton Raman Scattering in He^3-He^4 Solutions," *Phys. Rev. Lett.* **30** (May 28, 1973), pp. 1111-1114.

105. K. Andres, R. C. Dynes, and V. Narayanamurti, "Velocity Spectrum of Atoms Eva-porating from a Liquid He Surface at Low Temperatures," *Phys. Rev.* **A8** (November 1973), pp. 2501-2506; R. C. Dynes, V. Narayanamurti, and K. Andres, "Phonon and Roton Propagation in He II under Pressure," *Phys. Rev. Lett.* **30** (May 28, 1973), pp. 1129-1132; V. Narayanamurti, K. Andres, and R. C. Dynes, "Dispersion and Attenuation of Superthermal 'Monochromatic' Phonons in He II," *Phys. Rev. Lett.* **31** (September 10, 1973), pp. 687-690.

106. T. R. Brown and C. C. Grimes, "Observation of Cyclotron Resonance in Surface-Bound Electrons on Liquid Helium," *Phys. Rev. Lett.* **29** (October 30, 1972), pp. 1233-1236.

107. C. C. Grimes, T. R. Brown, M. L. Burns, and C. L. Zipfel, "Spectroscopy of Elec-trons in Image-Potential-Induced Surface States Outside Liquid Helium," *Phys. Rev.* **B13** (January 1976), pp. 140-147.

108. C. C. Grimes, "Structure of the Electron Gas at the Surface of Liquid Helium," *J. Phys.* **39, C6** (August 1978), pp. 1352-1357.

109. P. M. Platzman and H. Fukuyama, "Phase Diagram of the Two-Dimensional Elec-tron Liquid," *Phys. Rev.* **B10** (October 1974), pp. 3150-3158; R. W. Hockney and T. R. Brown, "A Lambda Transition in a Classical Electron Film," *J. Phys.* **C8,** (June 1975), pp. 1813-1822.

110. C. C. Grimes and G. Adams, "Observation of Two-Dimensional Plasmons and Electron-Ripplon Scattering in a Sheet of Electrons on Liquid Helium," *Phys. Rev. Lett.* **36** (January 19, 1976), pp. 145-148.

111. C. L. Zipfel, T. R. Brown, and C. C. Grimes, "Measurement of the Velocity Auto-correlation Time in a Two-Dimensional Electron Liquid," *Phys. Rev. Lett.* **37** (December 27, 1976), pp. 1760-1763.

112. E. P. Wigner, "On the Interaction of Electrons in Metals," *Phys. Rev.* **46** (December 1934), pp. 1002-1011.

113. C. C. Grimes and G. Adams, "Evidence for a Liquid-to-Crystal Phase Transition in a Classical, Two-Dimensional Sheet of Electrons," *Phys. Rev. Lett.* **42** (March 19, 1979), pp. 795-798.

114. D. S. Fisher, B. I. Halperin, and P. M. Platzman, "Phonon-Ripplon Coupling and the Two-Dimensional Electron Solid on a Liquid Helium Surface," *Phys. Rev. Lett.* **42** (March 19, 1979), pp. 798-801.

115. J. Bardeen, L. N. Cooper, and J. R. Schrieffer, "Theory of Superconductivity," *Phys. Rev.* **108** (December 1957), pp. 1175-1204.

116. See, for example: J. C. Wheatley, "Experimental Properties of Pure He^3 and Dilute Solutions of He^3 in Superfluid He^4 at Very Low Temperatures. Application to Dilution Refrigeration," *Progress in Low Temperature Physics*, Vol. VI, ed. C. J. Gorter (Amsterdam: North-Holland Publishing Co., 1970), pp. 77-161; L. D. Landau, "Oscillations in a Fermi Liquid," *Sov. Phys. JETP* **5** (August 1957), pp. 101-108.

117. K. A. Brueckner, T. Soda, P. W. Anderson, and P. Morel, "Level Structure of Nuclear Matter and Liquid He^3," *Phys. Rev.* **118** (June 1960), pp. 1442-1446.

118. P. W. Anderson and P. Morel, "Generalized Bardeen-Cooper-Schrieffer States and the Proposed Low-Temperature Phase of Liquid He^3," *Phys. Rev.* **123** (September 1961), pp. 1911-1934.

119. D. D. Osheroff, R. C. Richardson, and D. M. Lee, "Evidence for a New Phase of Solid He^3," *Phys. Rev. Lett.* **28** (April 3, 1972), pp. 885-888.

120. D. D. Osheroff, W. J. Gully, R. C. Richardson, and D. M. Lee, "New Magnetic Phenomena in Liquid Helium-3 Below 3mK," *Phys. Rev. Lett.* **29** (October 2, 1972), pp. 920-923.

121. A. J. Leggett, "Interpretation of Recent Results on He^3 Below 3mK: A New Liquid Phase?," *Phys. Rev. Lett.* **29** (October 30 1972), pp. 1227-1230; idem, "The Spin Dynamics of an Anisotropic Fermi Superfluid (^{3}He)," *Ann. Phys.* **85** (May 30, 1974), pp. 11-55.

122. P. W. Anderson and W. F. Brinkman, "Anisotropic Superfluidity in ^{3}He: A Possible Interpretation of Its Stability as a Spin-Fluctuation Effect," *Phys. Rev. Lett.* **30** (May 28, 1973), pp. 1108-1111; W. F. Brinkman and P. W. Anderson, *Proc. Nobel Symp. 24* (Uppsala: Nobel Foundation 1973), p. 116.

123. R. Balian and N. R. Werthamer, "Superconductivity with Pairs in a Relative *p* Wave," *Phys. Rev.* **131** (August 1963), pp. 1553-1564.

124. D. D. Osheroff and W. F. Brinkman, "Longitudinal Resonance and Domain Effects in the *A* and *B* Phases of Liquid Helium Three," *Phys. Rev. Lett.* **32** (March 18, 1974), pp. 584-587.

125. D. D. Osheroff, "Longitudinal and Transverse Resonance in the *B* Phase of Superfluid He^3," *Phys. Rev. Lett.* **33** (October 21, 1974), pp. 1009-1012.

126. W. F. Brinkman, H. Smith, D. D. Osheroff, and E. I. Blount, "Anisotropy in the *B* Phase of He^3," *Phys. Rev. Lett.* **33** (September 9, 1974), pp. 624-627.

127. H. Smith, W. F. Brinkman, and S. Engelsberg, "Textures and NMR in Superfluid ^{3}He-*B*," *Phys. Rev.* **B15** (January 1977), pp. 199-213.

128. D. D. Osheroff and P. W. Anderson, "Nuclear Magnetic Resonance of Superfluid He^3 near T_c in High Magnetic Fields," *Phys. Rev. Lett.* **33** (September 16, 1974), pp. 686-689.

129. See reference 122.

130. D. D. Osheroff and L. R. Corruccini, "Pulsed NMR Frequency Shifts in Superfluid ^{3}He," *Phys. Lett.* **51A** (May 5, 1975), pp. 447-448.

131. D. D. Osheroff and L. R. Corruccini, "Pulsed NMR Frequency Shifts in He^3 *B*," *Low Temperature Physics-LT14-Volume 1-Helium*, ed. M. Krusius and M. Vuorio (Amsterdam: North-Holland Publishing Co., 1975), pp. 100-103.

132. W. F. Brinkman and H. Smith, "Frequency Shifts in Pulsed NMR for ^{3}He(A)," *Phys. Lett.* **51A** (May 5, 1975), pp. 449-450; idem, "Large Angle Tipping Frequency Shifts in Pulsed NMR for ^{3}He(B)," *Phys. Lett.* **53A** (May 19, 1975), pp. 43-44.

133. D. D. Osheroff, S. Engelsberg, W. F. Brinkman, and L. R. Corruccini, "Surface Orientational Effects in B-He^3," *Phys. Rev. Lett.* **34** (January 27, 1975), pp. 190-193.

134. D. D. Osheroff, W. van Roosbroeck, H. Smith, and W. F. Brinkman, "Spin Waves in ^{3}He-*B*," *Phys. Rev. Lett.* **38** (January 17, 1977), pp. 134-137; D. D. Osheroff, "Textural Spin Waves in ^{3}HeB," *Physica* **90B** (1977), pp. 20-34.

135. P. W. Anderson and W. F. Brinkman, "Theory of Anisotropic Superfludity in ^{3}He," in *The Physics of Liquid and Solid Helium*, Part II, ed. K. H. Bennemann and J. B. Ketterson (New York: John Wiley & Sons, 1978), pp. 177-286.

136. P. W. Anderson and G. Toulouse, "Phase Slippage Without Vortex Cores: Vortex Textures in Superfluid ^{3}He," *Phys. Rev. Lett.* **38** (February 28, 1977), pp. 508-511.

137. D. D. Osheroff and M. C. Cross, "Interfacial Surface Energy Between the Superfluid Phases of He^3," *Phys. Rev. Lett.* **38** (April 18, 1977), pp. 905-909.

138. M. C. Cross, *Quantum Fluids and Solids*, ed. S. B. Trickey, E. D. Adams, and J. W. Duffy (New York: Plenum Press, 1977), pp. 183-194.

139. L. R. Corruccini and D. D. Osheroff, "Unusual Magnetic Relaxation in Superfluid ^{3}He," *Phys. Rev. Lett.* **34** (March 10, 1975), pp. 564-567.

140. A. Jayaraman and L. H. Cohen, "Phase Diagrams in High-Pressure Research," in *Phase Diagrams*, ed. H. Alpen (New York: Academic Press, 1970), p. 245.

141. D. B. McWhan, "The Pressure Variable in Materials Research," *Science* **176** (May 19, 1972), pp. 751-758.

142. D. N. Lyon, D. B. McWhan, and A. L. Stevens, "Cryostat for Studies at ~100 Kilobars at Liquid Helium Temperatures," *Rev. Sci. Inst.* **38** (September 1967), pp. 1234-1240.

143. A. C. Gossard, D. B. McWhan, and J. P. Remeika, "High Pressure Nuclear Resonance Study of the Metal-Insulator Transition of V_2O_3," *Phys. Rev.* **B2** (November 1970), pp. 3762-3768.

144. D. B. McWhan, "Neutron Scattering at 4.5 GPa and 20K," in *High Pressure Science and Technology*, Vol. 1, ed. K. D. Timmerhaus and M. S. Barber (New York: Plenum Press, 1979), pp. 292-296.

145. A. Jayaraman, A. R. Hutson, J. H. McFee, A. S. Coriell, and R. G. Maines, "Hydrostatic and Uniaxial Pressure Generation Using Teflon Cell Container in Conventional Piston-Cylinder Device," *Rev. Sci. Inst.* **38** (January 1967), pp. 44-49.

146. M. E. Fine, E. S. Greiner, and W. C. Ellis, "Transitions in Chromium," *J. Metals* **189** (1951), p. 56.

147. T. M. Rice, A. Jayaraman, and D. B. McWhan, "Pressure Effects in Itinerant Antiferromagnetism of Cr and Its Alloys," *J. Phys.* **32 C1**, (1971), pp. 39-45.

148. N. F. Mott, *Metal-Insulator Transitions* (London: Taylor and Francis, 1974).

149. D. B. McWhan, T. M. Rice, and J. P. Remeika, "Mott Transition in Cr-Doped V_2O_3," *Phys. Rev. Lett.* **23** (December 15, 1969), pp. 1384-1387.

150. D. B. McWhan, A. Menth, J. P. Remeika, W. F. Brinkman, and T. M. Rice, "Metal-Insulator Transitions in Pure and Doped V_2O_3," *Phys. Rev.* **B7** (March 1973), pp. 1920-1931.

151. A. Jayaraman, V. Narayanamurti, E. Bucher, and R. G. Maines, "Continuous and Discontinuous Metal Semiconductor Transition in Samarium Monochalcogenides Under Pressure," *Phys. Rev. Lett.* **25** (November 16, 1970), pp. 1430-1433.

152. G. H. Wannier, "The Statistical Problem in Cooperative Phenomena," *Rev. Mod. Phys.* **17** (January 1945), pp. 50-60.

153. G. Ahlers, "Critical Phenomena at Low Temperature," *Rev. Mod. Phys.* **52** (April 1980), pp. 489-503.

154. D. S. Greywall and G. Ahlers, "Second-Sound Velocity and Super-fluid Density in ^{4}He under Pressure near T_λ," *Phys. Rev.* **A7** (June 1973), pp. 2145-2162.

155. R. J. Birgeneau, H. Guggenheim, and G. Shirane, "Neutron Scattering Investigation of Phase Transitions and Magnetic Correlations in the Two-Dimensional Antiferromagnets K_2NiF_4, Rb_2MnF_4, Rb_2FeF_4," *Phys. Rev.* **B1** (March 1970), pp. 2211-2230; M. T. Hutchings, "Spin Dynamics in the One-Dimensional Antiferromagnet $(CD_3)_4NMnCl_3$," *Phys. Rev.* **B5** (March 1972), pp. 1999-2014; Y. L. Holt, "Dynamics of an $S = \frac{1}{2}$, One-Dimensional Heisenberg Antiferromagnet," *Phys. Rev. Lett.* **32** (January 28, 1974), pp. 170-173.

156. B. I. Halperin and P. C. Hohenberg, "Scaling Laws for Dynamic Critical Phenomena," *Phys. Rev.* **177** (January 1969), pp. 952-971.

157. R. A. Ferrell, N. Menyhärd, H. Schmidt, F. Schwabl, and P. Szëpfalusy, "Fluctuations and Lambda Phase Transition in Liquid Helium," *Ann. Phys.* **47** (May 1968), pp. 565-613.

158. See reference 153.

159. P. C. Hohenberg and B. I. Halperin, "Theory of Dynamic Critical Phenomena," *Rev. Mod. Phys.* **49** (July 1977), pp. 435-479.

160. P. A. Fleury and J. M. Worlock, "Electric-Field-Induced Raman Scattering in $SrTiO_3$ and $KTaO_3$," *Phys. Rev.* **174** (October 1968), pp. 613-623.

161. P. A. Fleury and K. B. Lyons, "Anharmonic Phonons and Central Peaks at Structural Phase Transitions," *Solid State Communications Special Issue on the Proceedings of the Joint Japan-USA Conference on Light Scattering,* **32** (October 1979), pp. 103-109.

162. J. A. Wilson, F. J. DiSalvo, and S. Mahajan, "Charge-Density Waves and Superlattices in the Metallic Layered Transition Metal Dichalcogenides," *Adv. Phys.* **24** (March 1975), pp. 117-201.

163. G. Ahlers and R. P. Behringer, "The Rayleigh-Benard Instability and the Evolution of Turbulence," *Prog. Theor. Phys. Suppl.* **64** (1978), pp. 186-201; G. Ahlers and R. W. Walden, "Turbulence near Onset of Convection," *Phys. Rev. Lett.* **44** (February 18, 1980), pp. 445-448.

Chapter 10

The Role
of Theoretical Physics
at Bell Laboratories

There is a complex relation between theoretical and experimental research at Bell Laboratories. Theoretical physicists have played an increasing role in research activities as the sophistication of physics research has increased. The shift of the center of theoretical work from classical physics to quantum mechanics resulted not only in important contributions to the understanding of ordered states of matter but also made possible highly effective research on localized states, random systems, many body problems, superconductivity, and phase transitions. The involvement of the theorists in diverse subfields of solid state physics contributed in an important way to the fruitful collaboration between the theorists and the experimentalists.

I. THE NATURE OF THEORETICAL PHYSICS

Theoretical physics can be defined as the invention and manipulation of concepts, using mathematics where necessary, to simplify the understanding of known physical phenomena and to predict new phenomena. The growth in the number of staff members who identify themselves professionally with theoretical physics has been a natural consequence both of the increasing variety of physical phenomena used in communication devices, and of the increasing maturity, and hence increasing conceptualization, of physics itself. At the time of this writing nearly all of these people are specialists in theoretical physics, and do no experimental work. Fifty years earlier, it was more common for theorists to be involved also in experimental work.

Whereas experimental research usually involves investing in complicated equipment specifically designed for a particular project,

Principal authors: P. W. Anderson, W. F. Brinkman, and C. Herring

theoretical work usually involves only intellectual commitments. A theorist, therefore, often works on a wide variety of projects. Theoretical contributions of Bell Labs scientists have covered areas as diverse as ionization in gases, superfluidity, chemical bonding, sintering, magnetic resonance, optical properties of transparent media, photoelectric emission, and so on. The esteem in which some of these contributions have been held by the scientific community is illustrated by the fact that of the twenty-eight times the annual Oliver E. Buckley Solid-State Physics Prize has been awarded by the American Physical Society up to 1980, eight have involved theoretical work (one of these in collaboration with experimental work) done largely or entirely at Bell Labs. Many other awards, including Nobel Prizes to three individuals, have been awarded to theoretical physicists for work done at Bell Labs. There have been dozens of other—and quite different—constellations of theoretical contributions of comparable importance. Many, though not all, have been integral parts of experimental programs described elsewhere in this history and will not be discussed in detail here. Perhaps the best way to convey a perspective on theoretical physics research over the years is to enumerate the major clusters of conceptual tools that have been applied to these many problems, and to illustrate them with a few selected samples.

Several important aspects of theoretical physics research are illustrated by the early work of H. Nyquist. Nyquist was intrigued by J. B. Johnson's discovery at Bell Labs in 1927-1928 that resistances made of quite diverse materials always acted as sources of white noise—the mean-square noise voltage in any frequency range being proportional to the product of the resistance and the absolute temperature, and independent of the material.[1] By a simple but ingenious combination of the canonical-distribution and detailed-balance concepts of statistical mechanics with his engineer's knowledge of transmission lines and impedance matching, Nyquist (who had joined Bell Labs by this time) proved that any type of circuit element with a frequency-dependent impedance must act as a noise source with a spectral density proportional to the real part of the impedance and to the absolute temperature.[2] This "Nyquist theorem" has been generalized into one of the most basic cornerstones of the understanding of the statistical mechanics of irreversible processes.

Nyquist's work is an example of an important development in theory consummated in a short time by a single person. In more recent history there have been a few such isolated "one-shot" contributions, but more often the major advances have been made in a series of related papers. These advances have usually, as in the thermal-noise case, been stimulated by contemporary experimental work; yet there are cases where important discoveries have been made in what at the time was a realm of pure imagination. Nyquist's fusing of concepts from two quite different fields, statistical mechanics and electrical engineering, points out what has been a particular strength of Bell Labs work in theoretical physics: the diversity of expertise among the theoretical staff, and the propensity of many of them to shift their attention from one area to another, transferring useful concepts in the process.

II. THE BUILDUP OF THE THEORETICAL PHYSICS EFFORT

Theoretical solid-state physicists have formed an indispensable part of the physics effort at Bell Laboratories since 1936, when W. Shockley joined the staff, and especially since the mid-1940s when J. Bardeen and a number of others in this field were added. The outstanding accomplishment of the late 1940s was the understanding of electrical transport and contact phenomena in semiconductors, and of the role of minority carriers and surface traps. Chapter 2 of this volume has described the intimate relationship between experimental work and theory in the discipline of electron waves in solids, a discipline whose further exploitation will be discussed below. But some of the same theorists also joined other colleagues in work on different types of properties of solids, often using tools from the realm of nonquantum physics. Thus in the late 1940s and early 1950s, "billiard-ball physics" was applied to problems of diffusion in crystals (as well as to phenomena in gas discharges by G. H. Wannier[3]) and, in conjunction with the theory of elasticity, to dislocations (the defects involved in plastic deformation) and to the problem of the energy associated with boundaries between crystal grains.[4] The theory of continuously varying states of magnetization was applied to the structure of the walls separating domains of opposite magnetization in ferromagnetic materials and to the resonance of magnetization oscillations in a high-frequency magnetic field. From C. Kittel's early work[5] on the theory of ferromagnetic resonance many interesting developments in the theory of magnetic resonance arose in conjunction with experiments throughout the 1950s. For example, H. Suhl's work on nonlinear pumping in ferromagnetic resonance was seminal in the development of the parametric amplifier, as well as important in its own right as a new approach to nonlinear problems.[6]

Another field of more or less classical physics was ferroelectrics, where Shockley stimulated theoretical work that elucidated the concept of displacive transitions caused by polarizable dipoles, which led eventually to P. W. Anderson's concept of the "soft mode."[7] This concept, Shockley's early work of the 1930s on order-disorder,[8] and Wannier's and Anderson's work on antiferromagnetism,[9,10] foreshadowed the interest in phase transitions in the 1970s. (Some of these developments are described in other sections of this chapter.)

Often the new insights gained in the late 1940s and early 1950s came merely because the increasing overall sophistication of physics research was causing theorists to scrutinize more carefully than ever before the relation of the concepts of classical physics to phenomena in solid bodies. The theory of sintering—the gradual growing together of solid particles when placed in contact at a high temperature—is one of the many examples of this. The motivation for such a change comes from the fact that sintering decreases the area of exposed surface. Recognition of this led C. Herring [Fig. 10-1] to examine critically the possible ways in which the surface tension of a crystal could depend on the orientation of the surface, and how diffusion currents could be controlled by the relative curvatures of different parts of a surface.[11] The outcome was a set of equations and principles that have facilitated the interpretation of many experiments in the areas of sintering, thermal etching, and high-temperature creep.

III. THE INCREASING ROLE OF QUANTUM MECHANICS – PHYSICS OF ORDERED STATES

While classical physics has continued to be an indispensable tool of Bell Labs theoreticians, its role since the early 1950s has been clearly subordinate to that of quantum mechanics. One of the most basic quantum-mechanical disciplines in solid state physics is the theory of electron waves in crystals. Progress in this area played an important role in the early semiconductor work mentioned above, and it became even more important in the 1950s and 1960s. The increasing sophistication of experiments on the transport properties and optical properties of semiconductors required a detailed understanding of the structure of the allowed and forbidden bands of energy for electron waves, the relation of energy to wavelength and direction of motion, and the often anisotropic responses of such electron waves to electric and magnetic fields. Bell Labs' physicists made many contributions to techniques for calculating energy bands, to calculating energy bands for specific materials, and to using these calculations to interpret optical properties.[12] Perhaps the most important of these was the development by J. C. Phillips, stimulated by Herring, of the pseudo-potential method for band structures.[13] [Fig. 10-2]

The study of interactions of magnetic electrons with nuclear moments—hyperfine interactions—has been a vital experimental tool in the use of electron paramagnetic resonance (EPR), nuclear magnetic resonance (NMR), and later, Mössbauer spectroscopy and laser probe methods. Early work in this field was done by Herring on the Knight shift in metals and by R. G. Shulman and coworkers on transferred hyperfine structure of magnetic materials.[14,15] These stud-

Fig. 10-1. C. Herring looking at a model of a Brillouin zone, which describes the periodicity of electron wave functions in momentum space.

ies elucidated the nature of chemical bonding as well as spin interactions. (See Chapter 1, section 2.1.)

Another important example of magnetic interaction is provided by pairs of neighboring magnetic atoms in insulators. It is the interaction of such pairs that causes the ordered-arrangements characteristic of ferromagnetism and antiferromagnetism. In insulators the magnetic atoms are normally separated from each other by a nonmagnetic atom. Although it had been suggested long ago that the magnetic atoms might interact through the intermediate one, it was only in 1959 that Anderson[16] showed convincingly how this interaction takes place and that it is deeply bound up with the "Mott-insulating" nature of these magnetic materials. Herring studied extensively the problem of magnetic interactions (see Chapter 1, section 1.4), itinerant electrons, and the asymptotic exchange interactions in insulators.[17]

In the late 1970s, there was increased attention to some problems that could be successfully attacked only because of the increasing power and sophistication of the computational tools available to the theorist. Much of the rapidly growing understanding of solid sur-

Fig. 10-2. D. R. Hamann (left) discusses his development in pseudopotential theory with J. C. Phillips. Hamann's and Schlüter's "norm-conserving" procedure enables pseudopotential calculations to reproduce full potential results accurately for the electronic structure of solids and surfaces.

faces and point defects falls in this category; for instance, the self-consistent calculation of the electronic band structure near a surface by J. A. Applebaum and D. R. Hamann, and the defect calculations by G. A. Baraff and M. Schlüter are major contributions.[18,19] Another trend is the formulation of empirical rules that can be used to order large amounts of data on complicated systems. This is a task that has usually been carried out by chemists and metallurgists, rather than by theoretical physicists whose training orients them more toward precise logical systems and calculations from first principles. However, some studies of chemical bonding in semiconducting and ionic compounds made in the early 1970s by Phillips showed that concepts suggested from the realm of theoretical physics can be of enormous assistance in the empirical correlation of data.[20]

IV. EXTENSION TO LOCALIZED STATES AND RANDOM SYSTEMS

Another important subject studied in the 1950s was that of the quantum mechanics of small numbers of electrons bound to one or several localized centers. For instance, the impurity centers that control the electrical properties of semiconductors were one early object of study. It is interesting to note that the classic theory relating the properties of such centers to the characteristics of the energy bands discussed in the preceding paragraph was worked out by W. Kohn and J. M. Luttinger largely while they were employed as summer visitors at Bell Labs.[21] A similar problem of weakly bound particles in semiconductors underlies the major advances in understanding the optical properties of semiconductors made by J. J. Hopfield and D. G. Thomas in their classic studies of exciton absorption and exciton-lightwave interactions.[22]

In its purest form, the research on electron waves in crystals and systems of locally bound electrons dealt merely with actual or possible energy levels or states of motion. To understand the many phenomena that are dynamic, rather than static, this research must be supplemented with another one—the determination of how electrons, atoms, and other particles shift about among their possible quantum states when disturbed by external fields and the random influences of thermal agitation. There are two basic approaches to this. The first, transport theory, emphasizes the Boltzmann equation and scattering, where Herring,[23] and later Luttinger and Kohn[24] made important contributions. Herring's work on the whole complex of thermal and electrical transport phenomena in semiconductors has become classic. A second approach, the fluctuation-dissipation concept, relates transport and dissipation phenomena to equilibrium fluctuations, with its origins in the work of Nyquist referred to earlier, and similar beginnings by Albert Einstein and Onsager. It was first made a practical method in a series of works by Anderson in the early 1950s on pressure broadening and exchange narrowing,[25] and it influenced work by M. Lax.[26] [Fig. 10-3] This approach underlies much of modern many-body theory, also to be discussed later. An example of the more recent applications was a series of studies by Lax and others on noise-producing fluctuations in systems whose state has been driven far from thermal equilibrium.[27] This has been applied to the understanding of fluctuations in the light output of lasers, an application at the forefront of laser experimental research at the time of this writing.

Bell Labs theoretical physicists have also contributed to the study of electron transport in random systems, such as impurity bands in semiconductors. The problem of densities of electronic states in such systems was studied by Lax and by J. R. Klauder using Lax's "multiple scattering theory."[28] P. Soven[29] and D. W. Taylor[30] made substantial contributions to the very powerful extension of this method, which became known as the coherent potential approximation. Lax also stimulated a numerical study of the one-dimensional problem by Phillips,[31] which led to certain exact results of H. L. Frisch and S. P. Lloyd.[32] This numerical study also led to a classic study by B. I.

Fig. 10-3. M. Lax examines an expression for quantum Markoffian noise.

Halperin and Lax of states deep in the band tails, important in the analysis of semiconductor lasers and as a testing ground for methodology.[33]

Anderson, noting a number of experimental anomalies that could not be explained by conventional transport theory, set up a model for systems with random positions of impurities and energy levels, and demonstrated the existence of localized states and of the "mobility edge."[34] This work, which has wide implications to the theory of random systems such as glasses, was a principal contribution for which Anderson was awarded the Nobel Prize in physics in 1977. [Fig. 10-4] Spin diffusion studies of the impurity bands in semiconductors were the initial motivation for this work. The basic theoretical understanding of the impurity band was also investigated by M. Pollak and T. H. Geballe, who studied the ac conductivity by phonon-assisted hopping.[35] This was stimulated by Lax and Anderson, and by the study of dc hopping conduction by E. Abrahams, which he did while spending a summer at Bell Labs.[36] The field then languished, except for some seminal work on the "percolation" theory of J. M. Hammersley,[37] until several works in the 1970s by Anderson and associates made further advances. Some examples are "tunneling systems" in glass by Anderson, Halperin, and C. M. Varma,[38] and two-electron centers by Anderson.[39]

Fig. 10-4. P. W. Anderson (left) being congratulated by A. M. Clogston, executive director of the Research, Physics, and Academic Affairs division from 1973 to 1982, upon receipt of the news that Anderson has been awarded the Nobel Prize in physics in 1977.

V. MANY-BODY THEORY – BROKEN SYMMETRY AND SUPERCON-DUCTIVITY

In the 1960s a lot of work at Bell Laboratories mirrored the trend of the times to pay strong attention to the discipline known as many-body theory. This was the study of the correlated motions of huge numbers of electrons or atoms, each of which exerts forces on all the others, and of the cooperative phenomena that arise in consequence. Some of the key works that foreshadowed this field were done at Bell Labs during the previous decade. Among the most important were the papers on spin waves in magnetic metals by Herring and Kittel where they calculated a "collective excitation" of an electron gas in a metal.[40] Also important was the work by Lax and Anderson on relaxation and Anderson's paper on the ground state of the antiferromagnet, which introduced the complex of ideas that became known as broken symmetry (that an asymmetric ground state has dynamical consequences, especially for the excitation spectrum of the system).[41]

Superconductivity and superfluidity are perhaps the most spectacular of the phenomena that require many-body theory to be understood. Major Bell Labs activity in these areas grew up after 1957, when Bardeen, L. Cooper, and J. R. Schrieffer at the University of Illinois put forth their Nobel Prize winning theory of superconductivity. (This was an outgrowth of some imaginative, though less successful work that Bardeen had done in 1950, when he was still at Bell Labs.)[42] The work done at Bell Labs in the late 1950s and early 1960s began with some clarifications of the Bardeen-Cooper-Schrieffer theory. In this work Anderson first applied the general theory of broken symmetry to this case, settling the question of gauge symmetry, and made a number of extensions of the theory.[43] In 1962, as a result of discussions of the broken symmetry concept with Anderson, B. Josephson, a student at Cambridge University in England, proposed the effect for which he won the Nobel Prize.[44] These ideas stimulated Anderson to develop the concept of "phase slippage" as the basic dissipative mechanism in superconductors and superfluids, including the hard superconducting materials from which superconducting magnets are made. The concept is analogous to "slip" in metals, which occurs when strain is relieved. In the 1970s the insights that led to the phase slippage idea had to be generalized to accommodate the topological multiplicity of defects that can occur in complicated systems such as liquid crystals and superfluid ^{3}He.[45]

Another important line of work in superconductivity is the exploration of the microscopic interactions of electrons and phonons that cause the phenomenon. This is one of the most quantitatively precise of any microscopic theories of material properties. Studies in this area were begun by Anderson and P. Morel,[46] following work elsewhere, especially by Eliashberg in the Soviet Union. Then the work was taken up by W. L. McMillan in collaboration with experiments by J. M. Rowell and others.[47] The relationship of these atomistic parameters to the wiggles in the current-voltage characteristics of high-resistance contacts between superconducting metals was developed and confirmed experimentally.

The work just described, like a great deal of the theoretical research at Bell Laboratories, involved an intimate collaboration between theorists and experimentalists. However, some of the theoretical work was of a purely conceptual or even speculative nature, extended far beyond the limits of existing experimental work, and did not lead to new experimental programs until many years later. An excellent example is provided by speculations, stimulated by the theory of superconductivity, on the possible existence of superfluid states of ^{3}He at extremely low temperatures.[48] The atoms of ^{3}He, which resemble electrons by having a nuclear spin and by obeying an exclusion principle, may be expected to become ordered at very low temperatures in a way similar to electrons in superconductors. However, because the forces between these atoms are quite different from those between electrons in a metal, this ordering should give rise to superfluid states with remarkable anisotropic properties. As was noted above, the theoretical predictions in the early 1960s by Anderson and Morel and by R. Balian and N. R. Werthamer of the existence of two possible forms of superfluid states of ^{3}He were indeed discovered experimentally. One result of interest is the relationship of the nature of the phases to the spin fluctuation theory of the nearly magnetic Fermi system, which has been exploited predominantly by W. F. Brinkman.[49]

Besides superconductivity and superfluidity, at the time of this writing, many other fascinating topics have engaged the attention of many-body theorists in the last two decades. Also active over the past 20 years has been the study of the solid state plasma or electron Fermi liquid in metals. P. A. Wolff was the first to point out that many metals provide ideal conditions for the study of quantum plasma physics. P. M. Platzman and Wolff have made many contributions in terms of applying the fundamental apparatus of Fermi liquid theory to real metals.[50] Another area of active study is the properties of impurities in metals, which can usually exchange electrons with the host and whose manifestation of magnetic properties will depend on the characteristics of this exchange. One special impurity is the core hole left behind in a high-energy excitation process. Bell Labs theorists have contributed to the elucidation of the strange Fermi-surface anomalies seen in X-ray spectra in metals. Another manifestation of these anomalies is the Kondo effect of enhanced magnetic scattering, a complex and fascinating effect first solved by Anderson, G. Yuval, and Hamann, applying the renormalization group method. This research was seminal to much of the research in physics in the 1970s.[51]

Another field of many-body physics where major developments occurred at Bell Labs was metal-insulator transitions, in which a change of pressure or temperature can cause a substance to change its conductivity discontinuously by many orders of magnitude.[52] One important theoretical development here was the work of Brinkman and T. M. Rice that was stimulated by experiments at Bell Labs on V_2O_3. An example of a model quantum liquid is the electron-hole liquid that is formed in semiconductors when electrons and holes, created by optical excitation, condense to form a metallic state.[53] Another field touched on was quantum crystals, crystals made of atoms so light that they have to be described as waves rather than as classical "billiard balls."[54]

VI. STATISTICAL MECHANICS AND PHASE TRANSITIONS

Other disciplines have also played significant roles in theoretical physics work at Bell Laboratories. One of the most important has been that of the statistical mechanics of phase transitions. This is the study of the "seesaw" region of the battle between interatomic forces of one kind or another, which strive to produce a long-range order in the arrangement or orientation of atoms or molecules in a medium, and the disordering effect of thermal agitation. It is here that the renormalization group method, in which the evolution of length and time scales are quantified has had its most important application. Building on work initiated elsewhere, P. C. Hohenberg and Halperin developed a detailed and comprehensive theory of dynamic phenomena at phase transitions.[55]

VII. CONCLUDING COMMENTS

Only a sample of the theoretical physics research at Bell Laboratories in the last few decades has been discussed in this chapter; hopefully, it has sufficed to convey something of the diversity of this work. Equally exciting theoretical work in astrophysics, biophysics, and plasma physics have been covered in other chapters. Bell Labs work has even ranged into other areas as remote as elementary-particle physics and pure mathematics related to physics; in another dimension, it has been fairly uniformly distributed over the whole range from collaborative work with experimentalists through interpretations of specific experiments by others to fundamental studies of basic theoretical concepts. Both kinds of diversity have helped its usefulness by facilitating the transfer of ideas—from one subject field to another or between the abstract and the concrete realms.

REFERENCES

1. J. B. Johnson, "Thermal Agitation of Electricity in Conductors," *Phys. Rev.* **32** (July 1928), pp. 97-109.
2. H. Nyquist, "Thermal Agitation of Electric Charge in Conductors," *Phys. Rev.* **32** (July 1928), pp. 110-113.
3. G. H. Wannier, "On the Motion of Gaseous Ions in a Strong Electric Field. I," *Phys. Rev.* **83** (July 1951), pp. 281-289; G. H. Wannier, "Motion of Gaseous Ions in a Strong Electric Field. II," *Phys. Rev.* **87** (September 1952), pp. 795-798.
4. W. T. Read and W. Shockley, "Dislocation Models of Crystal Grain Boundaries," *Phys. Rev.* **78** (May 1950), pp. 275-289.
5. C. Kittel, "Interpretation of Anomalous Larmor Frequencies in Ferromagnetic Resonance Experiment," *Phys. Rev.* **71** (February 1947), pp. 270-271; C. Kittel, "On the Theory of Ferromagnetic Resonance Absorption," *Phys. Rev.* **73** (January 1948), pp. 155-161.
6. P. W. Anderson and H. Suhl, "Instability in the Motion of Ferromagnets at High Microwave Power Levels," *Phys. Rev.* **100** (December 1955), pp. 1788-1789.
7. P. W. Anderson, "Qualitative Considerations on the Statistics of Phase Transition in Ferroelectrics of Type BaTiO$_3$," *Proceedings of the 2nd All-Union Conf. on the Physics of Dielectrics* (Moscow: Academy of Sciences of the USSR, 1960), pp. 290-296.
8. F. C. Nix and W. Shockley, "Order-Disorder Transformations in Alloys," *Rev. Mod. Phys.* **10** (January 1938), pp. 1-71.
9. G. H. Wannier, "Antiferromagnetism. The Triangular Ising Net," *Phys. Rev.* **79** (July 1950), pp. 357-364.
10. P. W. Anderson, "Antiferromagnetism. Theory of Superexchange Interactions" *Phys. Rev.* **79** (July 1950), pp. 350-356; idem, "Generalizations of the Weiss Molecu-

lar Field Theory of Antiferromagnetism," *Phys. Rev.* **79** (August 1950), pp. 705-710; idem, "An Approximate Quantum Theory of the Antiferromagnetic Ground State," *Phys. Rev.* **86** (June 1952), pp. 694-701.

11. C. Herring, "Surface Tension as a Motivation for Sintering," in *The Physics of Powder Metallurgy*, ed. W. E. Kingston (New York: McGraw-Hill, 1951), pp. 143-179; idem, "Effect of Change of Scale on Sintering Phenomena," *J. Appl. Phys.* **21** (April 1950), pp. 301-303.

12. A. P. Cracknell, *The Fermi Surfaces of Metals* (London: Taylor and Francis, 1971) D. L. Greenaway and G. Harbeke, *Optical Properties and Band Structure of Semiconductors, Volume 1* (Oxford: Pergamon, 1968).

13. J. C. Phillips, *Bonds and Bands in Semiconductors* (New York: Academic Press, 1973).

14. C. H. Townes, C. Herring, and W. D. Knight, "The Effect of Electronic Paramagnetism on Nuclear Magnetic Resonance Frequencies in Metals," *Phys. Rev.* **77** (March 1950), pp. 852-853; L. H. Bennett, R. E. Watson, and G. C. Carter, "Relevance of Knight Shift Measurements to the Electronic Density of States," *J. Res. NBS* 74A (1970), pp. 569-610.

15. R. G. Shulman and S. Sugano, "Calculation of the Crystal Field Splitting," *Phys. Rev. Lett.* **7** (September 1, 1961), pp. 157-159.

16. P. W. Anderson, "New Approach to the Theory of Superexchange Interactions," *Phys. Rev.* **115** (July 1959), pp. 2-13.

17. C. Herring, "Direct Exchange Between Well-Separated Atoms," in *Magnetism*, Volume IIB, ed. G. T. Rado and H. Suhl (New York: Academic Press, 1966), pp. 1-181.

18. J. A. Appelbaum and D. R. Hamann, "The Electronic Structure of Solid Surfaces," *Rev. Mod. Phys.* **48** (July 1976), pp. 479-496.

19. G. A. Baraff and M. Schlüter, "Self-Consistent Green's-Function Calculation of the Ideal Si Vacancy," *Phys. Rev. Lett.* **41** (September 25, 1978); D. R. Hamann, M. Schlüter, and C. Chiang, "Norm-Conserving Pseudopotentials," *Phys. Rev. Lett.* **43** (November 12, 1979), pp. 1494-1497; G. A. Baraff and M. Schlüter, "New Self-Consistent Approach to the Electronic Structure of Localized Defects in Solids," *Phys. Rev.* **B19** (May 1979), pp. 4965-4979.

20. See reference 13.

21. W. Kohn, "Shallow Impurity States in Silicon and Germanium," *Solid State Physics* 5, ed. F. Seitz and D. Turnbull (New York: Academic Press, 1957), pp. 257-320.

22. J. J. Hopfield and D. G. Thomas, "On Some Observable Properties of Longitudinal Excitons," *J. Phys. Chem. Solids* **12** (February 1960), pp. 276-284.

23. C. Herring, "Transport Properties of a Many-Valley Semiconductor," *Bell System Tech. J.* **34** (March 1955), pp. 237-290; C. Herring and E. Vogt, "Transport and Deformation-Potential Theory for Many-Valley Semiconductors with Anisotropic Scattering," *Phys. Rev.* **101** (February 1956), pp. 944-961.

24. W. L. Kohn and J. M. Luttinger, "Quantum Theory of Electrical Transport Phenomena," *Phys. Rev.* **108** (November 1957), pp. 590-611; idem, "Quantum Theory of Electrical Transport Phenomena. II," *Phys. Rev.* **109** (March 1958), pp. 1892-1909.

25. P. W. Anderson, "Pressure Broadening in the Microwave and Infra-Red Regions," *Phys. Rev.* **76** (September 1949), pp. 647-661.

26. M. Lax, "The Franck-Condon Principle and Its Application to Crystals," *J. Chem. Phys.* **20** (November 1952), pp. 1752-1760; H. Gummel and M. Lax, "Thermal Ionization and Capture of Electrons Trapped in Semiconductors," *Phys. Rev.* **97** (March 1955), pp. 1469-1470.

27. See, for example, the review of M. Lax, "Fluctuation and Coherence Phenomena in Classical and Quantum Physics," in *Statistical Physics, Phase Transitions, and Superfluidity*, Volume 2, ed. A. Chrétien, E. P. Gross, and S. Deser (New York: Gordon and Breach, 1968), pp. 269-478; also M. Lax and M. Zwanziger, "Exact Photocount Statistics: Lasers Near Threshold," *Phys. Rev.* **A7** (February 1973), pp. 750-771.

28. J. R. Klauder, "The Modification of Electron Energy Levels by Impurity Atoms," *Ann. Phys.* **14** (July 1961), pp. 43-76.

29. P. Soven, "Approximate Calculation of Electronic Structure of Disordered Alloys-Application to Alpha Brass," *Phys. Rev.* **151** (November 1966), pp. 539-550.

30. D. W. Taylor, "Vibrational Properties of Imperfect Crystals with Large Defect Concentrations," *Phys. Rev.* **156** (April 1967), pp. 1017-1029.

31. M. Lax and J. C. Phillips, "One-Dimensional Impurity Bands," *Phys. Rev.* **110** (April 1958), pp. 41-49.

32. H. L. Frisch and S. P. Lloyd, "Electron Levels in a One-Dimensional Random Lattice," *Phys. Rev.* **120** (November 1960), pp. 1175-1189.

33. B. I. Halperin and M. Lax, "Impurity-Band Tails in the High-Density Limit. I. Minimum Counting Methods," *Phys. Rev.* **148** (August 1966), pp. 722-740; idem, "Impurity-Band Tails in the High-Density Limit. II. Higher Order Corrections," *Phys. Rev.* **153** (January 1967), pp. 802-814.

34. P. W. Anderson, "Absence of Diffusion in Certain Random Lattices," *Phys. Rev.* **109** (March 1958), pp. 1492-1505.

35. M. Pollak and T. H. Geballe, "Low-Frequency Conductivity Due to Hopping Processes in Silicon," *Phys. Rev.* **122** (June 1961), pp. 1742-1753.

36. A. Miller and E. Abrahams, "Impurity Conduction at Low Concentrations," *Phys. Rev.* **120** (November 1960), pp. 745-755.

37. H. L. Frisch, J. M. Hammersley, and D. J. A. Welsh, "Monte Carlo Estimates of Percolation Probabilities for Various Lattices," *Phys. Rev.* **126** (May 1962), pp. 949-951.

38. P. W. Anderson, B. I. Halperin, and C. M. Varma, "Anomalous Low-Temperature Thermal Properties of Glasses and Spin Glasses," *Phil. Mag.* **25** (January 1972), pp. 1-9.

39. P. W. Anderson, "Model for the Electronic Structure of Amorphous Semiconductors," *Phys. Rev. Lett.* **34** (April 14, 1975), pp. 953-955.

40. C. Herring and C. Kittel, "On the Theory of Spin Waves in Ferromagnetic Media," *Phys. Rev.* **81** (March 1951), pp. 869-880; C. Herring, "Energy of a Bloch Wall on the Band Picture. I. Spiral Approach," *Phys. Rev.* **85** (March 1952), pp. 1003-1011; C. Herring, "Energy of a Bloch Wall on the Band Picture. II. Perturbation Approach," *Phys. Rev.* **87** (July 1952), pp. 60-70.

41. See reference 10.

42. J. Bardeen, "Zero-Point Vibrations and Superconductivity," *Phys. Rev.* **79** (July 1950), pp. 167-168; idem, "Wave Functions for Superconducting Electrons," *Phys. Rev.* **80** (November 1950), pp. 567-574.

43. P. W. Anderson, "Plasmons, Gauge Invariance, and Mass," *Phys. Rev.* **130** (April 1963), pp. 439-442; idem, "Coherent Excited States in the Theory of Superconductivity: Gauge and Invariance and the Meissner Effect," *Phys. Rev.* **110** (May 1958), pp. 827-835; idem, "Random-Phase Approximation in the Theory of Superconductivity," *Phys. Rev.* **112** (December 1958), pp. 1900-1916.

44. B. D. Josephson, "Possible New Effects in Superconductive Tunnelling," *Phys. Lett.* **1** (July 1, 1962), pp. 251-253.

45. P. W. Anderson and C. Toulouse, "Phase Slippage without Vortex Cores: Vortex Textures in Superfluid ^{3}He," *Phys. Rev. Lett.* **38** (February 28, 1977), pp. 508-511.

46. P. Morel and P. W. Anderson, "Calculation of the Superconducting State Parameters with Retarded Electron-Phonon Interaction," *Phys. Rev.* **125** (February 1962), pp. 1263-1271.

47. W. L. McMillan and J. M. Rowell, "Tunneling and Strong-Coupling Superconductivity," *Superconductivity*, Volume 1, ed. R. D. Parks (New York: Marcel Dekker, Inc., 1969), pp. 561-614.

48. P. W. Anderson and P. Morel, "Generalized Bardeen-Cooper-Schrieffer States and the Proposed Low-Temperature Phase of Liquid He³," *Phys. Rev.* **123** (September 1961), pp. 1911-1934; R. Balian and N. R. Werthamer, "Superconductivity with Pairs in a Relative *p* Wave," *Phys. Rev.* **131** (August 1963), pp. 1553-1564.

49. P. W. Anderson and W. F. Brinkman, *The Physics of Liquid and Solid Helium*, Part II., ed. K. H. Bennemann and J. P. Ketterson (New York: John Wiley & Sons, 1978), p. 177.

50. P. M. Platzman and P. A. Wolff, "Waves and Interactions in Solid State Plasmas," *Solid State Physics, Supplement 13.*, ed. H. Ehrenreich, F. Seitz, and D. Turnbull (New York: Academic Press, 1973).

51. J. Kondo, "Theory of Dilute Magnetic Alloys," *Solid State Physics* **23**, ed. F. Seitz, D. Turnbull, and H. Ehrenreich (New York: Academic Press, 1969), pp. 183-281; P. W. Anderson, "Kondo Effect III: The Wilderness - Mainly Theoretical," *Comments on Solid State Physics* **3** (February-March 1971), pp. 153-158; idem, "Kondo Effect IV: Out of the Wilderness," *Comments on Solid State Physics* **5** (March-April 1973), pp. 73-79.

52. See, for example, N. F. Mott, *Metal-Insulator Transitions* (London: Taylor and Francis, 1974).

53. T. M. Rice, "The Electron-Hole Liquid in Semiconductors: Theoretical Aspects," *Solid State Physics* **32**, ed. H. Ehrenreich, F. Seitz, and D. Turnbull (New York: Academic Press, 1977), pp. 1-86.

54. C. M. Varma and N. R. Werthamer, "Solid Helium," *The Physics of Liquid and Solid Helium*, Part I, ed. K. H. Bennemann and J. B. Ketterson (New York: John Wiley & Sons, 1976), pp. 503-570.

55. P. C. Hohenberg and B. I. Halperin, "Theory of Dynamic Critical Phenomena," *Rev. Mod. Phys.* **49** (July 1977), pp. 435-479.

Part II

Research in Materials

Overview –

Research in Materials

A good case can be made for the proposition that the progress of civilization is paced by the ability to master the limitations of the materials at hand. Relics from the Stone Age show that our primitive ancestors learned to make simple tools a million years ago. The ability to choose and manipulate the right kinds of stone must have been essential to our evolutionary survival. The stone knife and the stone-tipped arrow are, however, only products of human fabrication, not of discovery and modification. For that matter, the earliest uses of metals occurred with gold and silver, which are found in the pure state. Here, too, the objects formed from them require no intervention of the technologies that we associate with "materials," such as smelting, distillation, and synthesis.

The development of ceramics in early civilizations in the Middle East by 9000 B.C. constituted the earliest modification of the properties and the very nature of materials. The discovery of transparent glass made from sand and ash probably occurred around 4000 B.C. The extraction of workable metals from their ores was a major achievement. Probably the first metal to be liberated was lead, since the temperatures required to reduce common lead ores such as galena are easily obtained from wood fires. Indeed, it seems likely that the earliest discoveries of lead resulted from the accidental smelting of its ores at the earth's surface from the action of bonfires. Though copper sometimes occurs in its native state, its recovery from the common ores requires a higher technology than the recovery of lead, and the smelting of iron is a sophisticated technology that demands temperatures much higher than those of simple wood fires. Thus, the development of the ability to smelt metals was a major force that transformed the arts of peace and war.

An important consequence of early smelting was the discovery of alloys, beginning in the Mediterranean area in the fourth millenium B.C. The Bronze Age is named for the materials that made its civilization: The world changed when people learned to toughen soft copper by mixing tin or arsenic with it. The evolution of the metallurgy of iron around 2000 B.C. started the period that we now call the Iron

Age, a time of rapid development not only of the winning of iron, but also of a host of processes to fabricate steels. These metals and alloys from ancient times have in common that they can be derived from the reduction of minerals by carbon fires. A modern era of metals has emerged with the mastery of metals that cannot be reduced by carbon, notably aluminum, or that pose special problems of purity, such as titanium.

Synthetic organic materials—substances containing carbon compounds—began to enter the industrial scene in the first quarter of the 19th century. Prior to that time organic materials came from nature. Wood, cotton, silk, rubber, and tar were all used in the early telephone industry. The advent of the synthetic organic chemical industry, opened by the discoveries of man-made dyes and rayon textiles, led eventually to the massive manufacturing of polymers derived from petroleum and natural gas.

Future historians and archeologists may well talk about the Plastics Age or the Silicon Age. Certainly we know that progress in modern materials has had a profound impact on civilization in our lifetimes. Without question, the discoveries and developments in materials science in the past few decades surpass those of all previous civilizations.

The time span of the Bell System has seen a prodigious growth in the science and engineering of materials for communication. The earliest materials technology for telephony was borrowed directly from telegraphy, itself a new technology not many years before the invention of the telephone. The study of wood as the material for telephone poles took on a scientific character as the demands of the telephone plant increased. Methods for the preservation of wood outdoors became an early task for Bell Laboratories. This work was important not only to the telephone business, but also to the electric power industry, which followed the discoveries of Bell Laboratories with keen interest. Early work on copper wire for telephone transmission (discussed in Chapter 4 of the first volume in this series, *The Early Years*) also had wide impact on the power business. Materials research and development intended explicitly for telephony began, of course, with Alexander Graham Bell's empirical search for compositions with which to make his first working instrument, for example, his choice of "acidulated water."

The need for direct concern over materials goes far back in the telephone business. A chemical laboratory existed in the American Bell Telephone Company in 1895. It consisted of two employees, who probably were charged with analytical testing of materials. That activity continued and grew with the evolution of the American Telephone and Telegraph Company and the Western Electric Company. When in 1925 the engineering department of Western Electric became the Bell Telephone Laboratories, the staff in materials-related sciences numbered about fifty and comprised the chemical laboratory. These people, mostly chemists, metallurgists, and chemical engineers, were partly involved in testing materials of commerce for applicability in communications. However, they also explored new compositions of matter with the aim of finding improved alloys, ceramics, and electrical insulation.

R. R. Williams, the first chemical director, did much to organize the early growth of chemical and metallurgical technology at Bell Laboratories, and to guide the evolution of this activity from primarily a service organization into a research enterprise with long-range views of science. In order to bring about these ends, he enlisted the collaboration of some members of the science faculties of Yale University and Princeton University as advisors. Although the term "materials science" did not come into the technical language until the 1960s, the early work of Bell Laboratories emphasized scientific approaches to the evaluation of materials. Recruitment in the 1920s of young scientists and engineers such as R. M. Burns, G. T. Kohman, S. O. Morgan, J. H. Scaff, and E. E. Schumacher helped to set the pace of rapidly growing research activity in materials science. The search for materials having long, trouble-free life, studies of the effect of small amounts of impurities on the functioning of materials, and the development of standards and test methods by which to evaluate performance marked the early activities of a materials science department. With these beginnings, there developed a philosophy of coordinate responsibility with the apparatus departments for investigating and selecting materials used in telephone equipment.

Materials research, as an organized endeavor, calls upon the classic disciplines of chemistry, metallurgy, and physics. While metallurgy is commonly recognized as having to do with materials, all three are essential to what we now call materials research. Today materials research has an identity of its own in academic curricula. It has also achieved wide recognition as an interdisciplinary undertaking. Bell Laboratories was the first institution, industrial or academic, in which this interdisciplinary approach was stimulated, largely by the breadth and complexity of telecommunications. This experience has had wide influence. W. O. Baker, who as Vice President—Research, led much of the materials effort at Bell Laboratories, recognized early the importance of materials research and development to industry and to national security. He was a prime mover for the establishment, in the late 1950s and beyond, of a national program of materials science and development, especially in the federal government.

Materials research occupies, in turn, an important place in advancing the individual disciplines of which it is composed. The art of making sophisticated materials has often come before the basic understanding. For instance, the qualities of toughness and ductility in alloys were well under the control of fabricators many centuries before the concepts of defects, composition, and crystal structure became recognized. Much of the accomplishment in solid state physics has indeed depended upon the controlled manipulation of materials.

The following chapters tell some highlights of this important segment of Bell Laboratories' history: the challenge of problems related to materials, the remarkable achievements that have made possible subsequent triumphs in apparatus and equipment, and the resulting systems that depend jointly on hardware and software.

The initial chapter in this sequence is about Semiconductors, for no important class of modern materials is more closely associated with the achievements of Bell Laboratories. The field of semiconductors was an initiative for research at Bell Laboratories, and in so being was a natural home for an emerging population of solid state scientists. Not at all by chance, an important subset of talent arose in the persons of scientists who excelled in growing new and strange crystals.

The most important semiconductor is, of course, silicon, one of the most thoroughly understood elements, with germanium playing a closely parallel role, particularly in the invention of the transistor and in the advancement in the science of semiconductivity. The invention and perfection of the technique of zone refining, giving rise to semiconductor materials of unprecedented purity, not only accelerated the transistor technology but also provided a strong stimulus to the advancement of solid state science. The work in the III-V semiconductors was crucial to the invention of the light emitting diodes (LED) and the heterostructure lasers for optical communications.

The advances in metallic magnetic materials described in Chapter 12, following closely the advances in the physics of magnetic domains, as described in Chapter 1, have produced materials of unusually high permeability and low coercive force for electronic transformers and other applications, as well as the chromindur alloys and the unique cobalt/rare-earth alloys for permanent magnet application. The desirable high-resistivity magnetic oxides, such as the ferrites, were exploited for high-frequency device applications. The discovery of the magnetic garnets by Bell Labs scientists, and independently by the French at Grenoble, provided a strong stimulus for inventing materials particularly suited for memory devices.

Bell Laboratories' early and continued research activities in glasses—for vacuum tubes, capacitor dielectrics, acoustic delay lines, encapsulation of silicon diodes and transistors, as well as ceramic substrates—provided the Bell System with a reservoir of talent needed to make fundamental contributions to the evolution of glass fibers for optical communication. With the invention and perfection of the MCVD process, Bell Labs scientists have produced glass fibers with unprecedented low loss and high information-carrying capacity. This achievement was accompanied by the development of techniques for fiber drawing and coating, and thus for the production of glass fibers for optical waveguides with excellent tensile strength properties.

Polymers have always been used in telephony for electrical insulation. Stimulated by the requirement for long life, particularly in the insulation of undersea cables, Bell Labs scientists made fundamental contributions to the understanding of polymer-structure chain dynamics. They introduced the newly developed physics techniques of nuclear magnetic resonance and studied crystalline morphology in polymers. The advances in the understanding of polymer behavior gained thereby, coupled with the development of effective antioxidants techniques, served to establish the polymer polyethylene as a reliable insulator, even for the exacting requirements of ocean cables.

Research on superconducting materials at Bell Laboratories, described in Chapter 15, paralleled closely the fundamental microscopic research in physics, as discussed in Chapter 9, section I. The discovery of a large number of superconducting alloys and compounds and the advances in increasing transition temperatures, T_c, up to 23K, served to provide challenges to those concerned with the theory of superconductivity. The discovery that some superconducting materials, such as Nb_3Sn, can carry high electric currents and yet remain superconducting at high magnetic fields, brought about a marked increase in the application of superconducting materials as magnets for high-energy accelerators, for plasma-fusion research, and for NMR imaging of human organs.

The research dielectrics, described in Chapter 16, covers a broad range of materials from amorphous rubber and ceramics to the crystalline piezoelectric, ferroelectric, and nonlinear optical materials. A study of the rate of chemical combination of the ingredients of rubber, coupled with reproducible tests of viscosity and gel control, resulted in the early manufacture of rubber having desirable insulating and elastic properties. Similar attention to composition and processing led to the fabrication of ceramic materials possessing superior electrical insulating properties at the higher communications frequencies. Fundamental studies were carried out in the dielectric behavior of polar molecules in gases, liquids, and solids, including theoretical studies of liquid water.

In crystalline dielectrics, the phenomenon of piezoelectricity was studied in quartz, ethylene diamine tartrate (EDT), and ammonium dihydrogen phosphate (ADP), leading to the production of high-quality synthetic quartz crystals and to the design of many underwater sound devices. The studies of ferroelectric materials, as in the case of superconductors, paralleled closely the research in physics, as discussed in Chapter 9, section II. These were motivated by the potential application of ferroelectrics, having electrically reversible dipole moments, to memory devices. The discovery of a number of new ferroelectric materials served to demonstrate that ferroelectricity is not a rare phenomena in dielectric crystals that lack a center of symmetry. In the nonlinear optical crystals, the interest of Bell Labs scientists centered on laser crystals that can be optically pumped to emit coherent radiation of optical frequencies, on crystals that can be used for modulating carrier frequencies or can generate second harmonic frequencies, and on crystals of magnetic materials for new memory devices. These studies also paralleled the laser physics research, as discussed in Chapter 5, section VII.

The research activities described in Chapter 17 deal with conduction of electricity as encountered in storage batteries, relay and connector contacts, activation in carbon microphones, and emission from cathodes in electronic vacuum tubes. The studies of corrosion observed when silver is in contact with an insulating material, resulting in the production of metallic single-crystal whiskers, led to devising ways of inhibiting such growth, for example, by the use of a tin-clad solder finish. Similarly, stress-corrosion cracking caused by moisture or by nitrates has been eliminated by devising appropriate surface finishes. Studies of the chemistry of gold plating have led to the development of proper plating processes for obtaining wear-resistant electrical finishes. Advances in the understanding of the chemistry of gold plating have also helped in finding an appropriate gold-alloy overlay in palladium to produce excellent contact material for relays. Research on the chemistry of the conventional lead-acid battery have led to the introduction of a small amount of impurity in the lead (for example, 0.1 percent calcium) to optimize the electro-chemical behavior of batteries as used in the telephone plant. Despite the absence of a definitive theory of the process of electron emission from the nickel cathode, coated with a mixture of alkaline-earth oxides, as used in vacuum tubes, great improvements in the performance of these cathodes have been achieved by the control of the impurities in the nickel and the chemistry of the oxide reduction process.

Research activities leading to improvements in the mechanical properties of materials are discussed in Chapter 18. Studies of deformation texture in copper alloys, used in electronic equipment and electromechanical devices, have led to devising processes for strengthening these alloys. These included cold rolling and heat treatment at temperatures just below that were crystallization sets in. It was shown that the control of the small calcium impurity in lead-calcium alloys used in cable sheathing could more than double the strength of such sheaths. In polymer materials, the effect of the molecular weight distribution of polyethylene on sheath cracking was demonstrated, and that crosslinking by irradiation with high-energy electrons could greatly toughen the polymer coating used in wire insulation.

The research contributions to the broad range of processing techniques, except for the preparation of very low-loss optical fibers discussed in Chapter 13, are described in Chapter 19. These include contributions to crystal growth, zone refining, molecular beam epitaxy, ion implantation, masking, and fine-line lithography. Included also are theoretical contributions to crystal growth and imperfections. In crystal growth techniques, the contributions date back to the hydrothermal methods of growing single crystals, including the development of growth processes for large, optical quality synthetic quartz crystals, followed by the growth of magnetic garnet crystals for memory devices. In the growth of single crystals from the melt, outstanding contributions were to the growth of silicon, germanium, and III-V semiconductors, as well as to a variety of fluoride crystals used in physical research. The invention of zone refining complemented the techniques for obtaining single crystals of specified extremely low impurities. Contributions to the methods of introducing impurities include ion implantation, masking, and electron-beam and X-ray resist processes. The theoretical contributions to crystal growth and imperfections include effects of dislocations and vacancies on the molecular, microscopic, and macroscopic aspects of crystals. For the very thin layers of single crystal growth, the invention of the molecular beam epitaxial method stands out.

Important techniques for characterizing materials are discussed in Chapter 20. Bell Laboratories has long been a leader in this field. Special emphasis has been given to extreme precision and lowest levels of detectability.

The intervention of lasers, synchrotron storage rings, neutron sources, and plasmas has made possible a wide range of new understanding of atomic and molecular properties. Above all, the power of the modern computer has been enlisted to calculate the forces of chemical bonding, the dynamics of atoms and molecules in gases and at surfaces, the energy-band structures of solids, and the viscoelastic behavior of polymers.

A forecast of the future directions of materials science is intriguing but is probably a futile exercise. To be convinced of this point, one needs only to place oneself at the start of any decade in the history of Bell Laboratories and imagine what forecasts would have seemed plausible then. Some exciting developments are coming on the scene, and they tempt us to make some guesses. For example, nonequilibrium forms of matter are being discovered in large variety. New compositions are made in which alternate layers are constructed of different metals only a few nanometers thick. The properties of such special "alloys" have only begun to be explored. Whereas we have found fascination in the explicit characteristics of single crystals, an infinitude of structures and properties is possible in *amorphous* solids. A vast array of technologically important materials will surely emerge as fundamental understanding grows. History tells us that much, but little more.

W. P. Slichter
Executive Director—Research,
Materials Science,
and Engineering Division
Bell Laboratories
November, 1981

Chapter 11

Semiconductors — Silicon, Germanium, and III-V Compounds

Until the 1930s, the basic materials used to send electrical signals were metallic conductors and insulators. These broad categories of substances, together with the constituents of cathodes in vacuum tubes, accounted for most of the materials inventory of the telephone pathway. Certain specialized functions of current rectification and temperature-dependent resistance were performed by devices made of special materials such as transition metal oxides, silicon carbide, silicon, and germanium. As these materials became better characterized, it became clear that they and other substances exhibit electrical conductivity intermediate between that of metals and insulators. These materials came to be known as semiconductors. A theoretical basis for their behavior emerged through concepts of valence and conduction bands (see Chapter 2).

The culminating discovery of the transistor effect in 1947 brought into focus the importance of the basic properties of semiconductors as a class of materials. It also underscored the great importance of controlling the impurity content and crystalline perfection of the materials more generally. Related research activities on semiconductors are discussed in Chapter 2, Chapter 19, and section III of Chapter 5.

I. COMPOUND SEMICONDUCTORS FOR THERMISTORS AND VARISTORS

A major need of the Bell System has been the ability to transform, amplify, and modulate electrical signals. Until about 1930 the electrical materials generally used were metallic conductors and insulators.

Principal authors: J. K. Galt, W. G. Pfann, J. H. Scaff, R. W. Sears, C. D. Thurmond, J. H. Wernick, and A. H. White

Then semiconductors having electrical conductivity intermediate to that of metals and insulators emerged. *Thermistors* exhibited large variations of resistivity with temperature, and *varistors* showed non-ohmic variation of resistance with voltage.

1.1 Thermistors

A thermistor, or thermal resistor, is a circuit element with an electrical resistivity that varies sharply with changes in temperature.

1.1.1 Negative Temperature-Coefficient Thermistors

In the mid-1930s, O. E. Buckley (later to become president of Bell Laboratories) pointed to the need for a negative temperature-coefficient (NTC) thermistor that could be used in the underground transcontinental cable as a temperature compensator for the positive-coefficient metallic components. As a result, a variety of materials, in addition to those known to have NTC characteristics, were studied by G. L. Pearson, J. A. Becker, and C. B. Green.[1] The studies led to the development of a mixed oxide of nickel and manganese (20 percent nickel, 80 percent manganese), which became known as thermistor composition number 1, manufactured by Western Electric. It was used for the measurement of microwave power and also by the United States military as an infrared detector in World War II. It was later found that the addition of cobalt oxide to the NiO-Mn_2O_3 mixture further lowered the room-temperature resistance of the thermistor. Western Electric adopted the 52Mn-16Ni-32Co material as composition number 2. Composition numbers 1 and 2 still formed the bulk of Western Electric thermistor production in the 1970s. Thermistors have found a wide variety of practical applications in such functions as voltage regulation in power supplies, speech volume limitation, temperature compensation, and frequency control of oscillators used for signaling in *Touch-Tone** telephone station sets.

1.1.2 Positive Temperature-Coefficient Thermistors

In the late 1950s, ceramists became aware of the importance of grain-boundary chemistry in defining the properties of electronic ceramics. H. A. Sauer and S. S. Flaschen reported that when barium titanate ceramics are heated in an oxidizing atmosphere, oxygen is trapped along the grain boundaries, producing an insulating layer and

---

* Trademark of AT&T Co.

thereby a positive temperature-coefficient-of-resistance (PTC) thermistor.[2] When the thermistor is heated above the Curie temperature of $BaTiO_3$, which is adjustable from 50°C to 200°C through composition control, the resistivity increases by a factor of 10^4 to 10^7. On cooling, the resistivity drops again; thus the thermistor can act as a resettable fuse. Sauer and coworkers showed the importance of the gaseous ambient in the heat treatment and the metallization method on the properties of the thermistor.[3]

1.2 Varistors

Varistors are non-ohmic circuit elements with electrical resistivity that varies with the applied voltage. Two classes are described below: first, the cuprous oxide varistor, with resistance variation asymmetrical with respect to zero voltage—that is, the circuit element has rectifying properties—and second, the silicon carbide varistor, which is symmetrical with respect to $V = 0$ and used for protection from very high voltage surges.

1.2.1 The Cuprous Oxide Varistor

The cuprous oxide rectifier was described by L. O. Grondahl and P. H. Geiger in 1927.[4] Before 1950, the Cu_2O semiconductor was subject to intensive studies at Bell Laboratories. By simply heating a copper disc to 1000°C in air to form a layer of Cu_2O of about 0.01 centimeter (cm), it is possible to produce a rectifier whose forward and reverse currents at 1.0 volt differ by a factor of nearly 4000. W. H. Brattain and others showed that the current in Cu_2O is transported by positive holes excited from acceptor centers, which probably consist of vacant copper-ion lattice sites. The highly nonlinear electrical characteristic of the copper-oxide varistor made it particularly suitable for the function of modulator (or de-modulator) in telephone carrier systems. It was cheaper and more reliable than the electron tube, which it replaced. Its nonlinear current-voltage curve also found extensive application as a click reducer on telephone lines.

1.2.2 The Silicon Carbide Varistor

In the early 1930s, R. O. Grisdale introduced silicon carbide varistors as voltage limiters (shunts) to protect telephone lines from lightning strikes.[5] The silicon carbide varistor may be described as a symmetrical variable resistor, since it does not obey Ohm's law and its current-voltage (I-V) characteristics are the same for both directions of current. [Fig. 11-1]

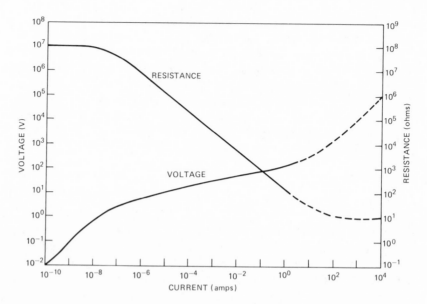

Fig. 11-1. Typical characteristics of a silicon carbon varistor, relating voltage and resistance to current.

In 1947, when the 500-type telephone set was being developed to replace the 300-type, lower-impedance varistors were needed as loop equalizers to compensate for differences in transmission and reception levels caused by different lengths of line. C. J. Frosch, H. F. Dienel, and their colleagues developed silicon carbide varistors composed of clay, carbon, and silicon carbide that exhibited lower impedance and current levels than had previously been attained.[6] For satisfactory, reproducible results, great care had to be taken in ceramic processing, especially with respect to particle size distribution, purity level, amount of clay and graphite, and sufficient water content in the mix for workable consistency. By attenuating the signal in short loops (near central offices), the silicon carbide varistor allowed longer loops than previously used.

II. SILICON AND GERMANIUM IN POINT-CONTACT RECTIFIERS

In the late 1930s, a radio research group led by H. T. Friis began to explore the potential of microwave communications. These high frequencies required a signal detector of very low shunt capacitance. R. S. Ohl, an electrical engineer, instinctively turned to the materials in vogue in the early days of radio, such as native lead sulfide (galena). Metallurgists at Bell Laboratories had been studying the preparation and properties of elemental silicon, one of the earth's most abundant elements which, however, occurs in nature only in chemical compounds. This research showed that polycrystalline silicon works well in point-contact detection of high frequency radio, although neither the electrical engineers nor the metallurgists understood the electrical phenomena.

In the early 1940s, wartime needs for point-contact rectifiers in microwave radar receivers became crucial, and extensive joint efforts with government and universities were undertaken. The limitations in the performance of these detectors were rightly ascribed to the variability in the properties of the materials. At Bell Labs a group of metallurgists under E. E. Schumacher (later to become metallurgical director) studied the preparation and properties of silicon. This work on materials contributed greatly to the development of the 1N21 series of point-contact rectifiers. Exciting advances in the undertaking of silicon and p-n junctions were also made. Following up on some earlier research on germanium by scientists at Purdue University, the Bell Labs metallurgists developed high-quality germanium ingots from which point-contact rectifiers were made.

2.1 Silicon Rectifiers

In the search for materials to meet the needs of microwave communications, much pioneering work was done on the metallurgy of silicon. The reactivity of this element in its molten state with container materials greatly complicated the preparation of ingots, which were indeed crude even by the earliest standards of single-crystal silicon in the 1950s.

A standardized design or "cartridge unit," coded 1N21, was adopted in 1941. It consisted of a ceramic sleeve that was threaded on the inside. A metal base fitting containing a wafer of silicon was screwed into one end of the sleeve; a tungsten wire spring assembly was screwed into the opposite end. The cartridge unit was first developed by Bell Labs for manufacture by Western Electric. [Fig. 11-2]

By 1945, a family of cartridge units tailored for use at the frequency bands of 1, 3, or 10 GHz had been developed at Bell Labs. A notable feature of this effort was the invention of a method of pointing the contact wires electrolytically, thereby eliminating a troublesome grinding procedure.[7] Another notable feature was that these units were tapped with tiny hammers to improve the stability and rectification ratio of the current-voltage characteristic, an empirical operation never well understood.

For the 24-GHz radar frequency (K Band), W. G. Pfann, following a prototype design of Ohl and G. Mueller, developed a shielded unit, the 1N26, having lower shunt capacitance and lower series inductance than the cartridge units. This was achieved by force fitting a silicon wafer assembly into one end of a metal sleeve and a contact spring assembly into the other end. The spring assembly contained an electropointed 0.005 cm tungsten wire that was spot welded to an axial pin molded in a hard plastic sleeve. A detailed account of the development of silicon point-contact rectifiers is given in a paper by J. H. Scaff and Ohl.[8]

2.2 Germanium Rectifiers

The Bell Labs metallurgical group led by Schumacher and Scaff also developed a germanium point-contact rectifier with a structure similar to the silicon cartridge unit, and limited numbers were manufactured

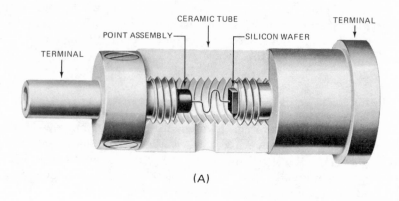

(A)

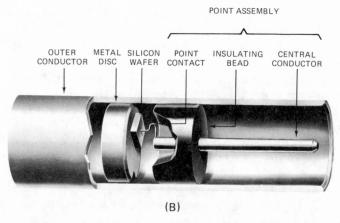

(B)

Fig. 11-2. (A) Drawing of IN2l, or cartridge, point-contact rectifier. The contact spring is a pointed, 0.012-inch-diameter tungsten wire bent into an "S" shape. (B) Drawing of IN26, or shielded coaxial, point-contact rectifier.

by Western Electric. These rectifiers had better rectifying properties than silicon units, partly because of improved electrical forming techniques, and were used in some radar receivers. More importantly, the same procedures that were developed by H. C. Theuerer for purifying germanium tetrachloride and preparing germanium ingots for the rectifiers were also used for preparing germanium for the first transistors.

III. SILICON AND GERMANIUM STUDIES BEFORE 1948

In 1945, a large fund of practical knowledge about silicon and germanium existed at Bell Labs, and a rich stockpile of ingots of these semiconductors became available for physics research initiated by J. Bardeen, Brattain, Pearson, W. Shockley, and others. The discovery of the transistor effect by Bardeen and Brattain in 1947 led to a marked increase in the materials research efforts on silicon and germanium.

3.1 Silicon Ingots with p- and n-Type Conductivity

In addition to work on silicon for point-contact rectifier applications, studies were conducted on the properties of silicon as a semiconductor. Although the first silicon ingots prepared by Scaff and Theuerer were polycrystalline and relatively impure, they revealed fundamental knowledge about semiconductors.

For their first experiment, Ohl and Scaff melted about 45 grams of the purest silicon commercially available (99.8 percent purity) under helium in a crucible of fused silica of roughly hemispherical shape. The molten silicon was frozen in place by slowly reducing the furnace power, so that the melt froze from the top downward and from the crucible walls radially inward.[9]

By examining a vertical cross section, Ohl showed that the polarity of point-contact rectification reversed as the distance to the center of the ingot decreased. The study also showed that a rectifying barrier which, upon illumination, produced a photovoltage existed between the two regions. Scaff and Ohl named the outer region "p-type" and the inner region "n-type," a most fortunate choice. [Fig. 11-3]

These p-n junctions aroused intense interest at Bell Labs. Pfann and Scaff [Fig. 11-4] applied microscopy and special etching techniques, and identified the p-n junction as a striated boundary separating the *p* and *n* regions of the ingot.[10] Further experiments by Theuerer showed the formation of the p-n junction to be a result of the normal segregation of unknown impurities during the freezing process.

These early ingots were badly cracked because they expanded when frozen and the silicon adhered to the crucible. The problem was

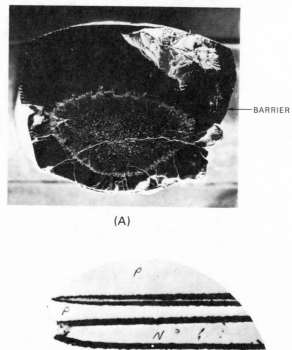

(A)

(B)

Fig. 11-3. (A) Early silicon ingot etched to show the photovoltaic p-n barrier, which separates the outer, p-type region from the inner, n-type region. (B) Photomicrograph of p-n barrier in early silicon ingot. The repetitions of p- and n- regions were caused by fluctuations in the growth rate of the solidifying melt.

solved by Theuerer by using a very thin-walled cylindrical crucible that was about 10 centimeters long. A 320-gram ingot was frozen directionally from the top downward by slowly raising the crucible from the furnace. Cracking caused by adhesion was avoided because the crucible was made so thin, by etching in hydrofluoric acid, that it was barely strong enough to hold the silicon granules. When contraction began, the crucible cracked, not the silicon. Such ingots provided p-type silicon for the 1N21 series of point-contact rectifiers.

Theuerer discovered that adding small amounts of boron (0.001 to 0.01 percent) increased the p-type conductivity of these ingots, and that as the boron content increased, the p-n junction moved closer to the bottom of the ingot. He suspected that phosphorus was somehow involved, for he had smelled traces of phosphine at times during ingot preparation. He concluded that phosphorus opposed boron and produced n-type conductivity, and further, that the p-n junction occurred because phosphorus segregated more readily than boron, so that its concentration overtook that of boron in the part of the ingot that froze last.

Using these concepts, Theuerer produced p-type ingots of highly uniform electrical conductivity (a desideratum for production) by

Fig. 11-4. W. G. Pfann, inventor of zone refining, shows the first zone-refined single crystal of germanium to J. H. Scaff, who pioneered in the growth of germanium and silicon ingots of either p-type or n-type conductivity.

adding boron and lesser amounts of phosphorus. Even though the phosphorus segregated faster, its concentration remained lower than that of boron, and a constant *difference* concentration was maintained.

From Theuerer's work emerged the basic generalization that elements of Group III (for example, boron or aluminum) produce p-type conduction in silicon, that elements of Group V (phosphorus, antimony, arsenic) produce n-type conductivity, and that these two kinds of impurity (acceptor and donor, respectively) compensate, atom for atom, so that the resultant conductivity is proportional to the difference in atomic concentrations. This remarkable piece of scientific detective work was accomplished without the help of chemical analysis, as the concentrations were too low for the analytical techniques then available.

This work, which is summarized in the classic paper of Scaff, Theuerer, and Schumacher was completed by 1945, but publication of it was delayed until 1949 because of military security restrictions.[11]

3.2 Germanium Ingots

Germanium ingots were prepared by Theuerer in a cylindrical graphite crucible by hydrogen reduction of very pure GeO_2.[12] In the same operation, the germanium was melted and frozen in the crucible from the bottom upward. The ingots thus obtained were polycrystalline, but with rather large grain size. They were usually n-type, with the conductivity increasing toward the top of the crucible. This was the material in which the transistor effect was discovered by Bardeen and Brattain.

IV. THE POINT-CONTACT TRANSISTOR

Soon after the discovery of the point-contact transistor, Pfann modified the structure of the 1N26 shielded point-contact rectifier to produce a plug-in point-contact transistor. The axial nickel pin was replaced by two parallel pins, with an offset C-spring welded to each pin. The germanium was n-type. [Fig. 11-5] A special method of electrical forming was developed, involving both the emitter and collector.[13] A phosphor bronze wire was used for the collector contact spring, and it was found later that the critical substance in the spring was the donor element phosphorus, which made possible the attainment of a current multiplication factor, α, much greater than the theoretical value of unity. This transistor was the prototype of the Type A transistor, which was manufactured by Western Electric for about ten years.

To improve the mechanical stability and electrical performance of the Type A transistor, which depended on mechanical spring pres-

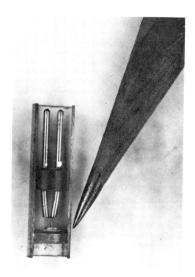

Fig. 11-5. A point-contact transistor with the outer sleeve cut away to reveal the interior. The two contact springs are composed of electro-pointed tungsten and phosphor bronze wire. The semiconductor crystal is n-type germanium.

sure, Pfann and coworkers developed a technique of alloying the contact springs to the germanium by passing a pulse of current through the original point contact. This technique also yielded better rectifying properties. Electrode materials that alloyed with germanium at low temperatures (for example, gold and aluminum) were used. Adding a small amount of antimony to the gold collector alloy had the same effect on α as using phosphor bronze.[14,15]

Although this improved transistor did not replace the Type A transistor because of the invention of the junction transistor, the alloying technique, using a gold-gallium alloy, was retained to make contact to the thin p-type base layer of the n-p-n transistor.

The alloying technique was also used by Pearson and P. W. Foy to fabricate a silicon diode rectifier.[16] The p-n junction, formed between the aluminum-doped p-type regrowth layer and the underlying n-silicon, had a reverse current of only 3×10^{-10} amp, and could be operated at 300°C. These devices became widely used commercially.

V. SILICON AND GERMANIUM STUDIES AFTER THE INVENTION OF THE TRANSISTOR

Demonstration of the transistor effect immediately created a demand for single crystals, higher purity, and greater uniformity of resistivity. The first efforts were directed toward germanium, because it was the semiconductor that showed the effect. Later, similar efforts were directed successfully toward silicon.

5.1 Germanium and Silicon Single Crystals for Junction Transistors, Grown by Crystal Pulling

A single-crystal growth technique, first used by J. Czochralski in 1917,[17] was adapted and improved in 1950 by G. K. Teal and J. B. Little for the growth of single crystals of germanium.[18] A seed crystal was lowered into a melt of germanium and then withdrawn slowly, usually with rotation, to produce crystals 8 centimeters long and 2.5 centimeters in diameter. The minority carrier lifetime, τ, in the germanium crystals grown in this way was strikingly greater than for polycrystalline germanium. The technique, which became known as crystal pulling or the Czochralski method, was widely applied and later extended to grow silicon crystals. By 1980, silicon crystals of a meter in length and over 10 centimeters in diameter were manufactured routinely.

In 1950, an important advantage of crystal pulling was that n-p-n junctions could be built into the growing crystal of germanium by perturbing the growth conditions. With the "double-doping" technique, pellets of gallium and antimony alloys of the semiconductor were added in quick succession to the melt of a growing n-type crystal to form an n-p-n transistor, as described in 1951 by Shockley, M. Sparks [Fig. 11-6], and Teal.[19] Although this growth technique was later superseded, this event was an important milestone in transistor science.

With the double-doping technique just described, only one n-p-n junction configuration could be grown in a Czochralski-type crystal. In 1953, R. N. Hall of the General Electric Company described a technique known as rate-growing with meltback, by which a series of n-p-n junctions could be grown into a germanium crystal.[20] By cycling the crystal pulling rate from fast to slow, the concentrations of gallium and antimony in the growing crystal were made to vary in such a way that a series of n-p-n junction configurations were formed. This technique was studied extensively at Bell Labs by H. E. Bridgers for germanium,[21] and by M. Tanenbaum and coworkers for silicon.[22]

These two methods were extremely important to the advance of the science of transistors, but they presented inherent problems for manufacture. The junctions were inside a crystal, usually curved in shape, and had to be sawed out of the crystal. The base (p-type) layer thickness was larger and less uniform than desired. The solution to these problems was later to emerge with the perfection of solid state diffusion techniques. (This topic is discussed in section 5.5.)

Fig. 11-6. M. Sparks fabricated the first junction transistor.

5.2 Zone Refining and Zone Leveling of Germanium

In 1951, Pfann invented a simple technique for ultrapurifying germanium that became known as zone refining.[23] It is described in some detail in section 2.1 of Chapter 19 in this volume. A 500-gram ingot of germanium was passed through six induction heating coils in a horizontal open boat of very pure graphite, with the result that over 80 percent of the ingot exhibited the intrinsic room-temperature resistivity of a very pure semiconductor. [Fig. 11-7] Low-temperature measurements by G. C. Dacey indicated an excess donor concentration less than 5×10^{12} atoms per cubic centimeter (cm^3), that is, less than one donor atom per 10^{10} atoms of germanium.

Another zone melting method invented by Pfann is zone leveling (also discussed in Chapter 19). Its object is to *add* a desired impurity uniformly along a single crystal. An oriented seed crystal is placed at one end of a horizontal carbon-coated boat of fused silica, abutting a pure (zone refined) germanium charge. A tiny pellet of antimony-germanium alloy is placed at the starting position of the zone. A molten zone is formed, melting a small part of the seed crystal, and the zone is passed along the charge. Using this technique, Pfann and K.

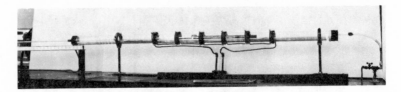

Fig. 11-7. Original zone refiner used to ultrapurify germanium. Each induction coil forms a molten zone that travels along the 1-1b ingot, thereby removing impurities from most of the ingot and concentrating them at the end.

M. Olsen[24] demonstrated that over 80 percent of the zone leveled crystal had a uniform concentration of 10^{15} antimony atoms per cm^3, as compared with a concentration varying from 10^{15} to 10^{16} antimony atoms per cm^3 in crystals grown by normal freezing (as in the Czochralski technique). The zone leveling method has been widely used in the manufacture of transistors and diodes.

5.3 Kinetics of Impurity Distribution During Crystal Growth

In a detailed experimental investigation coupled with a theoretical analysis, J. A. Burton, R. C. Prim, W. P. Slichter, and their colleagues studied the thermodynamic and kinetic aspects of the incorporation of impurities during growth of germanium crystals by the Teal-Little method.[25,26] They derived an equation relating the distribution coefficient of the solute to the freezing rate, the diffusivity of the impurity, and the thickness of the diffusion boundary layer at the growth interface. [Fig. 11-8] They found, among other effects, that variations in growth rate and stirring can change the impurity concentration by a factor of ten or more. Years later, L. O. Wilson made extensive computer calculations of the fluid flow during Czochralski growth.[27] Her results verified the Burton-Prim-Slichter analysis. She also calculated the solute distribution resulting from fluctuating growth rate, including cases where fluctuation amplitude is large enough to produce meltback. The Burton-Prim-Slichter equation has been widely used in research on crystal growth.

When a semiconductor crystal is grown, microscale fluctuations in growth rate cause microscale fluctuations in the concentration of a donor or acceptor and hence in electrical conductivity. Pfann and coworkers conceived a method of eliminating such conductivity fluctuations,[28] and with the help of L. P. Adda demonstrated it for a zone-leveled germanium crystal containing the acceptor indium as the major solute. The method is to have a small concentration of an opposite-type solute, in this case antimony, in the melt. The ratio of melt concentrations of major to minor solutes is made equal to the inverse ratio of the growth rate coefficients of the solutes. If this is done, the difference concentration in the solid and hence the electrical conductivity remains constant. For germanium with an indium-to-antimony ratio of 7 to 1, microscale fluctuations in conductivity were too small to measure. Furthermore, a deliberate, large change in growth rate changed the conductivity by less than 10 percent of that for indium alone. This microscale technique is analogous to the macroscale technique used by Theuerer to grow uniform ingots of p-type silicon (see section 3.1 of this chapter).

5.4 Silicon Single Crystals Grown by the Floating Zone Technique

Although silicon crystals were grown by crystal pulling by Teal and E. Buehler, contamination (mainly oxygen) from the fused silica crucible remained a serious drawback.[29] Theuerer invented the floating

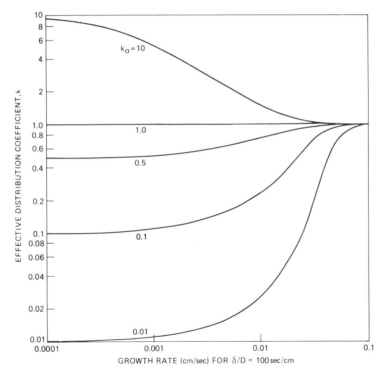

Fig. 11-8. Impurity distribution coefficient, k, as a function of growth rate calculated from the BPS equation for a value of the ratio of diffusion layer thickness, δ, to diffusivity, D, common in growth of germanium single crystals. k_0 is the value of k at zero growth rate. Note that all k's approach unity at large growth rates.

zone method, also called float zoning, and applied it to the growth of silicon single crystals of high quality.[30] Using zone refining and zone leveling, purity levels and uniformity of composition comparable to those obtained in germanium were achieved in silicon. (The floating zone method is discussed in more detail in Chapter 19, section 1.2.1.)

In float zoning, a vertical rod of silicon is clamped at both ends and a short molten zone extending through the cross section is formed. The zone is caused to traverse the rod by moving the rod through the induction heater, usually with rotation. The method is used worldwide, mainly for silicon but also for many other high-melting-point semiconductors, refractory oxides, and refractory metals. [Fig. 11-9]

5.5 Germanium and Silicon Transistors Made by Diffusion

The disadvantages of melt-grown, n-p-n junctions formed in the interior of the germanium crystals were pointed out in section 5.1. For silicon, these disadvantages were compounded by the problem of contamination from the crucible. Faced with the need of finding a solution to these important problems, a research effort was organized in 1953 under the leadership of N. B. Hannay.[31] Tanenbaum and coworkers used the rate-growing technique to make silicon n-p-n junctions and demonstrated that silicon was superior for transistors.[32] But further advances for both silicon and germanium awaited the perfection of solid state diffusion techniques for transistors.

The process of atomic diffusion from an external surface offered the possibility of fabricating thinner base layers and thus increasing the transistor cutoff frequency. This technique had the advantage of operating entirely within a solid phase of initially homogeneous composition, and of being slow enough to permit fine control of dimensions. It was known that diffusion constants differed widely among the electrically active impurities in germanium and silicon. In 1952, C. S. Fuller published a pioneering study of the diffusion of donors and acceptors in germanium, which provided a basis for diffusion technology.[33]

By the mid-1950s, improvements had been made in the cleanliness of heating methods, and the lowering of critical impurities in semiconductors. These advances made possible the fabrication of p-n-p and n-p-n configurations by diffusion. In 1956, the first transistor in germanium made by this method was reported by C. A. Lee.[34] He diffused a 1.5 micrometer (μm) layer of arsenic into p-type germanium, forming the base layer. He then diffused a thinner layer of aluminum to provide an emitter layer about 0.5 μm thick.

Also in 1956, Tanenbaum and D. E. Thomas described the results of their experiments with the diffused emitter and base-silicon transistor.[35] Fuller had shown that acceptors of low atomic weight diffuse much more rapidly than donors,[36] which made possible n-p-n structures by simultaneous diffusion of donors and acceptors of appropriately different surface concentrations. The first n-layer (the emitter) was formed because of the greater surface concentration of the donor (for example, antimony). The base formed beyond it because of the more rapid diffusion of the acceptor (for example, aluminum). The inner (collector) boundary of the base appeared where the diffused aluminum no longer over-compensated the n-type background doping of the original silicon. The base layers of the resulting transistors were 4-μm thick. Although the necessary heat treatments had reduced the recombination lifetime for the minority carriers to a fraction of a microsecond, these carriers could diffuse across this short distance with less than about 3 percent loss by recombination. Because the base layer was so thin, the carriers could reach the collector fast

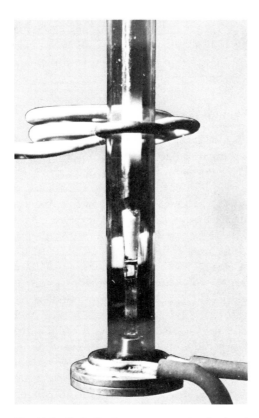

Fig. 11-9. Early floating zone apparatus developed by H. C. Theuerer and used to ultrapurify silicon. The molten zone is held in place by surface tension as it travels along the crystal.

enough to give rise to the observed high-frequency cutoff of 120 megahertz (MHz).

The solid state diffusion techniques released the n-p-n junction from its bondage to the interior of a bulk single crystal. Related techniques such as epitaxy and ion implantation followed, as described in sections 1.3 and 4.2 of Chapter 19. Perhaps most important of all, the diffusion techniques opened a pathway to fabricating solid state devices at the planar surface of a semiconductor. This in turn made possible, with the aid of masking and lithography techniques, the fabrication of thousands of electronic components on a single chip of semiconductor as used in integrated circuits.

VI. THE III-V SEMICONDUCTORS

Another major semiconductor materials effort involved the III-V compounds, especially gallium arsenide (GaAs), gallium aluminum arsenide ($Ga_{1-x}Al_xAs$), indium phosphide (InP), and gallium phosphide (GaP). These materials provide the basis for optoelectronic devices, primarily the heterostructure semiconductor lasers and the light-emitting diodes (LEDs). For more on this topic, see section 5.3 of Chapter 2 in this volume.

6.1 GaAs and InP Studies

In the early 1950s, a group led by J. A. Burton initiated research on III-V compound semiconductors. Indium antimonide single crystals were prepared by Tanenbaum, and their electrical transport properties and optical and magnetic properties were studied by J. P. Maita,[37] H. B. Briggs,[38] and G. L. Pearson.[39] The work was extended by H. J. Hrostowski to other Group III antimonides and to arsenides.[40] The initial studies indicated that the two most promising high band gap materials were GaAs and InP, and it was decided to concentrate on GaAs, primarily because of the high mobility of its conduction electrons and its energy gap, which is somewhat larger than that of silicon. J. M. Whelan applied the floating-zone crystal growth and purification techniques used by Theuerer in silicon to the work on GaAs and produced high-resistivity GaAs for exploratory device work. Doping studies were also carried out to measure the distribution coefficients of various impurities, particularly copper at its melting point in GaAs.[41,42]

In contrast to GaAs, InP exhibits a high dissociation pressure (27.5 atmospheres at its melting point of 1070°C), and this made it necessary to use pressurized vessels when growing crystals by the Czochralski process. By 1980, InP had emerged as the second most important III-V compound, because of its use as a substrate for lattice-matched double heterostructure LEDs, lasers, and detectors for optical communication at 1.3 μm and 1.55 μm. The first long-wavelength (1.3 μm) lightwave communication system to carry live telephone traffic used LEDs and detectors based on the InP/InGaAsP system.

6.2 GaP Studies

C. J. Frosch, M. Gershenzon, and D. F. Gibbs used the horizontal Bridgman method to produce boules of GaP from which large single-crystal regions with relatively homogeneous properties could be cut. Soon thereafter, crystal growth by the floating zone method was achieved by Frosch and L. Derick.[43] In addition, vapor phase growth was explored by Gershenzon and R. M. Mikulyak[44] and by Frosch.[45] Liquid phase epitaxy, described in section 6.3 below, was also adopted and has proved to be the best technique for studying luminescence in GaP and for fabricating the junctions.[46]

Efforts to fabricate LEDs from GaP started before 1962. Unwanted impurities had reduced power efficiency of diodes made in this early period. A major advance vital to the success of red GaP lamps was the discovery by R. A. Logan, H. G. White, and F. A. Trumbore that an annealing treatment increased the luminescent efficiency of p-n junctions in GaP by about a factor of four.[47] In these structures, about 2 percent of the carriers transported through the forward-biased junction recombined at the Zn-O impurity sites and emitted red photons. This 2 percent "quantum efficiency" was a new high, and made such structures attractive for device applications. It was later shown by C. H. Henry that this light was emitted primarily by an isoelectronic trap formed by a zinc atom and an oxygen atom on neighboring sites.[48]

In 1968, the feasibility of fabricating an efficient green LED by doping with nitrogen was demonstrated by Logan, White, and W. Wiegmann.[49] Thus, it was established that the isoelectronic trap provided the basis of LEDs made of GaP that generated either red or green light depending only on impurity content. In addition, it was shown by W. Rosenzweig, Logan, and Wiegmann that doping with a mixture of these defects made it possible to fabricate GaP diodes of variable hues between red and green.[50]

6.3 Liquid Phase Epitaxy for Light Emitting Diodes and Semiconductor Lasers

The research effort on GaAs at Bell Labs increased in the mid-1960s because of its relevance to semiconductor lasers. In 1965, M. B. Panish studied the bulk properties of GaAs grown from solutions of arsenic in gallium by liquid phase epitaxy (LPE). (This technique is described in section 1.3.3 of Chapter 19 in this volume.) Panish, H. J. Queisser, and others studied luminescence in this way and found that LPE is capable of producing very high quality GaAs material for optical devices.[51]

The LPE crystal growth technique was also used by Panish and S. Sumski to conduct studies that delineated the equilibrium chemical phase diagram of the Ga-Al-As system.[52] The information developed in these studies was the basis for the technique devised for fabricating some of the first heterostructure lasers.[53] In the early 1970s, work on the Ga-Al-As-P quaternary system made possible the fabrication of such lasers with phosphorus in the host lattice, a step that permitted precise tailoring of the lattice match in heterostructures for improvement in device life.[54]

6.4 Molecular Beam Epitaxy for Layers of III-V Compounds

At the time of this writing, the most recent contribution of Bell Labs scientists to the materials science of the III-V semiconductors is the invention by J. R. Arthur, and subsequent development by A. Y. Cho, of a novel method of crystal growth called molecular beam epitaxy (MBE).[55] This method, which is described in some detail in Section 1.3.4 of Chapter 19 in this volume, consists of growing a crystal layer by impinging beams of relevant molecular species from effusion ovens onto a substrate in what is otherwise a high vacuum. This method makes possible a new order of control of layer dimensions and doping profiles. A. C. Gossard and coworkers have demonstrated that it also enables the fabrication of structures with a very large number of thin layers (monolayer structures) and hence crystals with periodicities that do not occur in nature.[56] B. I. Miller and coworkers used the MBE technique to produce a room-temperature, long-wavelength (1.65 μm), double-heterostructure InGaAs laser.[57]

VII. TERNARY AND QUATERNARY SEMICONDUCTOR COMPOUNDS

A natural extension of the search for new semiconductors is to examine ternary compounds exhibiting diamond-like or tetrahedral coordination. The most interesting ternary cousins of the tetrahedral family are the I-III-VI$_2$ and II-IV-V$_2$ compounds such as $AgGaSe_2$ and $ZnGeP_2$, which usually have the chalcopyrite structure as in the mineral $CuFeS_2$.[58]

Ternary chalcopyrite crystals have properties that suggest possible technological applications in the areas of photovoltaic solar cells, infrared detectors, visible and infrared light-emitting diodes, optical parametric oscillators, up converters, and far-infrared generation. Several of the ternary compounds can be made both p-type and n-type. In addition, it has been found that two of them, $CuGaS_2$ and $CuAlS_2$, can be made p-type and have direct bandgaps in the visible and ultraviolet, respectively. They are unique in this respect, and have generated activity for applications to heterojunction lasers with large bandgap II-VI compounds, which can only be made n-type.

Because of their noncubic crystal structure, these compounds are optically birefringent, and have large nonlinear coefficients suitable for second harmonic generation of optical frequencies. The nonlinear properties of $AgGaS_2$ and $CuInS_2$ were summarized by G. D. Boyd, H. M. Kasper, and J. H. McFee.[59] The properties of $ZnGeP_2$, $ZnSiAs_2$, $CdGeP_2$, and $CdGeAs_2$ were studied by Boyd, E. Buehler, F. G. Storz, and J. H. Wernick.[60] Optical parametric oscillation was demonstrated in $ZnGeP_2$ in the infrared and submillimeter wave generation near 100 μm by Boyd, T. J. Bridges, C. K. N. Patel, and Buehler.[61]

These compounds are also of interest from a fundamental point of view because the chalcopyrite structure is the simplest, noncubic ternary analog of the well-understood cubic binary zinc-blende (ZnS) structure. The noncubic structure makes the ternary crystals differ from that of binary compounds in several nontrivial ways, such as the lifting of degeneracies and other interesting features in the energy-band structure.

Many other new ternary semiconductors were synthesized by Wernick in the mid-1950s. One such semiconductor, $AgSbTe_2$, has desirable thermolectric properties. It has a sodium chloride (NaCl) cubic-crystal structure, with the silver and antimony atoms randomly occupying the sodium sites. It conducts heat almost as poorly as glass. An InGaAs p-intrinsic-n (PIN) detector with sufficiently low dark current has been fabricated by R. F. Leheny and coworkers.[62] An InGaAs light emitting diode has been produced by T. P. Pearsall and coworkers.[63]

The first quaternary long-wavelength (1.0 μm) room-temperature laser (AlGaAsSb) was produced by R. E. Nahory and coworkers and stimulated a search for other quaternary lasers.[64]

VIII. SEMICONDUCTORS IN SOLAR PHOTOVOLTAIC CELLS

8.1 The Bell Solar Cell

The first silicon p-n junction solar cell was made at Bell Laboratories in 1941 by R. S. Ohl. However, this cell was inefficient because pure silicon was not yet available and, more importantly, because precisely positioned junctions, near the light-absorbing surfaces, could not be made. In 1947, Scaff and Theuerer made silicon photovoltaic cells by diffusing phosphorus into p-silicon and by diffusing boron into n-silicon, thereby forming large-area photovoltaic barriers near the surface of the silicon.[65]

The breakthrough leading to efficient solar cells came with Fuller's pioneering study of impurity diffusion as a means of p-n junction formation in germanium (see section 5.5 of this chapter). [Fig. 11-10] This study stimulated interest in the application of the diffusion techniques to solar photovoltaic cells for the conversion of solar energy to electricity. Pearson and Fuller made the first large-area silicon p-n junction by diffusing phosphorus or boron into material of the opposite conductivity type at temperatures above 1000°C.[66] They produced an efficient power rectifier covering an area of 0.75 cm² and yielding forward current up to 20 amps through a resistance of 0.08 ohm. Then D. M. Chapin, Fuller, and Pearson made a similar junction very close to a silicon surface which could be exposed to light. In 1954, they announced that the resulting photovoltaic cell, having an efficiency of 6 percent, was the most efficient means then available for converting sunlight into electrical energy.[67]

The commercial use of silicon solar cells began when they became the preferred source of electric power for space satellites. Silicon solar cells were used in the first orbiting satellite, Vanguard I, launched on March 17, 1958. Its radio transmitter, powered by solar cells, operated for eight years before radiation damage caused it to fail. Annual production of silicon solar cells for space applications rapidly increased, and then leveled off at quantities yielding something less than 100 kilowatts in the early 1970s.[68]

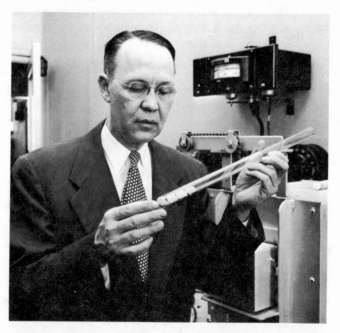

Fig. 11-10. C. S. Fuller holding a tube used to prepare silicon for use in the Bell solar battery.

8.2 Other Single-Crystal Semiconductor Solar Cells

Between 1974 and 1976, J. L. Shay, S. Wagner, and coworkers invented two new photovoltaic solar cells with solar power conversion efficiencies above 10 percent, generally considered the minimum efficiency suitable for large-scale applications. A heterojunction photovoltaic cell was prepared by growing a cadmium sulfide layer on a single crystal of copper indium diselenide.[69] A quantum efficiency of about 70 percent was measured over the entire wavelength range between 0.55 and 1.25 μm, and a solar power conversion efficiency of 12 percent was measured. Another heterojunction solar cell was prepared by growing a cadmium sulfide epitaxial layer on a substrate of single-crystal indium phosphide.[70] Preliminary devices showed a 15 percent efficiency for solar power conversion, which was comparable to commercial silicon solar cells.

8.3 Semiconductor-Liquid Junction Photovoltaic Cells

In 1976, A. Heller proposed the use of semiconductor-liquid junctions, similar to those used by W. H. Brattain and C. G. B. Garrett,[71] for solar cells that retain much of their single-crystal efficiency. Miller and Heller made such a cell by anodizing a cadmium metal sheet in a sulfide/disulfide solution, which also formed the junction with the semiconductor. This CdS cell had an efficiency of about 1 percent.[72] A later cell with an n-CdSe ceramic made by M. Robbins in 1977 had an efficiency of 5 percent.[73] To address the problem of electron-hole recombination at semiconductor grain boundaries, Heller suggested that strongly bound impurities be introduced at surfaces and grain boundaries to reduce electron-hole recombination. By dipping semiconductors in solutions of chemisorbed ions, Heller and B. A. Parkinson increased the efficiency of solar cells made with chemically vapor-deposited GaAs on graphite to 8 percent.[74]

The initial work at Bell Labs centered on n-type photoanodes in which holes produced by light shining on the semiconductor arrive at the semiconductor-liquid interface. Some of these holes may oxidize and corrode the exposed semiconductor surface. In p-type photocathodes, however, photogenerated electrons protect the semiconductor surface against oxidative corrosion. The problem with these photocathode-based cells was carrier recombination at the semiconductor-liquid interface. By strengthening the chemical bonds at the InP-liquid interface, recombination was reduced and 11.5-percent efficient singly crystalline cells, that were stable under intense irradiation, were made.[75] By introducing small amounts of hydrogen-evolution catalysts into the semiconductor interface, photogenerated electrons arriving at aqueous acid interfaces could be reacted with protons, reducing these to hydrogen. Thus Heller made 12-percent efficient cells that directly convert sunlight to hydrogen.[76]

REFERENCES

1. G. L. Pearson, "Thermistors, Their Characteristics and Uses," *Bell Laboratories Record* **19** (December 1940), pp. 106-111; J. A. Becker, C. B. Green, and G. L. Pearson, "Properties and Uses of Thermistors—Thermally Sensitive Resistors," *Bell System Tech. J.* **26** (January 1947), pp. 170-212.

2. H. A. Sauer and S. S. Flaschen, "Positive Temperature Coefficient of Resistance Thermistor Materials for Electronic Applications," *Proceedings of the Seventh Electronic Components Symposium,* Washington, D. C. (1956), pp. 41-46.

3. See reference 2. Also, H. A. Sauer and J. R. Fisher, "Processing of Positive Temperature Coefficient Thermistors," *J. Am. Ceramic Soc.* **43** (June 1960), pp. 297-301.

4. L. O. Grondahl and P. H. Geiger, "A New Electronic Rectifier," *Trans. AIEE* **46** (February 1927), pp. 357-366.

5. R. O. Grisdale, "Silicon Carbide Varistors," *Bell Laboratories Record* **19** (October 1940), pp. 46-51.

6. C. J. Frosch, "Improved Silicon Carbide Varistors," *Bell Laboratories Record* **32** (September 1954), pp. 336-340; H. F. Dienel, "Silicon Carbide Varistors: Properties and Construction," *Bell Laboratories Record* **34** (November 1956), pp. 407-411.

7. W. G. Pfann, "An Electrolytic Method for Pointing Tungsten Wires," *Trans. AIME* **175** (1948), pp. 606-610; idem, U.S. Patent No. 2,434,286; filed August 12, 1943; issued January 13, 1948.

8. J. H. Scaff and R. S. Ohl, "Development of Silicon Crystal Rectifiers for Microwave Radar Receivers," *Bell System Tech. J.* **26** (January 1947), pp. 1-30.

9. J. H. Scaff, "The Role of Metallurgy in the Technology of Electronic Materials," *Metallurgical Transactions* **1** (March 1970), pp. 561-573.

10. W. G. Pfann and J. H. Scaff, "Microstructures of Silicon Ingots," *J. Metals* **1**, *Trans. AIME* **185** (June 1949), pp. 389-392.

11. J. H. Scaff, H. C. Theuerer, and E. E. Schumacher, "p-Type and n-Type Silicon and the Formation of the Photovoltaic Barrier in Silicon Ingots," *J. Metals* **1**, *Trans. AIME* **185** (June 1949), pp. 383-388.

12. See reference 9.

13. W. G. Pfann, U. S. Patent No. 2,577,803; filed December 29, 1948, issued December 11, 1951.

14. W. G. Pfann, "Significance of Composition of Contact Point in Rectifying Junctions on Germanium," *Phys. Rev.* **81** (March 1951), p. 882; idem, U.S. Patent No. 2,920,425; filed September 14, 1950, issued August 23, 1960.

15. W. G. Pfann, U.S. Patent No. 2,792,538; filed September 14, 1950, issued May 14, 1957.

16. G. L. Pearson and B. Sawyer, "Silicon p-n Junction Alloy Diodes," *Proc. IRE* **40** (November 1952), pp. 1348-1351.

17. J. Czochralski, "Measuring the Velocity of Crystallisation of Metals," *Zeits. Phys. Chem.* **92** (April 24, 1917), pp. 219-221.

18. G. K. Teal and J. B. Little, "Growth of Germanium Single Crystals," *Phys. Rev.* **78** (June 1950), p. 647.

19. W. Shockley, M. Sparks, and G. K. Teal, "p-n Junction Transistors," *Phys. Rev.* **83** (July 1951), pp. 151-162.

20. R. N. Hall, "p-n Junctions Produced by Growth Rate Variation," *Phys. Rev.* **88** (October 1952), p. 139.

21. H. E. Bridgers, "Formation of p-n Junctions in Semiconductors by the Variation of Crystal Growth Parameters," *J. Appl. Phys.* **27** (July 1956), pp. 746-751.

22. M. Tanenbaum, L. B. Valdes, E. Buehler, and N. B. Hannay, "Silicon n-p-n Grown Junction Transistors," *J. Appl. Phys.* **26** (June 1955), pp. 686-692.

23. W. G. Pfann, "Principles of Zone Melting," *J. Metals* **4**, *Trans. AIME* **194**, (July

1952), pp. 747-753; idem, U.S. Patent No. 2,739,088; filed November 16, 1951, issued March 20, 1956.

24. W. G. Pfann and K. M. Olsen, "Purification and Prevention of Segregation in Single Crystals of Germanium," *Phys. Rev.* **89** (January 1953), pp. 322-323.

25. J. A. Burton, R. C. Prim, and W. P. Slichter, "The Distribution of Solute in Crystals Grown from the Melt. Part I. Theoretical," *J. Chem. Phys.* **21** (November 1953), pp. 1987-1991.

26. J. A. Burton, E. D. Kolb, W. P. Slichter, and J. D. Struthers, "Distribution of Solute in Crystals Grown from the Melt. Part II. Experimental," *J. Chem. Phys.* **21** (November 1953), pp. 1991-1996.

27. L. O. Wilson, "On Interpreting a Quantity in the Burton, Prim, and Slichter Equation as a Diffusion Boundary Layer Thickness," *J. Crystal Growth* **44** (1978), pp. 247-; idem, "A New Look at the Burton, Prim, and Slichter Model of Segregation During Crystal Growth from the Melt," *J. Crystal Growth* **44** (1978), pp. 371-; idem, "Analysis of Microsegregation in Crystals," *J. Crystal Growth* **48** (March 1980), pp. 363-366; idem, "The Effect of Fluctuating Growth Rates on Segregation in Crystals Grown from the Melt, I and II.," *J. Crystal Growth* **48** (March 1980), pp. 435-458.

28. W. G. Pfann, J. N. Hobstetter, and G. S. Indig, "Preventing Conductivity Fluctuations During Growth of a Semiconducting Crystal," *J. Appl. Phys.* **29** (August 1958), pp. 1238-1240.

29. G. K. Teal and E. Buehler, "Growth of Silicon Single Crystals and of Single-Crystal Silicon p-n Junctions," *Phys. Rev.* **87** (July 1952), p. 190.

30. H. C. Theuerer, "Removal of Boron from Silicon by Hydrogen Water Vapor Treatment," *J. Metals* **8**, *Trans. AIME* **206** (October 1956), pp. 1316-1319; idem, U.S. Patent No. 3,060,123; filed December 17, 1952, issued October 23, 1962.

31. N. B. Hannay, "Recent Advances in Silicon," in *Progress in Semiconductors*, Vol. 1, ed. A. F. Gibson (London: Heywood and Co., 1956), pp. 3-35.

32. See reference 22.

33. C. S. Fuller, "Diffusion of Donor and Acceptor Elements into Germanium," *Phys. Rev.* **86** (April 1952), pp. 136-137.

34. C. A. Lee, "A High-Frequency Diffused Base Germanium Transistor," *Bell System Tech. J.* **35** (January 1956), pp. 23-34.

35. M. Tanenbaum and D. E. Thomas, "Diffused Emitter and Base Silicon Transistors," *Bell System Tech. J.* **35** (January 1956), pp. 1-22.

36. C. S. Fuller, J. A. Ditzenberger, N. B. Hannay, and E. Buehler, "Resistivity Changes in Silicon Induced by Heat Treatment," *Phys. Rev.* **96** (November 1954), p. 833.

37. M. Tanenbaum and J. P. Maita, "Hall Effect and Conductivity of InSb Single Crystals," *Phys. Rev.* **91** (August 1953), pp. 1009-1010.

38. M. Tanenbaum and H. B. Briggs, "Optical Properties of Indium Antimonide," *Phys. Rev.* **91** (September 1953), pp. 1561-1562.

39. G. L. Pearson and M. Tanenbaum, "The Magnetoresistance Effect in InSb," *Phys. Rev.* **90** (April 1953), p. 153.

40. H. J. Hrostowski and M. Tanenbaum, *Physics* **20** (1954), p. 1065.

41. J. M. Whelan and G. H. Wheatley, "The Preparation and Properties of Gallium Arsenide Single Crystals," *J. Phys. Chem. Solids* **6** (August 1958), pp. 169-172.

42. J. M. Whelan, J. D. Struthers, and J. A. Ditzenberger, "Distribution Coefficients of Various Impurities in Gallium Arsenide," *Properties of Elemental and Compound Semiconductors*, Metallurgical Society Conferences **5** (New York: Interscience Publishers, 1960), pp. 141-151.

43. C. J. Frosch and L. Derick, "The Preparation and Floating Zone Processing of Gallium Phosphide," *J. Electrochem. Soc.* **108** (March 1961), pp. 251-257.

44. M. Gershenzon and R. M. Mikulyak, "Vapor Phase Preparation of Gallium Phosphide Crystals," *J. Electrochem. Soc.* **108** (June 1961), pp. 548-551.

45. C. J. Frosch, "The Epitaxial Growth of GaP by a Ga_2O Vapor Transport Mechanism," *J. Electrochem. Soc.* **111** (February 1964), pp. 180-184.

46. F. A. Trumbore, M. Kowalchik, and H. G. White, "Efficient Electroluminescence in GaP p-n Junctions Grown by Liquid-Phase Epitaxy on Vapor-Grown Substrates," *J. Appl. Phys.* **38** (March 15, 1967), pp. 1987-1988.

47. R. A. Logan, H. G. White, and F. A. Trumbore, "p-n Junctions in GaP with External Electroluminescence Efficiency ~2% at 25°C," *Appl. Phys. Lett.* **10** (April 1, 1967), pp. 206-208.

48. C. H. Henry and D. J. Dean, "New Red Pair Luminescence for GaP," *Phys. Rev.* **166** (February 1968), pp. 754-756.

49. R. A. Logan, H. G. White, and W. Wiegmann, "Efficient Green Electroluminescence in Nitrogen-Doped GaP p-n Junctions," *Appl. Phys. Lett.* **13** (August 15, 1968), pp. 139-141.

50. W. Rosenzweig, R. A. Logan, and W. Wiegmann, "Variable Hue GaP Diodes," *Solid-State Electron.* **14** (August 1971), pp. 655-660.

51. M. B. Panish, H. J. Queisser, L. Derick, and S. Sumski, "Photoluminescence and Solution Growth of Gallium Arsenide," *Solid-State Electron.* **9** (April 1966), pp. 311-314; H. J. Queisser and M. B. Panish, "Luminescence of Zinc Doped Solution Grown Gallium Arsenide," *J. Phys. Chem. Solids* **28** (July 1967), pp. 1177-1184; M. B. Panish, "Luminescence of Zinc Doped Solution Grown GaAs: The Effect of Arsenic Pressure," *J. Phys. Chem. Solids* **29** (February 1968), pp. 409-410.

52. M. B. Panish and S. Sumski, "Ga-Al-As: Phase, Thermodynamic and Optical Properties," *J. Phys. Chem. Solids* **30** (January 1969), pp. 129-137.

53. M. B. Panish, I. Hayashi, and S. Sumski, "A Technique for the Preparation of Low-Threshold Room-Temperature GaAs Laser Diode Structures," *IEEE J. Quant. Elect.* **QE5** (April 1969), pp. 210-211; M. B. Panish, S. Sumski, and I. Hayashi, "Preparation of Multilayer LPE Heterostructures with Crystalline Solid Solutions of $Al_xGa_{1-x}As$: Heterostructure Lasers," *Met. Trans.* **2** (March 1971), pp. 795-801.

54. G. A. Rozgonyi and M. B. Panish, "Stress Compensation in $Ga_{1-x}Al_xAs_{1-y}P_y$ LPE Layers on GaAs Substrates," *Appl. Phys. Lett.* **23** (November 15, 1973), pp. 533-535.

55. J. R. Arthur, U.S. Patent No. 3,615,931; filed December 27, 1968; issued October 26, 1971; J. R. Arthur and J. J. LePore, "GaAs, GaP, and $GaAs_xP_{1-x}$ Epitaxial Films Grown by Molecular Beam Deposition," *J. Vac. Sci. Tech.* **6** (July/August 1969), pp. 545-548; A. Y. Cho and J. R. Arthur, "Molecular Beam Epitaxy," *Progress in Solid-State Chem.* **10**, Part 3 (1975), pp. 157-191.

56. A. C. Gossard, P. M. Petroff, W. Wiegmann, R. Dingle, and A. Savage, "Epitaxial Structures with Alternate Atomic-Layer Composition Modulation," *Appl. Phys. Lett.* **29** (September 15, 1976), pp. 323-325.

57. B. I. Miller, J. H. McFee, R. J. Martin, and P. K. Tien, "Room-Temperature Operation of Lattice-matched $InP/Ga_{0.47}In_{0.53}$ As/InP Double-Heterostructure Lasers Grown by MBE," *Appl. Phys. Lett.* **33** (July 1, 1978), pp. 44-47.

58. J. L. Shay and J. H. Wernick, *Ternary Chalcopyrite Semiconductors: Growth, Electronic Properties, and Applications* (Oxford: Pergamon Press, 1975).

59. G. D. Boyd, H. M. Kasper, and J. H. McFee, "Linear and Nonlinear Optical Properties of $AgGaS_2$, $CuGaS_2$, and $CuInS_2$, and Theory of the Wedge Technique for the Measurement of Nonlinear Coefficients," *IEEE J. Quantum Elect.* **QE-7** (December 1971), pp. 563-573.

60. G. D. Boyd, E. Buehler, F. G. Storz, and J. H. Wernick, "Linear and Nonlinear Optical Properties of Ternary $A^{II}B^{IV}C_2^V$ Chalcopyrite Semiconductors," *IEEE J. Quantum Elect.* **QE-8** (April 1972), pp. 419-426.

61. G. D. Boyd, T. J. Bridges, C. K. N. Patel, and E. Buehler, "Phase-Matched Submillimeter Wave Generation by Difference-Frequency Mixing in $ZnGeP_2$," *Appl. Phys. Lett.* **21** (December 1, 1972), pp. 553-555.

62. R. F. Leheny, R. E. Nahory, M. A. Pollack, A. A. Ballman, E. D. Beebe, J. C. DeWinter, and R. J. Martin, "Integrated $In_{0.53}Ga_{0.47}As$ p-i-n FET Photoreceiver," *Electron. Lett.* **16** (May 8, 1980), pp. 353-354.

63. T. P. Pearsall, B. I. Miller, R. J. Capila, and K. J. Bachman, "Efficient Lattice-Matched Double-Heterostructure LEDs at 1.1 μm from $Ga_xIn_{1-x}As_yP_{1-y}$," *Appl. Phys. Lett.* **28** (May 1976), pp. 499-501.

64. R. E. Nahory, M. A. Pollack, E. D. Beebe, J. C. DeWinter, and D. W. Dixon, "Continuous Operation of 1.0 μm Wavelength $GaAs_{1-x}Sb_x/Al_yGa_{1-y} - As_{1-x}Sb_x$ Double-Heterostructure Injection Lasers at Room Temperature," *Appl. Phys. Lett.* **28** (January 1, 1976), pp. 19-21.

65. J. H. Scaff and H. C. Theuerer, U.S. Patent No. 2,567,970; filed December 24, 1947; issued September 18, 1951.

66. G. L. Pearson and C. S. Fuller, "Silicon p-n Junction Power Rectifiers and Lightning Protectors," *Proc. IRE* **42** (April 1954), p. 760.

67. D. M. Chapin, C. S. Fuller, and G. L. Pearson, "A New Silicon p-n Junction Photocell for Converting Solar Radiation into Electrical Power," *J. Appl. Phys.* **25** (May 1954), pp. 676-677.

68. M. Wolf, "Historical Development of Solar Cells," *Proc. 25th Power Sources Symp.* (1972), p. 120.

69. S. Wagner, J. L. Shay, P. Migliorato, and H. M. Kasper, "$CuInSe_2$/CdS Heterojunction Photovoltaic Detectors," *Appl. Phys. Lett.* **25** (October 15, 1974), pp. 434-435; J. L. Shay, S. Wagner, and H. M. Kasper, "Efficient $CuInSe_2$/CdS Solar Cells," *Appl. Phys. Lett.* **27** (July 15, 1975), pp. 89-90.

70. S. Wagner, J. L. Shay, K. J. Bachmann, and E. Buehler, "p-InP/n-CdS Solar Cells and Photovoltaic Detectors," *Appl. Phys. Lett.* **26** (March 1, 1975), pp. 229-230.

71. W. H. Brattain and C. G. B. Garrett, "Experiments on the Interface Between Germanium and an Electrolyte," *Bell System Tech. J.* **32** (January 1955), pp. 129-176.

72. B. Miller and A. Heller, "Semiconductor Liquid Junction Solar Cells Based on Anodic Sulphide Films," *Nature* **262** (1976), pp. 680-681; A. Heller and B. Miller, U.S. Patent No. 4,127,449; filed November 8, 1976; issued November 28, 1978.

73. B. Miller, A. Heller, M. Robbins, S. Menezes, K. C. Chang, and J. Thomson, Jr., "Solar Conversion Efficiency of Pressure Sintered Cadmium Selenide Liquid Junction Cells," *J. Electrochem. Soc.* **124** (1977), pp. 1019-1021; A. Heller, B. Miller, and M. Robbins, U.S. Patent No. 4,084,044; filed February 18, 1977; issued April 11, 1978.

74. B. A. Parkinson, A. Heller, and B. Miller, "Enhanced Photoelectrochemical Solar-Energy Conversion by Gallium Arsenide Surface Modification," *Appl. Phys. Lett.* **33** (September 15, 1978), pp. 521-523.

75. A. Heller, B. Miller, and F. A. Thiel, "11.5% Solar Conversion Efficiency in the Photocathodically Protected $p-InP/V^{3+}-V^{2+}$-HCl/C Semiconductor Liquid Junction Cell."

76. A. Heller and R. G. Vadimsky, "Efficient Solar to Chemical Conversion: 12% Efficient Photoassisted Electrolysis in the [p-type InP (Ru)]/Hcl-Kcl/Pt(Rh) Cell," *Hydrogen Phys. Rev. Lett.* **46**, (April 27, 1981), pp. 1153-1156.

Chapter 12

Magnetic Materials — Bubbles and Chromindur

The magnetic properties of matter have been important in telephony from the early years. Materials for permeable or permanent magnets had been explored empirically in the 19th century for a wide variety of applications. The early uses of electromagnets for telephone systems, in receivers, relays, and coils, pointed to the need for greatly improved magnetic materials. Here indeed were clear examples of the advancement of technology being paced by the materials available.

The long history of the Bell System's research and development effort on magnetic materials began around 1913, well before the founding of Bell Laboratories, with the pioneering work of G. W. Elmen on iron-nickel alloys and the discovery of Permalloy. In Bell Labs, successive studies led to a series of soft and hard magnetic materials that made possible a wide range of technological advances in telephone instruments, transmission systems, electromagnetic switching systems, and computer memory elements. On an entirely different front, research on magnetic oxides through the routes of ceramic science opened prospects for the development of high performance inductors, filters, and computer components. Related research activities on magnetic materials are discussed in Chapter 19, section I, and research on the physics of magnetic materials is discussed in Chapter 1, section I.

I. METALS AND ALLOYS

The history of Bell Laboratories accomplishments in the field of magnetic metallic materials can be viewed in terms of the two broad functional uses of such materials: soft magnetic materials with high permeability and low hysteresis loss, and hard magnetic materials for permanent magnet applications.

Principal authors: G. Y. Chin, J. F. Dillon, R. A. Laudise, J. H. Scaff, T. D. Schlabach, and J. H. Wernick

1.1 Soft Magnetic Materials

The earliest investigations at Bell Labs were concerned with magnetically soft materials. These were used in relays as cores and armatures, in receivers, ringers, and filters, and in loading coils, in various transformers as lamination cores, and in a variety of other electromagnetic devices. In these applications, the technical properties of interest were high permeability, low coercive force, low electrical losses in ac fields, and requisite saturation magnetization. The electrical power industry was also interested in these materials and properties, but it was concerned with strong currents, whereas communications most often dealt with weak-current devices. The special problems of communications usage required unique solutions in terms of soft magnetic materials and their processing, both in device designs and in design philosophy. In turn, these solutions characterized the special contributions of Bell Labs to soft magnetic metallic materials.

1.1.1 Iron and Low-Carbon Steel

Iron was the first important soft magnetic material. For many years, efforts were made to improve its magnetic qualities, especially its permeability. Efforts centered on increasing the purity of iron because

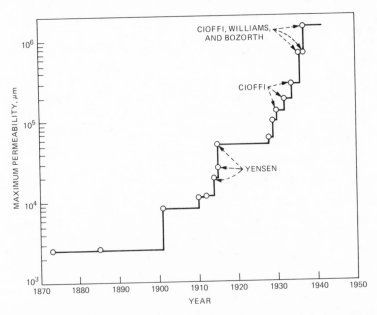

Fig. 12-1. Highest values of maximum permeability of iron reported in various years. The magnetic quality of iron has increased significantly as purification methods have been improved.

impurities such as carbon, oxygen, sulfur, and nitrogen, which enter the lattice interstitially, were known to limit its magnetic quality.

An important early contribution to this effort was the work at Bell Labs by P. P. Cioffi, whose method of purification, based on a technique first introduced by T. D. Yensen,[1] consisted of heating iron in very dry hydrogen at temperatures above 1300°C to its melting point for periods of up to 18 hours.[2] [Fig. 12-1] This treatment removed many of the interstitial impurities and increased the maximum permeability of commercial magnetic iron from its usual value of 5,000 to 10,000 to about 300,000.[3] [Fig. 12-2] Similar purification methods were later used by Bell Labs investigators to improve the magnetic properties of other soft magnetic alloys, notably Supermalloy and Supermendur.

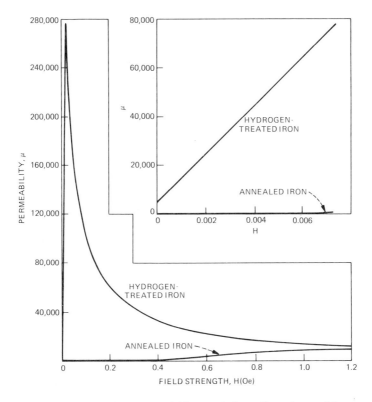

Fig. 12-2. Permeability versus field strength for ordinary iron and iron purified by heat treatment in hydrogen at 1500°C. Hydrogenization increases the magnetic softness of iron enormously.

During the early 1930s, J. H. Scaff studied the effect of gases and their removal on the properties of numerous metals and alloys, especially soft magnetic materials.[4] He constructed furnaces for preparing pure metals and alloys in a vacuum and in controlled atmospheres, and for studying metal purification in the liquid state. Later, these facilities were used in numerous investigations, including those by R. S. Ohl to prepare "pure" silicon and those by K. M. Olsen to prepare high-purity nickel and nickel alloys for long-lived vacuum tube filaments.

While magnetic iron was quite suitable and widely used for cores and armatures in relays, efforts after World War II began to focus on finding a less costly material and purification treatment. In the early 1950s, R. A. Chegwidden studied atmospheric effects on the heat treatment of cold-rolled steel, which was much less costly than magnetic iron but contained significantly more impurities. This work led to the commercial use of wet-forming gas (a mixture of nitrogen and hydrogen containing some H_2O) instead of expensive hydrogen for the heat treatment of cold-rolled steels for relays.

In addition to increasing the initial coercive force of magnetic iron and low-carbon steels, impurities were found to be responsible for further increases in coercivity on aging at moderate temperatures. E. A. Nesbitt showed that nitrogen, in particular, could increase the coercive force of magnetic iron upon aging at 100°C because of the precipitation of iron nitrides. These precipitates could be put back into solution at 150°C with a corresponding decrease in coercive force.[5]

In 1967, J. H. Swisher undertook a systematic study of the effect of impurities on the magnetic quality of iron and low-carbon steels.[6,7] He showed that carbon, nitrogen, and oxygen increase the coercivity of steels cooled rapidly from high temperatures, and that aging at 100°C is quite severe in nitrogen-containing steels but is not measurable in low-carbon-containing steels. He also showed that aging caused by oxygen, sulfur, and phosphorus is insignificant. Finally, he showed that steels suitable for many magnetic applications can be obtained without removing all of the carbon present, provided the remaining carbide particles are spherodized by annealing at temperatures below 727°C. In these studies, Swisher confirmed earlier work done by A. S. Wiseman at Western Electric's Hawthorne Works in Illinois.

1.1.2 Iron-Nickel Alloys

The pioneering work on Permalloys was done by G. W. Elmen.[8] This work was undertaken because of the need for material of higher permeability than was offered by the magnetic iron or silicon iron then available. Elmen showed that alloys containing from 30 to 90 percent nickel had higher initial permeabilities than any other material then known, and that those in the region of 78 percent nickel exhibited the highest initial permeabilities, especially when rapidly cooled. The 78.5 percent nickel alloy found its first commercial use in the continuous loading of submarine telegraph cable,[9] and thereafter in telephone transformers, coils, and sensitive relays.

Elmen was especially concerned with increasing the resistivity of certain Permalloys and investigated the effect of various additives on the magnetic properties of the compounds. Among the additives studied were copper, chromium, and molybdenum, but the most striking results were obtained with cobalt.[10] The iron-nickel-cobalt was of great scientific interest. It presented a range of compositions that, when properly heat treated, exhibited a constancy of permeability at low flux densities, a low hysteresis loss in the same region, and a constricted hysteresis loop at medium flux densities. Elmen and his colleagues gave the name Perminvar to alloys with these characteristics.[11]

Chromium and molybdenum were initially added to iron-nickel alloys to increase their resistivity and decrease their eddy-current losses. Subsequently, it was found that these additives also increased the permeability of iron-nickel alloys and simplified the heat treatment required to obtain high initial permeability. Molybdenum proved especially effective, and the composition containing 4 percent molybdenum, 79 percent nickel, and 17 percent iron (Mo Permalloy) became an important and widely used material.

During World War II, the use of high-purity techniques and hydrogen heat treatments greatly improved the magnetic properties of Permalloys. The most useful and remarkable of these is a material called Supermalloy, containing 5 percent molybdenum, 79 percent nickel, and 16 percent iron, developed by O. L. Boothby and R. M. Bozorth.[12] Supermalloy can exhibit initial permeabilities greater than 100,000 and maximum permeabilities over 1 million, making it attractive for transformers transmitting weak signals at audio and carrier frequencies.

After World War II, interest began to develop in a new class of applications for magnetic materials, namely, as memory elements in electronic computers. Permalloys seemed suitable for one type known as twistor memories. The basic element of these memories, a molybdenum Permalloy tape spirally wrapped around a copper conductor, senses the binary information stored in a nearby array of permanent magnets. [Fig. 12-3] For this type of application, the Permalloy must exhibit a coercive force suitable for switching at low magnetic fields and a hysteresis loop adequately square to provide sharp signals.

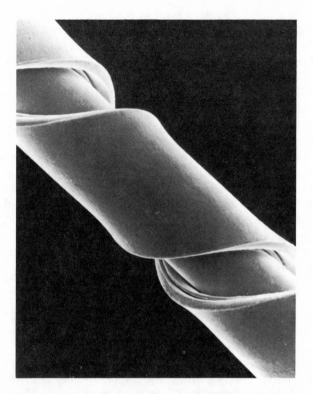

Fig. 12-3. Microphotograph of a small section of a piggyback twistor wire. Two tapes are wound on a 0.008-cm copper wire. The storage tape is made of the magnetically "hard" gold-iron-cobalt alloy, in which is written tiny permanent-magnet memory elements. The sense tape is made of the easily magnetizable Permalloy, used to detect the direction of magnetization of the storage elements.

In the early 1960s, the twistor program was accelerated by the designation of the permanent magnet twistor as the permanent magnet store in the Bell System No. 1 Electronic Switching System (ESS). It soon became apparent that a fundamental understanding of the interrelationship between mechanical processing and the development of magnetic anisotropy in Permalloy tapes was needed to ensure long-term reproducibility. This was provided by G. Y. Chin, who showed that the anisotropy in the Permalloy twistor tape was caused by a short-range directional order of nearest-neighbor atom pairs induced by plastic deformation.[13] Quantitative application of the directional-order theory to the actual crystallographic textures developed in the deformation of Permalloy wires and tapes provided a natural explanation to an observation made earlier by D. H. Wenny.

These studies had shown that tapes produced by roll flattening gave suitably square hysteresis loops, while those produced by drawing round wires through rectangular dies gave inferior loops. In addition, the knowledge gained from fundamental studies such as this enabled Chin and his colleagues at Bell Labs' Allentown laboratory to specify an optimum composition and processing procedure for the manufacture of twistor tapes in the No. 1 ESS program. Such knowledge also laid the groundwork for the later development by Chin, T. C. Tisone, and W. B. Grupen of optimum composition and processing of Permalloy tapes for the piggyback twistor, so essential to the early success of the electronic translator system (ETS) and the traffic service position system (TSPS).[14]

One of the most important applications for magnetic materials in telephone transmission has been in loading coils. In fact, it was this use that motivated Elmen's early work on Permalloys. The loading coil adds inductance to the telephone transmission line and decreases its loss. To maintain good transmission quality, coils are placed periodically along the transmission line. To reduce electrical losses, the magnetic core material used in these coils is in the form of insulated powder, and until 1927, that material was powdered iron. The development of Permalloys, with their higher permeability and resistivity, made it possible to make smaller loading-coil cores while reducing loss.[15] [Fig. 12-4] In 1927, the first Permalloy manufactured for loading coils was an 80%Ni-20%Fe alloy, for which C. V. Wahl and coworkers devised the novel method of adding a small amount of sulfur to make the Permalloy brittle for easy pulverization.[16]

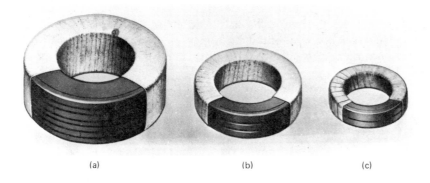

(a)   (b)   (c)

Fig. 12-4. Relative sizes of compressed powder cores for loading coils: (a) iron, (b) 80Ni-20Fe permalloy, (c) 81Ni-17Fe-2Mo Permalloy.

In addition to having loading coils with the desired inductance, it was extremely important that this value remain stable over the range of anticipated operating temperatures. By 1940, V. E. Legg and F. J. Given had accomplished this by adding a few tenths of one percent of an alloy that contained more molybdenum and had a lower Curie temperature and hence changed magnetic properties rapidly with temperature in the desired direction in the vicinity of room temperature.[17] This scheme of stabilization through control of Curie point has been widely applied to loading coils and to a variety of other high-quality filters and coils.

1.1.3 Vibralloy

Related to the efforts on magnetic materials were studies on constant elastic modulus materials, of which Vibralloy is a noteworthy example. This alloy, nominally containing 41.25 percent nickel, 9.0 percent molybdenum, 0.5 percent manganese, and 49.5 percent iron, was developed by M. E. Fine and W. C. Ellis in 1950 for use in the construction of small tuning forks in frequency-sensitive switches.[18] Depending on composition and processing, the elastic modulus of Vibralloy can be held substantially constant over a temperature range from −40°C to +100°C. In addition, since the alloy is a soft magnetic material, devices such as tuning forks or reed switches can be driven directly by means of a magnetic circuit. A commercial application was found in the *Bellboy** personal signaling set.

1.1.4 Iron-Cobalt Alloys

Because of their uniquely high saturation induction, iron-cobalt alloys received early attention for magnetic applications. In 1927, Ellis was the first to report on the high flux densities at medium magnetizing forces that could be achieved in the 50%Fe-50%Co alloy.[19] This alloy had been invented by Elmen in 1926 and given the name "Permendur" because its permeability "endured" to high values of flux density.

The simple binary alloy had one important drawback—while it was ductile and could be rolled when hot, it was extremely brittle when cold. In 1932, this limitation was overcome by J. H. White and Wahl by adding small amounts of vanadium to the alloy.[20] These new alloys became known as vanadium Permendurs, with the most widely used composition containing 2 percent vanadium, 49 percent iron, and 49 percent cobalt. While this alloy was suitable for various cores and for

---

* Trademark of AT&T Co.

pole pieces in loudspeakers, its most important Bell System use has been as the diaphragm in telephone receivers.[21]

In 1957, H. L. B. Gould and Wenny made substantial improvements in the magnetic and mechanical properties of the 2-percent vanadium alloy and named the improved alloy Supermendur.[22] They started with high-purity materials and used melting and purification in wet and dry hydrogen, and furnace cooling in a magnetic field. The resulting magnetic properties were a maximum permeability of 66,000, a coercive force of 0.2 oersted, and a residual induction of 21,500 gauss. These and other properties set new records and made the material attractive for high-quality transformers and magnetic amplifiers.

1.2 Hard and Semihard Magnetic Metallic Materials

Hard or permanent magnet materials are used to produce external magnetic fields of considerable strength and constancy without the expenditure of power. These materials are used in telephone receivers and ringers, in small motors and generators, and in various other devices. The properties used in evaluating the quality of materials for permanent magnet applications include the coercive force H_c, the residual induction, B_r, and the maximum energy product, $(BH)_m$. The term *semihard* refers to a class of permanent magnet materials having intermediate values of coercive force from a few oersteds up to perhaps 100 oersteds, and a fairly square hysteresis loop, making them suitable for various switching and memory applications.

1.2.1 Remalloy

The earliest permanent magnet materials were various high-carbon steels in which carbon played an essential role as the magnetic hardening agent. In 1931, K. S. Seljasator and B. A. Rogers of Western Electric found that useful permanent magnet properties could be obtained in iron-cobalt-molybdenum and iron-cobalt-tungsten alloys.[23] At Bell Laboratories a comprehensive study of the carbon-free Fe-Co-Mo system was initiated by E. S. Greiner, E. M. Tolman, and E. E. Thomas.[24] They identified the optimal compositions and heat treatments required to obtain the best permanent magnet properties. Alloys in the system became known as Remalloy or Comol.[25] They were the forerunners of a series of dispersal-phase, carbon-free permanent magnet materials. Two compositions achieved commercial importance: a 17%Mo-12%Co-71%Fe alloy with a $(BH)_m$ of 1.1×10^6 gauss-oersteds and a 20%Mo-12%Co-68%Fe alloy with a $(BH)_m$ of 1.3×10^6 gauss-oersteds. These alloys were hot formable and machinable. The 17-percent molybdenum alloy was first used in the Bell System in the HA1 telephone receiver introduced about 1937. The 20-percent alloy was used in the U-series of cup-shaped receivers first introduced in 1950 with the 500-type telephone handset and remained in use until it was replaced by Chromindur in 1980.

1.2.2 Vicalloy

Vicalloys, precipitation-hardened, carbon-free permanent magnet alloys formed of iron, cobalt, and vanadium, were discovered by Nesbitt and G. A. Kelsall in 1938.[26] They cover a composition range from 30 to 52 percent iron, 36 to 62 percent cobalt, and 4 to 16 percent vanadium and develop their permanent magnet properties by appropriate combinations of cold working and heat treatment. In contrast to most hard magnetic materials, which are brittle, these alloys are ductile and can be rolled to a thin sheet or drawn to a fine wire.

In 1939, Vicalloy I (38%Fe-52%Co-10%V), in the form of a narrow tape (0.002-inch thick by 0.050-inch wide), was used as the recording medium for weather and time announcements in Bell System Mirrophones.[27] In the mid-1960s, it was used for the memory card of the permanent magnet twistor (PMT) in the No. 1 ESS.[28] Here, in the form of a strip 0.001 inch thick by 6 inches wide, it is bonded to an aluminum card and photoetched to produce an array of tiny permanent magnets that are the heart of the memory. Their state of magnetization is sensed by the Permalloy twistor element described in section 1.1.2 of this chapter. To change information stored in the memory, the cards are removed and demagnetized and a new pattern of magnetization is applied. Such memories are called *semipermanent*.

1.2.3 Permanent Magnets for Magnetrons

During World War II, research and development of magnetic materials for normal Bell System use virtually ceased, giving way to programs essential to the war effort. One such program was directed toward providing improved permanent magnets in magnetrons for microwave radars. Cioffi designed the first permanent magnet structures for magnetrons from Alnico II, which was then the premier permanent magnet material. Later, based on information obtained from the Philips Research Laboratories in the Netherlands, Cioffi and Wenny developed Alnico V-type permanent magnets for magnetrons.[29] Precision sandcasting and magnetic-field, heat-treating facilities were developed for such magnets.

1.2.4 Remendurs

Remendur alloys are a family of semihard magnetic materials first described by Gould and Wenny in 1962. They contain from 2 to 5 percent vanadium with iron and cobalt in equal parts and are characterized by high remanence, a square hysteresis loop, and a coercive force controllable over a range from 20 to 50 oersteds. These alloys bridge the gap between the high permeability and low coercive force of vanadium Permendur and Supermendur and the high coercive force and low permeability of Vicalloy.

Remendur alloys were initially developed to provide a temperature-stable permanent magnet material for the ferreed switch in the No. 1 ESS.[30] [Fig. 12-5] Remendur in the form of plates energized by current pulses in the attached windings provided the magnetic field required to open or close the soft magnetic reed members contained in a sealed glass envelope.

In order to replace the reed elements in the sealed contact with a remanent magnetic material and eliminate the external plates, studies were undertaken to elucidate the effect of various heat treatments on these alloys and the nature of the phase transformations taking place.[31,32] A remanent-reed sealed contact and remreed network was developed for ESS using a Remendur alloy for the remanent-reed members. It was introduced into manufacture in 1972.[33] Similar

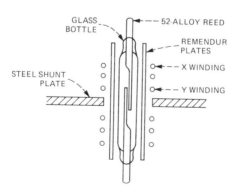

Fig. 12-5. Schematic of ferreed switch. Coincident current pulses in the horizontal (X) and vertical (Y) windings close the reeds, and the Remendur plate holds the reeds closed. A subsequent pulse in either winding opens the reeds.

ferreed and remreed contacts were subsequently produced throughout the world for the telecommunications industry.

1.2.5 Cobalt-Iron-Gold Semihard Magnetic Alloys

Another important contribution by Bell Labs scientists to semihard magnetic materials involved the cobalt-iron-gold alloys, which Nesbitt, Chin, and D. Jaffe developed for the permanent magnet element in the piggyback twistor memory.[34] [Fig. 12-6] This memory was used from the late 1960s to the mid-1970s in the ETS and TSPS units of electronic switching systems. The memory element of the twistor was composed of two magnetic tapes helically wrapped about a central copper conductor wire. The lower tape was a soft magnet made of Permalloy that performed the information-sensing function. The upper tape was a permanent magnet that performed an information-storage function. The permanent magnet required a medium coercive force of 13 to 15 oersteds, a square hysteresis loop, and near-zero magnetostriction to avoid problems from mechanical stressing. Starting with the binary cobalt-iron alloys in the vicinity of 90 percent cobalt that have a near-zero magnetostriction value, Nesbitt, Chin, and Jaffe developed an alloy of 82 percent cobalt, 12 percent iron, and 6 percent

Fig. 12-6. G. Y. Chin, co-inventor of cobalt-iron-gold semihard magnetic alloys and Chromindur magnet alloys.

gold, satisfying all the device requirements. The presence of gold helps to increase the coercive force by precipitation hardening. Later, during manufacture, the amount of gold was reduced to 4 percent.

1.2.6 *Cobalt/Rare-Earth Permanent Magnets*

About 1957, as a result of the increasing availability of rare earth elements, J. H. Wernick [Fig. 12-7] and Nesbitt [Fig. 12-8] started a rare earth alloy program directed toward discovering new magnetic materials and studying their properties. It soon became apparent to Wernick that, because of the nature of the chemistry of the rare earth elements, intermetallic compounds involving these elements would be important alloys. He prepared numerous new intermetallic compounds and systematically studied their structural and crystal-chemical relationships.[35]

Several of the newly synthesized rare earth intermetallic compounds in the Co_5Re family proved to be the basis of technologically important, new permanent-magnet materials.[36] These compounds exhibited the highest known $(BH)_m$ values (up to 30×10^6 gauss-oersteds) and thus permitted significant miniaturization of equipment. Permanent magnets based on Co_5Re phases are being manufactured throughout the world. Wernick, with Nesbitt and R. H. Willens, also invented the cobalt-copper/rare-earth class of permanent magnets, which exhibit extremely high intrinsic coercive force (about 30,000

Fig. 12-7. J. H. Wernick was responsible for the synthesis of many new magnetic rare earth intermetallic compounds.

oersteds) caused by the precipitation of a finely dispersed second phase when copper is present.[37]

1.2.7 Chromindur

The Remalloy used in the permanent magnet for the telephone receiver introduced in 1950 (U-receiver) had the disadvantage of being semibrittle and had to be hot formed near 1250°C into the cup shape required for the receiver magnet. [Fig. 12-9] Based on earlier work by H. Kaneko of Tohoku University in Japan,[38] Chin started the development of ductile chromium-cobalt-iron alloys. A task force was formed made up of personnel from both Bell Laboratories and

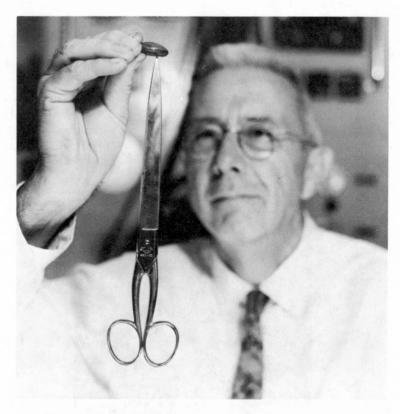

Fig. 12-8. Strength of Co_5Re magnet demonstrated by E. A. Nesbitt.

Western Electric.* The first ductile alloy developed, called Chromindur I, contained 15 percent cobalt. Subsequently, a second alloy called Chromindur II, containing only 10.5 percent of the costly cobalt and easier to process than Chromindur I, was developed and selected to replace Remalloy.[39] Full production was begun in mid-1980. Compared to Remalloy, the Chromindur alloys are better magnetically, mechanically tougher, and more corrosion-resistant.

Further research has resulted in even better Chromindur magnets, having energy products equivalent to the widely used Alnico alloys, but with the added advantage of being ductile and containing substantially less cobalt.[40] S. Jin used a new deformation-aging process to achieve a value of 5.5×10^6 gauss-oersteds for an 11.5%Co-33%Cr-55.5%Fe alloy similar to 24-percent cobalt Alnico V, and a value of 9.8

Fig. 12-9. Ring-shaped, Chromindur permanent magnet (bottom) used in the U-3 telephone receiver.

---

* Members of the task force from Bell Labs included: G. Y. Chin, S. Jin, J. T. Plewes, and B. C. Wonsiewicz from Murray Hill, and R. M. Hunt and J. E. Warren from Indianapolis. The members from Western Electric were S. Becker, C. T. Chen, P. Elarde, and C. Ghilarducci of the Hawthorne works, and C. M. Bordelon and G. Lunsford of the Shreveport works.

$\times 10^6$ gauss-oersteds for a 23%Co-2%Cu-33%Cr-42%Fe alloy, establishing a new record for chromium-cobalt-iron alloys.[41] Transmission-electron microscopy studies by S. Mahajan and coworkers and Mössbauer effect studies by M. Eibschütz and coworkers contributed to the basic understanding of the origin of the high coercivity in these new alloys.[42]

II. FERRITES

The discovery of magnetic ferrites by T. Takei in Japan,[43] and the subsequent exploratory research conducted at the Philips Laboratories in the Netherlands during World War II,[44] opened new vistas in the field of magnetic devices. The chemical formula for ferrites is MFe_2O_4, where M stands for any of the divalent ions magnesium, zinc, copper, nickel, iron, cobalt, or manganese, or a mixture of these ions. Except for compounds containing divalent iron ions, ferrites can be made with electrical resistivities in the range of 10^2 to 10^6 ohm-cm, contrasted with 10^{-5} ohm-cm for the ferromagnetic metals. This represents a major step forward for high-frequency applications.

For technical uses, dense polycrystalline bodies of ferrite compositions are made by ceramic procedures, which involve intimate mixing of fine powders of the appropriate oxides, compressing the mixture, and firing in carefully controlled atmospheres at temperatures of approximately 1100°C or 1200°C. Single crystals have been made by several techniques. The various members of the series displayed varied electrical and magnetic properties; the mixtures could therefore be tailored to fit a wide variety of technical requirements. Variations in the ceramic procedures provided another important means of adjusting properties.

2.1 Ferrites for Inductors and Filters

Before World War II, it was recognized that although inductor cores made of Permalloy dust were a great improvement over bulk Permalloy, because they reduced the eddy current loss and thus extended the useful frequency range of magnetic devices, they had reached the point of diminishing returns. The work of F. J. Schnettler and A. G. Ganz resulted in the development of a manganese-zinc ferrite for use at carrier frequencies of 100 kilohertz (kHz) and higher. One inductor, for example, occupied only one-third the volume of the metallic core it replaced, yet its quality was three times better and it was produced at one-sixth the cost.[45]

The production of manganese-zinc ferrites by Western Electric increased sharply with their incorporation into the *Touch-Tone** tele-phone introduced in the early 1960s. In the late 1970s, nearly 9 mil-lion new telephones equipped with *Touch-Tone* telephone dials were manufactured annually by Western Electric. The *Touch-Tone* tele-phone dial is a dual-frequency signal generator, at the heart of which are two ferrite-core transformers. The precisely tuned circuit demanded low magnetic loss and good stability with time and tem-perature. These, in turn, required sophisticated control of factors such as materials, chemistry, and processing through the use of small amounts of additives, such as calcium and silicon, that segregate to the grain boundaries and increase the electrical resistivity.[46]

In the 1960s and 1970s, Bell Labs scientists made several advances in linear ferrite properties in response to the rising need for high-quality linear devices in the transmission area. In the mid-1960s, the need for low-loss filters at frequencies up to 20 megahertz (MHz) for the L-4 carrier system resulted in the development of a process for making suitable nickel-zinc ferrites.[47] These were further improved until, by the mid-1970s, frequencies up to 100 MHz were possible. These advances were made by using cobalt additives and carefully controlled cooling. Very slow cooling in an oxidizing atmosphere near the Curie temperature allows the cation vacancies introduced by the oxidizing conditions to facilitate the diffusion of the cobalt ions and to trap the magnetic domain walls. The result is a movement of the domain-wall resonance peak to higher frequencies with consequent low loss.

A need for high-permeability ferrites for pulse transformers led to the development by J. F. Argyle in 1968 of a ferrite with μ of 10,000 using isostatic pressing. Improved compositions, whereby very low anisotropies and magnetostriction could be achieved, allowed M. D. Dixon to produce materials with permeabilities up to 25,000 at room temperature.

Ceramics research has led to a better understanding of the relation-ship between stoichiometry and magnetic behavior and advances in nonconventional powder-processing techniques, such as chemical coprecipitation and freeze drying, improved knowledge of sintering behavior, and the development of clean-burning binders that do not leave undesirable residues after sintering.

---

* Trademark of AT&T Co.

2.2 Ferrites for Microwave and Computer Applications

While the use of ferrites in inductors and transformers for carrier frequencies has had a major impact upon communications, its impact upon microwave and computer technology is of equal importance. The availability of magnetic oxides eventually led to the large family of nonreciprocal magnetic devices that play a key role in microwave technology. (Among these is the gyrator discussed in section 2.3.1 of Chapter 1.) The materials effort was due largely to L. G. Van Uitert, who proposed the substitution of nonmagnetic ions for magnetic ions in the ferrite structure to reduce internal fields and thereby lower the ferromagnetic resonance frequency.

In the computer field, A. Schonberg of Steatit-Magnesia AG. in Germany and workers at M.I.T.'s Lincoln Laboratories found a family of magnesium-manganese ferrites with remarkably square hysteresis loops. Potential uses of these square-loop ferrites in memory and other computer and switching applications were recognized. Schnettler developed some copper-manganese ferrites with good square-loop properties, as well as a magnesium-manganese-zinc ferrite composition that was used in the No. 101 ESS, in ferrod sensors for the No. 1 ESS, and elsewhere. Ferrite sheet memories made of a manganese-magnesium ferrite were developed by R. Meinken for use in electronic switching systems. These were replaced later by ferrite cores of a magnesium-manganese-zinc composition, which in turn gave way to semiconductor memories in the mid-1970s.

III. ORTHOFERRITES AND GARNETS

The initiation of research by S. Geller, M. A. Gilleo, and J. P. Remeika on the crystallization properties of the rare earth orthoferrites soon led to the discovery by Geller and Gilleo of another and much more important class of magnetic oxides, the ferrimagnetic garnets, of which yttrium iron garnet, $Y_3Fe_5O_{12}$, is a prototype. These garnets were independently discovered in France by F. Bertaut and F. Forrat. (See section 1.3.2 of Chapter 1.) This compound, commonly referred to as YIG, has a crystal structure identical to that of the naturally occurring semiprecious gem garnets, a complicated structure with cubic symmetry. The cubic-unit cell of the garnet structure contains 160 atoms with the metal ions located on three distinctly different kinds of crystallographic sites. [Fig. 12-10] There are eight chemical formula units in a unit cell of YIG. The Y^{3+} ions occupy 24 dodecahedral sites, and Fe^{3+} ions are on 16 octahedral sites and 24 tetrahedral sites. Ions at these positions are surrounded by eight, six, and four nearest-neighbor O^{2-} ions, respectively. As in the natural garnets, many substitutions can be made for the ions on each of these sites. Most notably, all of the 4*f* rare earth ions can be substituted for all or part of the Y^{3+} ions on dodecahedral sites, and nonmagnetic ions can preferentially replace Fe^{3+} ions on octahedral or tetrahedral sites. Thus, a great range of magnetic and crystallographic properties is accessible by adjusting the composition of ferrimagnetic garnets. Furthermore, large-sound single crystals can be grown from many of these compositions.

3.1 Garnets for Memory Devices

A. H. Bobeck's concept of using individual cylindrical domains (bubbles) in uniaxial single crystals to make high-speed memory devices with large information-storage capacities depended on finding magnetic materials with unique properties. When W. Shockley called a conference to discuss the possibility of a new type of device based on bubble domains, R. C. Sherwood who, with H. J. Williams, had been studying the domain behavior of the rare earth orthoferrites (ReFeO₃) immediately suggested that these orthoferrites possess magnetic behavior almost ideal for the device under consideration.[48-50] Van Uitert organized a program that was concerned with the growth

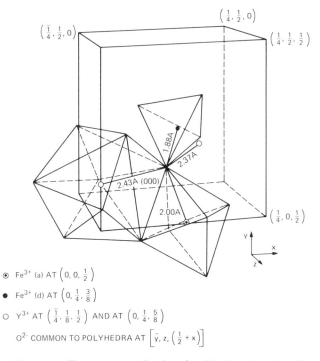

Fig. 12-10. The oxygen coordination of positive ions in yttrium iron garnet. [Gilleo and Geller, *Phys. Rev.* **110** (1958): 73].

of large orthoferrite single crystals, and later with magnetic garnets for the first prototype devices. Several orthoferrite single crystals were grown by Remeika early in the program.

A number of requirements must be met for a given material to be suitable for economical mass-memory devices based on bubbles. The material must possess a uniaxial anisotropy so that cylindrical domains can be created. The saturation moment must be low for the bubbles to be large enough for manipulation by an external field. The storage density of domains (or bits) must be of the order of 10^6 bits per square inch. Thus, the optimum domain diameter, determined by the magnitudes of the uniaxial anisotropy constant and the saturation magnetization, is of the order of a few micrometers. The bubbles must exhibit very low coercivity under an applied-field gradient and must have high mobility, since this determines the speed of the device. The coercivity and mobility requirements for bubbles place stringent demands on the quality of the single crystals; they must be relatively free of imperfections and compositional inhomogeneities.

Large crystals of orthoferrites for device studies were grown from PbO-PbF_2-B_2O_3 fluxes contained in platinum crucibles. Magnetic and device studies of single crystals of the orthoferrites and solid solutions among them showed that the bubble diameters and the temperature dependence of the magnetic properties around room temperature made the orthoferrites unattractive for mass storage devices, even though they exhibited large bubble mobilities.

The orthoferrite results suggested the preparation of cubic magnetic insulators, namely, the rare-earth iron garnets ($Re_3Fe_5O_{12}$). These garnets contained appropriate substitutions on the rare earth and iron sites to obtain a uniaxial anisotropy of proper magnitude and an optimum saturation moment, both of which led to optimum bubble diameter and nearly temperature-independent magnetic properties near room temperature.[51] Although the simple rare-earth iron garnets are ferrimagnetic and crystallographically cubic, they offered wide latitude for the control and adjustment of magnetic properties through the substitution of other rare earth and nonmagnetic aluminum and gallium atoms on the rare earth and iron sites, respectively.

Van Uitert produced the first large nonmagnetostrictive, uniaxial garnets suitable for bubble devices. These were grown from PbO-PbF_2-B_2O_3 fluxes and had varying compositions such as $Gd_{2.31}Tb_{0.60}Eu_{0.09}Fe_5O_{12}$. It was found that the noncubic symmetries required for uniaxial behavior existed under a particular growth facet of the large crystals.[52]

The technological impact of the work with garnets was enormous. Commercial mass memories were based on single-crystal garnet films epitaxially grown from fluxes by a technique developed by H. J. Levinstein and coworkers[53] onto large nonmagnetic gadolinium-gallium-garnet, single-crystal substrates grown by C. D. Brandle and A. J. Valentino.[54] Magnetic garnet compositions used in bubble-domain device technology at Western Electric[55] were optimized for mobility and speed through application of the understanding gained in the work described above.

IV. AMORPHOUS MAGNETIC MATERIALS

In 1960, W. Klement, R. H. Willens, and P. Duwez at the California Institute of Technology in Pasadena obtained amorphous or glassy metallic alloys by rapidly quenching them from the melt, at about $10^6 °C$ per second.[56] Soon thereafter, splat-cooled samples of glassy alloys containing transition metal elements were successfully prepared and found to be spontaneously magnetic at room temperature. This phenomenon of amorphous ferromagnetism became technologically interesting when H. S. Chen and C. E. Miller at Bell Labs developed a method for the continuous fabrication of long uniform ribbons of ferromagnetic glassy alloys by roller quenching.[57] The ribbons were produced by directing a molten stream between two counter-rotating rollers or onto the inside of a rotating drum. This advance led to an intense study of ferromagnetic glasses and to the discovery of many technically interesting properties, among which were high tensile strength, excellent corrosion resistance, and soft magnetic materials.

The ferromagnetic glassy alloys typically contain about 80 percent of one or more of the transition metals (iron, cobalt, nickel, chromium, manganese, and so on) with the remainder being boron, carbon, silicon, phosphorus, or aluminum. They are magnetically soft, with low losses in ac-power applications; some exhibit zero magnetostriction and low thermal expansion (invar) properties. Sherwood and coworkers at Bell Labs were the first to find alloys with zero magnetostriction, one such example being $(Fe_{0.04}Co_{0.96})_{0.75}$ $P_{0.16}B_{0.06}Al_{0.03}$.[58] Because of anisotropy acquired in the quenching process, infinite permeability should not be expected.[59] However, by minimizing the anisotropy with controlled annealing, low-field magnetic properties comparable or even superior to those of commercial Supermalloys have been achieved. Moreover, because of the larger resistivities of amorphous systems, the ferromagnetic glassy alloys can be used at much higher frequencies than the Supermalloys.

Sherwood was the first to observe a "spin-glass" transition in an iron-manganese metallic glass or, for that matter, in any concentrated magnetic material.[60] This is a transition to a frozen-in orientationally random arrangement of magnetic spins, that is, with no resulting bulk magnetic moment. Chen and his colleagues conducted extensive studies that resulted in a systematic understanding of the nature of the glassy state and the effect of alloy composition on glass-forming tendency and glassy-phase stability.[61]

In the late 1970s, a number of magnetic insulating materials have also been quenched into glassy forms. E. M. Gyorgy and coworkers have found that yttrium iron garnet, which is a room-temperature ferrimagnet in its crystalline form, exhibits a diffuse spin-glass ordering transition at about 30K when quenched from the melt as a glass.[62] Like their crystalline equivalents but unlike metallic glasses, the magnetic insulator glasses possess only near-neighbor magnetic exchange interactions. This means that magnetic measurements carry rather detailed information via the superexchange theory of the local symmetries, coordinations, and bonds present in the glassy state, information that is very difficult to acquire in such detail by any other method.[63]

REFERENCES

1. T. D. Yensen, "On the Road to Pure Iron and Some of Its Indicated Properties," *Trans. Am. Electrochem. Soc.* **56** (1929), pp. 215-222.
2. P. P. Cioffi, "Hydrogenized Iron of High Magnetic Permeability," *Nature* **126** (August 9, 1930), pp. 200-201; idem, "Hydrogenized Iron," *Phys. Rev.* **39** (January 1932), pp. 363-367.
3. P. P. Cioffi, H. J. Williams, and R. M. Bozorth, "Single Crystals with Exceptionally High Magnetic Permeabilities," *Phys. Rev.* **51** (June 1937), p. 1009.
4. J. H. Scaff and E. E. Schumacher, "Some Theoretical and Practical Aspects of Gases in Metals," *Bell System Tech. J.* **12** (April 1933), pp. 178-196.
5. R. M. Bozorth, *Ferromagnetism* (Princeton, N.J.: D. Van Nostrand Company, Inc., 1951), p. 38.
6. J. H. Swisher, A. T. English, and R. C. Stoffers, "Role of Specific Impurities on the Magnetic Properties of Low-Carbon Steels," *Transactions of the American Society for Metals* **62** (March 1969), pp. 257-262.
7. J. H. Swisher and E. O. Fuchs, "An Improved Forming Gas Heat Treatment for Low-Carbon Steels," *J. Iron and Steel Inst.* **208** (August 1970), pp. 777-778.
8. H. D. Arnold and G. W. Elmen, "Permalloy, A New Magnetic Material of Very High Permeability," *Bell System Tech. J.* **2** (July 1923), pp. 101-111; also, see the first volume of this series, *A History of Engineering and Science in the Bell System: The Early Years (1875-1925)*, ed. M. Fagen (Bell Telephone Laboratories, Inc., 1975), pp. 979-982.
9. G. W. Elmen, "Magnetic Alloys of Iron, Nickel, and Cobalt," *J. Franklin Inst.* **207** (May 1929), pp. 583-617; idem., *Electrical Engineering* **54** (December 1935), pp. 1292-1299.
10. G. W. Elmen, "Magnetic Properties of Perminvar," *J. Franklin Inst.* **206** (September 1928), pp. 317-338.
11. R. M. Bozorth, *Ferromagnetism* (Princeton, N.J.: D. Van Nostrand Company, Inc., 1951), pp. 160-180; also, see the first volume of this series, *A History of Engineering and Science in the Bell System: The Early Years (1875-1925)*, ed. M. D. Fagen (Bell Laboratories, Inc., 1975), p. 814.
12. O. L. Boothby and R. M. Bozorth, "A New Magnetic Material of High Permeability," *J. Appl. Phys.* **18** (February 1947), pp. 173-176.
13. G. Y. Chin, "Slip-Induced Directional Order in Fe-Ni Alloys. I. Extension of the Chikazumi-Suzuki-Iwata Theory," *J. Appl. Phys.* **36** (September 1965), pp. 2915-

2924; G. Y. Chin, E. A. Nesbitt, and J. H. Wernick, "Slip-Induced Directional Order in Fe-Ni Alloys. II. Experimental Observations," *J. Appl. Phys.* **38** (May 1967), pp. 2623-2629.

14. G. Y. Chin, T. C. Tisone, and W. B. Grupen, "Metallurgical Control of Magnetic Properties in Co-Fe and Ni-Fe Alloys for Memory Applications," *J. Appl. Phys.* **42** (March 1971), pp. 1502-1509.
15. See reference 9.
16. C. V. Wahl and J. H. White, U.S. Patent No. 1,739,052; filed January 30, 1929; issued December 10, 1929; also, see W. J. Shackelton and I. G. Barber, "Compressed Powdered Permalloy Manufacture and Magnetic Properties," *Trans. Am. Inst. Elec. Eng.* **47** (February 1928), pp. 429-437; W. C. Ellis and E. E. Schumacher, "A Survey of Magnetic Materials in Relation to Structure," *Bell System Tech. J.* **14** (January 1935), pp. 8-43.
17. V. E. Legg and F. J. Given, "Compressed Powdered Molybdenum Permalloy for High Quality Inductance Coils," *Bell System Tech. J.* **19** (July 1940), pp. 385-406.
18. M. E. Fine and W. C. Ellis, "Thermal Variation of Young's Modulus in Some Iron-Nickel-Molybdenum Alloys," *J. Metals* **3** (September 1951), pp. 761-764.
19. W. C. Ellis, "A Study of the Physical Properties of Electrolytic Cobalt and Its Alloys with Iron," *Rensselaer Polytechnic Institute Bulletin*, Engineering and Science Series, **No. 16** (June 1927).
20. J. H. White and C. V. Wahl, U.S. Patent No. 1,862,559; filed August 14, 1931; issued June 14, 1932.
21. V. E. Legg, "Survey of Magnetic Materials and Applications in the Telephone System," *Bell System Tech. J.* **18** (July 1939), pp. 438-464; also, see reference 9.
22. H. L. B. Gould and D. H. Wenny, "Supermendur. A New Rectangular Loop Magnetic Material," *Electrical Engineering* **76** (March 1957), pp. 208-211.
23. K. S. Seljasater and B. A. Rogers, "Magnetic and Mechanical Hardness of Dispersion-Hardened Iron Alloys," *Transactions of the American Society for Steel Treating* **19** (1932), pp. 553-572.
24. E. S. Greiner, E. M. Tolman, and E. E. Thomas, private communication, 1936.
25. R. A. Chegwidden, "A Review of Magnetic Materials Especially for Communication Systems," *Metal Progress* **54** (November 1948), pp. 705-714.
26. E. A. Nesbitt and G. A. Kelsall, "Vicalloy, a New Permanent Magnet Material," *Phys. Rev.* **58** (July 1940), p. 203; idem., U.S. Patent No. 2,190,667; filed April 9, 1938, issued February 20, 1940; E. A. Nesbitt, G. A. Kelsall, and K. S. Dunlop, U.S. Patent No. 2,298,225; filed December 30, 1939, issued October 6, 1942; E. A. Nesbitt, "Vicalloy—A Workable Alloy for Permanent Magnets," *Metals Technology* **13** (February 1946), pp. 1-11.
27. D. H. Wenny, "Some Magnetic Materials," *Bell Laboratories Record* **43** (June 1965), pp. 257-261.
28. See reference 27; also, see R. H. Meinken and L. W. Stammerjohn, "Memory Devices," *Bell Laboratories Record* **43** (June 1965), pp. 229-235.
29. J. B. Fisk, H. D. Hagstrum, and P. L. Hartman, "The Magnetron as a Generator of Centimeter Waves," in *Radar Systems and Components*, ed. members of the Technical Staff of Bell Telephone Laboratories (New York: D. Van Nostrand Company, Inc., 1949), pp. 56-237.
30. A. Feiner, "The Ferreed," *Bell System Tech. J.* **43** (January 1964), pp. 1-14.
31. W. E. Archer, K. M. Olsen, and P. W. Renaut, "Development of a Remanent Reed Sealed Contact," *Bell System Tech. J.* **55** (June 1976), pp. 511-535; R. J. Gashler, W. A. Liss, and P. W. Renaut, "The Remreed Network: A Smaller, More Reliable Switch," *Bell Laboratories Record* **51** (July/August 1973), pp. 203-207.
32. M. R. Pinnel, "Magnetic Materials for Dry Reed Contacts," *IEEE Transactions on Magnetics* **MAG-12** (November 1976), pp. 789-794.

33. S. Mahajan, M. R. Pinnel, and J. E. Bennett, "Influence of Heat Treatments on Microstructures in an Fe-Co-V Alloy," *Metallurgical Trans.* **5** (June 1974), pp. 1263-1272.

34. E. A. Nesbitt, G. Y. Chin, and D. Jaffe, "New Low-Magnetostrictive Permanent-Magnet Alloys," *J. Appl. Phys.* **39** (February 1968), pp. 1268-1269.

35. E. A. Nesbitt, J. H. Wernick, and E. Corenzwit, "Magnetic Moments of Alloys and Compounds of Iron and Cobalt with Rare Earth Metal Additions," *J. Appl. Phys.* **30** (March 1959), pp. 365-367; J. H. Wernick and S. Geller, "Transition Element—Rare Earth Compounds with the Cu_5Ca Structure," *Acta Crystallographica* **12** (September 1959), pp. 662-665.

36. E. A. Nesbitt, R. H. Willens, R. C. Sherwood, E. Buehler, and J. H. Wernick, "New Permanent Magnet Materials," *Appl. Phys. Lett.* **12** (June 1, 1968), pp. 361-362; E. A. Nesbitt and J. H. Wernick, *Rare Earth Permanent Magnets* (New York: Academic Press, 1973).

37. See reference 36; also, see E. A. Nesbitt, J. H. Wernick, and R. H. Willens, U.S. Patent No. 3,560,200; filed April 1, 1968; issued February 2, 1971.

38. H. Kaneko, M. Homma, and K. Nakamura, "New Ductile Permanent Magnet of Fe-Cr-Co System," *AIP Conf. Proc., No. 5, Magnetism and Magnetic Materials—1971,* Part 2, pp. 1088-1092.

39. G. Y. Chin, J. T. Plewes, and B. C. Wonsiewicz, "New Ductile Cr-Co-Fe Permanent Magnet Alloys for Telephone Receiver Applications," *J. Appl. Phys.* **49** (March 1978), pp. 2046-2048; S. Jin, G. Y. Chin, and B. C. Wonsiewicz, "A Low Cobalt Ternary Cr-Co-Fe Alloy for Telephone Receiver Magnet Use," *IEEE Transactions on Magnetics* **MAG-16** (January 1980), pp. 139-146.

40. G. Y. Chin, "New Magnetic Alloys," *Science* **208** (May 23, 1980), pp. 888-894.

41. S. Jin, "Deformation-Induced Anisotropic Cr-Co-Fe Permanent Magnet Alloys," *IEEE Transactions on Magnetics* **MAG-15** (November 1979), pp. 1748-1750; S. Jin, N. V. Gayle, and J. E. Bernardidi, "Deformation-Aged Cr-Co-Cu-Fe Permanent Magnet Alloys," *IEEE Transactions on Magnetics* **MAG-16** (September 1980), pp. 1050-1052.

42. S. Mahajan, E. M. Gyorgy, R. C. Sherwood, S. Jin, S. Nakahara, D. Brasen, and M. Eibschutz, "Origin of Coercivity in a Cr-Co-Fe Alloy (Chromindur)," *Appl. Phys. Lett.* **32** (May 15, 1978), pp. 688-690; M. Eibschütz et al., "Observation of Phase Separation in a Cr-Co-Fe Alloy (Chromindur) by Mössbauer Effect," *Appl. Phys. Lett.* **33** (August 15, 1978), pp. 362-363.

43. T. Takei, "Review of Ferrite Memory Materials in Japan," *Ferrites, Proceedings of the International Conference,* ed. Y. Hoshino, S. Iida, and M. Sugimoto (Baltimore: University Park Press, 1971), pp. 436-437.

44. J. L. Snoek, *New Developments in Ferromagnetic Materials* (New York: Elsevier Publishing Co., Inc, 1949).

45. H. A. Stone, Jr., "Ferrite Core Inductors," *Bell System Tech. J.* **32** (March 1953), pp. 265-291.

46. F. J. Schnettler, "Microstructure and Processing of Ferrites," *Physics of Electronic Ceramics, Part B,* ed. L. L. Hench and D. B. Dove (New York: Marcel Dekker, Inc., 1972), pp. 833-855.

47. P. I. Slick, U.S. Patent No. 3,533,949; filed November 21, 1967, issued October 13, 1970.

48. A. H. Bobeck, "Properties and Device Applications of Magnetic Domains in Orthoferrites," *Bell System Tech. J.* **46** (October 1967), pp. 1901-1925.

49. A. H. Bobeck, U. F. Gianola, R. C. Sherwood, and W. Shockley, U.S. Patent No. 3,460,116; filed September 16, 1966, issued August 5, 1969.

50. A. H. Bobeck, R. F. Fischer, A. J. Perneski, J. P. Remeika, and L. G. Van Uitert, "Application of Orthoferrites to Domain-Wall Devices," *IEEE Transactions on Magnetics* **MAG-5** (September 1969), pp. 544-553.

51. A. H. Bobeck, R. C. Sherwood, and L. G. Van Uitert, U.S. Patent No. 3,665,427; filed April 20, 1970, issued May 23, 1972.

52. See reference 51; also, see A. H. Bobeck, E. G. Spencer, L. G. Van Uitert, S. C. Abrahams, R. L. Barns, W. H. Grodkiewicz, R. C. Sherwood, P. H. Schmidt, D. H. Smith, and E. M. Walters, "Uniaxial Magnetic Garnets for Domain Wall 'Bubble' Devices," *Appl. Phys. Lett.* **17** (August 1, 1970), pp. 131-134; L. G. Van Uitert, W. A. Bonner, W. H. Grodkiewicz, L. Pictroski, and G. J. Zydzik, "Garnets for Bubble Domain Devices," *Materials Research Bulletin* **5** (September 1970), pp. 825-835.

53. H. J. Levinstein, S. Licht, R. W. Landorf, and S. L. Blank, "Growth of High-Quality Garnet Thin Films from Supercooled Melts," *Appl. Phys. Lett.* **19** (December 1, 1971), pp. 486-488.

54. C. D. Brandle and A. J. Valentino, "Czochralski Growth of Rare Earth Gallium Garnets," *J. Cryst. Growth* **12** (January 1972), pp. 3-8.

55. S. L. Blank, R. Wolfe, L. C. Luther, R. G. LeCraw, T. J. Nelson, and W. A. Biolsi, "Design and Development of Single-Layer, Ion-Implantable Small Bubble Materials for Magnetic Bubble Devices," *J. Appl. Phys.* **50** (March 1979), pp. 2155-2160.

56. W. Klement, Jr., R. H. Willens, and P. Duwez, "Non-Crystalline Structure in Solidified Gold-Silicon Alloys," *Nature* **187** (September 3, 1960), pp. 869-870.

57. H. S. Chen and C. E. Miller, "A Rapid Quenching Technique for the Preparation of Thin Uniform Films of Amorphous Solids," *Rev. Sci. Instrum.* **41** (August 1970), pp. 1237-1238.

58. R. C. Sherwood, E. M. Gyorgy, H. S. Chen, S. D. Ferris, G. Norman, and H. J. Leamy, "Ferromagnetic Behavior of Metallic Glasses," *AIP Conf. Proc.* **24** (1975), pp. 745-746.

59. H. S. Chen, S. D. Ferris, E. M. Gyorgy, H. J. Leamy, and R. C. Sherwood, "Field Heat Treatment of Ferromagnetic Metallic Glasses," *Appl. Phys. Lett.* **26** (April 1, 1975), pp. 405-406.

60. R. C. Sherwood, "Exchange Anisotropy in Metallic Glasses," *AIP Conf. Proc., No. 34, Magnetism and Magnetic Materials* (1976), pp. 327-330.

61. H. S. Chen, "Thermodynamic Considerations in the Formation and Stability of Metallic Glasses," *Acta Metallurgica* **22** (December 1974), pp. 1505-1571.

62. E. M. Gyorgy, K. Nassau, M. Eibschütz, J. V. Waszczak, C. A. Wang, and J. C. Shelton, "The Magnetic Properties of Amorphous $Y_3Fe_5O_{12}$," *J. Appl. Phys.* **50** (April 1979), pp. 2883-2886.

63. M. E. Lines, "Hard-Sphere Random-Packing Model for an Ionic Glass: Yttrium Iron Garnet," *Phys. Rev.* **B20** (November 1979), pp. 3729-3738.

Chapter 13

Glasses — Fiber Light Guides

The making of glass is almost as old as civilization, but the use of glasses for vessels, ornaments, and windows remained largely an art until the 17th century. At that time and later, the demand for optical glass grew rapidly and stimulated the development of improved recipes and processes. In the late 19th century, the development of chemical control and mechanical methods of manufacture changed glassmaking from a craft to a technology.

The Bell System has always been interested in the electrical properties of glasses. Early research and development work concentrated on glass requiring special properties, as in the application for capacitor dielectrics, close-spaced vacuum triodes, traveling wave tubes, and glass for bonding metals to ceramic systems. In the 1950s and 1960s, much work was done on glasses for acoustic delay lines having zero temperature coefficient of acoustic velocity, on glasses for encapsulants for semiconductor devices, on silica for helium diffusion, and on glasses for other applications. In the 1970s, research at Bell Laboratories turned vigorously to the optical qualities of glass for lightwave transmission systems and brought about marked improvements in transparency.

I. EARLY RESEARCH AND DEVELOPMENT

Glass has always been an important material in the Bell System, and its use in significant applications predated the organization of Bell Laboratories in 1925. In the early days, glass was used as the insulating material on telephone poles, as glass envelopes to enclose vacuum tubes, and in glass-to-metal seals in the bases of vacuum tubes. In more mundane applications, glass was used in panels, reinforced with wire mesh, in telephone booths, and for battery jars in central offices. In the telephone instrument itself, vitreous enameled number plates were used for telephone dials.

Investigations of new glass compositions and efforts to improve the properties of older products began in the early 1940s. Usually these activities involved uses of glass where the quantity of material or number of piece parts was too small to be of interest to traditional,

Principal authors: M. I. Cohen, R. A. Laudise, S. R. Nagel, A. D. Pearson, M. D. Rigterink, and J. H. Scaff

large scale, outside suppliers. Examples include the development of glasses that are stable at high temperatures and reducing atmospheres for use as adhesives and capacitor dielectrics in close-spaced triode and traveling wave tubes, as well as the glass protective coating applied to thermistors. Somewhat later, but falling into the same category, came the work by A. W. Treptow and L. A. Finneran on glass bonding for silver, copper, and other metal pastes.[1] This work involved the development of pastes containing powdered glass that were used to screenprint and fireprint wiring directly onto ceramic surfaces. The metal, glass, and ceramic system was engineered so that the glass effectively bonded the metal to the ceramic substrate, but also allowed sufficient electrical conductivity for the metal paths to function.

At the same time, there was considerable interest in applications where glass was present in a multiphase medium, but still performed an important function. An example of this is the low-loss steatites and alkaline-earth porcelain ceramics developed by M. D. Rigterink and R. O. Grisdale. These materials are composed of a mixture of polycrystalline and glass phases, the latter playing a dominant role in determining the electrical properties of these materials.[2]

1.1 Glasses for Acoustic Delay Lines and as Encapsulants for Semiconductor Devices

During the 1950s and into the 1960s, a considerable amount of work was done on acoustic delay lines. Fused silica, with a high degree of optical perfection and low acoustic loss, was one of the principal materials studied. In addition, multicomponent glasses were investigated in the mid-1960s by J. T. Krause. Although the acoustic losses of multicomponent glasses were higher, certain compositions were found that could be fabricated with a zero-temperature coefficient of acoustic velocity. Thus, a delay line could be developed whose acoustical delay was immune to changes in temperature, at least within reasonable limits. These developments proved to be of value, mainly in military systems.

Toward the end of the 1950s, chalcogenide glasses, which soften and melt at low temperatures, were investigated as an encapsulant for semiconductor devices. At that time, the active device chip had to be sealed within a metal can to protect it from the deleterious effects of the ambient environment. This situation, where a relatively inexpensive chip of silicon or germanium had to be enclosed in a relatively expensive metal can, was obviously undesirable. Chalcogenide glasses based on the parent system, arsenic trisulfide, were discovered by S. S. Flaschen, A. D. Pearson, W. R. Northover, and I. L. Kalnins. These glasses were successfully used to encapsulate silicon diodes that had remarkably stable and reproducible properties.[3] However, with the advent of planar technology in semiconductor devices, the need for such encapsulants disappeared.

At Bell Labs the work on chalcogenide glasses was followed by Pearson's discovery of switching phenomena and memory phenomena in semiconducting glasses.[4,5] The effects were unusual and exciting in the laboratory, but detailed studies showed that the stability and reliability of devices based on these phenomena did not satisfy Bell System requirements. Nevertheless, the work helped to stimulate a large number of practical and fundamental studies on amorphous semiconductors. Some of the higher-melting chalcogenide glass compositions were studied by C. R. Kurkjian and Krause in the early 1970s and remained of interest for possible use as acoustic delay lines when fashioned in fiber form. [Fig. 13-1]

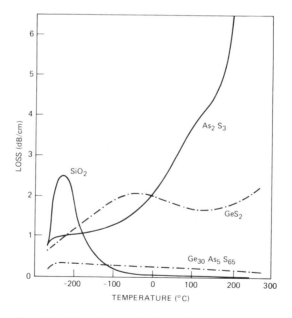

Fig. 13-1. Acoustic loss of various glasses as a function of temperature at 20 MHz. This behavior is characteristic of frequencies in the 5- to 20-MHz range, which are commonly used in acoustic delay lines. Note the low loss and the absence of a specific loss peak in the $Ge_{30}As_5S_{65}$ glass. [Krause et al., *Appl. Phys. Lett.* **17** (1970): 367].

1.2 Fused Silica for Helium Separation by Diffusion

In the mid-1950s, in the course of investigating the effect of helium diffusion in glass seals of the transatlantic cable, K. B. McAfee discovered that helium can be separated from a mixture of gases by diffusion in fused silica.[6] The helium atoms rapidly diffuse through the molecular structure of this glass, which cannot readily be penetrated by other atomic and molecular species. The helium-containing gas mixture is passed at elevated pressure through thin silica glass tubes. The helium diffuses preferentially through the tube wall and is recovered from the other side, while the rest of the gases in the mixture remain enclosed within the tube. The process produces extremely pure helium with impurity content of only a few parts per million. This process has been adopted commercially in applications requiring very pure helium.

1.3 Glazes for High-Alumina Ceramic Substrates

A particularly successful development, resulting from the work of F. V. DiMarcello, Treptow, and L. A. Baker, has been the high-quality glaze compositions for high-alumina ceramic substrates.[7] These glazes are coatings applied to substrates to improve their properties and offer a number of noteworthy features not previously available, including thermal expansion coefficients to match that of the substrate, better wetting characteristics to allow the application of thinner glaze coatings to substrates, high insulation resistance, and superior chemical stability. Subsequently, the selective glazing technique was realized that allows a glaze to be applied to specific areas of a substrate. This was particularly important for the development of integrated circuits. In an integrated circuit, the smooth surface provided by the glaze is necessary for capacitors, but is undesirable where resistors are to be fabricated because the glaze forms a thermal barrier that hinders the rapid dissipation of the heat developed by the resistors. These glaze compositions and selective glazing techniques are now widely used throughout the Bell System in integrated circuit technology.

1.4 Glasses for Other Applications

Other glass products realized during the 1950s and 1960s in which the contributions of Bell Labs scientists played an important role include compositions produced by Treptow and Rigterink for porcelain and enamel finishes for the side panels and shelves of telephone booths,[8] and tempered glass panels capable of withstanding considerable shock without breaking. Glass plane boards for electronic switching memories,[9] submerged glass floats for underwater sound systems for military applications, and glass-to-metal seals for submarine cable repeaters were also developed. The adequate specification of the necessary performance characteristics of all these products allowed a high level of trouble-free performance to be maintained in actual use.

Among the more fundamental investigations carried out during the 1960s were the studies of rare-earth-containing glasses in optical Faraday rotators[10] and in energy transfer processes.[11]

In the early part of 1970, very thin, precise, fused-silica disks were fabricated by J. C. Williams and his colleagues for use in low-pass filters for the millimeter waveguide system. The dimensional tolerances and quality required for the successful implementation of these achievements demanded adherence to much closer tolerances than had previously been necessary in the industry. The interaction of Bell Labs scientists with the outside suppliers helped establish reliable sources of supply for these components.

II. GLASS FOR OPTICAL COMMUNICATIONS

Perhaps the most important achievement of the 30 years of work in glass research at Bell Laboratories was laying the groundwork and assembling a group of people with broad expertise in the field of glass science and technology. These individuals, with their own broad backgrounds in glass science and their familiarity with the work of others in the field, were ready when the challenge of optical communications came along.

With the advent of the laser in the early 1960s, numerous possibilities for practical applications became apparent. The most exciting of these was the use of light to transmit information—optical communications.[12] As a basic idea, optical communications was not new. Alexander Graham Bell had demonstrated his photophone shortly after he invented the telephone. However, the practical application of optical communications and its integration into a nationwide network required more sophisticated techniques than were available to Bell in his pioneering work. Paramount among these was the need for an appropriate transmission medium. While optical signals can be sent through the atmosphere for considerable periods, interruptions inevitably occur during rainstorms, fog, and other atmospheric disturbances. A number of waveguiding methods were explored to avoid the shortcomings of the atmosphere. Laser beams were successfully guided within conduits by periodically refocusing the lightwave with mirror-pairs or with thermal-gradient gas lenses; both were demonstrated to have losses in the vicinity of 1 dB/km prior to 1970. (For more on this topic, see the section on lightwave transmission in the "Lightwave Communication" chapter of a subsequent volume in this series, entitled "Communications Sciences.") However, a technological competitor, the glass fiber, was demonstrated in 1970 to have a loss of 16 dB/km. The structural simplicity and mechanical flexibility of the fiber as well as its broader prospective field of application resulted in immediate concentration on this form of transmission medium.

2.1 Low-Loss Fiber as Optical Waveguides

Optical fiber waveguides are not new. The principle of the transmission and guidance of light by a high-index medium surrounded by a lower-index medium was demonstrated by J. Tyndall at the end of the 19th century. For light guidance in a fiber waveguide, a core of material with a given refractive index is fabricated. This core is surrounded by a cladding material of lower refractive index. For some years, optical fiber bundles have been used in medical endoscopes and in other applications requiring that light be transmitted for a few feet. However, for a communications system relying upon optical signals to be successful, light must be transmitted for many kilometers. Herein lay the research challenge. The glass must be extremely transparent so that a detectable signal emerges at the far end of a particular fiber.

The effort to develop a successful optical waveguide began at various laboratories around the world in the mid-1960s. K. C. Kao and G. A. Hockman of Standard Communications Laboratories in England reported measurements on commercially available bulk glasses with losses as low as a few decibels per kilometer (dB/km).[13] The first really low-loss glass fibers were prepared at Corning Glass Works in New York in 1970. As reported by R. D. Maurer, these single-mode fibers had a loss of about 20 dB/km for light with a wavelength of 0.6328 micrometer (μm).[14] In the technique developed at Corning, called the "soot process," vapor chlorides (for example, silicon tetrachloride) are converted to oxide soot by flame hydrolysis and then deposited on the outside of a cylindrical mandrel. The mandrel is subsequently removed, leaving a tube of compacted soot which is then consolidated at high temperature to a clear glass. Fiber is later drawn from the consolidated preform tube when the tube is heated. The soot process was important for establishing the feasibility of making low-loss fibers and has been developed into a viable manufacturing process.

Bell Laboratories has become known as one of the leaders in research and development in this field since its entry in 1967. Early studies by Pearson and W. G. French involved melting multicomponent glasses in a fairly conventional but very clean fashion to exclude impurities and to reduce absorption losses drastically (compared to glass then manufactured in the ordinary way). After obtaining appropriately purified chemicals, these workers eventually prepared some very low-loss glass compositions.[15] (Advances in purification and analysis of raw materials for production of glasses by melting are reviewed in Section 5.2 of Chapter 10.) The first low-loss fibers prepared at Bell Labs by deposition from the vapor phase were reported by French and coworkers in 1973.[16] The fused silica core and borosilicate cladding were deposited by chemical vapor deposition (CVD) inside a silica tube using silane, diborane, and oxygen as the starting materials. The tube was then collapsed into a solid rod from which the fiber was drawn. The lowest loss was about 6.5 dB/km at 0.8 μm. In 1974, this technique produced fiber losses of less than 2 dB/km, which represented the first time this low level had been achieved.[17] However, the deposition rates were too low to be feasible as a commercial process.

2.1.1 *The Modified Chemical Vapor Deposition (MCVD) Technique*

A dramatic improvement in process rates was realized in 1974 with the disclosure of a new process for forming glass fiber lightguides, invented by J. B. MacChesney and P. B. O'Connor.[18] [Fig. 13-2] The new process, Modified Chemical Vapor Deposition (MCVD) overcame

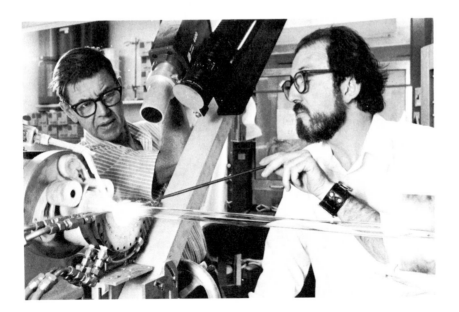

Fig. 13-2. J. B. MacChesney (left) and P. B. O'Connor, co-inventors of the MCVD technique in the process of making low-loss optical fibers. The silica tube and its contents are heated until they collapse into a solid glass rod, from which about 10 miles of fiber can be drawn.

the rate limitations of CVD techniques by using greatly increased reactant concentrations at high temperatures, resulting in the formation of particles which were deposited and simultaneously fused to form a glassy film; a two-order-of-magnitude increase in glass fabrication rate was realized. The technique is based on the high temperature oxidation of reagents within a rotating tube, typically fused silica, mounted in a glass working lathe and heated by a traversing oxyhydrogen burner. The reactants, such as $SiCl_4$, $GeCl_4$, $POCl_3$, CCl_2F_2 and BCl_3 are entrained in an oxygen gas stream, and because their vapor pressures are very high relative to those of any transition metal impurities, very high purity glass results. Because the system is closed to room atmosphere, special clean room requirements are unnecessary. Layer by layer of core and/or cladding material is deposited until sufficient material is accumulated; the composite tube is then heated to a higher temperature, causing it to collapse into a solid rod called a preform. The refractive index structure built into the preform is maintained when it is drawn into fiber. The technique can be used to realize virtually any desired refractive index profile required for either single mode or multimode lightguides by simply controlling the ratio of chemical reactants on each layer. Thus graded index cores were readily achieved for production of multimode fibers with low model dispersion. Moreover, the technique has allowed the fabrication of a wide variety of fiber types on the same equipment by simply changing the chemical delivery program.

Since the MCVD invention, subsequent studies focused on understanding the physics and chemistry of the process in order to obtain the best optical, dimensional, and mechanical properties of both the preform and the fiber drawn from it. The culmination of such work has been the successful implementation of this process into large scale, economic manufacture of lightguides by Western Electric beginning in 1979. By the early 1980s, this MCVD process had been widely adopted and accounted for the dominant fraction of lightguide fiber produced throughout the world.

Early multimode lightguides were designed for transmission in the 0.8 μm to 0.9 μm wavelength region, and routinely showed losses of 3 dB/km to 4 dB/km.[19] Bandwidths greater than 1 GHz were demonstrated by careful optimization of the chemical delivery program to grade the refractive index precisely.[20] With the achievement of successful operation of lasers and LEDs at longer wavelengths (greater than 1 μm), where the intrinsic fiber transmission losses were lower, further work focused on eliminating the hydroxl radical (OH) which causes strong absorption in this region. Chemical purification techniques for removing any source of hydrogen contamination were developed, including the invention of a photochlorination technique.[21,22] Techniques for the analysis of residual impurities were developed, including absorption spectroscopy for trace metals[23] and infrared spectroscopy for hydrogen species.[24] Multimode fibers with intrinsic losses of less than 0.5 dB/km at 1.3 μm were fabricated routinely with only 10 part-per-billion OH, giving rise to a 0.5 dB/km OH absorption peak at 1.39 μm.[25] With further chlorine drying this OH impurity was reduced to 1 part-per-billion and the OH peak to 0.05 dB/km.[26,27] [Fig. 13-3]

Improvements in lasers also made feasible the use of single mode fibers, which have lower losses and high bandwidths, especially for very long distance applications such as undersea systems. Single mode fiber designs with losses as low as 0.36 dB/km at 1.3 μm and 0.2 dB/km at 1.55 μm, with 40 km lengths were demonstrated.[28-30] A further advance was realized in a novel single mode structure, designed and fabricated to allow very high bandwidth (low dispersion) over the entire long wavelength region (1.3-1.6 μm).[31]

Scale up and optimization of the MCVD process for manufacturing implementation required understanding of the process mechanisms. Predictive studies of the equilibrium chemistry during all phases of the processing led to precise compositional and thus refractive index control in MCVD fibers.[32-34] The demonstration of thermophoresis, the net movement of a suspended particle in the direction of decreasing temperature, as the particulate deposition mechanism in MCVD played a key role in realizing higher deposition rates.[35-37] Studies of

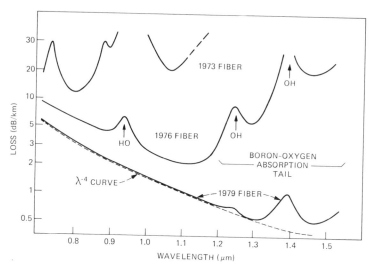

Fig. 13-3. Improvement in multimode fiber loss. Early fiber (1973) had a relatively high OH impurity concentration and contained boron. Improvement in water control further reduced fiber loss (1976). The 1979 fiber, which substituted phosphorus for boron and reduced the OH content, led to the realization of losses close to the theoretical limits (λ^{-4} curve).

viscous sintering as the fusion mechanism allowed optimization of the consolidation of each deposited layer in MCVD, without a degradation in optical properties at high rates.[38,39] Modelling of, and experiments on, the preform collapse rate and stability allowed further improvements in the total process time.[40] This understanding allowed the realization of MCVD fibers with optimized properties at deposition rates 20 times higher than the initial studies.[41,42]

A modification of the MCVD process, invented in 1980 by J. W. Fleming, and O'Connor,[43] utilizing a radio frequency plasma to enhance the MCVD process, resulted in even further improvements in process rate. A 5 MHz well-centered oxygen plasma, at or near atmospheric pressure inside a water-cooled glass substrate tube, is utilized to drive the chemical reaction to enhance the thermophoretic deposition of material. In this manner, reactant incorporation efficiencies of 80-100 percent (as compared to 30-60 percent in conventional MCVD) are realized, even at very high deposition rates. A separate heat

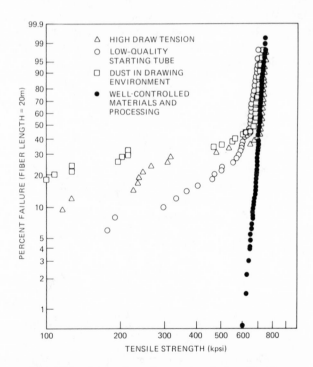

Fig. 13-4. Comparison of strengths of glass fiber drawn under well-controlled conditions with earlier fabrication processes. [Schonhorn et al., *Appl. Phys. Lett.* **29** (1976): pp. 712-714].

source is independently used to optimize the sintering. Very low losses (0.2 dB/km at 1.55 μm) have been achieved using this technique, as well as preforms yielding 40-km fiber lengths.[44]

2.1.2 Fiber Drawing, Coating, and Tensile Strength

Drawing the preform into a lightguide fiber is the second critical step in preparing glasses for optical communications. The final fiber diameter, its variation, and the mechanical and transmission properties were, to a large extent, determined on drawing. Fiber is drawn by feeding the preform into a very high temperature furnace (~ 2200°C) causing its tip to soften; the drawing force to convert the glass into approximately 0.013 cm diameter fiber is typically provided through a capstan.

The tensile strength of the fibers is important to ensure their survival through the rigors of cable manufacture and installation. The intrinsic strength of silica glass is high: tensile strengths well in excess of 1 million psi have been measured on short lengths of pristine fiber. However, this strength degrades through brittle fracture resulting from damage to the glass surface as microcracks form and grow when tensile loads are applied. A flaw only 2 μm in size will degrade the effective strength to 70,000 psi, a greater than ten-fold reduction. Thus, fiber drawing and coating techniques had to be developed to minimize such effects and to allow long lengths of high strength fiber to be fabricated. During 1975 and 1976, H. Schonhorn, Kurkjian, and coworkers demonstrated very high tensile strength silica fibers, achieved by drawing fibers with near perfect surfaces by using "clean" CO_2 laser heating and coating the fiber "in-line" to protect the pristine surface from damage.[45] [Fig. 13-4] H. N. Vazirani introduced a specially formulated, ultraviolet-curable liquid resin which was applied to the fiber, then cross-linked to form a tough, abrasion resistant protective coating.[46] Contactless, well-centered coatings were applied by employing a soft, flexible cone-shaped die developed by D. C. Hart and R. V. Albarino.[47] The die responded to forces generated by the flowing resin within it, to achieve self-centering of the fiber on the coating.

Long term aging or static fatigue effects in fibers have to be considered for reliability of systems using lightguides. J. Krause and coworkers studied the deterioration of fiber strength, due principally to the interaction of water vapor at the fiber surface.[48] This made it possible to define design criteria for guaranteeing reliability of fiber systems over time and in different environments.

To obtain high strength fiber in long lengths, many factors must be precisely controlled, as demonstrated by F. DiMarcello and coworkers.[49] Defect-free starting tubes are critical. The preform surface must be kept clean and flaw-free during fiber drawing and this can be accomplished by etching and/or firepolishing. A filtered, clean-air atmosphere is used during drawing to avoid sources of particle contamination. A special high-temperature, radio-frequency, inductively-heated zirconia furnace was developed, allowing particle-free, high-strength fiber with very precisely controlled dimensions to be drawn and coated. Clean, particle-free coatings were also shown to be important in achieving long-length, high-strength fiber. Implementation of proper drawing and coating operations have allowed production of optical waveguide fiber in kilometer lengths with tensile strengths in excess of 500,000 psi.[50]

A second approach to obtaining long lengths of high strength fiber is to develop high-strength, low-loss splicing techniques to fuse shorter high-strength lengths together. Krause and coworkers developed a special torch using chlorine and hydrogen for flame fusion of fibers, which resulted in the first very-high-strength splices simultaneously exhibiting low losses.[51] Hart and coworkers developed a practical recoating technique for such splices which did not damage the fiber and had approximately the same diameter as the original coating material.[52]

These steady improvements in fiber drawing, coating and splicing has allowed the practical attainment of very long lengths of high strength fiber. Such achievements made possible the fabrication of fiber for the first submarine lightguide sea trial in September, 1982, where high strength fibers passing a 200,000 psi prooftest level and splices with strengths in excess of 300,000 psi were utilized in long lengths successfully.

By the early 1980s, optical communications systems, involving several hundred thousand kilometers of fiber, had already found worldwide commercial use. These systems, which were made possible by research advances in semiconductor lasers and diodes, as well as the glass lightguide media described above, show promise for a rapidly expanding lightwave technology.

REFERENCES

1. A. W. Treptow and L. A. Finneran, "A Paste for Screen Printing and Firing Copper on Ceramic Bases," *Am. Ceramic Soc. Bull.* **39** (September 1960), pp. 453-455.

2. M. D. Rigterink and R. O. Grisdale, "Alkaline Earth Porcelains Possessing Low Dielectric Loss," *J. Am. Ceramic Soc.* **30** (March 1947), pp. 78-81.

3. S. S. Flaschen, A. D. Pearson, and W. R. Northover, "Formation and Properties of Low-Melting Glasses in the Ternary Systems As-Tl-S, As-Tl-Se, and As-Se-S," *J. Am. Ceramic Soc.* **43** (May 1960), pp. 274-278; S. S. Flaschen, A. D. Pearson, and I. L. Kalnins, "Improvement of Semiconductor Surfaces by Low-Melting Glasses, Possibly Functioning as Ion Getters," *J. Appl. Phys.* **31** (February 1960), pp. 431-432.

4. A. D. Pearson, W. R. Northover, J. F. Dewald, and W. F. Peak, Jr., "Chemical, Physical, and Electrical Properties of Some Unusual Inorganic Glasses," *Advances in Glass Technology*, Tech. Papers of the VIth International Congress on Glass, Washington D.C. (July 1962), pp. 357-365.

5. A. D. Pearson, "Memory and Switching in Semiconducting Glasses—A Review," *J. Noncrystalline Solids* 2 (January 1970), pp. 1-15.

6. K. B. McAfee, Jr., "Stress-Enhanced Diffusion in Glass. I. Glass Under Tension and Compression," *J. Chem. Phys.* 28 (February 1958), pp. 218-226; K. B. McAfee, Jr., "Stress-Enhanced Diffusion in Glass. II. Glass Under Shear," *J. Chem. Phys.* 28 (February 1958), pp. 226-229.

7. F. V. DiMarcello, A. W. Treptow, and L. A. Baker, "Glaze for Ceramic Substrates for Thin Films," *Am. Ceramic Soc. Bull.* 47 (May 1968), pp. 511-516.

8. K. D. Bartley, "The New Look in Public Telephone Stations," *Bell Laboratories Record* 44 (January 1966), pp. 16-19.

9. D. H. Wetherell, "Mechanical Design," *Bell Laboratories Record* 43 (June 1965), pp. 241-245.

10. S. B. Berger, C. B. Rubinstein, C. R. Kurkjian, and A. W. Treptow, "Faraday Rotation of Rare-Earth (III) Phosphate Glasses," *Phys. Rev.* 133A (February 1964), pp. 723-727.

11. A. D. Pearson and G. E. Peterson, "Energy Exchange Processes and Laser Oscillation in Glasses," *Proc. of the VIIth International Congress on Glass* (Brussels, 1965), pp. 10.1-10.11.

12. R. Komfner, "Optical Communications," *Science* 150 (October 1965), pp. 149-155.

13. K. C. Kao and G. A. Hockman, "Dielectric-Fibre Surface Waveguide for Optical Frequencies," *Proc. IEE* 113 (July 1966), pp. 1151-1158.

14. R. D. Maurer, "Glass Fibers for Optical Communications," *Proc. IEEE* 61 (April 1973), pp. 452-462.

15. A. D. Pearson and W. R. Northover, "Preparation and Properties of Ultrapure, Low Loss Sodium Borosilicate Glass," *Am. Ceramic Soc. Bull.* 57 (November 1978), pp. 1032-1033, 1038-1039.

16. W. G. French, A. D. Pearson, G. W. Tasker, and J. B. MacChesney, "Low-Loss Fused Silica Optical Waveguide with Borosilicate Cladding," *Appl. Phys. Lett.* 23 (September 15, 1973), pp. 338-339.

17. W. G. French, J. B. MacChesney, P. B. O'Connor, and G. W. Tasker, BSTJ Brief: "Optical Waveguides with Very Low Losses," *Bell System Tech. J.* 53 (May-June 1974), pp. 951-954.

18. J. B. MacChesney and P. B. O'Connor, U. S. Patent No. 4,217,027; filed 8/29/77, issued 8/12/80.

19. F. V. DiMarcello and J. C. Williams, "Reproducibility of Optical Fibers Prepared by a Modified Chemical Vapor Deposition Process," *Bell System Tech. J.* 57 (July-August 1978), pp. 1723-1734.

20. M. J. Buckler, J. W. Shiever, and F. P. Partus, "Bandwidth Optimization of Optical Fibers," Proc. 6th European Conf. on Optical Comm., York, England (1980).

21. R. L. Barns, E. A. Chandross, and C. M. Melliar-Smith, "The Photochemical Purification of Reagents used in the MCVD Process," Proc. 6th European Conf. Optical Comm., York, England (1980), pp. 22-28.

22. R. L. Barns, E. A. Chandross, D. L. Flamm, L. T. Manzione, and L. F. Thompson, U. S. Patent No. 4372,834; filed 6/19/81, issued 2/8/83.

23. T. Y. Kometani, "Flameless Atomic Absorption Spectrometric Determination of Ultratrace Elements in Silicon Tetrachloride," *Anal. Chem.* 49 (December 1977) pp. 2289-2291.

24. D. L. Wood, T. Y. Kometani, J. P. Luongo, and M. A. Saifi, "Incorporation of OH in Glass in the MCVD Process," *J. Amer. Ceram. Soc.* 62 (December 1979), pp. 638-639.

25. S. R. Nagel and M. A. Saifi, "Effect of Deposition Rate on Spectral Loss of $GeO_2-P_2O_5-SiO_2$, Graded Index Fibres," *Electron. Lett.* **16** (June 5, 1980), pp. 469-470; S. R. Nagel, S. G. Kosinski, and D. L. Brownlow, "Reduced Cycle Time MCVD," Tech. Dig., 3rd IOOC, San Francisco, CA., WA6.

26. K. L. Walker, J. B. MacChesney, and J. R. Simpson, "Reduction of Hydroxyl Contamination in Optical Fiber Preforms," *Electron. Lett.* **16** (June 5, 1980) pp. 86-88.

27. S. R. Nagel, S. G. Kosinski, and R. L. Barns, "Low OH MCVD Optical Fiber Fabrication," Fall Meeting, Glass Div., Amer. Ceram. Soc., *Ceramic Bulletin* **61** (August 1982), p. 882.

28. P. D. Lazay and A. D. Pearson, "Developments in Single Mode Fiber Design, Materials and Performance at Bell Laboratories," *J. Quant. Electron* **QE-18** (1982), pp. 504-510.

29. A. D. Pearson, P. D. Lazay, and W. A. Reed, BSTJ Brief: "Fabrication and Properties of Single-Mode Fiber Exhibiting Low Dispersion, Low Loss, and Tight Mode Confinement Simultaneously," *Bell System Tech. J.* **61** (February 1982), pp. 262-266.

30. A. D. Pearson, "Fabrication of Single-Mode Fiber at High Rate in Very Long Lengths for Submarine Cable," Tech. Dig., IOOC, San Francisco, CA. (April 27-29, 1981), p. 86, WA3.

31. L. G. Cohen, W. L. Mammel, and S. J. Jang, "Low-Loss Quadruple-Clad Single-Mode Lightguides with Dispersion Below 2 ps/km over the 1.28 μm - 1.65 μm Wavelength Range," *Electron. Lett.* **18** (1982), pp. 1023-1024.

32. D. L. Wood, K. L. Walker, J. R. Simpson, J. B. MacChesney, D. L. Nash, and P. Anguiera, "Chemistry of the MCVD Process for Making Optical Fibers," Proc. 7th European Conf. on Optical Comm., Denmark (September 8-11, 1981), pp. 1.2-1 - 1.2-4.

33. D. L. Wood, K. L. Walker, J. R. Simpson, J. B. MacChesney, and A. J. Ritger, "Reaction Equilibrium and Resultant Glass Compositions in the MCVD Process," Tech. Dig., Topical Meeting on Optical Fiber Comm., Phoenix, AZ (April 13-15, 1982), p. 10.

34. K. L. Walker and R. Csencsits, "Fluorine Chemistry in the MCVD Process," Fall Meeting, American Ceramic Soc. (1982).

35. P. G. Simpkins, S. Greenberg-Kosinski, and J. B. MacChesney, "Thermophoresis: The Mass Transfer Mechanism in Modified Chemical Vapor Deposition," *J. Appl. Phys.* **50** (September 1979), pp. 5676-5681.

36. K. L. Walker, G. M. Homsy, and F. T. Geyling, "Thermophoretic Deposition of Small Particles in Haminar Tube Flow," *J. Colloid and Interface Science* **69** (March 15, 1979), pp. 138-147.

37. K. L. Walker, F. T. Geyling, and S. R. Nagel, "Thermophoretic Deposition of Small Particles in the Modified Chemical Vapor Deposition (MCVD) Process," *J. Amer. Ceram. Soc.* **63** (September-October 1980), pp. 552-558.

38. K. L. Walker, J. W. Harvey, F. T. Geyling, and S. R. Nagel, "Consolidation of Particulate Layers in the Fabrication of Optical Fiber Preforms," *J. Amer. Ceram. Soc.* **63** (January-February, 1980), pp. 96-102.

39. S. G. Kosinski, L. Soto, S. R. Nagel, and T. Watrous, "Characterization of Germanium Phosphosilicate Films Prepared by Modified Chemical Vapor Deposition," Glass Div. Meeting, Amer. Ceram. Soc. (October 1981).

40. K. L. Walker, F. T. Geyling, and R. Csencsits, "The Collapse of MCVD Optical Preforms," Tech. Dig., 8th European Conference on Optical Comm., Cannes, France (September 21-24, 1982), p. 61.

41. J. R. Simpson, J. B. MacChesney, and K. L. Walker, "High Rate MCVD," *J. Non-Cryst. Solids* **38&39** (May-June 1980), pp. 831-836.

42. K. L. Walker and R. Csencsits, "High Rate Fabrication of Single Mode Fibers," Tech. Dig. Opt. Fiber Comm. (April 13-15 1982), pp. PDl-1-PDl-1, J. W. Fleming,

Jr., J. B. MacChesney, and P. B. O'Connor, U. S. Patent No. 4,331,462; filed 4/25/80, issued 5/25/82.

43. J. W. Fleming and P. B. O'Connor, "High Rate Lightguide Fabrication Technique," *Phys. of Fiber Optics: Advances in Ceramics, Vol. II* (1981), pp. 21-26.

44. J. W. Fleming and V. R. Raju, "Low-Loss Single-Mode Fibres Prepared by Plasma-Enhanced MCVD," *Electron. Lett.* **17** (November 12, 1981), pp. 867-868.

45. H. Schonhorn, C. R. Kurkjian, R. E. Jaeger, H. N. Vazirani, R. V. Albarino, and F. V. DiMarcello, "Epoxy-Acrylate-Coated Fused Silica Fibers with Tensile Strengths > 500 Ksi (3.5 GN/m^2) in 1-km Gauge Lengths," *Appl. Phys. Lett.* **29** (December 1976), pp. 712-714.

46. H. N. Vazirani, J. Schonhorn, and T. T. Wang, "UV-Cured Epoxy-Acrylate Coatings on Optical Fiber I and II, Chemistry and Application," Tech. Dig., Topical Meeting, Opt. Fiber Transm. II., Williamsburg, VA. (February 22-24, 1977), pp. TuB3-1-TuB3-4.

47. A. C. Hart, Jr. and R. V. Albarino, "An Improved Fabrication Technique for Applying Coating to Optical Fiber Waveguides," Tech. Dig., Topical Meeting, Opt. Fiber Transm. II., Williamsburg, VA. (February 22-24, 1977), pp. TuB2-1-Tub2-4.

48. J. T. Krause, "Transitions in the Static Fatigue of Fused Silica Fiber Lightguides," 5th European Conf. on Optical Comm., Amsterdam (September 17-19, 1979), pp. 19.1-1-19.1-H.

49. L. L. Blyler, Jr., and F. V. DiMarcello, "Fiber Drawing, Coating and Jacketing," *Proc. IEEE* **68** (October 1980), pp. 1194-1198.

50. F. V. DiMarcello, D. L. Brownlow, and D. S. Shenk, "Strength Characterization of Multikilometer Silica Fibers," Tech. Dig., 3rd IOOC, San Francisco, CA., 1981, MG6.

51. J. T. Krause, C. R. Kurkjian, and V. C. Paek, "Tensile Strengths >4 GPa for Lightguide Fusion Splices," *Electron. Lett.* **17** (October 15, 1981), pp. 812-813.

52. A. C. Hart and J. T. Krause, "Technique for Coating High Strength Lightguide Fusion Splices," Tech. Dig. Opt. Fiber Comm., Phoenix, AZ. (April 13-15, 1982), p. 44, THAA3.

Chapter 14

Polymers

Rubber, gutta percha, and paper comprised the early materials for wire insulation in telephony. Wax-impregnated paper was used in some capacitors. Hard rubber was used in some molded piece parts. These materials, based on natural products, are members of a broad class of substances called "polymers." The technology of the late 19th century and the early 20th century also produced synthetic substances such as cellulosic products and phenol-formaldehyde resins, which also found uses in the telephone plant. These early materials were derived in the chemical industry largely by opportune discoveries, not through fundamental research. However, the picture progressively changed in the 1930s and afterward. Synthetic polymers were discovered that depended upon simple molecules, instead of upon the architecture of cellulose and rubber. First, the products of the coal and coking industries produced the ingredients for large molecules such as the polyesters (for example, Mylar*) and the polyamides (nylons). Subsequent exploitation of petroleum and natural gas as raw materials has led to a vast number of wholly synthetic polymers used in textiles, tires, packaging films, paints, household items, toys, etc.

Bell Laboratories has been a pioneer in the discovery of new polymers, and in the measurement and understanding of their fundamental properties and engineering parameters. In particular, Bell Labs has responded to the Bell System's insistence on reliability by carrying out extensive research on the chemical and mechanical causes of the failure of polymers in service and of the means to extend lifetime. As a result, polymers, which in the public's mind are commonly seen as short-lived and disposable, have been made into durable substances that can be depended upon for long use.

I. THE EVOLUTION OF POLYMER CHEMISTRY

Until the late 1920s, chemists had believed that naturally occurring substances such as rubber, silk, and cellulose were indefinite organiza-

Principal author: W. P. Slichter

* Trademark of E. I. DuPont Co.

tions of rather simple molecules held together by forces of some special but undetermined character. Only with difficulty was the idea developed that these substances consisted of very large molecules composed of repeating structural units. These molecules became known as polymers, from the Greek *meros,* meaning *part.* The forces between molecules do, in fact, exert important influences upon the properties of polymers, just as they do in simple molecules. However, these forces are not unique. The molecules of polymeric substances follow the same laws of chemistry and physics that apply to simple substances.

In the 1920s, the work of H. Staudinger in Germany and W. H. Carothers in the United States led to the synthesis of long-chain molecules of definite structure and composition. These substances were excellent compounds for exploratory studies of the fundamental properties of polymers. For example, in the years just before World War II, chemists at Bell Laboratories examined the relationship of mechanical strength to molecular structure. C. S. Fuller showed that the way the various repeating units are combined and the regularity of the atomic positions in the units significantly affect such properties as elasticity and tensile strength. Fuller, W. O. Baker, and N. R. Pape demonstrated the importance of crystallinity, as determined by X-ray diffraction techniques, to the strength of polymers.[1] The growth of polymer science at Bell Labs helped set the pace for the development of the synthetic plastics industry in the United States.

II. SYNTHESIS AND MOLECULAR STRUCTURE OF POLYAMIDES AND COPOLYAMIDES

The growth of polymer science in the late 1930s had an impact on the Rubber Reserve program in the years prior to World War II. (For more on this topic, see section I of Chapter 16.) Although this work was important to the war effort, it had added significance in laying the groundwork for a broad understanding of the structure and properties of polymers. For little more than a decade, chemists had recognized that the source of the most remarkable physical properties of polymers—strength, elasticity, toughness, and others—lay in the great size of these molecules. But the differences that caused some polymeric substances to be elastic and others to be rigid were for the most part unknown. At Bell Labs, as elsewhere, chemists concluded correctly that such properties rest on a combination of the integrity of the long chain that is the backbone of every macromolecule, the specific interactions between a segment of a molecule and its neighbors, and chain stiffness.

In the 1940s, Baker, B. S. Biggs, Fuller, and their colleagues began systematically synthesizing many members of the families of polyesters and polyamides.[2] These substances belong to the important category of condensation polymers that had been investigated by Carothers of the Du Pont Company.[3] In the polyamides, for example, the condensation typically consists of the reaction of two entities, a diamine and a dibasic acid, with the release of a water molecule at every point of reaction. Bell Labs chemists synthesized a wide variety of members of this general family and determined their physical characteristics. X-ray diffraction studies of these polymers established that the solid contains a multitude of microcrystalline regions in which sections of the polymer chains are efficiently packed together. In particular, the amide groups were found to be arrayed in planes through the solid over distances that appeared to be at least as great as the dimensions of the microcrystalline regions, which typically are of the order of microns. The regular array of amide groups was ascribed to interaction through both dipolar attraction and hydrogen bonding. The coupling within these layers and the concentration of layers per unit-volume govern the internal energy, melting temperature, and mechanical strength of these solids. The importance of this coupling was emphasized in studies involving the synthesis of a series of polyamides and copolyamides, in which the latter consisted, for example, of the condensation products of a given diamine and two different dibasic acids in chosen proportions. In the simple polyamides, decreasing the amide content lowered the melting temperature and softened the solids. A corresponding trend in physical properties was observed as the disorder produced by copolymerization increased.[4] Similarly, Biggs and coworkers synthesized a series of polyamides and copolyamides in which the amino hydrogens were replaced to various extents with methyl or other alkyl groups. Once again, this had the effect of decreasing the dipolar coupling and hydrogen bonding with attendant changes in the physical properties.[5]

III. THE AGE OF PLASTICS – POLYETHYLENE

The discovery (and proliferation) of the substances now broadly classed as *plastics* (more accurately, polymers) brought about revolutionary changes in the design, manufacture, and performance of much of the telephone plant. The trend toward plastics was widely felt in the economy, where an important feature of these materials had been their cheapness. However, in the Bell System, such materials are of interest either for their novel or superior properties important to communications, or as successors to materials no longer available in the needed amounts. An example of the latter is the replacement of lead by polyethylene for cable jackets, which began in the late 1940s, when the supply of lead could no longer meet the demands of the expanding cable plant. Examples of plastics with superior properties are polyvinyl chloride used for indoor wire insulation and cable sheath, and acrylonitrile butadiene styrene (ABS), a commercial plastic used for station apparatus. Both of these families of plastics were introduced into the Bell System in the early 1950s. W. J. Clarke, J. B. DeCoste, J. B. Howard, and V. T. Wallder were involved in the development and engineering of these major classes of plastics.[6]

By 1975, the use of plastics in the Bell System had grown to such an extent that they accounted for more than half the volume of all materials being used for manufacture by Western Electric. Polyethylene is the plastic used most extensively in the Bell System and has consequently been investigated more extensively than any other polymer.

The polyethylene story began in the laboratories of Imperial Chemical Industries, Ltd. (I.C.I.) in England during the 1930s. Chemists studying the behavior of ethylene, $CH_2=CH_2$, at elevated temperature and pressure discovered a reaction product that was a white solid, flexible but fairly tough, and waxy to the touch. The compound was readily identified as a paraffinic hydrocarbon. In 1939, A. R. Kemp visited I.C.I. and brought back a small sample of polyethylene. Fuller, Howard, S. O. Morgan, and others recognized that such material would have excellent electrical properties at high frequencies because it was virtually free of polar groups. The suggestion was also made that polyethylene, consisting essentially of a chain of CH_2 groups, should be the simplest possible polymer and therefore should serve as a model for more complex systems. As so often happens, this expectation of simplicity was not borne out, but research into deviations from simplicity was undoubtedly more illuminating than studies of an ideally simple polymer would have been.

Because of their extensive background in the dielectric properties of matter, Bell Laboratories chemists and cable engineers were keen to examine the potential usefulness of polyethylene. In 1940, a large chunk of polyethylene about as big as a desk was imported from I.C.I. This material was cut into sheets and then into strips. Finally, it was punched into buttons about five-eighths of an inch in diameter and was used to insulate about nine miles of coaxial cable that was installed as a section of the Baltimore-Washington route. The polyethylene dielectric was used instead of insulators made of phenolic resins that were of lesser electrical quality. Although this primitive polyethylene was nonuniform and poorly characterized by modern standards, it represented the first commercial use of the material and served well in this installation for a number of years.

As already noted, severe pressures developed in the late 1940s to find an economically attractive replacement of lead as the material for use in cable sheath. Working with cable engineers, Wallder, Clarke, DeCoste, and Howard developed a cable sheathing compound made of polyethylene with about 1 percent carbon black as an additive.[7] The carbon black was incorporated as a screen against ultraviolet light. Although the expected service life of such compositions had yet to be demonstrated, laboratory experience indicated that 20 years or more should be expected in the field. Accordingly, in 1947, Western Electric began commercial production of polyethylene-sheathed cable.

It was not long before reports of trouble returned from the field, but of a totally unexpected sort. Disastrous cracking of the sheath was found again and again. F. W. Horn, C. F. Wiebusch, and other cable engineers worked with chemists such as Howard and Wallder to reproduce the cracking in the laboratory, simulating twists and bends and applying chemical environments typical of the field. The tests determined that mechanical stresses in the sheath, coupled with surface contamination from soaps or other surfactants, produced catastrophic failure of the sort found in service. Soaps had long been used as lubricants for pulling lead-sheathed cable through conduits and were needed also for plastic-sheathed cable.

The molecular basis for these failures was discovered by I. L. Hopkins, Baker, and Howard.[8] They realized that the stresses in the sheath were far more complicated than one-directional tension. Therefore, they used a stress-strain experiment in which a disk of polyethylene was deformed biaxially by stretching, much as a child does when blowing bubbles with bubble gum. They also showed that using solvent to remove the lower molecular-weight constituent of the polyethylene then in use made a dramatic improvement in the stress-cracking behavior. Later, in a series of experiments, H. D. Keith and F. J. Padden showed how the molecular weight affects the morphology. The chemical companies that supplied the polyethylene for cable sheath learned how to provide materials in which the whole molecular-weight distribution was shifted toward a higher average value, thereby minimizing the amount of low-molecular-weight polymer.

About 1949, the potential of polyethylene to replace paper pulp as a wire insulation was recognized. In the early 1950s, the superiority of polyethylene as a dielectric led to its selection as the insulating material for the first of the new generation of oceanic cables. The choice of polyethylene marked a major departure from the materials technology that had reigned for more than 80 years of oceanic telegraphy and telephony. Polyethylene at last provided an answer to the search begun by Williams 30 years earlier for the right cable insulation. (See section 3.4 below and section 1.1 of Chapter 16.)

3.1 Polyethylene Stabilization

The vulnerability of unprotected polyethylene to prolonged exposure to heat and light was known, in rudimentary terms, from the chemistry of rubber. In the late 1940s, a major effort to stabilize polymers was begun.

3.1.1 *Thermal Oxidation of Polyethylene*

Thermal oxidation, which results eventually in the mechanical and dielectric failure of polyethylene, has been studied extensively. F. H. Winslow [Fig. 14-1] devised an accelerated test in which the volume of oxygen at 1 atmosphere pressure reacting with a sample was measured at a series of elevated temperatures. Unprotected polyethylene rapidly takes up oxygen, but with an inhibitor present in the polymer, the rapid uptake is delayed until the inhibitor has been exhausted. Comparisons between potential stabilizers can be drawn from the length of time to failure at different temperatures. Substituted phenols and secondary aromatic amines, which were developed for the protection of natural rubber, were found to be moderately useful as thermal antioxidants with polyethylene. W. L. Hawkins,

Fig. 14-1. F. H. Winslow (left) and W. L. Hawkins conducted accelerated oxidation tests on polyethylene to determine the effectiveness of various thermal antioxidants.

R. H. Hansen, W. Matreyek, and Winslow found that carbon black has some effect as a stabilizer against the thermal oxidation, as well as being a light screen against photo-induced oxidation (see section 3.1.2 below).[9] However, when carbon black was present along with these phenols and amines, the protection was considerably reduced.[10] [Fig. 14-2] In contrast, certain sulfur-containing organic compounds were shown by Hawkins, V. L. Lanza, and Winslow to be excellent thermal antioxidants for polyethylene containing carbon black. For example 2-naphthol, a mild antioxidant for simple hydrocarbons, was found by Hawkins and his colleagues to be an effective stabilizer when made into a disulfide. This compound is not only more effective in the clear polymer than is 2-naphthol, but is also a much better antioxidant in the presence of carbon black. Similar effects have been observed with other thioethers. The favorable effect of carbon black on the protective activity of sulfur-containing compounds has been explored with a variety of systems, both aliphatic and aromatic.[11] These studies stemmed from accumulated information on the effectiveness of carbon black combined with organic sulfides and disulfides, as well as with elemental sulfur, in inhibiting polymer oxidation—even though these substances were poor antioxidants when present alone under comparable conditions. This research yielded a series of organosulfur compounds that are excellent thermal antioxidants in the presence of carbon black. Some of these have no appreciable activity as antioxidants in the clear polymer. This *syner-*

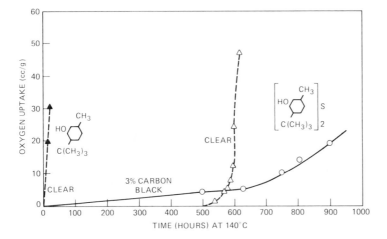

Fig. 14-2. Thermal oxidation rate of polyethylene containing a butylphenol, its corresponding thioether, and the thioether in the presence of carbon black. [Hawkins et al., *J. Appl. Polymer Science 1* (1959): 44].

gism was largely unexpected when the chemistry of sulfur was added to that of organic thermal antioxidants.

3.1.2 Photodegradation of Polyethylene

When polyethylene was first considered for cable sheath, the protection of polyethylene from ultraviolet light was studied by Wallder and his colleagues.[12] Following the practice for the protection of rubber insulation on outdoor wire, they specified the addition to the plastic of from 1 to 3 percent carbon black to serve as a screen to absorb the ultraviolet light. In particular, the investigators showed that the protection is better with small carbon particles and depends upon how thoroughly the particles are dispersed in the plastic. A major advance in this work was the use of indoor weathering tests under intense artificial light to accelerate the degradative processes.[13] Concurrently, samples of carbon-loaded polyethylene were put outdoors in test plots in various parts of the country. The slow deterioration of these samples over the course of several decades has paralleled the changes predicted from the accelerated tests.

The primary processes of oxidative photodegradation of polyethylene are less understood than those of thermal oxidation. Photolysis depends on the absorption of light energy, but little or no solar radiation with wavelengths shorter than about 300 nanometers is transmitted by the earth's atmosphere. On the other hand, a paraffinic hydrocarbon such as "pure" polyethylene does not absorb light appreciably in the visible part of the spectrum. Winslow, Matreyek, and A. M. Trozzolo showed that the rate of outdoor oxidation of unprotected polyethylene typically undergoes a tenfold seasonal change, corresponding quite closely to the seasonal variation in the intensity of the sun's spectrum.[14] Because pure hydrocarbons absorb very little of the ultraviolet component of sunlight, the oxidative photodegradation of polyethylene is partly ascribed to impurities in the chain that absorb energy in this region of wavelength. The carbonyl group ($C=O$) can be incorporated both as an impurity during polymerization and as a product of processing at elevated temperatures. Because carbonyl groups are always present at low levels in polyethylene, Trozzolo and Winslow postulated a photochemical mechanism involving the absorption of light by a carbonyl group, the photolysis of a carbon-carbon bond to produce chain scission, followed by an oxidative chain reaction that used hydroperoxide intermediate.[15]

3.2 Nuclear Magnetic Resonance Studies of Polymer-Chain Structure

Nuclear magnetic resonance (NMR) in solids and liquids, observed in 1945 by E. M. Purcell's group at Harvard University in Massachusetts[16] and by F. Bloch's group at Stanford University in California,[17] opened vast new areas of physics and chemistry. Indeed, NMR spectroscopy has become a basic tool for chemists and has been adopted by polymer chemists in particular. Much of the development of NMR as a powerful technique to study the structure and stereochemistry of polymer chains was the work of F. A. Bovey. [Fig. 14-3] Extending the techniques of high-resolution NMR spectroscopy, he showed that NMR can be used to ascertain the configuration of monomer sequences in a macromolecule. In an important series of studies

Fig. 14-3. F. A. Bovey seated before the electromagnet of a high-resolution nuclear magnetic resonance spectrometer used for the study of the structure and chain dynamics of macromolecules.

on vinyl polymers, for example, Bovey and his colleagues used proton magnetic resonance to measure the preferred geometrical placement of the sequences of monomer in the chains. He also applied the method to study polymer conformation—that attribute of the molecuar shape that changes as the result of thermal motion—and related his observations to matters such as the statistical thermodynamics of chain motion.

The ability to resolve molecular structures from the NMR spectra generally increases with increasing radio frequency of the spectrometer. Thus, Bovey's early work at 60 megahertz (MHz) was capable only of establishing rather short-range structures along the chain, notably dyads and triads of monomeric groups.[18] However, the structural arrangements of polymer chains became much clearer with extension of the experiments to high radio frequency. At 220 MHz, F. Heatley and Bovey observed the conformation of tetrad and pentad sequences of monomer groups in polyvinyl chloride.[19] The interpretation of the NMR spectra of polymers was helped by the use of high-speed computation. Bovey and L. C. Snyder showed that computers could be used to simulate the NMR of even complicated chain structures in polymers.[20] The NMR line-splittings and shapes for polymers are generated in the computer on the basis of information derived from the spectra of simple analogous molecules. Comparison between actual and simulated spectra tests the merit of structures postulated for the polymer chains.

An old question with polyethylene, concerning the kind and amount of chain branching, was addressed by Bovey through NMR of ^{13}C. Although the NMR signal strength from ^{13}C is weak compared to that of the proton, because the abundance of the ^{13}C isotope is only about 1 percent, the ^{13}C NMR spectra are spread out and are largely free from overlaps that obscure the spectra of proton magnetic resonance. Not long after the discovery of polyethylene, the observation had been made that the molecular structure is more complicated than that of a simple CH_2 chain. In particular, measurements by infrared spectroscopy showed bands ascribed to CH_3 groups, the presumed entities at the ends of paraffin molecules. This information, combined with measurements of average molecular weight and shape, showed that low-density polyethylenes contain a mixture of branches. The number and size of these branches were known qualitatively to vary with the conditions of polymerization, but there was no direct quantitative information on branching. Bovey's NMR studies identified and measured the ethyl, *n*-butyl, *n*-amyl, *n*-hexyl, and longer branching in polyethylene for the first time.[21] [Fig. 14-4] In a spectrum of a low-density polyethylene, the peaks are assigned in terms of information from model compounds. The intensities of these peaks give a quantitative measure of the relative abundance of the different types of

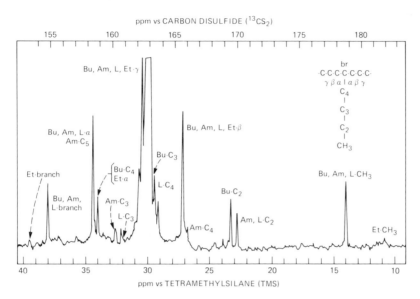

Fig. 14-4. ^{13}C NMR spectrum of a low-density polyethylene in trichlorobenzene solution. The diagram at the upper right shows the nomenclature used for the carbons associated with a branch. The end carbon, C_1, is designated as CH_3; Et = ethyl, Bu = *n*-butyl, Am = *n*-amyl, and L = *n*-hexyl and longer. ppm is the departure, in parts-per-million, from the true value of the nuclear magnetic moment of ^{13}C. [Bovey et al., *Macromolecules* **9** (1976): 78].

branches. It was demonstrated that *n*-butyl groups outnumber other short groups by three or four to one, which is consistent with a mechanism of an intramolecular reaction of the growing chain radical postulated many years earlier by Du Pont chemists but never before shown quantitatively.

3.3 Morphology of Polyethylene

Polymers exhibit certain important properties that stem from the very great length of the molecules. One such attribute is the molecular organization or *morphology* of the solid state. The morphology of polyethylene has received particular attention because of the presumed simplicity of that polymer. As noted earlier, the existence of crystallinity in solid polymers was known from pioneering studies by X-ray diffraction, many of which were carried out at Bell Laboratories. The crystalline regions of polymers are not visible to the naked eye. Indeed, polymeric solids prepared from the melt never achieve complete crystalline order but, instead, are some sort of inhomogeneous composition in which substantial amounts of noncrystalline (*amorphous*) material are mingled with the crystalline. This state of affairs was explained, quite satisfactorily for a time, by the entanglement of the long chains and by the broad spectrum of molecular lengths. Each of these factors was presumed to limit the ultimate degree of order in the solid.

The first indication that it was possible to obtain fairly large (greater than 1000Å) single crystals of polymers from solution came in early studies by K. H. Storks in 1938.[22] He made electron diffraction measurements of thin films of gutta-percha* (the *trans* isomer of natural rubber) that had been cast from solution in chloroform. The diffraction spots proved the existence of microscopic crystals in the film, and their pattern showed that the molecular axes were perpendicular to the plane of the film. Storks pointed out that the film thickness was much less than the total length of a macromolecule and that this could occur if the molecules were folded back on themselves. Unfortunately, the work of Storks was ahead of its time. Nearly 20 years later, R. Jaccodine at Bell Labs, A. Keller at the University of Bristol, E. W. Fischer at the University of Mainz, and P. H. Till of DuPont grew lamellar single crystals of polyethylene from dilute solution.[23] Electron diffraction studies showed that the molecules were perpendicular to the faces of the lamellar. Again, chain folding was invoked as an explanation.

Although the picture of an ill-defined mingling of amorphous and crystalline material lent itself to a general explanation of mechanical attributes such as strength and flexure, it was plainly not complete. In the late 1940s, investigators of solid polyethylene at I.C.I. in England found ordering that was visible with an optical microscope on a scale far larger than the estimated sizes of the crystalline regions. In polyethylene, this ordering consists of intimately packed spheres or near-spheres and makes up the whole of the solid. These structures are commonly called *spherulites*, a term adopted from mineralogy, where it is used for structures consisting of assemblages of fine crystals radiating from a point. Spherulites are found in a wide variety of polymers.

H. D. Keith and F. J. Padden developed a phenomenological theory of spherulitic crystallization aimed at explaining the mechanisms of forming spherulites in systems of all known types. They noted that all spherulite-forming melts have viscosities that are much higher than those of simple liquids and crystallize much more slowly. As a consequence, these melts can be greatly supercooled in contrast with most crystallizing melts. The growth of a spherulite from a super-

---

* Gutta-percha is a hard, but deformable, hydrocarbon produced by the solidification of milky juices from certain trees in Malaysia. Its structure is intimately related to that of rubber; in fact, it is an isomer of rubber—it has the same atomic composition but different atomic structure.

cooled melt always begins with a primary nucleus and proceeds with the development of radial fibers of crystals that ultimately fill the volume occupied by the spherulite. This mode of growth requires that the fibers branch in a noncrystallographic manner and at small angles, which is in marked contrast to the dendritic branching found in the rapid solidification of metals and many other compounds. Keith and Padden reasoned that a difference in composition between the virgin melt and the residual melt controls the crystallization of fibers in the spherulites.[24] Although segregation of components was well known in the growth of crystals from melts or solutions, the existence of such a process in a homopolymer such as polyethylene had not been previously known. Keith and Padden made the important suggestion that molecules of lower molecular weight or of irregular configuration are rejected preferentially by growing crystals and that their diffusion plays a vital part in governing overall morphology. [Fig. 14-5]

This work led to important discoveries about the mechanical properties of polymers. The morphological evidence on solution-grown single crystals and on lamellae in spherulitic structures strongly suggested that the chain folding found in the former is also a structural

Fig. 14-5. H. D. Keith carried out pioneering research on crystalline morphology in polymers.

feature in the latter. However, the mechanical properties of spherulites suggested that there must be strong, direct coupling between
lamellae. Such intercrystalline connections were found by Keith, Padden, and R. G. Vadimsky in electron microscopic studies of spherulites
produced by the crystallization of polyethylene-paraffin mixtures.[25]
[Fig. 14-6] The existence of abundant, highly organized tie links
between adjacent fibers in the spherulites was shown by removing the
intervening paraffin molecules with a suitable solvent.

3.4 Polyethylene and the Ocean Cable Problem

The emergence of polyethylene as the material of choice for cable
sheath and wire insulation led to its introduction in the early 1950s
into the technology of ocean cables. Although the amounts of polymer used for ocean cable are small compared to the quantities used for
cable sheath and wire insulation, the performance requirements are as
severe. Inadequacies in the cable-core material of the 1920s posed one
of the first challenges to chemists at Bell Labs. At the end of World
War II, renewed impetus was given to the design of submarine cables.
Chemists took up the problem of restricting dipolar content. They

1µm

Fig. 14-6. Intercrystalline links in the neighborhood of interspherulitic
boundaries in a thin film of polyethylene crystallized from a solution of a
paraffinic solvent. [Keith, Padden, and Vadimsky, *J. Appl. Phys.* **42**
(1971): 4586].

recognized that pure polyethylene is essentially nonpolar, and worked toward a synthetic polymeric compound based on polyethylene that would obviate the problems encountered earlier with impurities contained in naturally occurring hydrocarbon polymers. Based on the work of Hopkins and coworkers on the mechanical failure of biaxially stressed polyethylene, Howard and Wallder devised a formula of polyethylene plus 5 percent butyl rubber to be used as the dielectric in the SB Submarine Cable Systems. This design was used in the transatlantic cable that was put in service in 1956. [Fig. 14-7] The system had a capacity of 64 voice channels. Its success led to the design and deployment of a system called SD with 128 two-way channels. The SD required a dielectric of substantially improved quality and uniformity. A pure polyethylene resin of high molecular weight was chosen.

Further ocean cable systems followed in quick succession, through the 4200-channel SG system that was put in place in the 1970s. These developments put severe demands upon the performance requirements of the polyethylene dielectric. As had been the case several decades before, the limitation of the dielectric behavior was the dipolar content. In polyethylene, the principal dielectric losses arise from polar impurities, such as residues of the catalyst used in the polymerization process, and from chemicals added to protect the polymer from oxidation during cable manufacture. Howard and Wallder worked with suppliers to bring about a dramatic decrease in the inherent losses arising from residual impurities in the polyethylene. Hawkins and Wallder also devoted much effort to the selection of antioxidant additives that are virtually nonpolar. The progress in decreasing the dielectric loss was so great that new sensitivity and accuracy were needed to measure the electrical qualities of materials. In response, D. W. McCall, and G. L. Link and G. E. Johnson pushed the capability for the accurate measurement of dielectric loss over frequencies in the megahertz range far beyond that previously achieved.[26]

This record of meeting the successive demands for better dielectric performance in cable from one generation to the next is matched by the course of mechanical requirements. The diameter of the dielectric for each new cable system was greater than that of its predecessor (for example, 1.0 inch in the SD cable and 1.5 inches in the SF cable). Experience had shown that the molecular weight had to be high enough to avoid the risk of stress cracking, yet not too high to be processable. Moreover, the mechanical stress on the dielectric from bending and pulling, together with the stresses on the outer sheath during the cable-laying operation, imposed severe engineering requirements upon the plastics. T. W. Huseby and S. Matsuoka analyzed these mechanical and structural factors and related them to basic properties of the polymer.[27] For example, the outer jacket not only protects the

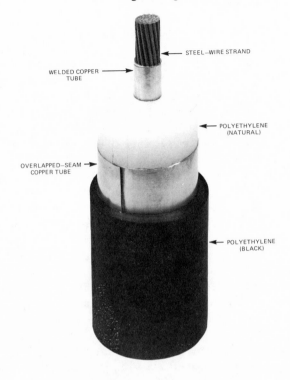

STEEL—WIRE STRAND

WELDED COPPER
TUBE

POLYETHYLENE
(NATURAL)

OVERLAPPED—SEAM
COPPER TUBE

POLYETHYLENE
(BLACK)

Fig. 14-7. Polyethylene in an undersea cable.

outer conductor from abrasion during handling, but also, by compression, keeps it from wrinkling during bending. This wrinkling has to be avoided, for it leads to cracking of the copper and ultimately to failure of the outer conductor. Therefore, in the total design of the cable, the jacket must have optimal thickness and stiffness. Matsuoka experimented with the performance of the cable jacket in reverse-bend tests, using various thicknesses of the jacket and various polyethylenes. The Young's modulus of the polyethylene was found to determine the performance. For a given thickness of jacket, polyethylenes having a Young's modulus above a certain level were found to perform satisfactorily, whereas those of lower modulus could not prevent failure of the outer conductor.

IV. MOLECULAR MOTION IN POLYMERS

Many of the mechanical and electrical properties of interest in the practical use of polymers originate in the motions of segments of the macromolecules. Such motions are present in the liquid state, but also occur extensively in the solid state. In combination with the structural aspects of solid polymers, motions of portions of the long chains and of attached groups strongly influence the physical properties of the material. W. P. Mason, Baker, H. J. McSkimin, and J. H. Heiss pioneered in establishing the nature of these motions in liquids at ultrasonic frequencies.[28]

The processes involving motions in solids (or liquids) are commonly referred to as *relaxation phenomena* and are described in terms of relaxation times, or the reciprocal of the frequency at which the maximum dissipation of energy occurs. Much of the phenomenological understanding of polymer solids is based on measuring relaxation times through the use of electrical, mechanical, or spectroscopic methods. At Bell Laboratories, such methods have been useful in defining the behavior of polymers for applications in communications.

An early contribution in this area was an extensive study by Baker and W. A. Yager of the dielectric properties of some linear polyesters and polyamides.[29] (For more on this topic, see section II of this chapter.) Baker and Yager observed a substantial dielectric polarization contributed by motion of the polar groups. At the frequencies used, which ranged from 1 kilohertz (kHz) to 75 MHz, the loss maxima in the polyamides occurred at much higher temperatures (typically in the range 90°C to 140°C) than in the polyesters (−25°C to +20°C). The difference in behavior between these two families of polar polymers indicates a significantly higher constraint to motion for the amide groups compared to the ester groups. (It was noted in the discussion of polyamides and copolyamides that the strong interactions between polyamide chains influence the structures and melting temperatures of the polyamides.) [Fig. 14-8]

Baker and Yager focused their studies of polyamides on nylon 6-10. (The numbers refer to the number of carbon atoms in the diamine and dibasic acid, respectively.) McCall and E. W. Anderson studied the dielectric relaxation of a number of linear polyamides.[30] [Fig. 14-9] Two relaxation processes were identified over a range of temperature and frequency. The data for the polyamides were quite similar. The inhomogeneities in the nylons, and in other polymers exhibiting similar behavior, were attributed to the crystalline-amorphous character of the materials. The dielectric effect at low frequency was believed to come from the transport of ions (perhaps including protons) within the amorphous regions.

The use of NMR spectroscopy to examine molecular motion in solid polymers is another important application and was widely explored by D. C. Douglass, McCall, W. P. Slichter, and their colleagues.[31] While NMR is valuable for structural studies of solids, including polymers, its greatest strength is in the examination of molecular motions. The frequency ranges to which the NMR relaxations are especially sensitive are from 10 kHz to 100 kHz and from 10 MHz to 100 MHz.

Fig. 14-8. W. O. Baker made fundamental contributions to the crystal structure and dielectric properties of crystalline polymers. He later became vice president for research and then president and chairman of the board of directors of Bell Laboratories.

In studies at Bell Labs, this method has been particularly useful in detecting and distinguishing motions of chain segments in polymers and substituent groups. An early application was Slichter's study of NMR in polyamides, which showed the onset of rotation of chain segments some 20 or 30 degrees below the melting temperature.[32] [Fig. 14-10] The temperatures at which the motion developed were found to be higher as the polar content of the polymer increased, that is, as the hydrocarbon segments between the amide groups shortened. The nuclear magnetic relaxations in polyamides come primarily from the protons in these chain segments, for these are the most numerous protons. Therefore, NMR observations of the behavior of the hydrocarbon segments and dielectric experiments on the behavior of the polar groups are complementary. [Fig. 14-11]

In recent years, computer simulation has provided a view supporting that obtained by experiments. The Brownian motion of polymer chains was first simulated on a computer by E. Helfand, Z. R. Wasserman, and T. A. Weber.[33] One goal was to determine how sizable

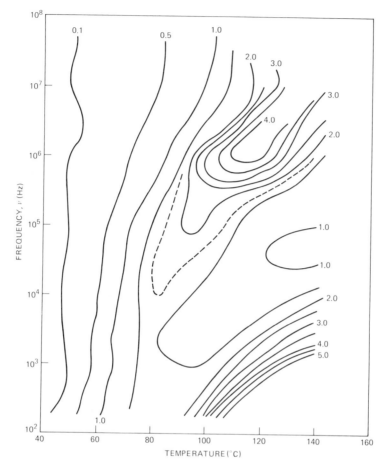

Fig. 14-9. Contour diagram of the dielectric loss, ϵ'', as a function of frequency and temperature. The data are for nylon 6-9, but the general features are common to linear polyamides. [McCall and Anderson, *J. Chem. Phys.* **32** (1960): 238].

motions can occur in a small section of the chain without having to pull along the whole molecule. A crank-like mode of motion was observed to occur frequently, and was an important contributor to the required localization of the motion. In addition to Brownian motion simulation of single molecules, the molecular dynamics of a collection of macromolecules was also first simulated by Weber and Helfand.[34] This revealed not only a detailed view of the molecular motions, but also provided a picture of the arrangements of polymer chains in the amorphous state.

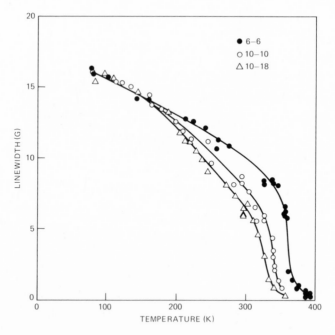

Fig. 14-10. Variation of NMR linewidth with temperature in nylons 6-6, 10-10, and 10-18. The appearance of line narrowing with increasing temperature indicates the onset of molecular motion. [Slichter, *J. Appl. Phys.* **26** (1955): 1100].

V. DIVALENT CARBON CHEMISTRY

Because of the pervasive importance of tetravalent carbon, the chemistry of molecular species in which the valence state of at least one carbon atom is *less* than four is of great interest. These species comprise the most important intermediates between reactants and products in organic chemistry. Trivalent carbon derivatives, notably free radicals, have been observed directly by a variety of methods, especially by electron paramagnetic resonance (EPR) spectroscopy. The first observation of a long-lived or "stable" free radical by EPR was made at Bell Labs in 1949 by A. N. Holden and colleagues, who studied the compound diphenylpicryl hydrazyl.[35] Numerous other free radicals, both stable and highly reactive, have since been studied by Bell Labs chemists.

The more elusive divalent carbon intermediates have come under intense study since the early 1960s. These species are frequently called carbenes, although chemists also refer to divalent carbon intermediates as derivatives of methylene, $-CH_2-$. For many years, methylene was thought to be an intermediate in a variety of reactions,

Fig. 14-11. W. P. Slichter pioneered in the application of nuclear magnetic resonance techniques to the study of molecular motion in polymers.

but it was not detected by direct physical measurement until some studies of electronic spectra by G. Herzberg in Canada in 1961.[36] An important question had to do with the shape of the triatomic fragment: Is it bent, like the water molecule, or is it linear? The correct answer would say much about the electronic configuration of methylene and hence about the kinds of chemistry in which the reactive intermediate might be expected to take part. The experimental evidence from electronic spectroscopy seemed to support the picture of a linear molecule,[37] whereas calculations from the theory of chemical bonding led to the conflicting view that the HCH angle is 129°, not 180°.[38] This disparity between experiment and theory remained unresolved for a decade until studies by E. Wasserman and colleagues confirmed the theoretical view of a bent HCH triplet. Their work involved EPR studies of methylene that had been formed from a parent compound by ultraviolet illumination in a frozen xenon matrix at extremely low temperature. Under such conditions this reactive species was stable enough for observation.

This work on the simplest member of the methylene family followed studies by Wasserman, Trozzolo, R. W. Murray, and others of the much more stable aromatic derivatives, the arylmethylenes.[39] In these compounds the interaction of the aromatic rings with the unbonded electrons of the methylene has a major effect. With the aid of electronic spin resonance (ESR) and electronic spectroscopy, the ground states of these molecules have been studied, and the geometric structures of a number of these compounds have been unambiguously determined.

REFERENCES

1. C. S. Fuller, "Mixed Linear Condensation Polymers," *Industrial and Engineering Chemistry* **30** (April 1938), pp. 472-477; C. S. Fuller, W. O. Baker, and N. R. Pape, "Crystalline Behavior of Linear Polyamides. Effect of Heat Treatment," *J. Am. Chem. Soc.* **62** (December 1940), pp. 3275-3281.

2. See reference 1; also, see C. S. Fuller and C. L. Erickson, "An X-Ray Study of Some Linear Polyesters," *J. Am. Chem. Soc.* **59** (February 1937), pp. 344-351; W. O. Baker, C. S. Fuller, and J. H. Heiss, Jr., "Macromolecular Properties of Linear Polyesters: Molecular Weight Determinations on ω-OH-Undecanoic Self-Polyesters," *J. Am. Chem. Soc.* **63** (August 1941), pp. 2142-2148.

3. W. H. Carothers, *Collected Papers of Wallace Hume Carothers on High Polymeric Substances*, ed. H. Mark and G. S. Whitby (New York: Interscience Publishers, Inc., 1940).

4. W. O. Baker and C. S. Fuller, "Macromolecular Disorder in Linear Polyamides. Relation of Structure to Physical Properties of Copolyamides," *J. Am. Chem. Soc.* **64** (October 1942), pp. 2399-2407.

5. W. O. Baker and C. S. Fuller, "Intermolecular Forces and Chain Configuration in Linear Polymers—The Effect of N-Methylation on the X-ray Structures and Properties of Linear Polyamides," *J. Am. Chem. Soc.* **65** (June 1943), pp. 1120-1130; B. S. Biggs, C. J. Frosch, and R. H. Erickson, "Melting Points of N-Substituted Polyamides," *Industrial and Engineering Chemistry* **38** (October 1946), pp. 1016-1019.

6. J. B. Howard, "Stress Cracking," in *Crystalline Olefin Polymers*, ed. R. A. V. Raff and K. W. Doak (New York: Interscience Publishers, Inc., 1964), pp. 47-103.

7. V. T. Wallder, W. J. Clarke, J. B. DeCoste, and J. B. Howard, "Weathering Studies on Polyethylene," *Industrial and Engineering Chemistry* **42** (November 1950), pp. 2320-2325.

8. I. L. Hopkins, W. O. Baker, and J. B. Howard, "Complex Stressing of Polyethylene," *J. Appl. Phys.* **21** (March 1950), pp. 206-213.

9. W. L. Hawkins, R. H. Hansen, W. Matreyek, and F. H. Winslow, "The Effect of Carbon Black on Thermal Antioxidants for Polyethylene," *J. Appl. Polymer Science* **1** (Jan./Feb. 1959), pp. 37-42.

10. W. L. Hawkins and M. A. Worthington, "Carbon Black as a Catalyst in the Oxidation of Antioxidants," *J. Polymer Science* **62** (December 1962), pp. S106-S107.

11. W. L. Hawkins, V. L. Lanza, and F. H. Winslow, U.S. Patent No. 2,889,306; filed July 15, 1957, issued June 2, 1959; W. L. Hawkins, V. L. Lanza, B. B. Loeffler, W. Matreyek, and F. H. Winslow, "New Thermal Antioxidants for Polyethylene Containing Carbon Black," *J. Appl. Polymer Science* **1** (Jan./Feb. 1959), pp. 43-49; W. L.

Hawkins and H. Sautter, "Synergistic Antioxidant Combinations. Mechanism of Stabilization with Organo-Sulfur Compounds," *J. Polymer Science* **1A** (November 1963), pp. 3499-3509.

12. See reference 7.

13. J. B. Howard and H. M. Gilroy, "Natural and Artificial Weathering of Polyethylene Plastics," *Polymer Eng. Sci.* **9** No. 4, (1969), pp. 286-294.

14. F. H. Winslow, W. Matreyek, and A. M. Trozzolo, "Polymers Under the Weather," *SPE J.* **28** (July 1972), pp. 19-24.

15. A. M. Trozzolo and F. H. Winslow, "A Mechanism for the Oxidative Photodegradation of Polyethylene," *Macromolecules* **1** (Jan./Feb. 1968), pp. 98-100.

16. E. M. Purcell, H. C. Torrey, and R. V. Pound, "Resonance Absorption by Nuclear Magnetic Moments in a Solid," *Phys. Rev.* **69** (January 1946), pp. 37-38.

17. F. Bloch, W. W. Hansen, and M. Packard, "Nuclear Induction," *Phys. Rev.* **69** (February 1946), p. 127.

18. F. A. Bovey, E. W. Anderson, and D. C. Douglass, "Polymer NMR Spectroscopy. X. The Use of H^1-H^1 Spin Decoupling in the Elucidation of Polymer Structure," *J. Chem. Phys.* **39** (September 1963), pp. 1199-1202.

19. F. Heatley and F. A. Bovey, "Polymer Nuclear Magnetic Resonance Spectroscopy. XVI. Poly(vinyl Chloride) at 220 MHz," *Macromolecules* **2** (May/June 1969), pp. 241-245.

20. F. A. Bovey, F. P. Hood, III, E. W. Anderson, and L. C. Snyder, "Polymer NMR Spectroscopy. XI. Polystyrene and Polystyrene Model Compounds," *J. Chem. Phys.* **42** (June 1965), pp. 3900-3910.

21. F. A. Bovey, F. C. Schilling, F. L. McCrackin, and H. L. Wagner, "Short-Chain and Long-Chain Branching in Low-Density Polyethylene," *Macromolecules* **9** (Jan./Feb. 1976), pp. 76-80.

22. K. H. Storks, "An Electron Diffraction Examination of Some Linear High Polymers," *J. Am. Chem. Soc.* **60** (August 1938), pp. 1753-1761.

23. R. Jaccodine, "Observations of Spiral Growth Steps in Ethylene Polymer," *Nature* **176** (August 1955), pp. 305-306; A. Keller, "A Note on Single Crystals in Polymers: Evidence for a Folded Chain Configuration," *Phil. Mag.* **2** (1957), p. 1171; E. W. Fischer, "Staten-und spiralförniges Kristalwachtum bei Hochpolymeren," *Z. Naturforsch* **12a** (1957), p. 753; P. H. Till, "The Growth of Single Crystals of Linear Polyethylene," *J. Polymer Science* **24** (1957), p. 301.

24. H. D. Keith and F. J. Padden, Jr., "A Phenomenological Theory of Spherulitic Crystallization," *J. Appl. Phys.* **34** (August 1963), pp. 2409-2421; idem, "Spherulitic Crystallization from the Melt. I. Fractionation and Impurity Segregation and Their Influence on Crystalline Morphology," *J. Appl. Phys.* **35** (April 1964), pp. 1270-1285.

25. H. D. Keith, F. J. Padden, Jr., and R. G. Vadimsky, "Intercrystalline Links in Polyethylene Crystallized from the Melt," *J. Polymer Science* Part A2, **4** (April 1966), pp. 267-281; idem, "Intercrystalline Links: Critical Evaluation," *J. Appl. Phys.* **42** (November 1971), pp. 4585-4592.

26. D. W. McCall, in *Polyethylene*, ed. A. Renfrew and P. Morgan (London: Iliffe & Sons, Ltd., 2nd ed, 1957); G. L. Link and G. E. Johnson, "High Resolution Measurement of the Dielectric Loss Angle at 30 MHz," *1972 Ann. Rep. Conf. Elec. Insul. Dielectr. Phenom., Nat'l. Acad. Sci.* (1973).

27. T. W. Huseby and S. Matsuoka, "Mechanical Properties of Solid and Liquid Polymers," *Materials Science and Engineering* **1** (March 1967), pp. 321-341.

28. W. P. Mason, W. O. Baker, H. J. McSkimin, and J. H. Heiss, "Mechanical Properties of Long Chain Molecule Liquids at Ultrasonic Frequencies," *Phys. Rev.* **73** (1948), pp. 1074.

29. W. A. Yager and W. O. Baker, "The Relation of Dielectric Properties to Structure of Crystalline Polymers. I. Polyesters," *J. Am. Chem. Soc.* **64** (September 1942), pp.

2164-2171; W. O. Baker and W. A. Yager, "The Relation of Dielectric Properties to Structure of Crystalline Polymers. II. Linear Polyamides," *J. Am. Chem. Soc.* **64** (September 1942), pp. 2171-2177.

30. D. W. McCall and E. W. Anderson, "Dielectric Properties of Linear Polyamides," *J. Chem. Phys.* **32** (January 1960), pp. 237-241.

31. W. P. Slichter, "NMR Studies of Multiple Relaxations in Polymers," *J. Polymer Science*, Part C, No. 14, (1966), pp. 33-48; D. W. McCall and D. R. Falcone, "Nuclear Magnetic Relaxation in Seven Polymers," *Trans. Faraday Soc.* **66** (1970), pp. 262-272; W. P. Slichter, "NMR Studies of Solid Polymers," in *NMR: Basic Principles and Progress*, **4**, ed. P. Diehl, E. Fluck, and R. Kosfeld (Berlin: Springer-Verlag, 1971), pp. 209-231; D. W. McCall, "Nuclear Magnetic Resonance Studies of Molecular Relaxation Mechanisms in Polymers," *Accounts of Chemical Research* **4** (June 1971), pp. 223-232.

32. W. P. Slichter, "Proton Magnetic Resonance in Polyamides," *J. Appl. Phys.* **26** (September 1955), pp. 1099-1103.

33. E. Helfand, Z. R. Wasserman, and T. A. Weber, "Brownian Dynamics Study of Polymer Conformational Transitions," *J. Chem. Phys.* **70** (February 1979), pp. 2016-2017; idem, "Brownian Dynamics Study of Polymer Conformational Transitions," *Macromolecules* **13** (May/June 1980), pp. 526-533.

34. T. A. Weber and E. Helfand, "Molecular Dynamics Simulation of Polymers. I. Structure," *J. Chem. Phys.* **71** (December 1979), pp. 4760-4762.

35. A. N. Holden, C. Kittel, F. R. Merritt, and W. A. Yager, "Determination of g-Values in Paramagnetic Organic Compounds by Microwave Resonance," *Phys. Rev.* **77** (January 1950), pp. 147-148.

36. G. Herzberg, "The Spectra and Structures of Free Methyl and Free Methylene," *Proc. Roy. Soc. (London)* **A262** (July 18, 1961), pp. 291-317.

37. J. M. Foster and S. F. Boys, "Quantum Variational Calculations for a Range of CH_2 Configurations," *Rev. Mod. Phys.* **32** (April 1960), pp. 305-307.

38. E. Wasserman, W. A. Yager, and V. J. Kuck, "EPR of CH_2: A Substantially Bent and Partially Rotating Ground State Triplet," *Chem. Phys. Lett.* **7** (November 15, 1970), pp. 409-413; E. Wasserman, V. J. Kuck, R. S. Hutton, and W. A. Yager, "Electron Paramagnetic Resonance of CD_2 and CHD. Isotope Effects, Motion, and Geometry of Methylene," *J. Am. Chem. Soc.* **92** (December 1970), pp. 7491-7493; E. Wasserman, V. J. Kuck, R. S. Hutton, E. D. Anderson, and W. A. Yager, "^{13}C Hyperfine Interactions and Geometry of Methylene," *J. Chem. Phys.* **54** (May 1971), pp. 4120-4121.

39. A. M. Trozzolo, "Electronic Spectroscopy of Arylmethylenes," *Accounts of Chemical Research* **1** (November 1968), pp. 329-335; A. M. Trozzolo and E. Wasserman, "Structure of Arylcarbenes," *Carbenes*, Volume II, ed. R. A. Moss and M. Jones, Jr. (New York: John Wiley & Sons, 1975), pp. 185-206.

Chapter 15

Superconductors

Research on superconducting materials began with the discovery of super-conductivity by Kamerlingh Onnes at Leiden in 1911. Onnes and his col-leagues observed that the electrical voltage across a wire of solid mercury car-rying an electric current dropped abruptly to zero at a characteristic tempera-ture, T_c, of 4.2K. The phenomenon was observed by him in other metals at other T_c's, and has since been seen in many metals and compounds. At Bell Laboratories the materials effort has resulted in contributions along three different lines: the discovery of a large number of superconductors, the increase in T_c, the onset of superconductivity temperature, and the discovery that some superconducting compounds and alloys have very large current-carrying capacity at high magnetic fields. These advances in superconducting materials provided continuous challenges to those with primary interest in the microscopic theory of the phenomenon of superconductivity, and led to the explanation of such physical phenomena as the absence of the isotope effect in ruthenium, the high currents measured in the superconducting Nb_3Sn, or in trends of T_c with electron-per-atom ratio across the Periodic Table, as dis-cussed in Chapter 9, section I.

I. NEW SUPERCONDUCTING ELEMENTS, ALLOYS, AND COMPOUNDS

In 1955, B. T. Matthias showed empirically that there is a correlation of T_c with the average valence electron per atom ratio of a supercon-ducting element or alloy.[1] [Fig. 15-1] He pointed out that T_c has max-ima near 5 and 7 electrons per atom and a minimum at 6. Use of this "rule" and his extensive knowledge of the properties of atoms in the Periodic Table enabled Matthias subsequently to discover many super-conducting materials. The efforts of Matthias, T. H. Geballe, and their coworkers doubled the number of known superconductors in the 1959 to 1972 period.[2] Intermediate-phase crystal structures favorable for superconductivity were identified and classified.[3] The role of localiza-

Principal authors: P. A. Fleury, T. H. Geballe, and J. M. Rowell

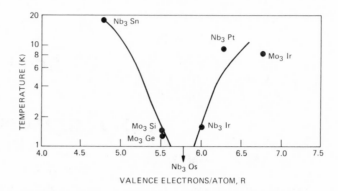

Fig. 15-1. Superconducting transition temperatures of compounds with the "beta-tungsten" structure as a function of valence electrons per atom. In this crystal structure, which is particularly favorable for the occurrence of superconductivity, the transition metal atoms (e.g., Nb, Mo) form long chains that interlace the structure. [Matthias, *Phys. Rev.* **97** (1955): 75].

tion and virtual bound states and of charge transfer in *d*- and *f*- band compounds and alloys was explored.[4,5]

A number of novel systems were also shown to be superconducting, for example, the layer compound formed by introducing alkali metals between the layers of a graphite crystal, as suggested by N. B. Hannay in 1965.[6] This research showed that the "first-stage" compounds with alternating carbon-alkali metal layers were superconducting, whereas the electrically more nearly two-dimensional higher-stage compounds (with adjacent carbon layers) were not. Observations that alkali-metals could be reversibly intercalated between the layers of MoS_2, a semiconductor, and could result in superconducting compounds led Geballe, F. Gamble, and F. J. DiSalvo, then at Stanford University to discover a large number of new, superconducting, layered compounds. The intercalation of involving large organic molecules into TaS_2 resulted in superconductors with large, anisotropic, two-dimensional properties. Studies of the intercalation of alkali-metals also led to the development of new materials for storage batteries by Gamble and coworkers at Exxon Corporation, and by DiSalvo, D. W. Murphy, and coworkers at Bell Labs.

In 1971, R. Chevrel at Rennes, France, discovered a new class of true ternary compounds, MMo_6S_8 and MMo_6Se_8, where M is a third element such as lead, tin, or copper.[7] Shortly thereafter, Matthias and coworkers showed that many of these compounds were superconducting with high (up to 15K) transition temperatures.[8] O. Fischer and his group at Geneva found that these compounds maintained their superconductivity at fields as high as 600 kilogauss (kG).[9] This discovery of superconductivity and high critical fields in true ternary compounds created a flurry of activity in this area.

In 1977, Matthias, E. Corenzwit, and coworkers discovered a second class of ternary compounds based on the general formula $M\text{Rh}_4\text{B}_4$, where M was a transition or rare earth element.[10] These compounds showed either magnetism or superconductivity; one unique compound, ErRh_4B_4, displayed the properties of both. When the temperature was lowered, the material first became superconducting at 8.5K and, as the temperature was lowered further to 0.95K, it became ferromagnetic and lost its superconducting properties. The subtle interplay of superconductivity and magnetism displayed in this compound stimulated further research in this field. A new family of ternary rare earth, rhodium stannide compounds, exhibiting either superconductivity or magnetic ordering, was discovered and prepared in single-crystal form by J. P. Remeika and coworkers in 1980. One of these compounds, erbium rhodium stannide, is both superconducting ($I_c = 1.3\text{K}$) and magnetic ($T \sim 0.5\text{K}$).[11]

II. INCREASE IN THE TEMPERATURE OF ONSET OF SUPERCONDUCTIVITY

The maximum known T_c advanced steadily following the discovery of superconductivity in mercury in 1911. In 1952, Hardy and J. K. Hulm at the University of Chicago investigated superconductivity in the intermetallic compounds of transition metals with silicon or germanium. They observed that the crystal structure similar to that of β-tungsten appeared favorable for superconductivity, and that V_3Si, one of these "β-tungstens," had a T_c of 17K. Matthias also pursued superconductivity in this structure and in 1954, with Geballe, S. Geller, and Corenzwit, reported that Nb_3Sn was superconducting at 18K.[12]

Early work by A. M. Clogston and V. Jaccarino on the Knight shift and susceptibility on β-tungsten materials required that the Fermi level intersect an extremely narrow peak in the electronic density of states.[13] Most subsequent thinking about these materials has incorporated these ideas. It has been found that increasing T_c above 18K required flirting with crystalline stability. By quenching the melt onto a cold substrate, Matthias and coworkers were able to change the transition temperature of Nb_3Ge, which is normally very sharp around 6K, to a broad transition starting at 17K.[14] They attributed the increase in T_c to the approach to the ideal 3:1 stoichiometry and predicted further increase if the ordering of the niobium and germanium atoms on their respective lattice sites were more nearly perfect. On the other hand, R. H. Willens and coworkers increased the T_c of Nb_3Al to 18.8K after a special preparation that involved an exothermic reaction between niobium and aluminum powder.[15] Geballe, Corenzwit, and Matthias experimented with a mixture of various ratios of Nb_3Al to Nb_3Ge. They narrowed down this mixture to 80 percent Nb_3Al and 20 percent Nb_3Ge after hearing that work by scientists in the Soviet

Union showed that such a mixture had a higher T_c than either of the two starting compounds. In 1967, this led to the synthesis of the first superconductors with T_c above the boiling point of hydrogen (20.4K).[16] In 1973, Gavaler at the Westinghouse Electric Company discovered that Nb_3Ge films could be prepared by sputtering to produce T_c above 22K. This was almost immediately confirmed by L. R. Testardi, J. H. Wernick, and W. A. Royer, who prepared Nb_3Ge films with an onset of the transition just above 23K, the highest transition produced as of the early 1980s.[17]

Testardi reasoned that if a superconducting material could be prepared in the vicinity of a structural transition and metastably maintained in that atomic configuration, it should exhibit a superconducting T_c. [Fig. 15-2] Working with J. J. Hauser, Testardi verified this novel idea by preparing thin films of molybdenum-rhenium alloys at different deposition temperatures. When the deposition temperature was close to the structural transformation temperature of the alloy, the resulting metastable films exhibited superconducting T_c of approximately 15K, more than twice the bulk value.[18] This discovery set the search for high-temperature superconductors off in a new direction. Testardi, together with Wernick and Royer, discovered dozens of new metastable phases—including some with other remarkable properties, such as corrosion resistance and hardness exceeding that of any known metal.[19] In 1975, the use of epitaxial growth to stabilize high-T_c superconducting compounds, in particular Nb_3Ge and Nb_3Si, was suggested by C. K. N. Patel and P. K. Tien, and by Geballe.[20] A study carried out by A. H. Dayem, Geballe, and coworkers from Stanford University showed that it is possible to use a polycrystalline film (for example, a Nb_3Ir film) as a substrate for the epitaxial growth of a second film (for example, Nb_3Ge) whose lattice matches that of the substrate.[21] The study also demonstrated that this epitaxial growth can extend the phase boundaries of a given crystalline structure far beyond its boundaries in thermodynamic equilibrium.

III. HIGH-FIELD SUPERCONDUCTORS

The high-field behavior of Nb_3Sn was ignored for approximately five years after its high T_c was determined, probably because earlier attempts to manufacture superconducting magnets had failed and because it generally had been assumed that critical fields and superconducting currents would only increase in proportion to T_c. However, in 1960, R. Kompfner, while visiting M.I.T.'s Lincoln Laboratories, observed the performance of a superconducting solenoid magnet wound with niobium and used by S. H. Autler for a solid state maser. It produced a magnetic field of 4.3 kOe. Kompfner's report of

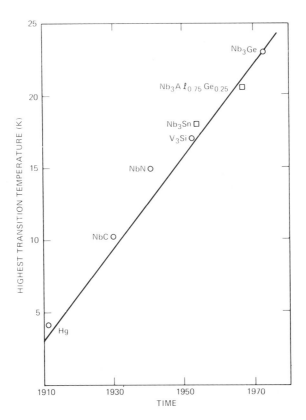

Fig. 15-2. The contribution by Bell Labs scientists to the increase in the maximum superconducting transition temperature, T_c, is indicated by the squares. The superconductor Nb_3Sn became the most important material for use in superconducting magnets, giving fields of 150 kG. The $Nb_3Al_{0.75}Ge_{0.25}$ superconductor was the first material that reached a T_c above the boiling point of hydrogen (20.4 K). Despite intensive research in many institutions, as of 1981 no material with a T_c higher than that of Nb_3Ge had been reported.

this observation to Matthias and others at Bell Labs stimulated further research on superconducting materials. With a ductile alloy of $Mo_{75}Re_{25}$ prepared by E. Buehler and drawn into wire form by the Chase Brass Company in New York, J. E. Kunzler [Fig. 15-3] produced useful super currents yielding magnetic fields up to 15 kOe.[22] This coil of Mo-Re alloy was coated with gold, which facilitated the drawing process and helped in electrically stabilizing the superconducting coil by protecting it from destruction should the material be inadvertently overloaded and return to the normal state. The coil was the subject of a patent granted to Geballe.[23]

Fig. 15-3. In 1960, J. E. Kunzler discovered that some superconducting wires (for example, Nb_3Sn) can carry electric currents up to 10^5 amps/cm^2 at magnetic fields as high as 88 kG.

The use of the Mo-Re alloy did not lead to superconducting currents at fields greater than 18 kG. However, a big increase in both field and current-carrying capacity was obtained by Kunzler when brittle Nb_3Sn was produced in wire form by reacting niobium and tin in niobium tubes. The discovery of "high-field superconductivity" took place late in 1960 when Kunzler and coworkers showed that at 4.2K the Nb_3Sn wires had critical current densities of 10^5 amps/cm^2, which was 50 times those of the bulk ingots, at magnetic fields as high as 88 kOe.[24] [Fig. 15-4] Later specific heat measurements on similar materials by F. J. Morin and coworkers showed that a very large fraction of the sample remains superconducting in these high fields.[25] [Fig. 15-5] The somewhat arbitrary figure of 88 kOe arose from the fact that it was the highest magnetic field that could be attained at Bell Labs in J. K. Galt's Bitter-type solenoid, an apparatus he had acquired because he thought that it was important to have a state-of-the-art, high-field magnet available in any basic research institution.

The excitement surrounding the discovery of such high critical fields in Nb_3Sn can be partially sensed by reading the account given in the paper "The Road to Superconducting Materials" by Hulm,

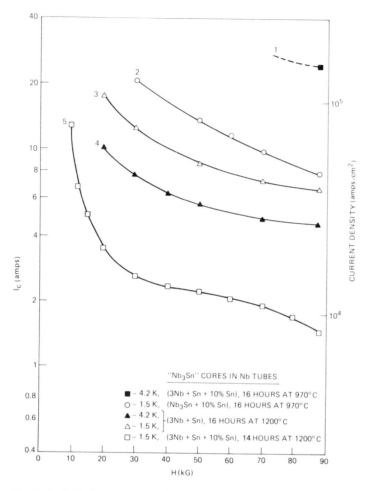

Fig. 15-4. Critical current vs. applied magnetic field for niobium-clad cores of Nb$_3$Sn. The outside diameter of the cores was about 0.015 cm, and that of the niobium jackets was about 0.038 cm. The "+10%Sn" in the table legend means 10 wt.-percent more tin than is required to form Nb$_3$Sn, assuming no reaction with the niobium tube. The magnetic field was perpendicular to the direction of the current. Each experimental point represents the maximum current, at the value of magnetic field indicated, for which no voltage drop along the sample was observed—the smallest detectable voltage being a few hundredths of a microvolt. [Kunzler et al., *Phys. Rev. Lett.* **6** (1961): 91].

Kunzler, and Matthias where they give details of the "scotch bet," which was paid at the rate of one bottle for every 3 kOe over 25 kOe.[26] At a celebration party following the discovery, G. Indig prompted Matthias to write down other ductile magnet materials, which he did on the inside cover of a matchbook. Among these were

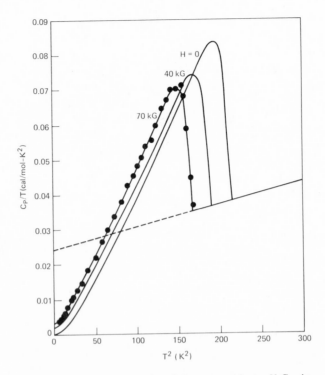

Fig. 15-5. The heat capacity of the superconductor V_3Ga, in fields of 0, 40, and 70 kG. The dashed line represents the extrapolated behavior expected for the normal state based on measurements above the critical temperature (14.66K). The persistence of the peak in the heat capacity in such high magnetic fields and the smallness of the intercept at 0K are evidence that a large degree of superconductivity remains in high magnetic fields. This experiment eliminated the possibility that at high fields such materials exhibited superconductivity only in filaments. [Morin et al., *Phys. Rev. Lett.* **8** (1962): 275].

NbZr and NbTi alloys, which were the basis of a valuable patent, as NbTi has been the most important magnet material for two decades.

The discovery that specific-heat measurements of Nb_3Sn showed it to have the largest known linear coefficient in temperature-dependent specific heat imparted a special urgency to a complete understanding of high-field and high-temperature superconductors. Kunzler, Buehler, and F. S. L. Hsu worked to fabricate an ultrahigh-field (greater than 100 kOe) superconducting magnet based on Nb_3Sn. The technique of Nb_3Sn core wire was developed, and magnets operating at 70 kOe were soon achieved. These Nb_3Sn magnets are often wound from a pre-reacted multifilamentary wire, but for some applications the magnet is wound before the Nb_3Sn is reacted by the solid state diffusion of Nb and Sn, the method pioneered by Kunzler, Buehler, and Hsu.

Many of the high-T_c and high-current-carrying superconducting compounds have been discovered to be susceptible to radiation damage. The T_c of several materials that belong to the β-tungsten class, such as V_3Si, was shown by A. R. Sweedler and coworkers at Brookhaven National Laboratory to be sensitive to radiation damage.[27] It was then shown by J. M. Poate and coworkers that there was a universality of behavior for superconductors having the same crystal structure as V_3Si, subject to α-particle irradiation such that the T_c drops rapidly at first with increasing dosage and then levels off at higher dosage to some low value of T_c.[28] This final saturated value was the same as that obtained if the compound was prepared in the disordered state. Similar behavior was also shown to occur in the ternary boride compounds by J. M. Rowell, R. C. Dynes, and P. H. Schmidt.[29]

The impact of superconductivity research at Bell Laboratories has been widespread. As mentioned above, NbTi was the material of choice for superconducting magnets up to 100 kOe, whereas Nb_3Sn came to be routinely used up to 150 kOe. In addition to revolutionizing the use of high magnetic fields in research laboratories and at national magnet facilities, at the time of this writing, superconducting magnets have found extensive use as bending magnets of high-energy accelerators, and have become crucial for the production of the high fields over large volumes required to confine plasmas to produce fusion energy. In Japan, a superconducting magnet was also used to levitate a high-speed train. In the 1980s, as this volume was being produced, a very rapidly growing application for such magnets has been for NMR imaging of the human body, a technique which may replace X-ray imaging in some cases. Thus, superconductivity, regarded in the early 1960s as an exotic effect occurring at temperatures that were impractical commercially, has become the workhorse of modern technology. Even electrical power may be generated by superconducting machines within the next two decades.

REFERENCES

1. B. T. Matthias, "Empirical Relation Between Superconductivity and the Number of Valence Electrons per Atom," *Phys. Rev.* **97** (January 1955), pp. 74-76.
2. B. W. Roberts, "Survey of Superconductive Materials and Critical Evaluation of Selected Properties," *J. Phys. Chem. Ref. Data* **5** (1976), pp. 581-821.
3. B. T. Matthias, T. H. Geballe, and V. B. Compton, "Superconductivity," *Rev. Mod. Phys.* **35** (January 1963), pp. 1-22.
4. T. H. Geballe, B. T. Matthias, B. Caroli, E. Corenzwit, G. W. Hull, Jr., and L. D.

Longinotti, "3*d* Elements in Superconducting PdSb," *Phys. Rev.* **169** (May 1968), pp. 457-465.

5. T. H. Geballe, B. T. Matthias, V. B. Compton, E. Corenzwit, G. W. Hull, Jr., and L. D. Longinotti, "Superconductivity in Binary Alloy Systems of the Rare Earths and of Thorium with Pt-Group Metals," *Phys. Rev.* **137** (January 1965), pp. A119-A127.

6. N. B. Hannay, T. H. Geballe, B. T. Matthias, K. Andres, P. Schmidt, and D. Mac-Nair, "Superconductivity in Graphitic Compounds," *Phys. Rev. Lett.* **14** (February 15, 1965), pp. 225-226.

7. R. Chevrel, M. Serget, and J. Prigent, "Sur de Nouvelles Phases Sulfurées Ternaires du Molybdéne." *J. Solid State Chem.* **3** (November 1971), p. 515-519.

8. B. T. Matthias, M. Marezio, E. Corenzwit, A. S. Cooper, and H. E. Barz, "High-Temperature Superconductors, the First Ternary System," *Science* **175** (March 1972), pp. 1465-1466.

9. O. Fischer, "Chevrel Phases: Superconducting and Normal State Properties," *Appl. Phys.* **16** (May 1978), p. 1-28.

10. B. T. Matthias, E. Corenzwit, J. M. Vandenberg, and H. E. Barz, "High Superconducting Transition Temperatures of New Rare Earth Ternary Borides," *Proc. Nat'l. Acad. Sci.* **74** (April 1977), pp. 1334-1335.

11. J. P. Remeika, "A New Family of Ternary Intermediate Superconducting Magnetic Stannides," *J. Solid State Comm.* **34** (1980), pp. 923-926.

12. B. T. Matthias, T. H. Geballe, S. Geller, and E. Corenzwit, "Superconductivity of Nb_3Sn," *Phys. Rev.* **95** (September 1954), p. 1435.

13. A. M. Clogston, "Impurity States in Metals," *Phys. Rev.* **125** (January 1962), pp. 439-443; A. M. Clogston and V. Jaccarino, "Susceptibilities and Negative Knight Shifts of Intermetallic Compounds," *Phys. Rev.* **121** (March 1961), pp. 1357-1362.

14. B. T. Matthias, T. H. Geballe, R. H. Willens, E. Corenzwit, and G. W. Hull, Jr., "Superconductivity of Nb_3Ge," *Phys. Rev.* **139** (August 1965), pp. A1501-A1503.

15. R. H. Willens, T. H. Geballe, A. C. Gossard, J. P. Maita, A. Menth, G. W. Hull, Jr., and R. R. Soden, "Superconductivity of Nb_3Al," *Solid State Comm.* **7** (June 1969), pp. 837-841.

16. G. Arrhenius, E. Corenzwit, R. Fitzgerald, G. W. Hull, Jr., H. L. Luo, B. T. Matthias, and W. H. Zachariasen, "Superconductivity of $Nb_3(Al,Ge)$ Above 20.4K," *Proc. Nat'l. Acad. Sci.* **61** (October 1968), pp. 621-628.

17. L. R. Testardi, J. H. Wernick, and W. A. Royer, "Superconductivity with Onset Above 23K in Nb-Ge Sputtered Films," *Solid State Comm.* **15** (July 1974), pp. 1-4.

18. L. R. Testardi, J. J. Hauser, and M. H. Read, "Enhanced Superconducting T_c and Structural Transformation in Mo-Re Alloys," *Solid State Comm.* **9** (November 1971), pp. 1829-1831.

19. L. R. Testardi, W. A. Royer, D. D. Bacon, A. R. Storm, and J. H. Wernick, "Exceptional Hardness and Corrosion Resistance of Mo_5Ru_3 and W_3Ru_2 Films," *Metal. Trans.* **4** (September 1973), pp. 2195-2198; also, see reference 17.

20. A. H. Dayem, U.S. Patent No. 4,242,419; filed December 29, 1977, issued December 30, 1980.

21. A. H. Dayem, T. H. Geballe, R. B. Zubeck, A. B. Hallack, and G. W. Hull, Jr., "Epitaxial Growth of High T_c Superconducting Nb_3Ge on Nb_3Ir," *Appl. Phys. Lett.* **30** (May 15, 1977), pp. 541-543; idem, "Epitaxial Growth of Nb_3Ge on Nb_3Ir and Nb_3Rh," *J. Phys. Chem. Solids* **39** (1978), pp. 529-538.

22. J. E. Kunzler, E. Buehler, F. S. L. Hsu, B. T. Matthias, and C. Wahl, "Production of Magnetic Fields Exceeding 15 Kilogauss by a Superconducting Solenoid," *J. Appl. Phys.* **32** (February 1961), pp. 325-326.

23. T. H. Geballe, U.S. Patent No. 3,109,963; filed August 29, 1960; issued November 5, 1963.

24. J. E. Kunzler, E. Buehler, F. S. L. Hsu, and J. H. Wernick, "Superconductivity in Nb₃Sn at High Current Density in a Magnetic Field of 88 kgauss," *Phys. Rev. Lett.* **6** (February 1, 1961), pp. 89-91.

25. F. J. Morin, J. P. Maita, H. J. Williams, R. C. Sherwood, J. H. Wernick, and J. E. Kunzler, "Heat Capacity Evidence for a Large Degree of Superconductivity in V₃Ga in High Magnetic Fields," *Phys. Rev. Lett.* **8** (April 1, 1962), pp. 275-277.

26. J. K. Hulm, J. E. Kunzler, and B. T. Matthias, "The Road to Superconducting Materials," *Physics Today* **34** (January 1981), pp. 34-37, 40-43.

27. A. R. Sweedler, R. G. Schweitzer, and G. W. Webb, "Atomic Ordering and Superconductivity in High-T_c A-15 Compounds," *Phys. Rev. Lett.* **33** (July 15, 1974), p. 168-172.

28. J. M. Poate, L. R. Testardi, A. R. Storm, and W. M. Augustyniak, "⁴He-Induced Damage in Superconducting Nb-Ge Films," *Phys. Rev. Lett.* **35** (November 10, 1975), pp. 1290-1293.

29. J. M. Rowell, R. C. Dynes, and P. H. Schmidt, "The Effect of Damage on the Superconducting and Magnetic Transitions in ErRh₄B₄," *Solid State Comm.*, **30** (1979), pp. 191-194.

Chapter 16

Dielectrics for Insulators, and for Electronic and Optical Applications

Among the early demands upon the newly formed Bell Laboratories was the need to improve the electric properties of materials used as insulators for wire, cable, and vacuum tubes, and as dielectrics in capacitors. The small electrical currents and the spectrum of frequencies characteristic of telephony imposed new challenges to the technology of dielectrics and insulators. Radio communication and long distance telephony emerged together in the 1920s and 1930s, with requirements for materials that respond with minimum energy loss to the spectra of alternating voltages. These requirements were seen to go far beyond the problems of simple resistive attenuation.

Interest in the theory of the dielectric behavior of matter was being developed in Germany, through the research of P. J. W. Debye, and in the United States by J. H. Van Vleck. These studies developed concepts of the electric dipolar character of molecules and of the polarizability of electric charge in matter. This fundamental work was appreciated early by scientists at Bell Laboratories, who applied the concepts to research on cable and capacitors. Interest in dielectric behavior continued actively as the electromagnetic frequencies used in communication have increased, until now they occupy the spectra of light. Although the optical behavior of matter is an old subject, the research entered new arenas through discoveries of nonlinear effects in matter found with the intense optical excitation by lasers.

Principal authors: G. Y. Chin, R. A. Laudise, G. T. Kohman, R. C. Miller, S. O. Morgan, M. D. Rigterink, W. P. Slichter, F. J. Stillinger, J. H. Wernick, A. H. White, and J. C. Williams

517

I. RUBBER

1.1 Insulation for Submarine Cables

One of the early activities in materials research was related to submarine cables. Shortly after World War I, an attempt to use telegraph cables for the telephone had failed. F. B. Jewett (president of Bell Laboratories from 1925 to 1940) realized that the trouble lay in the dielectric material gutta-percha, which had been used as insulation for undersea telegraphic cable ever since the pioneering installations of the 1860s. Part of the problem lay in the severity of the demands of telephony compared with those of telegraphy: intelligible transmission of complex signals at the frequencies of speech is affected by the capacitance of the cable to a much greater degree than is transmission of the simpler current and voltage alternations encountered in telegraphy.

A group of chemists under R. R. Williams and A. R. Kemp studied the electrical and mechanical characteristics of gutta-percha and rubber.[1] H. H. Lowry and G. T. Kohman, who had been recruited by Williams, carried out extensive studies on how water is absorbed by rubber and gutta-percha.[2] They showed that impurities inherent in the natural hydrocarbons are particularly sensitive to the presence of water. These impurities were found to be proteins, originating in the trees from which the rubber was extracted. A process for washing rubber at elevated temperature and pressure was developed to remove the proteins and other electrolytic impurities. The processed rubber was found to be electrically stable in the presence of water. Further, Kemp and his colleagues discovered a substance that offered the dimensional stability and flexibility necessary at the cold temperatures of the ocean floor.[3] This substance, a blend of the two purified hydrocarbon isomers, rubber and gutta-percha, was called paragutta and was successfully used in cables between Key West, Florida, and Havana, Cuba, and between the California mainland and Catalina Island.

1.2 Continuous Vulcanization Process

Another major advance occurred in the improved vulcanization of rubber. Ever since 1839, when Charles Goodyear learned how to change gum rubber into a strong, permanently elastic material, the conversion of this hydrocarbon into useful objects had largely been done on a batch basis. Thus, coils of wire insulated with raw rubber to which sulfur had been added were batch cured in a steam chamber. This process took an hour or more for each batch of wire. Kemp, in separate studies with A. N. Gray and J. H. Ingmanson, developed a chemical termed an ultra-accelerator that greatly speeded the curing process.[4] Thus, the batch process was eliminated. Instead, the rubber insulation was continuously extruded onto the conductor, and the wire passed immediately through a long steam chamber. Curing took only a minute, and the finished wire was continuously wound on drums. This "continuous vulcanization" process revolutionized the wire industry and has been licensed widely.

1.3 Rubber for National Defense

A national crisis arose when war in the Pacific cut off shipments of natural rubber from the Far East. Chemistry had to fill the gap in the United States supply of this basic material, but the technology had never been tested in this country. German chemists, on the other hand, had long been active in finding ways to synthesize materials of natural origin, such as dyes and rubber. Toward the end of World War I, they had produced an unsatisfactory ersatz rubber. But by 1934, the German chemical firm I. G. Farben had successfully synthesized a useful rubber.

While rubber companies in the United States had been experimenting with synthetic substitutes for natural rubber for some time, they had not advanced very far with problems of raw materials and finished properties. In 1942, a large program was laid out by the government, under the sponsorship of the Reconstruction Finance Corporation, Office of Rubber Reserve. A number of industrial and academic laboratories took part in the research. Bell Laboratories, through the work of W. O. Baker, C. S. Fuller, and J. H. Heiss, made essential contributions to the characterization and control of experimental compounds.[5]

In surprisingly short order, the emergency program under the Office of Rubber Reserve produced a product that, although made from the same ingredients as the Germans' artificial rubber, was clearly different and superior. The American product was given the general name GR-S, an abbreviation of Government Rubber-Styrene. Efficient manufacturing required knowledge of the intimate details of its structure. The rate of chemical combination of the key ingredients, butadiene and styrene, differed from the rate at which each combined with itself. The composition of the product therefore differed from that of the ingredients. Baker and Fuller developed an optical method of measuring the styrene content of GR-S, thus permitting close control over the average composition.[6] They also developed tests of viscosity and of gel content to monitor the compounding of the rubber. The term "compounding" embraces the various mechanical operations that are carried out on a rubber, such as mixing in fillers and pigments, prior to vulcanization. Control of the starting material and the processing was shown to be essential to successful manufacture of the product.

The program, in which Bell Labs chemists played a central part, produced the first GR-S in December 1943, just 16 months after the planners first met. By 1945, the annual production of GR-S exceeded 700,000 tons. This achievement was a vital element in the prosecution of the war. Moreover, the science and technology developed with such urgency formed the basis of much of the postwar rubber industry.

II. CERAMICS FOR HIGH-FREQUENCY INSULATION

The increasing use of higher frequencies in communications before and during World War II required the development of improved insulating materials because the electrical porcelains used for insulation at low frequencies, such as those used with power and lighting systems, were inadequate for high frequencies. In particular, such materials dissipated excessive amounts of energy at high temperatures and even suffered breakdown. In addition, the demand for increased precision of electronic components required substantial improvement in the control of composition and processing in ceramics.

2.1 High-Performance Ceramic Steatite

M. D. Rigterink [Fig. 16-1] and his colleagues discovered many high-performance ceramics, and improved the process for manufacture of others, particularly the steatites.[7] [Fig. 16-2] These materials take their name from the mineral steatite, also known as soapstone in its more impure form, but more widely known as talc. Rigterink prepared synthetic steatites from mixtures of about 60 percent talc, 30 percent clay, and 10 percent alkaline earth oxides. Under controlled heat treatment at 1200°C to 1400°C, the alkaline earth oxides melt and combine with part of the magnesia, alumina, and silica contained in the talc and clay. Upon cooling, crystalline transformations occurs, causing the material to shrink and to become dense and hard. Rigterink and his colleagues also experimented with the grinding and mixing of the raw materials, the times and temperatures of the heating, and the program of cooling. The close attention to the process resulted in a family of ceramics possessing superior electrical properties and mechanical strength.

2.2 High-Alumina Ceramics

Since about 1955, the growth of the electronics industry has led to greater use of high-alumina compositions (those containing more than 85 percent by weight of aluminum oxide or alumina, Al_2O_3) as insulating materials rather than porcelain or steatite. High-alumina ceramics have excellent dielectric properties, great mechanical

Fig. 16-1. M. D. Rigterink was a leader in the studies and
the development of ceramic materials for electrical insulators
at high frequencies.

strength, high thermal conductivity, and ease of metallization (joining
ceramics to metal components by means of high-temperature
processes). They were particularly useful in miniaturized vacuum
tubes and in hermetically sealed terminals that served as leadout
bushings for oil-filled transformer housings.

However, one of the major applications for alumina in electronics
has been as substrate material for thin-film circuits. The history of the
development of alumina substrates is recounted by J. C. Williams, who
was intimately associated with the project.[8] A major requirement of a
substrate, especially for use with thin-film capacitors, is an extremely
smooth [less than 0.03 micrometer (μm)] surface texture. At first, during the development of tantalum-film technology, soft glass (composed of soda, lime, and silica) served as the substrate. Unfortunately,
the high alkali (sodium) content of such glasses degraded the insulation resistance and promoted corrosion of the tantalum film. With the
availability of fine-grain and low-soda aluminum oxide powders from
commercial producers, the Bell Labs group developed high-alumina

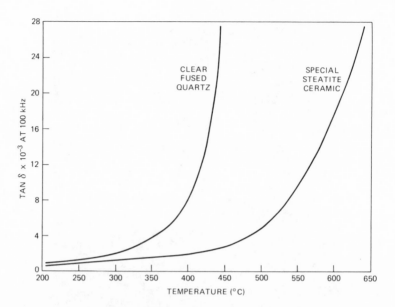

Fig. 16-2. Variations with temperature of the dielectric losses at 100 kHz of clear fused quartz and a steatite ceramic.

substrates with smooth as-fired surface finish, improved mechanical strength, and inertness to tantalum corrosion. A notable achievement during this period was the development, first by H. W. Stetson and W. Gyurk and later by R. Mistler and D. Shanefield of the Western Electric Engineering Research Center, of 0.05 μm surface-finish substrates using a combination of ultrafine powders and improved firing technology to maintain a fine-grain size with high density.

2.2.1 Substrate Glazes

While as-fired surface finishes of 0.05 μm on alumina substrates had become practical, they were still inadequate for use beneath thin-film capacitors. Consequently, a smoother surface was achieved by selectively glazing the substrate in the areas where the capacitors were located. In 1969, F. V. DiMarcello and collaborators obtained a patent for a series of lead-bismuth borosilicate glaze compositions for use with high-alumina substrates that provided a unique combination of properties capable of satisfying a stringent set of requirements.[9] In addition to providing a surface finish of less than 0.025 μm, and withstanding the environments associated with the processing and application of tantalum thin-film circuitry, these glazes were especially designed to be applied at thicknesses of less than 10 μm to minimize the effect of the step between the glazed and unglazed portions of the substrate.

During the late 1960s and early 1970s, the technology of glaze preparation was transferred to a commercial supplier and the application technique was developed and put into production at the Allentown, PA, site of Western Electric. Since that time, several Western Electric locations have used these glazed substrates in the manufacture of tantalum thin-film circuits for a variety of Bell System applications.

An extension of this work during the 1970s by DiMarcello, led to a series of lead-free and bismuth-free glazes that could be used in applications requiring resistance to chemically reducing atmospheres during high-temperature processing.

2.3 Ceramic Processing

In contrast to metal systems, ceramics must be fabricated without the use of extensive melting or deformation. Packed particles are typically sintered together at high temperatures, with the minimization of total surface energy as the driving force.

In early technical ceramics, naturally occurring minerals such as clay, potash, feldspar, and silica were generally ground and mixed. Early improvements were made by better grinding and by utilizing purified fine-particle alkaline earth carbonates as part of the raw materials. The trend toward refined raw materials continued with the use of pure alumina (Al_2O_3) fine powder for substrate and ferric oxide (Fe_2O_3) powder for ferrites.

Rigterink, F. J. Schnettler, and their colleagues extended the chemical refining techniques to include the chemical preparation of total compositions, thereby eliminating the normal mixing and grinding steps. Work done in the late 1960s and early 1970s on precipitation from solutions, freeze drying, and liquid-liquid drying of solutions may be cited as examples.[10,11] With these techniques, the ceramic powder largely retains the intimate mixing of the components in the liquid solution. Further advantages include very closely controlled compositions and fine particle sizes. A large array of solution-preparation processes became available.

The need for better forming techniques led from simple, uniaxial die pressing of dried powders to the isostatic pressing technique in which the more uniformly pressed, unfired parts could be sintered to higher densities with less shape distortion. Better pressing was also achieved by using spray drying of powder slurries as a means of making dense free-flowing agglomerates of the powders for uniform die filling. Research on organic additives to the pressing powder for higher unfired strengths and densities also contributed to improvements in the forming technology. In the mid-1970s high sintered densities and improved ceramic microstructures were attained by the development of various hot-pressing techniques by M. F. Yan and D.

W. Johnson in sintering ceramics with controlled amounts of low melting temperature composition.[12,13]

The use of these ceramic techniques led to the development of highly active oxide catalysts on ceramic supports.[14] These were prepared either by putting very fine oxide catalysts, made by freeze drying, onto corrugated ceramic supports, or by freeze drying solutions directly on porous supports for a very homogeneous distribution of catalyst.

III. DIELECTRICS

The dielectric behavior of materials received early attention in the chemical laboratory. In Germany during the period 1910-1930, P. J. W. Debye had developed theoretical models for the dielectric behavior of matter. (Debye emigrated to the United States and joined the chemistry faculty of Cornell University. He served as a consultant to Bell Laboratories in the late 1940s.) Debye concluded that the response of matter to fluctuating electric fields must depend on the separation of charge in the molecules and on the constraints to motion that the molecules experience from their neighbors. He also saw that these constraints must vary with the temperature. He developed some inherently simple equations to describe dielectric behavior in molecular terms.[15] Debye's treatment was directed primarily at understanding the response of polar molecules in gases or dilute solutions to fluctuating electric fields. In such media the dielectric behavior is ascribed to the rotation of molecules that have permanent electric dipole moments owing to the presence of polar groups.

3.1 Electric Dipoles in Organic Liquids

Because of the importance to telephony of using insulating materials in the presence of alternating fields, a basic research program on dielectrics was undertaken by Bell Labs chemists in the late 1920s. Extensive experiments examined the relationships of molecular structure and polarity to dielectric behavior. S. O. Morgan [Fig. 16-3] and Lowry studied the dielectric constants and densities of a number of organic compounds, such as the methyl and ethyl halides, as liquids, as solids, and in solution.[16] Organic halides were dissolved in nonpolar solvents at successively greater dilution, and the measured dielectric constants were extrapolated to infinite dilution. In this manner, the dissolved molecules were represented as being arbitrarily far from each other and, therefore, free of the strong dipole-dipole forces characteristic of the pure liquid and especially the crystalline lattice. The dipole moments were then calculated from the measured dielectric constants and were found to agree satisfactorily with values

Fig. 16-3. S. O. Morgan conducted fundamental studies on the effect of molecular motion on the dielectric properties of organic molecules.

obtained by other investigators who had studied the same compounds in the gaseous state. This finding enhanced the understanding of the constraints on rotational motion of polar molecules in the liquid state.

3.2 Dielectric Properties of Organic Solids

In most atomic and molecular crystals, the atoms or molecules are virtually devoid of motion through the lattice. However, molecules that are sufficiently symmetrical may be able to undergo rotation about one or more axes in their lattice positions. When such molecules contain polar groups that experience motion, the dielectric constant of the solid resembles that of the corresponding liquid. Indeed, early work by W. A. Yager, A. H. White, and Morgan on camphor (which is a nearly spherical molecule with an attached hydroxyl group) established the presence of molecular rotation in that substance many degrees below the melting point.[17] Similarly, White and Morgan found a premelting rotational transition in some polar derivatives of ethane.[18] Other studies by White, B. S. Biggs, and Morgan showed that molecular rotation may occur in the crystalline form of benzene derivatives, provided certain requirements of symmetry are met.[19] Such motion was detected in molecules that are geometrically symmetrical about one axis but are electrically asymmetrical. A simple example is methylpentachlorobenzene. Here, the CH_3 group and the five chlorine atoms are sufficiently similar in size that the molecule can be regarded as geometrically symmetrical, but sufficiently dissimilar in polarity that the whole molecule has a net dipole moment.

Work of this sort led to the realization that polar organic molecules could be useful replacements for paraffinic waxes as dielectric materials in capacitors. The large increase in dielectric constant brought about by this substitution permitted a substantial decrease in the size of capacitors. Halowax, a chlorinated naphthalene, was developed for this purpose by Kohman. The key to his success was the identification and removal of certain impurities that caused instability in the electrical behavior. These studies of relatively simple dielectrics formed the basis for meeting the highly demanding requirements imposed by later advances in communications.

3.3 Theoretical Studies of Molecular Behavior of Liquid Water

It was inevitable that research attention would eventually turn to that most important of polar dielectrics, liquid water. The Bell System has always had scientific and technological concern with this substance and its solutions for both its constructive as well as destructive properties. On the constructive side, many of Western Electric's manufacturing processes require water as a medium, as illustrated in its electroplating activities. On the destructive side, of course, corrosion is an unwelcome concomitant of telephone equipment in high-humidity field locations. However, in spite of the obvious fundamental importance of water in virtually all areas of materials science, chemistry, and biology, the situation, even as late as the mid-1960s, was one of ignorance about the molecular nature of this substance.

With these factors providing a powerful inducement, F. H. Stillinger initiated a theoretical program designed to fill the knowledge gap.[20-25] [Fig. 16-4] Using established methods of quantum mechanics and statistical mechanics, he first studied the complex intermolecular forces operating between water molecules, and then assembled that knowledge into predictions about the way the water molecules arrange themselves and move about in the liquid phase. This process had become feasible because of the increasing power and availability of digital computers.

Fig. 16-4. F. H. Stillinger created a fundamental theory for the statistical mechanics of liquid water, which has been applied to physical, biological, geological, and meteorlogical phenomena.

One of the more vivid products of this theoretical study of water was a set of stereoscopic pictures of submicroscopic regions in the liquid comprising a few hundred molecules. These three-dimensional views showed for the first time how the hydrogen bonds linking neighbor molecules are spatially arranged, particularly in comparison with their orderly arrangement in the ice crystal. As a result it was learned that water consists of a random hydrogen-bond network with frequent strained and broken bonds, and with the participating molecules constantly moving to restructure the network. Insights gained in this manner have been used to explain the unusual physical properties of liquid water in pure form and as a solvent, and to show how it operates in maintaining the native form of large biological molecules through "hydrophobic interactions."

By coincidence, this research on the molecular behavior of water began at about the time that "polywater" burst onto the scene, thanks to a group of imaginative physical chemists in the Soviet Union, raising the possibility that a drop of this substance would eventually rigidify the Earth's oceans. Stillinger's theoretical work helped to allay such fears by showing that pure water would not polymerize. At the same time, D. L. Rousseau at Bell Labs repeated the polywater "experiments" and showed that they were artifacts caused by impurities.[26] (For more on this topic, see section 5.2 of Chapter 20.)

3.4 Microwave Ceramic Dielectrics

In conventional microwave transmission, resonating metal waveguide cavities are used as filters while the control frequencies are obtained either by multiplying the output of a quartz-crystal resonator or by using the output of Invar cavity-stabilized diode oscillators. Until the 1970s, ceramic resonators were not useful because of their poor temperature stability and large dielectric losses. In 1973, H. M. O'Bryan, J. K. Plourde, and coworkers developed a new barium titanate compound ($Ba_2Ti_9O_{20}$) that combined low dielectric loss ($Q >$ 8000) with excellent temperature stability (frequency change of approximately 2 parts per million per degree centigrade).[27] The crystalline structure of $Ba_2Ti_9O_{20}$ allowed its oxygen octahedra to shift with temperature so that decreases in dielectric constant caused by thermal expansion were nearly compensated for by increases in polarization. Processing controls prevented dielectric loss caused by aliovalent impurities, oxygen deficiency, second phase, and/or microcracks.

The resonators are used in the form of unmetallized disks that, because of a relatively high dielectric constant (approximately 40), are able to confine most of the electromagnetic fields within the ceramic. The geometry and size of the resonator determine which resonance frequency between 1 and 8 gigahertz (GHz) is selected. Cost, size, and performance advantages accompany the use of dielectric resonators in filters and oscillators. Also, unlike waveguide resonators, the reduced size of ceramic resonators permits their easy incorporation into microwave integrated circuits. [Fig. 16-5]

The titanate microwave dielectric resonator was first used in 1976 in the TD-2 radio system (4 GHz), which helped expand its capacity from 1200 voice channels to 1500 channels. Subsequent improvements, which included further use of dielectric resonators and GaAs FET solid state amplifiers, boosted the capacity to 1800 voice channels. In the early 1980s, new digital radio systems such as DR6-30 (6 GHz) and DR11-40 (11 GHz) made extensive use of dielectric resonators. Dielectric resonators have also been designed as part of the channel combiner in AMPS (advanced mobile phone service), the cellular radio system developed by the Bell System.

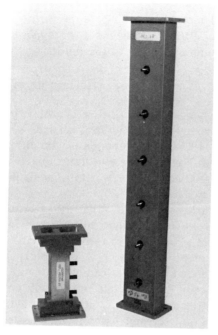

Fig. 16-5. Ceramic resonator filter (left) compared with a copper cavity waveguide filter for 4-GHz application. The reduction in size made possible by the new ceramic resonators is significant.

IV. PIEZOELECTRICS

Crystalline dielectrics that lack a center of symmetry (acentric crystals) can possess the important electrical property of piezoelectricity, that is, the generation of an electrical polarization upon application of mechanical stress. An outstanding example is a quartz crystal.

After the discovery of piezoelectricity in quartz by Pierre and Jacques Curie in 1880, the property remained essentially a scientific curiosity until World War I. In 1917, P. Langevin of France and A. M. Nicolson, then in the research department of Western Electric, initiated studies to use piezoelectric devices for submarine detection.

Many individuals at Bell Labs contributed to establishing quartz as the material for filters, oscillators, and frequency standards during the 1920s and 1930s. W. P. Mason investigated the elastic, dielectric, and piezoelectric properties of a number of piezoelectric materials and was instrumental in the design of many quartz crystal devices.[28-30] He was responsible for the design of ethylene diamine tartrate (EDT) and ammonium dihydrogen phosphate (ADP) underwater sound devices.[31]

Mason was awarded more than 190 patents during his career at Bell Labs; his book, *Piezoelectric Crystals and Their Application to Ultrasonics,* published in 1950, remains a bible in the field.[32]

4.1 Ammonium Dihydrogen Phosphate (ADP) – A Quartz Substitute

Submarine attacks on shipping during World War II caused sharp cuts in many imports—especially natural quartz, which came chiefly from Brazil. In the 1950s, this dependence on Brazilian quartz was relieved by a process for making synthetic quartz of high quality. However, in the immediacy of the wartime need, Bell Labs chemists sought other natural materials.

A satisfactory quartz substitute must be strongly piezoelectric. Piezoelectricity had long been known to originate in detailed aspects of the crystal structure. However, to recognize that a substance can be piezoelectric is not to say how strongly it is piezoelectric, or that it has other qualities needed for large-scale manufacture and use. Apart from natural quartz, only Rochelle salt was widely known in the early 1940s as a piezoelectric material, and its erratic behavior cast doubt upon the usefulness of a crystal grown from aqueous solution. A major advance was made at Bell Labs with the discovery of the effectiveness of ammonium dihydrogen phosphate as a piezoelectric substance by W. L. Bond and A. N. Holden.

Bond surveyed the five volumes of P. Groth's *Chemische Kristallographie* and selected for closer study those species whose crystal class lacked a center of inversion and could therefore exhibit a piezoelectric effect. This in turn led A. N. Holden to grow small crystals of some of these species. Holden and Bond verified that materials that were crystallographically compatible with the piezoelectric effect always exhibited the effect. In particular, they discovered this effect in ADP.

The work of A. C. Walker and Kohman led to the growth of large crystals of ADP in the laboratory.[33] These crystals were big enough so that plates with the desired orientation and dimensions for use in electrical measurements could be cut from them. Crystals were grown from solutions containing seed crystals, or by feeding a solution saturated at one temperature into a vessel containing seed crystals held at a slightly lower temperature. (This technique is described in more detail in section 1.1 of Chapter 19.)

4.2 Synthetic Quartz Crystals

The development of the hydrothermal growth process for producing large, optical quality, high-purity synthetic quartz crystals for piezoelectric applications is another success story in crystal growth (see section 1.1 of Chapter 19). [Fig. 16-6] Following closely upon the

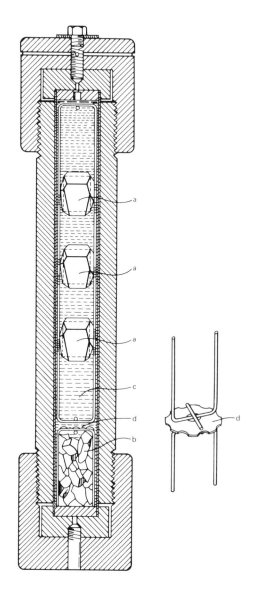

Fig. 16-6. Cylindrical autoclave for growing quartz crystals synthetically: (a) quartz seeds; (b) quartz mass serving as nutrient; (c) aqueous alkaline solution serving as transport medium; (d) G. T. Kohman's baffle. The baffle—shown in perspective on the right with a portion of its wire support— restricts the convective flow of the aqueous medium between the area of dissolution (below) and deposition (above) and keeps the two regions functionally distinct. [Adapted from G. T. Kohman, U.S. Patent No. 2,895,812].

announcement of results obtained by Walker and E. Buehler on the growth of large quartz crystals,[34] other institutions adopted their method for the commercial production of quartz. Western Electric's success in quartz production is also due in part to the work of R. A. Laudise and R. A. Sullivan, the Western Electric engineer who directed the initial commercial production.[35] Laudise's contribution, based upon systematic studies of the growth kinetics, resulted in an optimum process that doubled the growth rate.[36]

The mechanical Q, which is inversely proportional to loss, is a measure of the sharpness of the resonance of a quartz oscillator. High Qs are desirable for drivers or resonators. Beginning in 1958, Laudise, A. A. Ballman, D. W. Rudd, and E. D. Kolb made steady improvements in Q (greater than 10^6) for commercial crystals by adding lithium and nitrite ions to the growth solution. By choice of growth conditions and by choice of seed orientation and perfection, Qs equivalent to natural quartz at commercially useful growth rates were ultimately attained. Until about 1974, the high-purity quartz nutrient used for the commercial process was obtained from Brazil. Driven by the possibility that Brazil, in concert with other potential foreign suppliers of high-purity nutrient, might try to manipulate the source of supply, new North American sources were found by Bell Laboratories materials scientists.[37]

4.3 Other Piezoelectric Crystals

Holden undertook intensive development of procedures for growing large crystals. He designed an apparatus in which seeds mounted on a spindle revolved back and forth to circulate the supersaturated aqueous solution past the growing surfaces.[38] The availability of this technique made it very attractive to return to the search for quartz substitutes after World War II. This search was guided by the principle that if a molecular species lacks certain specified symmetry elements (one example of which is a center of inversion), any crystal made of this species will lack that symmetry element too, and can therefore be piezoelectric. By following this rule, Holden prepared a number of materials unknown to the crystallographic literature, every one of which was piezoelectric.

Another piezoelectric material of interest, even though it was not used commercially, was developed by Holden and coworkers. This material was a modified Rochelle salt crystal, obtained by substituting heavy water (D_2O) for ordinary water of hydration.[39] This substitution raised the useful operating temperature of the material from 23.5°C to 34.5°C, and reduced its dielectric constant and its lower critical temperature, leaving it otherwise unchanged.

One very gratifying byproduct of Holden's work on piezoelectric crystals was the writing of a popular book on crystals and crystal growing by Holden and P. Singer—the most widely read book to come out of Bell Laboratories in the 20 years following its publication.[40]

The piezoelectric material lithium tantalate ($LiTaO_3$) was also studied. It was first grown in single-crystal form by B. T. Matthias and J. P. Remeika.[41] It was later grown in large high-quality form by Ballman,[42] and its properties were characterized by A. W. Warner.[43] This material has a large coupling between applied electric fields and mechanical motions (electromechanical coupling coefficient). Furthermore, it is possible to cut plates of lithium tantalate with crystal orientations such that their resonant vibrational frequency has a zero-temperature coefficient, a property that is essential for many applications (only in quartz and lithium tantalate is this possible). Two early applications for this material recently initiated at Western Electric were a testing circuit for mobile radios and a filter for the Data Under Voice (DUV) system.

4.4 Piezoelectric Ceramics

4.4.1 Sodium Potassium Niobate

In the early 1950s, Remeika used improved crystal-preparation techniques to grow crystals of many binary oxide compounds, some of which Matthias and coworkers discovered to be ferroelectric. Among the ferroelectric compounds were sodium niobate and potassium niobate. Later, as ceramic transducers were sought for ultrasonic delay-line applications, a mixed niobate with the composition $K_{0.5}Na_{0.5}NbO_3$ was found by L. Egerton and D. M. Dillon to be attractive for its combination of relatively low dielectric constant (approximately 400), high electromechanical coupling, and large frequency constant (resonant frequency times thickness).[44] The alternative material, lead zirconate/lead titanate, had too large a dielectric constant (approximately 1,700).

The preparation of the niobate as a ceramic proved difficult, however, because the high sintering temperature needed for densification also reduced the niobium ion (causing high dielectric loss) and promoted grain growth (causing low mechanical strength). These difficulties were successfully overcome by Egerton and C. A. Bieling, who introduced an acid leaching to define the metal stoichiometry (that is, the niobium to alkali ratio). Hot pressing provided densification without excessive grain growth, while annealing techniques replaced the oxygen lost at high temperature. When the delay lines required larger transducer sections (up to 15 centimeters long), a technique called hot isostatic pressing was successfully applied to niobate.[45] In this process, preformed rods are sealed in thin-walled platinum vessels, heated to an appropriate temperature, and the whole assembly collapsed under controlled helium-gas pressure. Within the vessel, an oxygen source such as barium peroxide, which decomposes at elevated temperatures, prevents reduction of the niobate. This process was used to prepare transducers for dispersive delay lines in the Nike-X missile defense system. Such transducers found wide application in manufacture outside Bell Laboratories for military applications.

4.4.2 Lead Zirconate/Lead Titanate Compositions

Piezoelectric materials exhibit high electromechanical coupling efficiencies and are therefore very useful as transducers for the conversion of electrical to mechanical energy and vice versa. The early piezoelectric ceramics used for this purpose were based on barium titanate,[46] but its piezoelectric properties degraded over time. In 1955, interest turned from barium-titanate-based transducers to the more stable, higher-output lead zirconate/lead titanate (PZT) compositions developed at the National Bureau of Standards. Ceramic compositions with good thermal stability, slow aging, better mechanical strength, and higher coupling were developed for piezoelectric devices. Poled ceramics of these compounds have been investigated at Bell Labs for use in microphones, receivers, channel bank filters, key pads, and more recently, as acoustic signal devices. For example, a coin sensor consisting of three lead zirconate/lead titanate pads is being used in the signal unit of the dial-tone-first coin telephone. The impact of a coin falling on the ceramic generates a voltage that is used in the logic circuit of the totalizer to sum the coins deposited.

V. FERROELECTRICS

Another important property of some acentric crystals is ferroelectricity—the presence of a spontaneous electric dipole moment that is electrically reversible. A substantial fraction of the known ferroelectric crystals were discovered at Bell Labs, largely by Matthias and Remeika in collaboration with Holden and E. A. Wood.

5.1 New Ferroelectric Crystals

Matthias initiated a search for new ferroelectric materials. He began with crystals having the so-called perovskite structure, of which $BaTiO_3$ is a prototype. With the aid of optical instrumentation designed by Bond, Matthias and Remeika examined crystals optically at temperatures above room temperature and came to the realization that $BaTiO_3$ is not unique, but that many crystals have structures that can be made to exhibit ferroelectricity with appropriate atomic substitutions such as strontium for barium and zirconium for titanium in $BaTiO_3$. Ferroelectricity could also be achieved by changing valence but maintaining the perovskite structure as in potassium niobate or sodium tantalate. Without such changes the crystal may be antiferroelectric (adjacent unit cells oppositely charged).

Matthias started looking for ferroelectricity in piezoelectric materials that do not have the perovskite structure. While examining a collection of piezoelectric crystals that Holden had accumulated in the course of a search for a quartz substitute, Matthias discovered ferroelectricity in guanidine aluminum sulfate hexahydrate, one of a new class of materials having trigonal crystal structure, with interesting ferroelectric properties.[47] This was soon followed by the discovery of ferroelectricity in ammonium sulfate,[48] and in glycine sulfate[49] and its isomorphous selenate, and in still another class of materials characterized by dicalcium strontium propionate. While these discoveries did not result in a ferroelectric material with properties superior to $BaTiO_3$ for memory and switching applications (for example, high transition temperatures or better resistivity), it did demonstrate that ferroelectricity is far from being a rare phenomenon.

The lead zirconate/lead titanate ceramics, which have been discussed above in connection with their piezoelectric properties, are also ferroelectric. In 1965, G. H. Haertling of Sandia Laboratories showed that hot-pressing compositions containing small amounts of lanthanum produced a transparent ceramic with interesting electro-optic properties. The application of an electric field to selected areas in thin sections of this ceramic altered the domain structure in those areas and hence their birefringence. Thus, this ceramic could be used as a memory or as a light gate. Research at Bell Laboratories on novel processing techniques made important contributions to improving optical quality of the material. D. B. Fraser, H. M. O'Bryan, and J. Thomson improved the homogeneity by adding lanthanum as an aqueous solution and enhanced pore removal by using oxygen as the hot-pressing atmosphere.[50]

VI. PYROELECTRICS

The class of acentric crystals that shows a temperature dependent, spontaneous, electric dipole moment includes, but is larger than, the ferroelectrics; such crystals are pyroelectric, that is, exhibit a voltage upon a change of temperature. Examples of materials discovered at Bell Laboratories that are ferroelectric and have pyroelectric properties of technical interest are triglycene sulfate (TGS) discovered by Matthias, C. E. Miller, and Remeika,[51] strontium barium niobate grown by Ballman[52] and characterized by A. M. Glass,[53] and polyvinyl fluoride (PVF_2) films discovered by J. G. Bergman, J. H. McFee, and G. R. Crane.[54] Thermal pyroelectric detectors made from TGS are manufactured by a number of different companies and, at the time of this writing, are more sensitive than any other thermal detector operating at room temperature. Strontium barium niobate is of interest as a detector of laser beams because of its rugged character and high responsivity. PVF_2 has a somewhat lower figure of merit as a detector of radiation than the others, but films of it are readily available in large areas, it is cheap, and it can be fabricated into almost any form.

VII. OPTICAL AND NONLINEAR OPTICAL MATERIALS

The invention of the laser by A. L. Schawlow and C. H. Townes stimulated L. G. Van Uitert to set up a laboratory devoted to the growth of large optical-quality crystals, some of which require the addition of controlled amounts of optically active impurities. Of the vast number of materials prepared in single-crystal form by Van Uitert [Fig. 16-7] and his associates, those relevant to telecommunications include laser crystals that can be optically pumped to emit coherent radiation at optical frequencies, nonlinear optical crystals for generating other coherent carrier frequencies, crystals of materials possessing optical properties (exhibiting a large electro-optic effect, for example) for modulating, or impressing information on the carrier frequency, and crystals of magnetic materials for new memory devices. (For more on this topic, see section 1.1 of Chapter 19.)

7.1 Laser Crystals

The first low-threshold laser crystal, grown by L. F. Johnson and K. Nassau, was calcium tungstate doped with trivalent neodymium (Nd^{3+})ions.[55] In the initial experiments, doping with Nd^{3+} ions without charge compensation with 1^+ ions gave rise to the formation of Ca^{2+} ion vacancies, and resulted in a broadened fluorescent linewidth. If the Nd^{3+} ions are charge compensated by codoping with Na^{1+} ions at Ca^{2+} sites, then all the Nd^{3+} ions experience a similar local crystalline electric field, the fluorescent linewidth is narrowed, and the laser threshold is lowered. By proper choice of Nd^{3+} and Na^{1+} concentration, the first continuous-wave (cw), room-temperature solid state laser was made.[56]

An even lower threshold resulted when Nd^{3+} was substituted for Y^{3+} in yttrium aluminum garnet (YAG), where no charge compensation was required.[57] In this material, the transition from the ground state to the broad absorption band (corresponding to the optimum

Fig. 16-7. L. G. Van Uitert invented processes for growing novel nonlinear crystals.

pump frequencies) in YAG:Nd corresponds to a region of high output in ordinary tungsten lamps. Thus, YAG:Nd can be pumped with an incandescent lamp, eliminating the need for flash lamps and capacitor banks in the pump. The first continuous-wave YAG:Nd crystals were grown from a flux by Van Uitert and his associates.

7.2 Nonlinear and Electro-Optic Crystals

A property of dielectrics that was almost unobservable before the invention of the laser is nonlinearity, that is, variation of the effective dielectric constant with the amplitude of the applied optical electric field. The nonlinear effects make possible second harmonic generation (SHG) of light and the production of sum and difference frequencies (modulation) as well as optical parametric oscillation. A tunable optical parametric oscillator (OPO) was first demonstrated by J. A. Giordmaine and R. C. Miller in 1965, using a $LiNbO_3$ oscillator crystal.[58] This achievement was in part made possible through the efforts of G. D. Boyd and coworkers who first realized that $LiNbO_3$ had great potential for such a device.[59] Ballman, [60] Nassau, and H. J. Levinstein[61] were responsible for growing the crystals used in these initial experiments. Temperature-tuned $LiNbO_3$ crystals have been used in commercial optical parametric oscillators. An even better material for such oscillators, $Ba_2NaNb_5O_{15}$, was grown by J. J. Rubin and used to demonstrate oscillation by R. G. Smith and coworkers.[62] Its nonlinear optical properties were investigated by J. E. Geusic and coworkers.[63] It is not used as widely as $LiNbO_3$ because of the difficulty encountered in growing good single crystals. Iodic acid was studied by S. K. Kurtz, T. T. Perry, and Bergman.[64] A material with even larger nonlinearity, 2-methyl-4-nitroaniline, was studied by B. F. Levine and coworkers.[65] Successful preparation of these materials in the form of high-quality single crystals has been the result of important improvements in crystal growth techniques and advances in materials science.

Bell Labs scientists grew single crystals, studied their stoichiometry, and discovered the highly efficient nonlinear properties of the II-IV-V_2 and I-III-VI_2 semiconductors such as $ZnGeP_2$ and $AgGaSe_2$. These materials were used in frequency mixers and infrared-pumped OPOs in the wavelength range of 1 μm to 12 μm.[66]

Laudise, Van Uitert, Ballman, and their colleagues devised a highly successful search strategy for nonlinear optical and modulator materials. For second-harmonic generation, the material should possess a crystal structure that lacks a center of symmetry and should exhibit a birefringence greater than the dispersion in indices of refraction. For a modulator material, their first requirement was the same, but they sought small or zero birefringence, plus a large electro-optic effect. In addition, they limited their search to materials capable of being grown as single crystals by the Czochralski technique. This program was quite successful and led to the discovery of such materials as lithium niobate, lithium tantalate, and barium sodium niobate.

The discovery by Ballman and Nassau that $LiNbO_3$ could be pulled with comparative ease and that its large nonlinear optical coefficients and birefringence made it useful for harmonic generation and parametric experiments led to an intense interest in this material.[67,68] Crystal structure, dielectric, thermodynamic, and other studies by S. C. Abrahams, Nassau, and Levinstein provided a reasonably complete description of lithium niobate.[69] Lack of stoichiometric uniformity seriously affected its properties. A great deal of work was then undertaken to understand the phase relationships in the lithium niobate system in order to grow large homogeneous crystals. It was shown that growth from a melt containing 48.6 mol percent lithium oxide virtually eliminates birefringence variations in the crystals. Although poling procedures are complicated by the fact that the Curie temperature is close to the melting temperature, single-domain material has become easy to obtain.

Barium sodium niobate, like lithium niobate, was shown by Van Uitert and associates to be "pullable" with comparative ease.[70] It had the additional advantage of a much higher resistance to laser damage than lithium niobate, which, coupled with its large coefficient of harmonic generation and birefringence, made it particularly attractive for optical parametric experiments.[71] Barium sodium niobate is structurally similar to the tetragonal tungsten bronzes.[72] At 260°C, it undergoes a transition from tetragonal to orthorhombic (transition temperature is stoichiometry dependent) and twins when passed through this range. However, appropriate stress treatment can be used to produce untwinned specimens.

Among the important results of studies of this material is an understanding of the role of expansion in the destructive cracking that had been severely limiting the yields of useful crystals.[73] Cracking occurs because the c-axis coefficient of expansion undergoes a rapid change in the vicinity of the Curie temperature. Thus, if crystals pass through this temperature region in a thermal gradient, the large mechanical stresses cause cracking. However, cracking can be avoided if the puller is arranged with an isothermal zone above the melt, so that the crystal temperature is kept above about 600°C until growth is complete. The entire crystal is then slowly cooled, through the ferroelectric transition, to below 300°C. Work on the $Na_2O\text{-}BaO\text{-}Nb_2O_5$ phase diagram provided a reasonably complete picture of the phase relationships in the region of $Ba_2NaNb_5O_{15}$, and the problem of compositional inhomogeneities was reduced by the proper choice of liquid composition for growth, as was done for lithium niobate.

The achievements in the growth of high-quality single crystals, having the desired nonlinear optical properties, are excellent examples of the outcome of interaction between materials researchers and physicists involved in lightwave communications research.

REFERENCES

1. R. R. Williams and A. R. Kemp, "Submarine Insulation with Special Reference to the Use of Rubber," *J. Franklin Inst.* **203** (January 1927), pp. 35-61.

2. H. H. Lowry and G. T. Kohman, "The Mechanism of the Absorption of Water by Rubber," *J. Phys. Chem.* **31** (January 1927), pp. 23-57.

3. A. R. Kemp, "Paragutta, a New Insulating Material for Submarine Cables," *J. Franklin Inst.* **211** (January 1931), pp. 37-57; idem, "Paragutta," *Bell Laboratories Record* **9** (May 1931), pp. 422-425.

4. A. R. Kemp and A. N. Gray, U.S. Patent No. 2,047,736; filed August 11, 1930, issued July 14, 1936; A. R. Kemp and J. H. Ingmanson, "High-Speed Vulcanization of Rubber," *Indus. Eng. Chem.* **29** (July 1937), pp. 782-788.

5. C. S. Fuller, "Some Recent Contributions to Synthetic Rubber Research," *Bell System Tech. J.* **25** (July 1946), pp. 351-384.
6. W. O. Baker, "Molecular Requirements for Synthetic Rubbers," *Bell Laboratories Record* **23** (April 1945), pp. 97-100.
7. M. D. Rigterink, "Ceramics for Electrical Applications," *Bell Laboratories Record* **25** (December 1947), pp. 464-468.
8. J. C. Williams, "Evolution of Ceramic Substrates for Thick and Thin Film Components and Circuits in the United States," *Bull. Am. Ceram. Soc.* **56** (June 1977), pp. 580-585.
9. F. V. DiMarcello and A. W. Treptow, U.S. Patent No. 3,470,002; filed January 30, 1967, issued September 30, 1969; F. V. DiMarcello, A. W. Treptow, and L. A. Baker, "Glaze for Ceramic Substrates for Thin Films," *Bull. Am. Ceram. Soc.* **47** (May 1968), pp. 511-516.
10. F. J. Schnettler, F. R. Monforte, and W. W. Rhodes, "A Cryochemical Method for Preparing Ceramic Materials," *Science of Ceramics* **4**, ed. G. H. Stewart (British Ceramic Society, 1968), pp. 79-90; M. D. Rigterink, "Advances in Technology of the Cryochemical Process," *Bull. Am. Ceram. Soc.* **51** (February 1972), pp. 158-161; R. E. Jaeger and T. J. Miller, "Preparation of Ceramic Oxide Powders by Liquid Drying," *Bull. Am. Ceram. Soc.* **53** (December 1974), pp. 855-859.
11. D. W. Johnson, Jr., and P. K. Gallagher, "Reactive Powders from Solution," *Ceramic Processing Before Firing*, ed. G. Y. Onoda, Jr., and L. L. Hench (New York: John Wiley & Sons, 1978), pp. 125-139.
12. M. F. Yan and D. W. Johnson, Jr., "Impurity-Induced Exaggerated Grain Growth in Mn-Zn Ferrites," *J. Am. Ceram. Soc.* **61** (July/August 1978), pp. 342-349.
13. M. F. Yan and D. W. Johnson, Jr., "Sintering of High Density Ferrites," *Materials Science Research—Volume 11—Processing of Crystalline Ceramics*, ed. H. Palmour, III, R. F. Davis, and T. M. Hare (New York: Plenum Press., 1978), pp. 393-402.
14. D. W. Johnson, Jr., P. K. Gallagher, F. Schrey, and W. W. Rhodes, "Preparation of High Surface Area Substituted $LaMnO_3$ Catalysts," *Bull. Am. Ceram. Soc.* **55** (May 1976), pp. 520-523; D. W. Johnson, Jr., P. K. Gallagher, F. J. Schnettler, and E. M. Vogel, "Novel Preparative Techniques for Supported Oxide Catalysts," *Bull. Am. Ceram. Soc.* **56** (September 1977), pp. 785-788.
15. P. J. W. Debye, *Polar Molecules* (New York: Dover Publications, Inc. 1929).
16. S. O. Morgan and H. H. Lowry, "Dielectric Polarization of Some Pure Organic Compounds in the Dissolved, Liquid, and Solid States," *J. Phys. Chem.* **34** (November 1930), pp. 2385-2432.
17. W. A. Yager and S. O. Morgan, "Transitions in Camphor and Chemically Related Compounds. I. Dipole Rotation in Crystalline Solids," *J. Am. Chem. Soc.* **57** (November 1935), pp. 2071-2078; A. H. White and S. O. Morgan, "Transitions in Camphor and Chemically Related Compounds. II. Vibration of Atomic Groups," *J. Am. Chem. Soc.* **57** (November 1935), pp. 2078-2086.
18. A. H. White and S. O. Morgan, "Molecular Rotation in Crystalline Disubstituted Ethanes," *J. Chem. Phys.* **5** (August 1937), pp. 655-665.
19. A. H. White, B. S. Biggs, and S. O. Morgan, "Dielectric Evidence of Molecular Rotation in the Crystals of Certain Benzene Derivatives," *J. Am. Chem. Soc.* **62** (1940), pp. 16-25.
20. F. H. Stillinger, Jr., "Effective Pair Interactions in Liquids. Water," *J. Phys. Chem.* **74** (October 1970), pp. 3677-3687.
21. D. Hankins, J. W. Moskowitz, and F. H. Stillinger, Jr., "Water Molecule Interactions," *J. Chem. Phys.* **53** (December 15, 1970), pp. 4544-4554.
22. A. Rahman and F. H. Stillinger, Jr., "Molecular Dynamics Study of Liquid Water," *J. Chem. Phys.* **55** (October 1971), pp. 3336-3359.

23. A. Ben-Naim and F. H. Stillinger, Jr., "Aspects of the Statistical-Mechanical Theory of Water," in *Water and Aqueous Solutions,* ed. R. A. Horne (New York: John Wiley & Sons, 1972), pp. 295-330.

24. A. Rahman and F. H. Stillinger, Jr., "Hydrogen-Bond Patterns in Liquid Water," *J. Am. Chem. Soc.* **95** (November 1973), pp. 7943-7948.

25. F. H. Stillinger, Jr., "Theory and Molecular Models for Water," *Advances in Chemical Physics—Non-Simple Liquids* **31** (New York: John Wiley & Sons, 1975), pp. 1-101.

26. D. L. Rousseau and S. P. S. Porto, "Polywater: Polymer or Artifact?" *Science* **167** (March 1970), pp. 1715-1719.

27. H. M. O'Bryan, Jr., J. Thomson, Jr., and J. K. Plourde, "A New $BaO-TiO_2$ Compound with Temperature-Stable High Permittivity and Low Microwave Loss," *J. Am. Ceram. Soc.* **57** (October 1974), pp. 450-453; J. K. Plourde, D. F. Linn, H. M. O'Bryan, Jr., and J. Thomson, Jr., "$Ba_2Ti_9O_{20}$ as a Microwave Dielectric Resonator," *J. Am. Ceram. Soc.* **58** (Sept./Oct. 1975), pp. 418-420.

28. W. P. Mason, "Electrical Wave Filters Employing Quartz Crystals as Elements," *Bell System Tech. J.* **13** (July 1934), pp. 405-452.

29. W. P. Mason, "A New Quartz-Crystal Plate, Designated the GT, Which Produces a Very Constant Frequency over a Wide Temperature Range," *Proc. IRE* **28** (1940), pp. 220-223.

30. A. N. Holden and W. P. Mason, "The Elastic, Dielectric, and Piezoelectric Constants of Heavy-Water Rochelle Salt," *Phys. Rev.* **57** (January 1940), p. 54.

31. W. P. Mason, "The Elastic, Piezoelectric, and Dielectric Constants of Potassium Dihydrogen Phosphate and Ammonium Dihydrogen Phosphate," *Phys. Rev.* **69** (March 1946), pp. 173-194.

32. W. P. Mason, *Piezoelectric Crystals and Their Application to Ultrasonics* (Princeton, N.J.: D. Van Nostrand Co., 1950), p. 508.

33. A. C. Walker, "Piezoelectric Crystal Culture," *Bell Laboratories Record* **25** (October 1947), pp. 357-362.

34. A. C. Walker and E. Buehler, "Growing Large Quartz Crystals," *Indust. Eng. Chem.* **42** (July 1950), pp. 1369-1375.

35. R. A. Laudise and R. A. Sullivan, "Pilot-Plant Production—Synthetic Quartz," *Chem. Eng. of Prog.* **55** (1959), pp. 55-59.

36. R. A. Laudise, "Kinetics of Hydrothermal Quartz Crystallization," *J. Am. Chem. Soc.* **81** (February 1959), pp. 562-566; idem, "Hydrothermal Synthesis of Single Crystals," in *Progress in Inorganic Chemistry, Volume III,* ed. F. A. Cotton (New York: John Wiley & Sons, 1962), pp. 1-47.

37. E. D. Kolb, K. Nassau, and R. A. Laudise, "New Sources of Quartz Nutrient for the Hydrothermal Growth of Quartz," *J. Crystal Growth* **36** (November 1976), pp. 93-100.

38. A. N. Holden, "Apparatus for Growing Single Crystals from Solution," *Phys. Rev.* **68** (December 1945), p. 283.

39. A. N. Holden, G. T. Kohman, W. P. Mason, and S. O. Morgan, "Heavy Water Rochelle Salt," *Phys. Rev.* **56** (August 1939), p. 378; A. N. Holden and W. P. Mason, "The Elastic, Dielectric, and Piezoelectric Constants of Heavy-Water Rochelle Salt," *Phys. Rev.* **57** (January 1940), pp. 54-56.

40. A. N. Holden and P. Singer, *Crystals and Crystal Growing* (New York: Doubleday & Company, Inc., 1960).

41. B. T. Matthias and J. P. Remeika, "Ferroelectricity in the Ilmenite Structure," *Phys. Rev.* **76** (December 1949), pp. 1886-1887.

42. A. A. Ballman, "Growth of Piezoelectric and Ferroelectric Materials by the Czochralski Technique," *J. Am. Ceram. Soc.* **48** (February 1965), pp. 112-113.

43. A. W. Warner, M. Onoe, and G. A. Coquin, "Determination of Elastic and

Piezoelectric Constants for Crystals in Class (3*m*)," *J. Acoust. Soc.* **42** (October 1966), pp. 1223-1231; A. W. Warner and A. A. Ballman, "Low Temperature Coefficient of Frequency in a Lithium Tantalate Resonator," *Proc. IEEE* **55** (March 1967), p. 450.

44. L. Egerton and D. M. Dillon, "Piezoelectric and Dielectric Properties of Ceramics in the System Potassium-Sodium Niobate," *J. Am. Ceram. Soc.* **42** (September 1959), pp. 438-442.

45. L. Egerton and C. A. Bieling, "Isostatically Hot-Pressed Sodium-Potassium Niobate Transducer Material for Ultrasonic Devices," *Bull. Am. Ceram. Soc.* **47** (December 1968), pp. 1151-1156.

46. W. P. Mason, "Electrostrictive Effect in Barium Titanate Ceramics," *Phys. Rev.* **74** (November 1948), pp. 1134-1147.

47. A. N. Holden, B. T. Matthias, W. J. Merz, and J. P. Remeika, "New Class of Ferroelectrics," Letters to the Editor, *Phys. Rev.*, **98** (April 15, 1955), p. 546.

48. A. N. Holden, W. J. Merz, J. P. Remeika, and B. T. Matthias, "Properties of Guanidine Aluminum Sulfate Hexahydrate and Some of Its Isomorphs," *Phys. Rev.* **101** (February 1956), pp. 962-966; B. T. Matthias and J. P. Remeika, "Ferroelectricity in Ammonium Sulfate," *Phys. Rev.* **103** (July 1956), p. 262.

49. B. T. Matthias, C. E. Miller, and J. P. Remeika, "Ferroelectricity of Glycine Sulphate," Letters to the Editor, *Phys. Rev.*, **104** (November 1, 1956), pp. 849-850.

50. D. B. Fraser, H. M. O'Bryan, Jr., and J. Thomson, U.S. Patent No. 3,718,723; filed October 23, 1970, issued February 27, 1973.

51. See reference 49.

52. A. A. Ballman and H. Brown, "The Growth and Properties of Strontium Barium Metaniobate, $Sr_{1-x}Ba_xNb_2O_6$, A Tungsten Bronze Ferroelectric," *J. Crystal. Growth* **1** (December 1967), pp. 311-314.

53. A. M. Glass, "Ferroelectric $Sr_{1-x}Ba_xNb_2O_6$ as a Fast and Sensitive Detector of Infrared Radiation," *Appl. Phys. Lett.* **13** (August 15, 1968), pp. 147-149.

54. J. G. Bergman, Jr., J. H. McFee, and G. R. Crane, "Pyroelectricity and Optical Second-Harmonic Generation in Polyvinylidene Fluoride Films," *Appl. Phys. Lett.* **18** (March 1, 1971), pp. 203-205.

55. L. F. Johnson and K. Nassau, "Infrared Fluorescence and Stimulated Emission of Nd^{3+} in $CaWO_4$," *Proceedings of the Institute of Radio Engineers* **49** (November 1961), pp. 1704-1706; D. F. Nelson and W. S. Boyle, "A Continuously Operating Ruby Optical Maser," *Appl. Optics* **1** (March 1962), pp. 181-183.

56. L. F. Johnson, G. D. Boyd, K. Nassau, and R. R. Soden, "Continuous Operation of the $CaWO_4$:Nd^{3+} Optical Maser," *Proc. IRE* **50** (February 1962), p. 213; K. Nassau and G. M. Loiacono, "Calcium Tungstate—III. Trivalent Rare Earth Substitution," *J. Phys. Chem. Solids* **24** (December 1963), pp. 1503-1510; K. Nassau, "Calcium Tungstate—IV. The Theory of Coupled Substitution," *J. Phys. Chem. Solids* **24** (December 1963), pp. 1511-1517.

57. J. E. Geusic, H. M. Marcos, and L. G. Van Uitert, "Laser Oscillations in Nd-Doped Yttrium Aluminum, Yttrium Gallium, and Gadolinium Garnets," *Appl. Phys. Lett.* **4** (May 15, 1964), pp. 182-184.

58. J. A. Giordmaine and R. C. Miller, "Tunable Coherent Parametric Oscillation in $LiNbO_3$ at Optical Frequencies," *Phys. Rev. Lett.* **14** (June 14, 1965), pp. 973-976.

59. G. D. Boyd, R. C. Miller, K. Nassau, W. L. Bond, and A. Savage, "$LiNbO_3$: An Efficient Phase Matchable Nonlinear Optical Material," *Appl. Phys. Lett.* **5** (December 1, 1964), pp. 234-236.

60. See reference 42.

61. K. Nassau and H. J. Levinstein, "Ferroelectric Behavior of Lithuim Niobate," *Appl. Phys. Lett.* **7** (August 1, 1965), pp. 69-70.

62. J. J. Rubin, L. G. Van Uitert, and H. J. Levinstein, "The Growth of Single Crystal Niobates for Electro-Optic and Non-Linear Applications," *J. Crystal Growth* **1** (December 1967), pp. 315-317; R. G. Smith, J. E. Geusic, H. J. Levinstein, J. J. Rubin, S. Singh, and L. G. Van Uitert, "Continuous Optical Parametric Oscillation in $Ba_2NaNb_5O_{15}$," *Appl. Phys. Lett.* **12** (May 1, 1968), pp. 308-310.

63. J. E. Geusic, H. J. Levinstein, J. J. Rubin, S. Singh, and L. G. Van Uitert, "The Nonlinear Optical Properties of $Ba_2NaNb_5O_{15}$," *Appl. Phys. Lett.* **11** (November 1, 1967), pp. 269-271; idem, "The Nonlinear Optical Properties of $Ba_2NaNb_5O_{15}$," *Appl. Phys. Lett.* **12** (March 15, 1968), p. 224.

64. S. K. Kurtz, T. T. Perry, and J. G. Bergman, Jr., "Alpha-Iodic Acid: A Solution-Grown Crystal for Nonlinear Optical Studies and Applications," *Appl. Phys. Lett.* **12** (March 1, 1968), pp. 186-188.

65. B. F. Levine, "An Organic Crystal with an Exceptionally Large Optical Second-Harmonic Coefficient: 2-methyl-4-nitroaniline," *J. Appl. Phys.* (April 1979), pp. 2523-2527.

66. E. Buehler, J. H. Wernick, and J. D. Wiley, "The ZnP_2—Ge System and Growth of Single Crystals of $ZnGeP_2$," *J. Electron. Mat.* **2** (August 1973), pp. 445-454; H. M. Kasper, "Formation, Stoichiometry, and Properties of $I-III-VI_2$ Semiconducting Crystals," *Proc. Seventh International Symposium on the Reactivity of Solids*, Bristol, 17-21 July 1972, ed. J. S. Anderson, M. W. Roberts, and F. S. Stone (London: Chapman and Hall, 1972), pp. 46-55; G. D. Boyd, E. Buehler, and F. G. Storz, "Linear and Nonlinear Optical Properties of Zinc Germanium Phosphorus (2) and Cadmium Selenide," *Appl. Phys. Lett.* **18** (April 1, 1971), pp. 301-304; G. D. Boyd, H. M. Kasper, and J. H. McFee, "Linear and Nonlinear Optical Properties of Silver Gallium Sulfide, Copper Gallium Sulfide, and Copper Indium Sulfide, and Theory of the Wedge Technique for the Measurement of Nonlinear Coefficients," *IEEE J. Quantum Electron.* **QE-7** (December 1971), pp. 563-573.

67. A. A. Ballman, "Growth of Piezoelectric and Ferroelectric Materials by the Czochralski Technique," *J. Am. Ceram. Soc.* **48** (February 1965), pp. 112-113; R. C. Miller, G. D. Boyd, and A. Savage, "Nonlinear Optical Interactions in $LiNbO_3$ Without Double Refraction," *Appl. Phys. Lett.* **6** (February 15, 1965), pp. 77-79.

68. G. D. Boyd, R. C. Miller, K. Nassau, W. L. Bond, and A. Savage, "$LiNbO_3$: An Efficient Phase Matchable Nonlinear Optical Material," *Appl. Phys. Lett.* **5** (December 1, 1964), pp. 234-236; R. C. Miller, G. D. Boyd, and A. Savage, "Nonlinear Optical Interactions in $LiNbO_3$, without Double Refraction," *Appl. Phys. Lett.* **6** (February 15, 1965), pp. 77-79.

69. S. C. Abrahams, H. J. Levinstein, and J. M. Reddy, "Ferroelectric Lithium Niobate 5 Polycrystal X-ray Diffraction Study Between 24° and 1200°C," *J. Phys. Chem. Solids* **27** (1966), pp. 1019-1026.

70. L. G. Van Uitert, J. J. Rubin, and W. A. Bonner, "K-1—Growth of $Ba_2NaNb_5O_{15}$ Single Crystals for Optical Applications," *IEEE J. Quantum Electron.* **QE4** (October 1968), pp. 622-627.

71. A. Ashkin, G. D. Boyd, J. M. Dziedzic, R. G. Smith, A. A. Ballman, J. J. Levinstein, and K. Nassau, "Optically-Induced Refractive Index Inhomogeneities in $LiNbO_3$ and $LiTaO_3$," *Appl. Phys. Lett.* **9** (July 1, 1966), pp. 72-74.

72. P. B. Jamieson, S. C. Abrahams, and J. L. Bernstein, "Ferroelectric Tungsten Bronze-Type Crystal Structures. II. Barium Sodium Niobate $Ba_{(4+x)}Na_{(2-2x)}Nb_{10}O_{30}$," *J. Chem. Phys.* **50** (May 1969), pp. 4352-4363.

73. A. A. Ballman, J. R. Carruthers, and H. M. O'Bryan, Jr., "Growth of Uncracked Barium-Sodium Niobate Crystals," *J. Crystal Growth* **6** (Jan./Feb. 1970), pp. 184-186.

Chapter 17

Electric Currents and Electrical Conduction

Electric currents are intrinsic to the behavior and the usefulness of many materials. From the early years of Bell Laboratories, the electrical properties of contact materials were recognized as being critical to the satisfactory performance of switching equipment. Discoveries of the thermionic emission of materials led to greatly improved cathodes for electron tubes. Fundamental studies in electro-chemistry have led to technological advances in the fundamental understanding of phenomena in corrosion and of processes in electroplating. In addition, much basic work on the behavior of storage batteries has been done at Bell Laboratories. Carbon has also been studied extensively, both as a constituent of the microphone and as a material for fixed resistors and surge protectors.

I. ELECTROCHEMISTRY – CORROSION, ELECTROPLATING, AND BATTERIES

Electrochemistry and related subjects have long been of interest at Bell Laboratories because of the widespread use of electrochemical processes in the manufacture of Bell System equipment and because of the occurrence of degradation caused by electrochemical phenomena. Corrosion and tarnish processes may adversely affect the electrical performance, reliability, and life of equipment, while electroplating is frequently the method of choice in applying metallic finishes for corrosion protection. In addition, daily use is made of the electrical energy storage provided by batteries in an extremely practical application of electrochemistry.

In general, electrochemical processes involve the transfer of charge across interfaces, demonstrating a close relationship between electrochemistry and surface chemistry.

Principal authors: P. C. Milner and A. H. White

1.1 Corrosion

Corrosion is responsible for losses of hundreds of millions of dollars annually to the telephone plant. It occurs in a wide variety of forms, ranging from general deterioration to catastrophic attack. It is highly dependent on local conditions, such as high humidity, the presence of specific ionic contaminants, and thermal cycling. Studies of corrosion have occupied the attention of Bell Laboratories scientists and engineers since the earliest times.

1.1.1 Metallic Whisker Growth

One example of corrosion is observed when silver is in contact with an insulating material under an applied positive potential. The silver is oxidized and transported ionically across or through the insulating material to a conductor under lower potential, where it is redeposited as the metal in dendritic form. The extent of the attack may be almost imperceptible, even at the time the dendrites have caused electrical breakdown or shorts between the two conductors. In the mid-1950s, G. T. Kohman, H. W. Hermance, and G. H. Downes investigated this phenomenon and showed that it required the absorption of water by the insulating material to provide the medium for the ionic transport and that it therefore depended on the ambient humidity as well as on the type of insulating material involved.[1] Silver appears unique among metals in requiring only water for this type of migration and failure to occur. Other metals require complexing contaminants in addition to water, although it has been found that the electrolytic corrosion products formed with water alone can cause problems with leakage, as R. P. Frankenthal and W. H. Becker demonstrated in 1979 for gold metallizations in electronic circuits.[2]

A different source of dendritic metal growth was identified in 1948. An investigation of electrical failures of channel filters showed that these failures were caused by bridging of circuit components by conducting filamentary growths, called whiskers, which caused short circuits. The growths were found to be metallic single crystals growing from an electroplated zinc finish used on a mounting plate in these filters.[3] Later research showed that such crystals could form on electroplated tin and cadmium as well as on zinc. Generally, the crystals were about 3 micrometers (μm) in diameter and up to 0.6 centimeter long. Because of their length and high metallic conductivity, they posed a significant hazard in electronic circuits. Studies by S. M. Arnold led to the discovery that whisker growth could be substantially repressed by small alloy additions to the finish.[4] As a result, a tin-lead solder finish has been adopted for use throughout the Bell System and much of the electronics industry.

The research on the spontaneous growth of whiskers on electroplated finishes led to other studies of whiskers. C. Herring and J. K. Galt used tin whiskers obtained from an electroplated finish to study the elastic properties of metallic crystals without dislocations.[5] R. S. Wagner and W. C. Ellis developed the vapor-liquid-solid (VLS) mechanism to grow silicon crystals.[6]

1.1.2 Stress-Corrosion Cracking

Metals and alloys that are stressed in a corrosive environment can be subject to mechanical failures caused by stress-corrosion cracking. Generally, the amount of visible gross corrosion associated with stress-corrosion attack is extremely small, making it a particularly insidious phenomenon. The environment causing attack is usually specific to the metal or alloy involved. In the case of an iron-nickel-cobalt alloy used for making glass-to-metal seals in hermetic packages for electronic devices, investigations by R. G. Baker and A. Mendizza showed that the cracking agent was moisture and that stress-corrosion cracking could be prevented if the entire surface of the alloy was coated with a suitable material such as solder.[7]

A dramatic incident of stress-corrosion failure occurred in some central offices in the Los Angeles area in the early 1960s, when thousands of nickel-brass springs in wire spring relays broke. The environmental agent responsible for these failures was hard to identify. The breakage was found to occur where wires with a normally positive electric potential emerged under a moderate spring stress from the molded plastic base of the relay through a surface covered with a layer of fine dust. Extensive studies by N. E. McKinney and Hermance showed that the cracking agent was the nitrate contained in this dust, which was itself noticeably hygroscopic at relative humidities greater than about 50 percent.[8] It was found that the applied potential enhanced the susceptibility of nickel-brass to stress-corrosion cracking at relatively low levels of nitrate in the presence of elevated humidity, and this led to a change in the spring material from nickel-brass to a copper-nickel alloy. In further investigations, the nitrate contamination levels at sites throughout the Los Angeles area were measured to determine where the hazards to equipment operation were greatest; these results correlated well with the distribution anticipated from the sources of nitrogen oxides and the topography.[9]

1.2 Electroplating

Thin layers of copper, nickel, and precious metals are widely used as protective finishes on components. They are commonly deposited by electroplating. Since the 1950s, chemists at Bell Laboratories have worked on improving the understanding and control of electroplating, with particular attention to the deposition of gold. The need for a neutral or mildly acidic gold-plating system for use in plating printed wiring boards was addressed by R. A. Ehrhardt.[10] He found that excellent deposits could be produced from an electrolyte with a hydrogen-ion concentration corresponding to a pH ranging from 5 to 6, prepared from dibasic ammonium citrate and sodium or potassium aurocyanide. These and similarly buffered solutions are now widely used for soft (pure) gold plating in a variety of electronic applications, and they provided the basis for the development of the hard (alloy) gold-plating systems that are used to produce wear-resistant electrical contact finishes. These finishes typically contain about 0.1 weight-percent cobalt or nickel as a hardening agent. However, G. B. Munier made the surprising discovery that they also contained a few tenths of a weight-percent carbon and, when dissolved, left an insoluble residue that has been termed "polymer."[11] The carbon and the polymer derive from the cyanide of the aurocyanide complex and are, together with the hardness of the deposits, apparently responsible for the excellent wear characteristics of these golds.

In studies of carbonaceous contaminants in pure gold deposits, H. A. Reinheimer found that the carbon content and hardness of the deposits could be varied by controlling the plating conditions.[12] These findings have been used in the development of additive-free, hard gold plating, which provides wear-resistant deposits of higher ductility and greater thermal stability of contact resistance than the customary alloy-hardened golds.[13]

Electroless plating of copper, nickel, and silver, wherein the metal is deposited by an autocatalytic chemical process rather than by electrolytic reduction, has been practiced for many years. The first such process for gold was invented by Y. Okinaka, using potassium borohydride as the reducing agent.[14] The process produces soft gold deposits with characteristics comparable to those of electrolytic deposits and, like other electroless processes, is capable of being initiated by transition-metal catalysts. This allows selective plating on insulating substrates or on electrically isolated areas, a capability useful in the manufacture of electronic components and devices.

Attention has also been directed to the plating of noble metal alternatives to gold for electrical contact uses. Ruthenium was considered a prime candidate for this purpose by virtue of its lower cost and the environmental stability of the conducting dioxide that it forms, but it was difficult to produce consistently sound deposits using existing plating processes. Work by A. Heller, B. Miller, and R. G. Vadimsky led to the synthesis of a pure ruthenium salt that involved the nitrogen-bridged anionic complex $[Ru_2N(H_2O)_2Cl_8]^{3-}$ and its use in a plating cell with the anode isolated by a cation-exchange membrane separator to produce high-quality deposits.[15] The process operated at a constant current efficiency, and the ruthenium produced was resistant to cracking under thermal stress at the thicknesses useful in contact applications.

1.2.1 *Specification of Electroplated Finishes*

Many of the electroplating studies at Bell Laboratories have been concerned with the application of existing technology in the manufacture of specific products, both by Western Electric and by outside suppliers. As a result, a rationale for the specification of electroplated finishes based on end-point requirements has been developed. These requirements concern the characteristics of the finish as applied instead of dealing with the method of application; this approach has become generally adopted by government and industry. It assures that a finish will serve its intended function, which has been particularly important in the use of electroplated gold for such critical applications as electrical contact finishes. The advantages of end-point specifications for gold deposits have been discussed by Baker and T. A. Palumbo, who list the characteristics measured and illustrate the problems encountered when the requirements are not met.[16]

1.3 Batteries

Stationary batteries are used in every Bell System central office to provide load leveling and standby power, and they have been the subject of research at Bell Laboratories since 1930. Typical central-office usage involves what is known as float operation, in which the batteries are maintained at a full state of charge and are only infrequently recharged because of an interruption of commercial power service. This differs considerably from cycle operation, with its succession of charges and discharges. Initial studies were aimed at determining whether there might be design changes that would improve performance in float service.

1.3.1 *Lead-Calcium Alloys for Batteries*

Attention was soon directed to the lead-antimony alloys used in the grids of the conventional lead-acid battery plates, where it was recognized that antimony caused undesirable electrochemical changes in cell behavior. The highly anodic conditions at the positive grid caused antimony to be slowly leached and deposited as metallic antimony on the surface of the negative plate, giving rise to an undesirable aging process. H. E. Haring and U. B. Thomas recognized that the aging problems encountered with lead-antimony might be overcome by using lead alloys with low levels of alloying constituents that were electronegative to lead.[17] They initiated studies of the age-hardening, lead-calcium alloys containing about 0.1 percent or less of calcium that had been investigated by E. E. Schumacher and G. M. Bouton. These alloys had been found to have metallurgical and physical properties that compared favorably with those of lead-antimony.[18] Laboratory studies of lead-calcium confirmed its superior electrochemical behavior, but longer-term results from test cells in service showed considerable variability in positive grid and post corrosion and established the need for accurate analysis and control of the calcium content of the alloy. The required rapid calcium analysis technique was developed by Bouton and G. S. Phipps,[19] and in 1950, cells with lead-calcium alloy grids containing 0.065 to 0.085 percent calcium began to be used in the Bell System.

Such cells became widely used for float service, and this concept of achieving low self-discharge rates through the use of low-level alloying constituents that are electronegative to lead was applied elsewhere in the development of "maintenance-free" lead-acid batteries for automotive use. At Bell Labs, further developments have resulted in the design and manufacture of a novel cylindrical cell that makes possible the use of pure lead as the grid material.[20] This provides improved positive grid-corrosion behavior in long-term float service.

1.3.2 Nickel-Cadmium and Non-Aqueous Battery Materials

Work has also been carried out on other secondary battery systems. Sealed nickel-cadmium alkaline cells were studied in the early 1960s by D. C. Bomberger and L. F. Moose,[21] and were used in the original Telstar satellite, and programs for their improvement have continued. Attention was focused on positive-active (cathode) materials for high-energy-density lithium secondary cells that utilize nonaqueous electrolytes and operate at ambient temperatures. What was desired was an electronically conducting material that could be reversibly oxidized and reduced without changing the shape and structure, in a process that involves the solid-state transport of lithium ions. A surprising number of compounds with such properties were found in the late 1970s; among them are layered transition metal dichalcogenides such as VSe_2, and transition metal oxides such as V_6O_{13}.[22,23] The understanding gained in fundamental studies of these materials opens up new options for practical battery systems.

II. RELAY AND CONNECTOR CONTACTS

The performance and reliability of relay and connector contacts have long been important to the Bell System and have been studied at Bell Laboratories for many years. In the early 1950s, W. P. Mason and coworkers applied photoelastic techniques to study stress-strain patterns in polymers.[24,25] They simulated the stress-strain conditions that existed in the solderless wrapped connector developed by H. A. Miloche and R. F. Mallina.[26,27] [Fig. 17-1] The stress-strain conditions between the wrapped wire and the terminal permitted solid-state diffusion but did not permit cold welding. Mason's results led to the prediction of a life of over 40 years for the connectors under any likely ambient conditions.

In the early use of silver contacts in connectors, problems were encountered from the formation of insulating films in a sulfiding environment. This led to the introduction of gold plating to increase the reliability of these contacts. However, in 1960, Egan and Mendizza found that the silver sulfide that formed in the pores of the plated gold crept rapidly over the gold surface, resulting in the undesireable silver sulfide film.[28] Their investigation led ultimately to the complete abandonment of gold-plated silver as a contact material.

The effect of contaminants more generally on the performance of relay and connector contacts was the subject of many studies and the results of these investigations have had a widespread influence on the

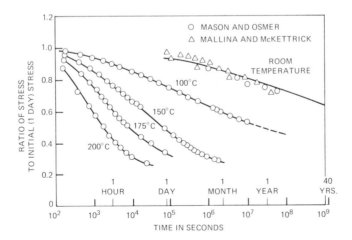

Fig. 17-1. Relaxation of stress in tinned copper wire in solderless wrapped connections, as a function of time and temperature.

selection of contact materials and design. In a systematic study of relay contact contamination, Hermance [Fig. 17-2] and T. F. Egan found that an amorphous, brownish, insulating organic deposit was formed on non-arcing palladium contacts.[29] Laboratory investigations showed that this material was produced when metals, particularly those of the palladium and platinum groups, were rubbed together in the presence of low concentrations of a wide variety of organic vapors. The vapors were apparently adsorbed on the metal surface and then frictionally activated and polymerized, which led to the use of the term "frictional polymer" to describe the material, and to the adoption of a practice of evaluating new contact materials with regard to the formation of such frictional polymers. Fortunately, gold and its alloys produce very few frictional polymers, and a thin gold-alloy overlay on palladium provided good contact material and improved relay performance greatly.[30]

Fig. 17-2. H. W. Hermance studied the impact of contaminants on relay contacts in the telephone plant.

III. OXIDE-COATED CATHODES FOR VACUUM TUBES

The operation of vacuum tubes depends upon thermionic emission of electrons from a cathode into a vacuum, preferably from a surface of low and stable work function. In the early tubes the cathode was simply a hot filament whose surface had been treated in empirically determined ways to lower its work function. A major improvement appeared in the late 1920s in the form of the indirectly heated oxide cathode. This is heated by a tungsten filament with insulation provided to separate it from the nickel cathode, which is coated with a mixture of alkaline earth oxides. The mixture contains barium oxide and the oxides of strontium and calcium. The nickel substrate is lightly doped with magnesium or some other element capable of slowly reducing the oxide to produce free, low work-function atoms, such as barium.

The oxide-coated cathode was the subject of enormous development efforts, which gradually improved its performance and life. During manufacture, however, the cathode continued to be prone to activity "busts," which could often be traced to minute quantities of contaminants such as sulfur or chlorine. At Bell Labs a number of researchers tried to remedy this situation. Among the first were J. A. Becker and R. W. Sears, who, as early as 1930, cited evidence that the emission was determined by the condition of the oxide surface.[31] Probably the last was a group under the direction of A. H. White that made use of the post-World War II theories of semiconduction in a research program aimed at understanding barium oxide as an n-type semiconductor. Unfortunately, an oxide cathode is more complicated than this because it is a very porous structure with a major part of its conductivity arising from electrons in the pores, especially at high temperatures.[32] Indeed, its structure is so complicated that as of the time of this writing there is no generally accepted model of the physics of the oxide-coated cathode, even as to the location of the seat of thermionic emission. [Fig. 17-3]

Nevertheless, the work of H. E. Kern and his collaborators provided the necessary high-purity nickel alloys and brought the chemistry of this cathode under good control.[33] They showed that cathode activation and life are controlled by the rate of diffusion of reducing agents such as carbon, zirconium, or magnesium from the interior to the surface of the nickel core. The reducing agent reacts with the oxide coating to generate free alkaline earth atoms necessary for electron emission and for maintaining the electrical conductivity of the oxide coating.

Even after the transistor had largely displaced vacuum tubes in electronic circuitry, the thermionic cathode still had important applications as an essential source of electron emission in gas lasers. D. Mac-

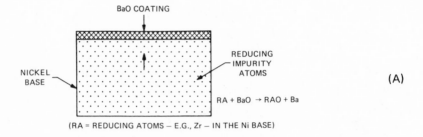

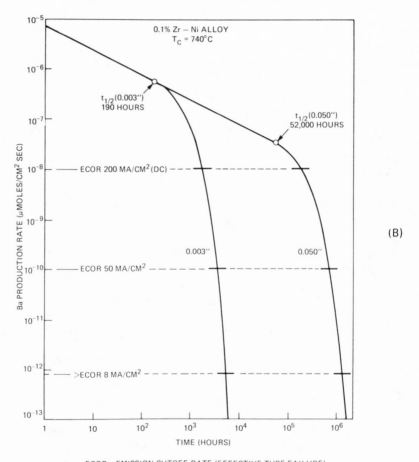

ECOR = EMISSION CUTOFF RATE (EFFECTIVE TUBE FAILURE)
$t_{1/2}$ = TIME OF ORIGINAL CONCENTRATION OF Zr
            TO BE REDUCED TO ONE-HALF

Fig. 17-3. (A) Schematic of an oxide cathode. (B) Effect of nickel thickness on cathode life.

Nair devised a matrix-type cathode that provides good electron emission under exposure to reactive gases such as CO_2, O_2, H_2O, and Cl_2, most of which poison emission from conventional porous oxide-coated cathodes.[34] These designs include a great variety of barium-strontium oxide cathodes in varied matrix structures. Most spectacular, however, was the $BaZrO_3$ cathode that gives copious electron emission in carbon dioxide and other oxidizing atmospheres.

IV. CARBON MICROPHONES AND CARBON RESISTORS

4.1 Microphone Carbon

Throughout the history of telecommunications, granulated carbon has proved to be the most satisfactory active, nonlinear element in a transducer for converting acoustical into electrical energy. Condenser and moving-coil microphones provide much more faithful reproductions of the signal, but they do not amplify it. As early as 1930, the electrical power output of the carbon transmitter was of the order of 1000 times greater than the acoustical power input. The cost of supplying this much gain to the subscriber's set by any other means was prohibitive until the advent of the electronic telephone that could provide gain. The polymer-foil electret microphone, first developed in 1966 by G. M. Sessler and J. E. West,[35] and further developed by J. B. Baumbauer and A. M. Brzezinski in 1979,[36] provided an inexpensive microphone of small size, having lower noise and distortion than the carbon transmitter.

Before 1931, manufacture of microphone carbon started with anthracite coal purchased from a particular mine in eastern Pennsylvania. This coal was crushed in a specified manner, sifted, purified in a stream of air, and roasted according to a procedure that had been carefully studied by H. H. Lowry and his colleagues.[37] This procedure produced particles of nearly uniform size and spherical shape and reduced the hydrogen content of the carbon without leaving pores that would have adsorbed atmospheric gases and impaired performance. A deposit of pyrolytic carbon, formed from the decomposition of methane gas, smoothed the surface of the granules further and increased their elastic modulus. As a consequence, there was a great improvement in the performance, reproducibility, and reliability of transmitter carbon. This work also provided a method of selecting another source of supply after the original mine had been exhausted. Thus after 1931, the making of microphone carbon started with anthracite coal purchased from a different mine in eastern Pennsylvania.

During the early 1930s, F. S. Goucher and his colleagues clarified the physics of this material by a series of studies of contacts between individual carbon granules.[38] They established that at any given applied force the current-voltage curve of the contact was reversible and ohmic, providing that care was taken to avoid heating. They found the contact resistance between granules to be a function of contact area which, in turn, was a function of the applied force. This latter function was complicated by the fact that the carbon surfaces were visibly rough, as seen under the microscope. The temperature coefficient of resistance was shown to be the same as that of disordered carbon, even in the presence of adsorbed gases that increased the resistance. This eliminated various hypotheses that had invoked field emission or a special surface layer to explain the electrical properties. J. R. Haynes verified the assumption of elastic deformation implicit in all this work by showing that the stress-strain curve between two particles was reversible up to a total displacement of 3×10^{-6} cm, which is greater than that present in commercial contacts.[37] [Fig. 17-4] These contributions to the physics of the carbon

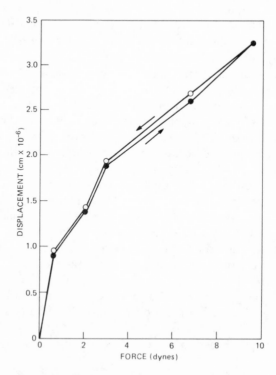

Fig. 17-4. Typical force-displacement characteristic of a carbon contact.

transducer stimulated and supplemented improved transmitter design,[38] even though a complete physical theory of this complicated aggregate has not yet been achieved.

4.2 Ceramic Core for Deposited-Carbon Resistors

The advent of precise electronic equipment, such as that used in radar during World War II, imposed stringent demands on the technology of resistors, capacitors, and other components.[41] (For more on this topic see the second volume of this series, "National Service in War and Peace," pp. 142-143.) This in turn led to the invention of deposited-carbon resistors, which had critical applications in electronic systems.[39] [Fig. 17-5] These resistors were made by putting down a thin film of carbon on the surface of a ceramic core. The resistance values were varied by means of spirals that were cut through the carbon film and were accurately controlled by the size of the ceramic core, the resistivity of the deposited film, and the length of the spiral. The quality of the ceramic core was quickly perceived to be basic to the success of the design. The core had to have high insulation resistance at all operating temperatures and low ionic conduction to avoid resistance changes caused by electrolytic polarization. Perfection of the surface structure and freedom from contami-

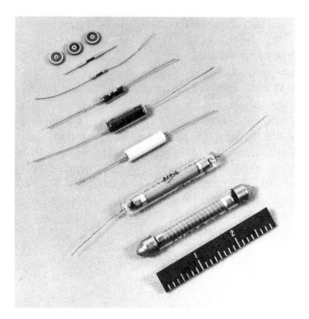

Fig. 17-5. Typical examples of several varieties of deposited carbon resistors.

nation were important to the integrity of the deposited carbon. To satisfy these requirements, M. D. Rigterink chose a composition of fine-grained raw materials, such as kaolin and precipitated carbonates of alkaline earths, which are capable of thorough mixing and fine grinding.[42] Careful studies were made of the time and temperature regimes needed to achieve the fine-grained structure responsible for the excellent adherence of carbon films.

This technology, which was so useful to the progress of high-frequency electronics during the war, also formed the basis for meeting the even greater demands of electronics in the age of solid-state devices.

4.3 Polymer Carbonization and Voltage Surge Protectors for Telephone Lines

In the late 1940s, F. H. Winslow and W. O. Baker initiated a study aimed at producing small carbon spheres from crosslinked styrene polymers obtained by suspension polymerization. Their experiments were stimulated by an interest expressed by a Bell Labs Station Apparatus Group in obtaining small carbon spheres of the same size and properties as those of the microphone granules made from anthracite. Polymer spheres were preoxidized at 250°C and carbonized by a group engaged in pyrolitic states, supervised by R. O. Grisdale. Winslow and Baker succeeded in making the desired carbon balls, although for economic reasons these spheres did not go into production. But in the course of their research they advanced the understanding of the mechanism of crosslinking in polymer carbonization.[43] This pyrolytic carbon process has been used in the preparation of heat shields for protecting space vehicles during reentry into the earth's atmosphere.

These carbonization ideas proved to be very useful in an application in the voltage surge protectors used with every Bell System telephone line. C. W. Wilkins and coworkers experimented with other binders for the coke, keeping in mind the crosslinking principles established by Winslow and Baker, and came up with binders that are furfuryl alcohol and phenol-formaldehyde based, which polymerize and carbonize in a manner similar to that observed above.

The same carbonization process may prove useful in developing bound carbon for replacement of certain gold-plated contacts now in use.

REFERENCES

1. G. T. Kohman, H. W. Hermance, and G. H. Downes, "Silver Migration in Electrical Insulation," *Bell System Tech. J.* **34** (November 1955), pp. 1115-1147.

2. R. P. Frankenthal and W. H. Becker, "Corrosion Failure Mechanisms for Gold Metallizations," *J. Electrochem. Soc.* **126** (October 1979), pp. 1718-1719.

3. K. G. Compton, A. Mendizza, and S. M. Arnold, "Filamentary Growths on Metal Surfaces—'Whiskers,'" *Corrosion* **7** (October 1951), pp. 327-334.

4. S. M. Arnold, "Repressing the Growth of Tin Whiskers," *Plating* **53** (January 1966), pp. 96-99.

5. C. Herring and J. K. Galt, "Elastic and Plastic Properties of Very Small Metal Specimens," *Phys. Rev.* **85** (March 1952), pp. 1060-1061.

6. R. S. Wagner and W. C. Ellis, "Vapor-Liquid-Solid Mechanism of Single Crystal Growth," *Appl. Phys. Lett.* **4** (March 1, 1964), pp. 89-90.

7. R. G. Baker and A. Mendizza, "The Susceptibility of Iron-Nickel-Cobalt Alloys to Stress Corrosion Cracking," *Electro-Technology* **11** (October 1963), pp. 11-12.

8. N. E. McKinney and H. W. Hermance, in "Stress Corrosion Testing," *ASTM Special Publication No.* **425** (1967).

9. H. W. Hermance, C. A. Russell, E. J. Bauer, T. F. Egan, and H. V. Wadlow, "Relation of Airborne Nitrate to Telephone Equipment Damage," *Environ. Sci. Technol.* **5** (September 1971), pp. 781-785.

10. R. A. Ehrhardt, "Acid Gold Plating," *Technical Proceedings of the 47th Annual Convention Am. Electroplaters' Soc.* (Newark, N.J.: American Electroplaters' Society, Inc., 1960), pp. 78-82.

11. G. B. Munier, "Polymer Codeposited with Gold During Electroplating," *Plating* **56** (October 1969), pp. 1151-1157.

12. H. A. Reinheimer, "Carbon in Gold Electrodeposits," *J. Electrochem. Soc.* **121** (April 1974), pp. 490-500.

13. F. B. Koch, Y. Okinaka, C. Wolowodiuk, and D. R. Blessington, "Additive-Free Hard Gold Plating for Electronics Applications—Part I—Physical Aspects," *Plating and Surface Finishing* **67** (June 1980), pp. 50-54; idem, "Additive-Free Hard Gold Plating for Electronics Applications—Part II—Chemical Aspects," *Plating and Surface Finishing* **67** (July 1980), pp. 43-45.

14. Y. Okinaka, "Electroless Gold Deposition Using Borohydride or Dimethylamine Borane as Reducing Agent," *Plating* **57** (September 1970), pp. 914-920.

15. A. Heller, B. Miller, and R. G. Vadimsky, U.S. Patent No. 4,082,624; filed December 3, 1976, issued April 4, 1978.

16. R. G. Baker and T. A. Palumbo, "The Case for End-Point Requirements in Gold Plating Specifications for Electronic Equipment," *Plating* **58** (August 1971), pp. 791-800.

17. H. E. Haring and U. B. Thomas, "The Electrochemical Behavior of Lead, Lead-Antimony, and Lead-Calcium Alloys in Storage Cells," *Trans. Electrochem. Soc.* **68** (October 1935), pp. 293-307.

18. E. E. Schumacher and G. M. Bouton, "Age Hardening Lead-Calcium Alloys," *Metals and Alloys* **1** (March 1930), pp. 405-409.

19. G. M. Bouton and G. S. Phipps, "Rapid Determination of the Calcium Content of Lead-Calcium Alloys by Titrating in the Molten State with Metallic Antimony," *Trans. Electrochem. Soc.* **92** (October 1947), pp. 305-311.

20. D. E. Koontz, D. O. Feder, L. D. Babusci, and H. J. Luer, "Reserve Batteries for Bell System Use: Design of the New Cell," *Bell System Tech. J.* **49** (September 1970), pp. 1253-1278.

21. D. C. Bomberger and L. F. Moose, "Nickel-Cadmium Cells for the Spacecraft Battery," *Bell System Tech. J.* **42** (July 1963), pp. 1687-1702.

22. D. W. Murphy and J. N. Carides, "Low Voltage Behavior of Lithium/Metal Dichalcogenide Topochemical Cells," *J. Electrochem. Soc.* **126** (March 1979), pp. 349-351.

23. D. W. Murphy, P. A. Christian, F. J. DiSalvo, and J. N. Carides, "Vanadium Oxide Cathode Materials for Secondary Lithium Cells," *J. Electrochem. Soc.* **126** (March 1979), pp. 497-499.

24. W. P. Mason and T. F. Osmer, "Part II--Necessary Conditions for Obtaining a Permanent Connection in Solderless Wrapped Connections," *Bell System Tech. J.* **32** (May 1953), pp. 557-590.

25. W. P. Mason and O. L. Anderson, "Stress Systems in the Solderless Wrapped Connection and Their Permanence," *Bell System Tech. J.* **33** (September 1954), pp. 1093-1110.

26. H. A. Miloche, "Mechanically Wrapped Connectors," *Bell Laboratories Record* **29** (July 1951), pp. 307-311.

27. R. F. Mallina, "Solderless Wrapped Connections. Part I. Structure and Tools," *Bell System Tech. J.* **32** (May 1953), pp. 525-555.

28. T. F. Egan and A. Mendizza, "Creeping Silver Sulfide," *J. Electrochem. Soc.* **107** (April 1960), pp. 353-354.

29. H. W. Hermance and T. F. Egan, "Organic Deposits on Precious Metal Contacts," *Bell System Tech. J.* **37** (May 1958), pp. 739-768.

30. T. F. Egan, U.S. Patent No. 2,812,406; filed March 2, 1954, issued November 5, 1957.

31. J. A. Becker, "Phenomena in Oxide Coated Filaments," *Phys. Rev.* **34** (November 1929), pp. 1323-1351; R. W. Sears and J. A. Becker, "The Origin of Thermionic Electrons from Oxide Coated Filaments," *Phys. Rev.* **37** (June 1931), p. 1681.

32. *Semiconductors*, ed. N. B. Hannay (New York: Reinhold Publishing Corporation, 1959), pp. 293-300 and 548-576.

33. H. E. Kern, "Research on Oxide-Coated Cathodes," *Bell Laboratories Record* **38** (December 1960), pp. 451-456; idem, "Emission and Life of Practical Oxide Cathodes as Limited by Diffusion and Chemical Reaction Phenomena," in *Report on Twenty-Third Annual Conference on Physical Electronics* (M.I.T., 1963), pp. 106-113.

34. D. MacNair, "Study of Electron Emitters for Use in Gas Lasers," *IEEE J. Quantum Electronics* **QE5** (September 1969), pp. 460-470.

35. G. M. Sessler and J. E. West, "Foil-Electret Microphones," *J. Acoust. Soc. Am.* **40** (December 1966), pp. 1433-1440.

36. J. C. Baumbauer, Jr. and A. M. Brzezinski, "The EL2 Electret Transmitter; Analytical Modeling, Optimization and Design," *Bell System Tech. J.* **58** (September 1979), pp. 1557-1578.

37. H. H. Lowry, "On the Nature of 'Active' Carbon," *J. Phys. Chem.* **34** (January 1930), pp. 63-73.

38. F. S. Goucher, "Microphonic Action in Telephone Transmitters," *Science* **72** (November 7, 1930), pp. 467-470; idem, "Recent Advances in Microphonic Research," *Bell Laboratories Record* **13** (July 1935), pp. 332-336.

39. M. D. Rigterink and R. O. Grisdale, "Alkaline Earth Porcelains Possessing Low Dielectric Loss," *J. Am. Ceram. Soc.* **30** (March 1, 1947), pp. 78-81; also, see the second volume of this series, *A History of Engineering and Science in the Bell System: National Service in War and Peace (1925-1975)*, ed. M. D. Fagan (Bell Telephone Laboratories, 1978), pp. 142-143.

40. See, for example, A. F. Bennet, "An Improved Transmitter for Operators' Use," *Bell Laboratories Record* **10** (February 1932), pp. 182-186; W. C. Jones, "Instruments for the New Telephone Sets," *Bell System Tech. J.* **17** (July 1938), pp. 338-357; A. H. Inglis, "Transmission Features of the New Telephone Sets," *Bell System Tech. J.* **17** (July 1938), pp. 358-380.

41. M. D. Rigterink and R. O. Grisdale, "Alkaline Earth Porcelains Possessing Low Dielectric Loss," *J. Am. Ceram. Soc.* **30** (March 1, 1947), pp. 78-81; also, see the second volume of this series, *A History of Engineering and Science in the Bell System: National Service in War and Peace (1925-1975)*, ed. M. D. Fagan (Bell Telephone Laboratories, 1978), pp. 142-143.

42. M. D. Rigterink, U.S. Patent No. 2,386,633; filed October 10, 1944, issued October 9, 1945.

43. F. H. Winslow, W. O. Baker, N. R. Pape, and W. Matreyek, "Formation and Properties of Polymer Carbon," *J. Polym. Sci.* **16** (April 1955), pp. 101-120.

Chapter 18

Improving the Mechanical Properties of Materials

The mechanical properties of materials have often been prominent in the design of telephone equipment. The classic concerns of metallurgy with the strength of metals and alloys have interested Bell Laboratories over the years, with special attention to critical uses such as relay springs, connectors, lead alloy sheathing for cables, and storage battery electrodes. The advent of polymers as structural materials focused new attention on mechanical properties and failure mechanisms. Bell Laboratories chemists did much to bring scientific and engineering understanding to the mechanical behavior of these materials.

I. STRENGTHENING OF METALS AND ALLOYS

Nonferrous metals and alloys are of major importance in the Bell System because of the large consumption of these materials. The need for long life, and economy, resulted in efforts to improve these materials. The developments often centered on improving mechanical strength and minimizing ultimate mechanical failures caused by fatigue, creep, or stress relaxation. In pursuit of these goals, contributions were also made in the field of materials testing.

1.1 Copper-Based Alloys

Copper alloys have always been of great interest to the Bell System because of their wide use in telephone apparatus such as switches, relays, keys, and jacks. In these electromechanical devices, copper alloys most often are used in the form of flat springs that are subjected to repeated bending, and it is vital that they perform this function reliably over many years. In addition, such spring elements had to be

Principal authors: G. Y. Chin, D. W. McCall, T. D. Schlabach, and W. P. Slichter

reasonable electrical conductors, capable of being soldered, and had to exhibit adequate corrosion resistance in the environments in which they were placed. Of these requirements, long life under conditions of repeated bending was the most critical and prompted early studies on the strengthening of copper alloys.

In one early study, W. C. Ellis and E. E. Schumacher [Fig. 18-1] examined precipitation, or age hardening, in brass and bronze alloys containing nickel and silicon.[1] They showed that the elastic strength of these alloys could be two to four times that of the same alloys without nickel and tin, that prior cold work increased the rate of age hardening, and that subsequent cold work increased the ultimate tensile or breaking strength without improving elastic strength. While their improved alloys were not used, their findings about the role of cold work proved important in later studies. They also discovered age hardening in copper-titanium alloys.[2]

Concurrent with these studies, J. R. Townsend and C. H. Greenall devised the first fatigue-test machine for sheet metals and used it to characterize the fatigue strength of copper alloys then commonly used for springs in electromechanical devices.[3] This method of testing was adopted by the metal industry and widely used in fatigue investigations. Further, because the springs were often bent into complex

Fig. 18-1. E. E. Schumacher (left) and W. C. Ellis, pioneers in the research and development of lead-based alloys and strong advocates of the importance of high purity in metals and alloys.

shapes for use in electromechanical devices, it became necessary to develop forming-test methods and establish forming limits for these materials. The work, done by G. R. Gohn, followed earlier work done at Western Electric and established an industry-wide standard.[4] Bell Laboratories also played a substantial role in establishing industry specifications and in standardizing thickness gauges for copper-alloy sheet materials.

In the 1950s and 1960s, Gohn and coworkers undertook a series of investigations on the mechanical properties of copper-alloy sheet materials. These included nickel-silver, phosphor-bronze, and copper-beryllium alloys, the most important copper alloys then used in electromechanical devices.[5] Their findings were useful in relating elastic strength to composition.

1.1.1 Texture-Strengthened Copper Alloys

By the 1960s, as electronic equipment and associated electromechanical devices became miniaturized, even stronger copper alloys were needed to meet the higher operating stresses encountered. This demand renewed the interest of G. Y. Chin, B. C. Wonsiewicz, and R. R. Hart in strengthening copper alloys.

The background for this work dated to Chin's earlier studies of the effect of crystallographic texture on the magnetic properties of Permalloy undertaken for the twistor memory program (see section 1.1.2 of Chapter 12). That work led to a series of basic investigations, including computer simulation studies, on the development of deformation textures by Chin and coworkers.[6] The fundamental knowledge acquired in these studies, in turn, formed a base on which Chin, Wonsiewicz, and Hart built to attain remarkable strengthening in already-known copper alloys.[7] [Fig. 18-2] This strengthening was achieved by extensively cold rolling these alloys and then heat treating them below their recrystallization temperature. This technique combined the strengthening conferred by cold work with that obtained by crystallographic texture in the deformed material and by precipitation hardening. These alloys possessed improved fatigue strength and resistance to stress relaxation together with acceptable formability.

Demands for improved alloys created parallel demands for improved methods of testing. An important aspect of this was that in many miniaturized designs, particularly those for connectors, stress relaxation replaced fatigue as a limiting design criterion. Stress relaxation resulted in the loss of forces needed to ensure good electrical contact or mechanical movement. A. Fox devised new tests for evaluating this property in wire and strip material.[8] Further, the high strength of these alloys uncovered inadequacies in the classical method of measuring elastic strength,[9] which led G. F. Weissmann to investigate alternate methods. In 1973, he developed a new measurement technique and a novel apparatus popularly called the "tic-toc" in which the test could be conducted. The apparatus subjects the specimen to a metronome-like oscillation and measures the number of cycles to failure.[10] This test has the advantage that it measures elastic strength in spring materials in the way that they are stressed in service.

1.1.2 *Spinodal Copper Alloys*

In 1971, J. T. Plewes began a fundamental study of alloys that could be made to undergo a particular type of metastable phase transformation known as spinodal decomposition. This transformation resulted in a finely modulated microstructure, with the possibility of substan-

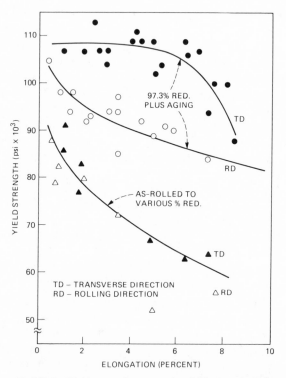

Fig. 18-2. Yield strength measured at 0.01 percent strain (a common reference offset) vs. elongation of a standard, 2-inch-long tensile bar of texture-strengthened phosphor bronze (upper curves) compared with conventionally prepared bronze (lower curve). [Hart, Wonsiewicz, and Chin, *Metall. Trans.* **1** (November 1970)].

tial alloy strengthening. Unfortunately, such alloys were frequently brittle and unsuitable for use. Plewes, however, found that this embrittling grain boundary phase could be suppressed by cold working prior to aging at the spinodal decomposition temperature. Very strong and ductile alloys could then be obtained.[11] He demonstrated this strengthening for a family of copper-nickel-tin alloys. In addition to excellent strength and ductility, these alloys possessed good fatigue and stress-relaxation characteristics.

Later, Plewes showed that the addition of a fourth element to these copper-nickel-tin alloys, notably, niobium in very low concentrations, eliminated the need for cold work prior to aging to obtain ductility. This made it possible to consider the use of these alloys in the form of high-strength castings. The spinodal copper-nickel-tin alloys developed by Plewes found use in a variety of applications in the Bell System, such as relays and connectors, as well as in various outside applications.

1.2 Lead-Based Alloys

Until 1947, Bell System transmission and exchange area cables were covered by lead or lead alloy sheaths to provide environmental protection. However, high cost and deficiencies in performance of the earliest sheaths of pure lead or lead and 3 percent tin alloy prompted studies to find improved sheathing materials. The most important of these were the lead-antimony, lead-calcium, and lead-silver alloys.

1.2.1 Lead-Antimony Alloy Sheaths

Schumacher, G. M. Bouton, and F. C. Nix studied the lead-antimony system to alleviate the difficulties encountered at Western Electric in the introduction of lead-antimony alloys for sheath manufacture and to understand the mechanism of precipitation hardening (then a fairly new concept) that was responsible for the improved mechanical properties of these alloys.[12,13] Precipitation hardening depends upon supersaturating a solid-solution alloy by quenching and then aging at some intermediate temperature to precipitate out a finely dispersed second phase. In this way, significant improvements in the mechanical strength, hardness, and resistance to fatigue failure can be obtained in suitable alloys. From this work, the 99 percent lead, 1 percent antimony composition was developed, which became the standard sheathing alloy for both power cables and communications cables throughout the United States. At the same time, Townsend and Greenall carried out fatigue studies on lead and lead-antimony alloys.[14] They developed laboratory fatigue tests that could produce the same type of fatigue failures as those encountered in the field, and which could be used to predict the field fatigue performance of other lead-sheath alloys. Fatigue testing of sheath materials was carried out for many years together with creep tests, which were also important to the successful use of cables.[15]

1.2.2 Lead-Calcium Alloys

In 1930, Schumacher and Bouton, confirming independent studies of Dean and Ryjord at Western Electric, showed that lead-calcium alloys subjected to precipitation hardening could develop greater strength, hardness, and resistance to fatigue and creep failure than the 99 percent lead, 1 percent antimony alloy. They also established the solid-solubility limits for calcium in lead and showed that strengthening was achieved at very low calcium-content levels. In a typical alloy containing 0.04 percent calcium, ultimate tensile strengths of about 5,250 pounds per square inch (psi) were obtained, as compared with 2,200 psi for pure lead.[16] [Fig. 18-3] Although lead-calcium alloys did not replace lead-antimony in cable sheathing, they did find use in the late 1960s in large-diameter sleeves for joining lead-sheathed cables. Also, lead-calcium alloys later replaced lead-antimony grids in lead-acid storage batteries. To control the low but precise calcium content required for these alloys, Schumacher and Bouton developed a rapid, visual, quantitative test suitable for factory use.[17]

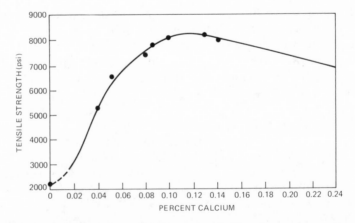

Fig. 18-3. Variation of tensile strength with calcium content of hardened lead-calcium alloys. [*Trans. Electrochemical Soc.* (October 1935): 313].

1.2.3 Lead-Silver Alloys

One of the last Bell Laboratories developments in strengthened lead alloys occurred in 1945 when Bouton, K. M. Olsen, and Schumacher reported on the improved strength, hardness, and creep resistance of lead alloys containing from 0.004 to 0.15 percent silver.[18] These were intended for use as sleeves to join pressurized, lead-sheathed cables, but they were never used because polyethylene began to replace lead as the standard cable sheathing material.

1.3 Zinc-Based Alloys

Zinc-based alloy die castings produced by many suppliers appear in countless products. Originally developed as economical substitutes for aluminum alloys, early die castings failed because of intercrystalline cracking and swelling caused by lead and tin impurities in the zinc. In the early 1930s, Bell Laboratories cooperated with industry in developing a series of zinc-based die casting alloys, known as *Zamak**[*] alloys, which were free of such problems, and which became the industry standard for small parts production.[19]

Knowledge gained from these early studies was later applied by Bouton and P. R. White to develop a superior solder for aluminum.[20]

II. STRENGTHENING OF POLYMERS

Polymeric materials are useful in diverse applications because they exhibit unusual combinations of mechanical properties. Properties of interest include elastic modulus, impact strength, and elongation to fracture or yield. A great deal of fruitful work has been carried out to tailor mechanical properties through admixture of nonorganic materials (for example, fiber glass and other composites), mixing of polymers to form polymer alloys, and thermal and mechanical processing. Many polymers crystallize to only a limited extent and thus even pure homopolymers can behave as composites. In viscoelastic materials, which manifest characteristics of both solids and liquids simultaneously, the mechanical properties of importance are often more complex than encountered with simple liquids or crystalline solids. The mode of failure (that is, the limit of strength) may involve creep, crazing, cracking (perhaps influenced by environmental agents), and other less familiar behaviors.

---

* Trademark of New Jersey Zinc Company.

2.1 Polyethylene in Cables

The mechanical integrity of polymers employed as sheath material in cables is a matter of primary importance. The sheath is subjected to many forms of abuse in manufacture, storage, delivery, installation, and service. W. O. Baker, I. L. Hopkins, and J. B. Howard demonstrated the importance of molecular weight, particularly the elimination of the lower range of the molecular weight distribution, as a critical factor in sheath cracking.[21] They also recognized the significance of biaxial stress and developed test methods relevant to cable sheath cracking. (See section III of Chapter 14.)

2.2 Crosslinked Polyvinyl Chloride Wire Insulation

Wire used in switchboards, distributing frames, and other telephone applications is often subject to severe abrasive stresses. Historically, a layer of textile fiber was served or braided outside the plastic insulation to toughen the structure, but the manufacturing process was slow and expensive. In the early 1970s, L. D. Loan introduced a superior process in which polyvinyl chloride (PVC) is compounded with a crosslinking agent and then extruded onto the conductor.[22,23] This wire is subsequently irradiated by an intense beam of high-energy electrons that causes the insulation to crosslink. The resulting insulation is mechanically tough and can be used directly with no textile protective coating. Other properties are also favorable. By 1981, this process became the standard method of making insulation for wires used in electric circuits.

2.3 High-Impact Polymers

Glassy polymers have desirable mechanical rigidity, but they are brittle. Rubbery polymers do not shatter, but they are soft and unsuited to many structural applications. By combining the two materials, it is possible to obtain the desireable properties of both. Rigid, high-impact compositions can be obtained by compounding rubber spheres into a glassy matrix. G. H. Bebbington demonstrated that scrap plastic from discarded telephone housings and handsets can be formulated with PVC and iron oxide to produce a useful, general-purpose, high-impact molding compound.[24] This material is used in a number of applications, including internal parts for telephones.

2.4 Failure Mechanisms

There has been a long-term interest at Bell Laboratories in polymer strength and mechanisms of failure. In addition to the work of Baker and Hopkins in connection with molecular weight and biaxial stress, H. D. Keith, F. J. Padden, and R. G. Vadimsky studied microscopic deformations of polyethylene spherulites and discovered a subtle structural feature, the intercrystalline link, that is believed to play an important role in endowing polyethylene with its useful high modulus.[25] (See section 3.3 of Chapter 14.) T. T. Wang, M. Matsuo, and T. K. Kwei modeled the inception of fracture in polystyrene composites incorporating rigid and rubbery spherical reinforcements.[26] They correctly predicted craze initiation behavior on the basis of a principal strain criterion.

Mechanical failure depends upon many factors including chemical composition, average molecular weight and distribution, molecular orientation, thermal history, specimen configuration, and stress geometry. S. Matsuoka and coworkers succeeded in developing a theoretical framework that allowed failure model (that is, brittle vs. ductile) and conditions of failure to be predicted on the basis of minimal experimental measurements.[27,28] This system provided design engineers with a valuable procedure in the important matter of material selection. [Fig. 18-4]

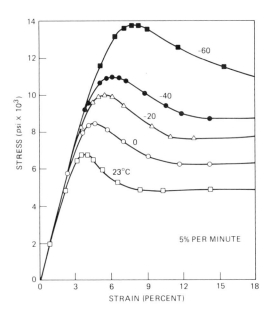

Fig. 18-4. Stress-strain behavior of polyvinyl chloride. Solid lines represent theoretical calculations, based on a rather complicated parametric formulation of postulated polymer structure, which give excellent agreement with the indicated experimental results.

III. RESEARCH AND DEVELOPMENT WORK AT BELL LABS ON WOOD POLES AND ON THEIR PRESERVATION

In the early days of telephony, the poles used to support conductors were of naturally durable species—chestnut, northern white cedar, and western red cedar.[29] Later, these were butt treated with coal tar creosote, and still later, AT&T pioneered in the use of pressure, full-length creosoted southern pine poles, which had a physical life equal to or longer than that of the durable species, even when butt treated. By the mid-1950s, the Bell System pole plant of some 22 million poles was 100 percent treated and predominantly southern pine.[30]

When Bell Laboratories was founded, a timber group was organized in the new Outside Plant Development Department to work with the Chemical Research Department to improve the telephone pole. R. E. Waterman was in charge of the wood preservation program. By 1934, research led to the development of accelerated procedures for the chemical and biological evaluation of wood preservatives. The results of their first endeavors, as reported by R. R. Williams, Waterman, C. O. Wells, F. C. Koch, and W. McMahon, involved the use of small stakes, 1 inch to 2 inches in diameter, treated to graduated retentions of preservatives and set out in test-plot environments to determine the amount of preservative necessary to prevent decay and termite attack.[31] This method became a published industrial standard.

Analytical methods were also developed to measure the amounts of preservatives in test stakes and standard poles. These techniques, coupled with the work of the development group in analyzing sapwood thickness data on hundreds of thousands of poles, with the contribution of W. A. Shewhart and others in the Quality Assurance Department, resulted in a statistical sampling procedure for acceptance of treated poles.

A fast method to bioassay ground-contact wood preservatives was conceived by J. Leutritz.[32] In this procedure, small sapwood pine cubes are treated to graduated levels of preservative and exposed to wood-destroying fungi for 90 days. The threshold level at which no decay takes place can be measured and compared for different preservatives. This procedure has had an impact on the testing of wood preservatives in government laboratories throughout the world. A paper by R. H. Colley offers a wealth of information on the subject of preservative evaluations.[33]

REFERENCES

1. W. C. Ellis and E. E. Schumacher, "Heat Treatment and Mechanical Properties of Some Copper-Zinc and Copper-Tin Alloys Containing Nickel and Silicon," *Am. Inst. Mining and Metal. Eng., Tech. Pub.* **188** (March 1929); idem, "Effect of Combina-

tions of Strain and Heat Treatment on the Properties of Some Age-Hardening Copper Alloys," *Am. Inst. Mining and Metal. Eng., Tech. Pub.* **395** (February 1931).

2. E. E. Schumacher and W. C. Ellis, "Age-Hardening of Copper-Titanium Alloys," *Metals and Alloys* **2** (September 1931), pp. 111-112.

3. J. R. Townsend and C. H. Greenall, "Fatigue Studies of Non-Ferrous Sheet Metals," *Bell System Tech. J.* **8** (July 1929), pp. 576-590; C. H. Greenall and G. R. Gohn, "Fatigue Properties of Non-Ferrous Sheet Metals," *Proc. Am. Soc. Testing Materials* **37** (1937), pp. 160-191.

4. G. R. Gohn, "The Forming Properties of Some Non-Ferrous Sheet Metals," *Proc. Am. Soc. Testing Materials* **36** (1936), pp. 207-220.

5. G. R. Gohn, G. J. Herbert, and J. B. Kuhn, "The Mechanical Properties of Copper-Beryllium Alloy Strip," *Am. Soc. Testing Materials, Special Tech. Pub.* **367** (1964).

6. B. C. Wonsiewicz and G. Y. Chin, "Plane Strain Compression of Copper, Cu 6 Wt. Pct A, and Ag 4 Wt. Pct Sn Crystals," *Metall. Trans.* **1** (October 1970), pp. 2715-2722.

7. R. R. Hart, B. C. Wonsiewicz, and G. Y. Chin, "High Strength Copper Alloys by Thermomechanical Treatments," *Metall. Trans.* **1** (November 1970), pp. 3163-3172.

8. A. Fox, "The Effect of Extreme Cold Rolling on the Stress Relaxation Characteristics of CDA Copper Alloy 510 Strip," *J. Materials* **6** (June 1971), pp. 422-435; idem, "A Simple Test for Evaluating Stress Relaxation in Bending," *Mat. Res. Stds.* **4** (September 1964), pp. 480-481.

9. B. C. Wonsiewicz and R. R. Hart, "Finite Strain and the 0.01 Percent Offset Yield Strength," *J. Testing and Evaluation* **1** (September 1973), pp. 412-415.

10. G. F. Weissmann, "Determination of Mechanical Design Properties of Materials," *J. Testing and Evaluation* **1** (March 1973), pp. 133-138.

11. J. T. Plewes, "High-Strength Cu-Ni-Sn Alloys by Thermomechanical Processing," *Metall. Trans.* **6A** (March 1975), pp. 537-544.

12. E. E. Schumacher and G. M. Bouton, "The Solid Solubility of Antimony in Lead as Determined by Conductivity Measurements on Cold-Worked Alloys," *J. Am. Chem. Soc.* **49** (July 1927), pp. 1667-1675.

13. E. E. Schumacher and F. C. Nix, "The Solidus Line in the Lead-Antimony System," *Trans. Am. Inst. Mining and Metal. Eng., No.* **1636-E** (February 1927).

14. J. R. Townsend, "Fatigue Studies of Telephone Cable Sheath Alloys," *Proc. Am. Soc. Testing Materials* **27** (1927), pp. 153-166; J. R. Townsend and C. H. Greenall, "Fatique Studies of Telephone Cable Sheath Alloys," *Proc. Am. Soc. Testing Materials* **30** (1930), pp. 395-405.

15. G. R. Gohn, S. M. Arnold, and G. M. Bouton, "Creep Tests on Some Extruded Lead and Lead-Alloy Sleeves and Tapes," *Proc. Am. Soc. Testing Materials* **46** (1946), pp. 990-1024.

16. E. E. Schumacher and G. M. Bouton, "Age Hardening Lead-Calcium Alloys," *Metals and Alloys* **1** (March 1930), pp. 405-409.

17. E. E. Schumacher and G. M. Bouton, "A Rapid Visual Test for the Quantitative Determination of Small Concentrations of Calcium in Lead," *Bell System Tech. J.* **20** (October 1941), pp. 434-438.

18. G. M. Bouton, K. M. Olsen, and E. E. Schumacher, U.S. Patent No. 2,449,566; filed June 8, 1945, issued March 7, 1950.

19. C. H. Mathewson, "The Processing and Uses of Metallic Zinc and Zinc-Base Alloys—Grades of Zinc and Fields of Use," in *Zinc, The Science and Technology of the Metal, Its Alloys, and Compounds* (New York: Reinhold Corp., 1959), pp. 386-389.

20. G. M. Bouton and P. R. White, "A Method of Soldering Aluminum," *Bell Laboratories Record* **36** (May 1958), pp. 157-160.

21. I. L. Hopkins, W. O. Baker, and J. B. Howard, "Complex Stressing of Polyethylene," *J. Appl. Phys.* **21** (March 1950), pp. 206-213.

22. W. A. Salmon and L. D. Loan, "Radiation Crosslinking of Poly(vinyl chloride)," *J. Appl. Polymer Sci.* **16** (March 1972), pp. 671-682.

23. L. D. Loan, W. A. Salmon, and J. R. Austin, "Continuous Radiation Crosslinking of Poly(vinyl chloride)," *SPE Antec* **18** (1972), pp. 636-637.

24. G. H. Bebbington, "Recycling ABS Waste as a Flame Retardant Molding Compound," *SPE Antec* **25** (1979), pp. 877-880.

25. H. D. Keith, F. J. Padden, Jr., and R. G. Vadimsky, "Intercrystalline Links in Polyethylene Crystallized from the Melt," *J. Appl. Polymer Sci.* **A2, 4** (April 1966), pp. 267-281.

26. T. T. Wang, M. Matsuo, and T. K. Kwei, "Criteria of Craze Initiation in Glassy Polymers," *J. Appl. Phys.* **42** (October 1971), pp. 4188-4196.

27. S. Matsuoka, H. E. Bair, S. S. Bearder, H. E. Kern, and J. T. Ryan, "Analysis of Non-Linear Stress Relaxation in Polymeric Glasses," *Polymer Eng. and Sci.* **18** (November 1978), pp. 1073-1080.

28. S. Matsuoka, "Free Volume, Excess Entropy and Mechanical Behavior of Polymeric Glasses," *Polymer Eng. and Sci.*, **21** (1981).

29. F. L. Rhodes, *Beginnings of Telephony* (New York: Harper & Brothers, 1929).

30. G. Q. Lumsden, "The Physical Life of Wood Poles," *Am. Inst. Elec. Eng.* (February 3, 1955).

31. R. R. Williams, "Chemical Studies of Wood Preservation, I. The Problem and Plan of Attack," R. E. Waterman and C. O. Wells, "II. Sampling Poles for Chemical Analysis," *Indust. Eng. Chem., Analytical Edition* **6** (September 15, 1934), pp. 308-314; R. E. Waterman, F. C. Koch, and W. McMahon, "Chemical Studies of Wood Preservation. III. Analysis of Preserved Timber," R. E. Waterman and R. R. Williams, "IV. Small Sapling Method of Evaluating Wood Preservatives," *Indust. Eng. Chem., Analytical Edition* **6** (November 15, 1934), pp. 409-418.

32. J. Leutritz, Jr., "A Wood-Soil Contact Culture Technique for Laboratory Study of Wood-Destroying Fungi, Wood Decay and Wood Preservation," *Bell System Tech. J.* **25** (January 1946), pp. 102-135.

33. R. H. Colley, "The Evaluation of Wood Preservatives," *Bell System Tech. J.* **32** (January 1953), pp. 120-169; ibid (March 1953), pp. 425-505.

Chapter 19

Crystal Growth and Other Processing Techniques

The preparation of materials of desired specification and the discovery of new techniques play key roles in any research program in the physical sciences. Indeed, a fortunate synergism has developed at Bell Laboratories in the fields of solid state science and in research on the growth of crystals. These mutually supporting ventures have in turn led to new basic science in the understanding of defects, dislocations, and impurities, and to new technologies for the processing of materials. The successes have been especially fruitful with semiconductors, for which methods of preparation are tightly linked to physical understanding.

Assembled in this chapter are processing techniques that Bell Laboratories scientists have either invented or to which they have contributed in a major way. Most of the techniques have also found their way into important technological applications, as in the case of crystal growth, zone refining, diffusion of impurities in semiconductors, molecular beam epitaxy, ion implantation, or oxide masking. Techniques for the fabrication of low-loss glass fibers as optical waveguides are described in Chapter 13.

I. CRYSTAL GROWTH

The importance of single crystals is apparent throughout the discussion of the modern history of crystalline materials. The first advantage is the elimination of grain boundaries, which represent serious flaws in materials such as silicon or germanium. Impurities diffuse much more rapidly along grain boundaries than through the volume of a crystal, which makes it difficult to control diffusion profiles. Impurities also tend to collect at grain boundaries and form precipitates that can short out devices or otherwise ruin their characteristics.

Principal authors: K. A. Jackson, R. A. Laudise, H. J. Leamy, D. W. McCall, M. B. Panish, W. G. Pfann, L. F. Thompson, C. D. Thurmond, and J. H. Wernick

Modern devices are therefore made of single crystals and are free of grain boundaries. Even dislocations have been virtually eliminated, and point defects are increasingly being brought under control.

Another advantage of materials in monocrystalline form stems from the anisotropy of their properties. For example, the frequency of a quartz oscillator depends on the orientation of the crystal as well as on dimensions. Quartz oscillators are made from precisely oriented single crystals. They are used extensively in the Bell System for multiplexing and demultiplexing signals, and even more commonly in watches and clocks for precise time control.

Single crystals are also advantageous when excellent optical quality is required, as in lasers, nonlinear optic, and optical modulator applications. Various aspects of single crystal growth have been summarized by R. A. Laudise.[1]

1.1 Growth from Solution — Ammonium Dihydrogen Phosphate, Quartz, and Garnets for Bubble Memory

Early crystal-growth efforts at Bell Laboratories involved the growth of crystals from aqueous solution containing seed crystals, that is, by feeding a solution saturated at one temperature into a vessel containing seed crystals held at a slightly lower temperature. [Fig. 19-1] For good crystal growth, the nutrient solution must be uniformly supplied to the growing face of the crystals, and the degree of supersaturation of the solution must be carefully controlled through precise regulation of the temperature. The circulation of the solution around the growing crystal must also be controlled. Failure to exercise these controls can cause multitudes of extraneous small crystals to form spontaneously in the solution and to settle out as waste on the bottom of the tank. Such seeds can also attach themselves to the faces of the desired crystals, thus disrupting their orderly growth. The knowledge of crystal growth gained in laboratory studies was successfully applied by G. T. Kohman, A. C. Walker, and A. N. Holden to the production of synthetic ammonium dihydrogen phosphate (ADP) crystals.[2] (See section IV of Chapter 16.)

Another notable achievement at Bell Labs in the field of crystal growth was the development of the hydrothermal growth process for producing large, optical quality, high purity synthetic quartz crystals. [Fig. 19-2] This work, begun in 1945, was motivated initially by the need for a reliable domestic supply of this strategic material. The work expanded greatly in the mid-1950s and involved Walker, Kohman, E. Buehler, and Laudise. [Fig. 19-3] The efforts of Walker and coworkers continued the work done in Germany during World War II in which quartz crystals were grown in an isothermal system from a

Fig. 19-1. The radial crystallizer tank for the synthetic crystal structure. The stainless steel gyrator has arms with methacrylate frames on which the seed plates are held as shown.

vitreous silica nutrient.[3] The German process was too slow to be commercially feasible.

The growth of large flawless crystals having high mechanical Q, suitable for piezoelectric devices, was first achieved in 1948 by Buehler and Walker.[4] Their procedure involved a vertical autoclave, a crystalline quartz nutrient, a temperature gradient between the seeds and nutrient, and pressures of the order of 1,700 atmospheres. Buehler and Walker also found that sodium hydroxide solutions were excellent solvents at higher pressures. The high yields of large crystals that they obtained were, in large measure, caused by the introduction of a baffle, which effectively divided the autoclave into two nearly isothermal regions, one for dissolution and the other for crystallization.[5] The large isothermal-crystallization zone permitted the growth of many large crystals at a nearly uniform rate. This research helped to establish Western Electric's outstanding position in the production of synthetic quartz crystals.

Single crystals were also used for studying the structure of materials using X-ray diffraction (see section 2.1 of Chapter 8). Single crystals, even small ones, are preferred for such studies, especially if the structure is complex. Crystal growth from solution was extensively investigated by Holden (see section 4.3 of Chapter 16). Water-soluble crystals are not widely used in practical applications because they tend to be attacked by moisture in the atmosphere. Growth of water-insoluble crystals from molten fluxes was initiated by J. P. Remeika in 1952.[6] The use of fluxes for the growth of single crystals sometimes produced new compounds with unique physical properties. For example, in 1960 Remeika discovered a $GaFeO_3$ single crystal which exhibited piezoelectricity and ferromagnetism simultaneously.[7] Much later, working with metal solvents, he found a new family of ternary

1 cm

Fig. 19-2. Synthetic quartz crystal.

Fig. 19-3. E. Buehler, R. A. Laudise, and G. T. Kohman (left to right) standing near a steel tank used in the production of large, optical quality, high-purity synthetic quartz crystals by hydrothermic growth.

intermetallic compounds (rare-earth rhodium stannides), some of which exhibited superconductivity and magnetic ordering sequentially.[8] Another use of the flux method was made by L. G. Van Uitert for the growth of garnet single crystals.[9] In this application a molten mixture of PbO, B_2O_3, and PbF_2 in a platinum crucible was used as the growth medium. The first crystals grown for possible application to bubble memory devices were the orthoferrites (see section III of Chapter 12). However, detailed magnetic and device studies with the orthoferrites showed that these materials were unattractive for mass-storage devices, but that the rare-earth iron garnets ($Re_3Fe_5O_{12}$), containing appropriate substitutions on the rare-earth and iron sites, would yield a uniaxial anisotropy of proper magnitude and an optimum saturation moment. Previous work by S. Geller, M. A. Gilleo, and coworkers had shown that the crystal chemistry of the garnets offered wide latitude for the control (and adjustment) of magnetic properties through such substitutions. (For more on this topic see section 1.3.2 of Chapter 1.)

The first large, nonmagnetostrictive, uniaxial garnets suitable for bubble devices were grown from $PbO-PbF_2-B_2O_3$ fluxes by Van Uitert and had such compositions as $Er_2TbAl_{1.1}Fe_{3.9}O_{12}$ and other multielement garnets containing 12 oxygen atoms, up to 5 atoms of iron, and two or three rare earth atoms. In 1970, A. H. Bobeck and Van Uitert discovered that the appropriate departure from cubic symmetries required for uniaxial behavior existed under a particular growth facet of the large crystals.[10]

As a result of this work, Western Electric began manufacture of mass memories in the early 1970s, based on single-crystal garnet films epitaxially grown from fluxes by a technique developed by H. J. Levinstein and coworkers.[11] The films are grown onto large, nonmagnetic, gadolinium gallium garnet (GGG), single-crystal substrates grown by C. D. Brandle and A. J. Valentino.[12] W. A. Bonner and Van Uitert showed that substitutions of Ca^{2+} ions on the rare earth sites, together with substitutions of Ge^{4+} or Si^{4+} ions on the tetrahedral iron sites, resulted in single-crystal films whose lattices matched that of GGG and reduced temperature sensitivity while retaining high bubble mobilities.[13] At the time of this writing magnetic garnet compositions used in bubble-domain device technology in production at Western Electric,[14] optimized for mobility and speed, have the formula $Y_{1.25} Lu_{0.45} Sm_{0.4} Ca_{0.9} Fe_{4.1} Ge_{0.9} O_{12}$.

1.2 Growth from the Melt

In the early days of the transistor, the semiconductors available were impure and polycrystalline. In addition to developing methods for purifying the materials, it was necessary to solve the problems associated with melting these materials at high temperatures (for example, 1412°C for silicon). A new high-purity grade of fused silica had to be developed as the crucible for holding the silicon. Gas atmospheres that would not contaminate the material had to be found. The timely invention of zone refining by W. G. Pfann was a major contribution that helped bring the impurities in germanium and silicon under control. (See section 5.2 of Chapter 11.)

Two methods of growing single crystals from the melt were in use in a few laboratories at that time. One was the method used by P. W. Bridgman at Harvard University.[15] It consisted of putting the material in a container with a pointed tip, melting the contents in a furnace, and then slowly lowering the container and melt out of the furnace so that it gradually froze from the lower end. This method had the disadvantage that it was difficult to seed the melt to obtain a single crystal with a predetermined orientation. Usually, crystals grown by this method had a random axial orientation.

The second method for forming crystals by growth from a melt was by the Czochralski technique.[16] This method could produce a large boule with a predetermined orientation by using a seed crystal and careful control. In the original process, metal was fused in an oxide crucible using a resistance furnace and held at a temperature just above the melting point. A small seed crystal was then dipped into the melt and slowly pulled out.

G. K. Teal and J. B. Little greatly improved the Czochralski method for silicon growth by introducing a radio-frequency heating source and a carbon susceptor. The latter was fitted to and heated a fused silica crucible that contained the metalloid. Later, Van Uitert converted the process to the growth of oxide crystals, such as sodium-doped yttrium aluminum garnet and many electro-optic and acousto-optic materials, by the direct radio-frequency heating of a noble metal, crucible susceptor that contained an oxide melt. This process has proven to be of great advantage for the growth of large oxide crystals of optical quality and has supplanted the flame-fusion technique for the preparation of crystals for lasers and for substrates for silicon on sapphire and garnet bubble-domain films.[17]

Modern production methods of growing single crystals evolved from the early work. Induction heating became the common method of applying the heat necessary to melt these materials and maintain them at a carefully controlled temperature. The crystals, and sometimes the crucibles, are rotated to improve radial thermal symmetry, resulting in better uniformity. The pullers, as refined over the years, bear little resemblance to those used in the early years for making laboratory crystals and produce routinely crystals 30 to 90 centimeters long and over 10 centimeters in diameter. [Fig. 19-4]

At the time of this writing, variations of these two basic methods are in use. GaAs used as substrate material (for example, in heterostructure lasers) is grown in a horizontal crucible, using a seed. InP is grown by liquid phase encapsulation, which is a variation of Czochralski growth in which the melt is covered with a layer of flux,

Fig. 19-4. Lead molybdate single crystal being grown from the melt.

such as molten boron oxide, which serves to inhibit, to a large extent, the evaporation of phosphorus from the melt.

1.2.1 Growth of Silicon Crystals by Float Zoning

In 1956, H. C. Theuerer [Fig. 19-5] invented another important method of melt growth, known as float zoning.[18] In this method, only a small zone in a vertical bar of the material is heated by a radio frequency coil and melted. The liquid is held in place by surface tension. This method can be used to produce high-resistivity silicon because it is relatively free from oxygen contamination, which is present in the Czochralski method because of the dissolution of the SiO_2 crucible. In 1972, J. R. Carruthers performed experiments to simulate a floating zone in zero gravity and to study convection in the

Fig. 19-5. H. C. Theuerer prepares to place a thin film substrate into "getter sputtering" equipment. Theuerer devised getter sputtering — a technique which improves on high-vacuum cathode sputtering for depositing thin metal films of high quality.

floating zone by using two immiscible liquids of the same density.[19] Both Czochralski and floating-zone crystals are rotated during growth to improve the thermal symmetry. By 1980, the floating zone method had become widely used to produce silicon single crystals for electronic applications.

1.2.2 Growth of Fluoride Crystals

In the early 1960s, much interest in fluoride compounds was generated by the availability of single crystals with high optical quality produced by H. J. Guggenheim.[20] Guggenheim devised techniques to overcome the corrosion problems encountered in using the Stockbarger-Bridgman method of growing fluoride crystals from the melt. The corrosion arose from the high reactivity of the molten fluoride and the hydrogen fluoride gas. Using a platinum crucible and an ambient containing a partial pressure of hydrogen fluoride, he was able to grow fluoride crystals with oriented-seed nucleation. Incongruently melting compounds such as Rb_2MnF_4 were pulled from a nonstoichiometric melt.[21] It was found that an excess of the alkali fluoride could shift the phase equilibria sufficiently to permit the desired compound to crystallize on an oriented-seed crystal. The technique was used for growing MgF_2 and MnF_2 crystals doped with V^{2+}, Ni^{2+}, and Co^{2+} for tunable phonon-terminated lasers, and for the rare-earth doped BaY_2F_8 lasers.[22] It has also been used for the family of antiferromagnetic, piezoelectric crystals $BaMF_4$,[23] where M is manganese, iron, cobalt, or nickel, as well as for neutron and optical investigation of magnons in NiF_2.[24]

1.3 Epitaxial Growth and Thin Films

1.3.1 Chemical Vapor Deposition

Chemical vapor deposition (CVD) is a method of growing epitaxial layers of, for example, silicon on silicon, by the use of a volatile molecule such as $SiCl_4$, which is reduced by H_2, to deposit silicon on the sample. This process has the advantage of high deposition rates—up to 2 micrometers (μm) per minute—and has been an important part of silicon technology since it was introduced by Theuerer in 1960.[25] This process was explored in several laboratories as part of a search for the best method of growing epitaxial silicon. One of the first studies was reported by Theuerer, who investigated doping of the epitaxial layers to produce p-n junctions.[26]

By 1962, CVD had emerged as the method of choice for producing epitaxial silicon layers at Western Electric, where it is in widespread use in semiconductor production.

1.3.2 Liquid Phase Epitaxy

The technique of liquid phase epitaxy (LPE) for the growth of crystalline layers became important during the 1960s in connection with the research then being carried out on light-emitting devices based on GaAs. The technique, which is the growth of an oriented crystalline layer of material from a saturated or supersaturated liquid solution onto a crystalline substrate, was first initiated by H. Nelson at RCA,[27] who grew layers of germanium from germanium dissolved in indium and GaAs from GaAs dissolved in tin.

The growth of GaAs from solutions of arsenic in gallium was undertaken at Bell Labs by M. B. Panish in 1965. Panish, H. J. Queisser, and others demonstrated that GaAs grown from gallium-rich solution had high luminescence efficiency.[28,29] [Fig. 19-6] The LPE studies were extended in 1966 to include the Al-Ga-As ternary system to permit phase studies and epitaxial layer growth of $Al_xGa_{1-x}As$ on GaAs. During the mid-1960s, it became clear that multi-epitaxial layers (called heterostructures by Panish and I. Hayashi) would be needed for heterostructure lasers and light-emitting diodes. The feasibility of such devices was demonstrated in the late 1960s,[30-32] and the success of the LPE technique for multilayer semiconductor epitaxy led to a worldwide effort on the growth of heterostructures.

During the 1970s, a large variety of III-V and II-VI layered structures for semiconductor devices were grown by the LPE technique in

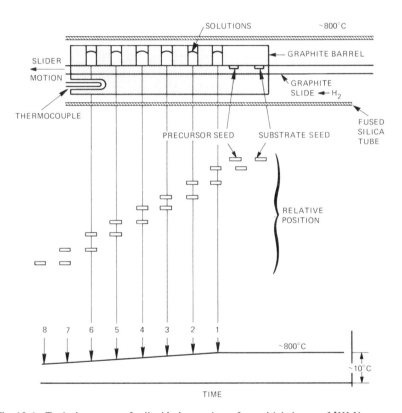

Fig. 19-6. Typical apparatus for liquid phase epitaxy for multiple layers of ˆIII-V compounds. Solutions containing the appropriate concentrations of the required elements (e.g., gallium, aluminum, arsenic, tin) as dopants are inserted in the chambers of the graphite barrel as indicated. Each solution composition is chosen to yield a desired layer composition and doping. By the use of a slider within the barrel, a precursor seed and a substrate seed (e.g. GaAS) may be brought into contact with each solution. The precursor seed tends to bring each solution to saturation relative to the group V element. Growth is on the substrate seed, which is successively translated under each solution while cooling at 0.1°C to 0.5°C per minute. The relative seed positions for growth of successive layers are illustrated. Other versions of the LPE apparatus permit the use of thin solutions and intentional supersaturation.

spite of the fact that it is inherently difficult to obtain a high degree of reproducibility or a highly uniform growth of large areas, as is desirable in semiconductor technology. Most of the layered structures were used for the fabrication of light emitters in a large range of wavelengths. By the early 1980s, the LPE technique was still the major method used for the growth of semiconductor heterostructures for light emitting diodes.

1.3.3 Molecular Beam Epitaxy

In the mid-1960s, J. R. Arthur initiated a study of the interaction of beams of gallium atoms and arsenic molecules on heated GaAs surfaces.[33] Utilizing modulated beams, he observed that while the sticking coefficient for gallium on a GaAs crystal surface was unity, the sticking coefficient of arsenic (from As_2 molecules) was small, and highly dependent on the gallium coverage of the surface. By making the arsenic beam intensity higher than that of gallium, he was able to achieve a deposit of one arsenic atom on the surface for each added gallium atom. This observation provided the basis for an epitaxial growth technique for stoichiometric GaAs that did not require precise control over the As/Ga beam intensity ratios provided the arsenic beam was significantly more intense than the gallium beam.

Although there had been a previous history of thin-film epitaxial growth in semiconductors with evaporative techniques, the layers were of poor or undetermined semiconductor quality. Arthur and A. Y. Cho recognized that thermal molecular and atomic beams were potentially useful for epitaxial growth of high-quality compound semiconductor layers of desirable thickness. The very versatile vacuum epitaxial-growth technique subsequently developed largely by Cho is called molecular beam epitaxy (MBE).[34]

In 1969, Cho began a detailed series of studies of MBE growth of GaAs. These included studies of surface structure and morphology, doping, transport and optical properties, and possible device applications. The use of glancing incidence, high-energy electron diffraction (HEED) techniques produced patterns from diffraction from reconstructed surface structures on the growing crystal surfaces. These studies showed that extremely smooth layers could be grown, and that both the surface structures and the properties of the epitaxial material could be modified by changing the ratio of the constituents in the beams.[35] Additional molecular beams of selected impurity atoms were used to dope the epitaxial layers during growth.[36] The mobility and optical properties of doped layers revealed that with suitable care the MBE layers of GaAs could be as high in crystal quality as the best material grown by other techniques.[37] In addition, a precision was attained in dimensional control over the layer thickness and doping profile that was previously not available. [Fig. 19-7]

The application of MBE GaAs for varactor diodes,[38] impatt diodes,[39,40] and field effect transistors[41,42] were explored in the mid-1970s. It is particularly attractive for GaAs devices that take advantage of its suitability for their layer growth. A striking example of this is a GaAs millimeter-wave-mixer diode that makes possible extremely low noise receivers (300K at 80 GHz) for radio astronomy and satellite communications experiments.[43]

One of the early objectives of MBE studies was the achievement of multilayered semiconductor structures for semiconductor injection lasers (see section III of Chapter 5) and the demonstration that more complex structures for integration of the laser with other components

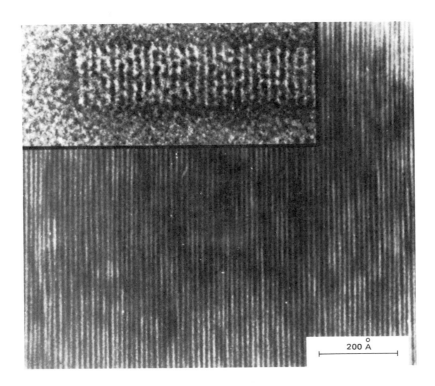

Fig. 19-7. Monolayer structures — so called because each layer consists of a small integer number of atomic monolayers — represent the ultimate in layer-thickness dimensional control achieved by molecular beam epitaxy. The structure illustrated consists of alternating layers of GaAs and AlAs, each two monolayers thick. For comparison, the tobacco mosaic virus is shown in the inset at the same magnification. [Inset from Finch, *J. Mol. Biol.* **8** (1964): 872.]

could be made. Cho's early studies of MBE in $Al_xGa_{1-x}As$ showed that the addition of an aluminum beam with suitable shuttering procedures yielded epitaxial structures of $GaAs/Al_xGa_{1-x}As$ with more than adequate dimensional control.[44] In the mid-1970s, W. T. Tsang used MBE to grow double heterostructure wafers from which double heterostructure lasers with exceptionally low threshold current density and high uniformity have been fabricated. In addition, Cho, Tsang, and M. Ilegems demonstrated that shadow masking can be used to produce complex three-dimensional $GaAs/Al_xGa_{1-x}As$ structures with excellent lateral and vertical dimensional control as a possible technology for the preparation of wafers for integrated-optics structures.[45,46]

1.3.4 Vapor-Liquid-Solid Growth

In the early 1960s, R. S. Wagner and W. C. Ellis discovered the vapor-liquid-solid (VLS) growth mechanism for whisker-like or needle-like crystals.[47] The discovery was the culmination of many years of study of whisker growth at Bell Labs. As noted in section 1.1.1 of Chapter 17, in the early 1950s, it was found that tiny whiskers of zinc shorted out closely spaced, electroplated circuit components. After extensive experiments, practical means were found to alleviate this problem, as described by S. M. Arnold.[48] In 1952, C. Herring and J. K. Galt guessed that very thin whiskers, because they contained no or few dislocations, should exhibit the theoretical strength of a perfect crystal, and they demonstrated this convincingly by bending whiskers of tin, grown from an electroplate.[49] (This is discussed further in section 1.1.1 of Chapter 17.)

Wagner and Ellis studied the growth of silicon whiskers from the vapor, using a procedure described by E. S. Greiner and coworkers.[50] Silicon and iodine were sealed in a reaction tube in a two-zone furnace. Uncontrolled whisker growth from the disproportionation of SiI_2 vapor was found. At that time, it was thought that a single screw dislocation running up the center of the whisker (an axial screw dislocation) and providing an active growth site at the tip, was responsible for the growth of whiskers. Two main facts emerged from these studies: an impurity, such as gold, had to be present and the whiskers were perfect crystals without an axial screw dislocation, as demonstrated by K. A. Jackson and Wagner.[51] These whiskers were not growing by the accepted mechanism.

Wagner and Ellis then demonstrated that the impurity was forming a molten alloy droplet on the silicon. [Fig. 19-8] This liquid droplet had a higher sticking coefficient for the silicon atoms arriving from the gas phase than did the solid silicon, so the whiskers grew with the droplet riding on top. Silicon atoms deposited on a droplet, diffused through the droplet, and adsorbed on the solid whisker. Understanding the process made it possible to grow vertical arrays of silicon whiskers or needles by depositing a patterned array of gold dots on a suitably oriented silicon crystal as the substrate. The VLS process provided a novel mechanism for the growth of whiskers[52] such that even trace amounts of impurity can cause uncontrolled whisker growth from the vapor. The VLS method is a very general method of controlled whisker growth applicable to many materials.

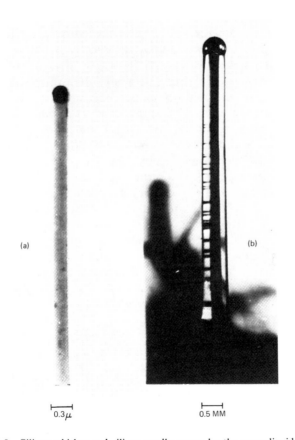

(a)

(b)

├──────┤
0.3μ

├──────┤
0.5 MM

Fig. 19-8. Silicon whisker and silicon needle grown by the vapor-liquid-solid mechanism. (a) Electron transmission photograph of whisker grown by iodide disproportionation. The growth was interrupted suddenly by quenching to freeze the gold-rich silicon alloy at the tip. (b) Optical photograph of needle with gold-rich tip grown from a (111) silicon crystal substrate by the hydrogen reduction of $SiCl_4$ for one hour, with a gold particle used as the alloying agent.

1.3.5 Splat Cooling

In 1960, a new method for rapidly quenching materials from the liquid state to obtain metastable phases was reported by P. Duwez, R. H. Willens, and W. Klement at the California Institute of Technology.[53] At Bell Labs, this technique, called splat cooling, was advanced by Willens and Buehler and applied to the quenching of reactive and refractory alloys.[54]

Solid-state rapid quenching is a technique that has been used extensively to produce metastable phases. However, the techniques commonly used for quenching solids, that is, quenching by immersion in liquids or gas blasts, do not usually cool the material rapidly enough to produce metastable alloys from molten material. To achieve the high quench rates required, it is necessary to have intimate contact between a thin molten film and a solid heat sink that extracts the heat by conduction cooling. A molten drop of material is propelled at high velocity by means of a shock tube against a curved copper strip at grazing incidence. The drop is spread into a thin foil, and the curvature of the strip ensures intimate contact between the copper strip and the molten material. This technique has resulted in quenching-rate values as high as 10^9 kelvins per second (K/sec). The technique was further advanced when Willens and Buehler devised a radio-frequency heating technique where the sample was supported on a water-cooled silver hearth with the radio-frequency energy coupled into the sample by a radio-frequency concentrator. The concentration of energy was large enough to melt the most refractory materials known (melting temperature >4000K) in about 1 second.

At some sacrifice of cooling rate, other techniques that used quenching principles, such as the roller quenching process used at Bell Labs by H. S. Chen and C. E. Miller,[55] allowed strip materials to be produced continuously. The cooling rates were of the order of 10^5 to 10^6 K/sec, which were high enough to yield metastable phases in many alloy systems.

When molten alloys are subjected to these cooling rates, it is possible to increase the solubility of elements in each other (even sometimes to the limit of complete solubility), to change the stoichiometry and order in existing phases, to create new intermediate crystalline phases, and in some alloy systems, to create metallic or semiconducting glasses. The resulting rapidly quenched alloys are found to have unique electronic, magnetic, and mechanical properties in many instances. Using splat-cooling techniques, Willens, B. T. Matthias, and their coworkers demonstrated the effect of rapid cooling on the stoichiometry, order, and the Nb_3Ge superconducting transition temperature, T_c, which was increased from 6K to 17K.[56] They also succeeded in producing a stoichiometric NaCl-type structure in MoC with a T_c of 14.3K, the highest of the transition-metal carbides.

E. A. Nesbitt and coworkers demonstrated that the magnetic properties of some iron-cobalt-vanadium alloys could be modified by splat cooling to produce a collection of superparamagnetic particles that continually and reversibly transformed to single-domain ferromagnetic particles.[57] This property permitted the fabrication of a high-sensitivity inductance thermometer by Willens, Buehler, and Nesbitt.[58] Using this technique, the coercive force of Vicalloy was increased[59] from 400 to 600 oersteds (Oe) and the coercive force of the MnAl magnetic alloy from 600 to 2100 Oe with a corresponding increase in the energy product from 0.4 to 1.6×10^6 gauss-oersteds.

The most unique structures produced by this quenching technique are the metallic glasses with their ultra-soft magnetic properties (see section IV of Chapter 12).

1.3.6 Sputter Deposition of Thin Films

Sputtering is the ejection of atoms from a solid as a result of a cascade of collisions initiated by an incident energetic particle striking the solid surface. The rudiments of this phenomenon were understood very early, and it was recognized that the process could be used either to erode a solid or to deposit the eroded material on another substrate. Sputtering has played an important role in Bell System technology from the very early years, with two applications dating from the 1930s: the manufacture of diaphragms for carbon broadcasting transmitters,[60] and the deposition of a conducting gold layer on the wax surface of an original phonograph record as a first step in making a master.

Sputtering by direct-current or radio-frequency discharge in argon gas was first considered in 1956 by H. Basseches as a possible deposition technique for producing metal films for resistor applications. The desirability of examining materials other than carbon and additives to carbon became evident after studies by Basseches and others pointed to basic long-term instabilities of borocarbon films used for resistors. Sputtering appeared to provide a method for preparing materials that had desirable resistor properties such as high stability, low temperature coefficient of resistance, and good adherence. It also seemed that sputtering could be developed to be a controlled and reproducible process.

In 1957, Basseches designed a system that had the versatility and flexibility to explore a wide variety of materials and process parameters. In the initial studies a variety of materials were sputtered on many substrates, including semiconductors, and it became clear that the potentialities of sputtered films extended well beyond that of resistive films for discrete resistors.[61] Effort soon focused on tantalum because it could be used for both resistors and capacitors. In 1959, D.

A. McLean demonstrated the use of tantalum for microcircuits,[62] and R. W. Berry and D. J. Sloan developed tantalum printed capacitors.[63,64] In 1961 and 1962, Basseches studied the sputtering process and performed the first oxidation and stability studies on tantalum films.[65-67]

Further work by D. Gerstenberg and C. J. Calbick indicated some of the influence of impurity elements such as nitrogen, carbon, and oxygen.[68] This led to the development of tantalum-nitride by Gerstenberg.[69] By mid-1959, the development of a production sputtering capability was initiated at the Engineering Research Center of Western Electric in Princeton, New Jersey, which resulted in an inline machine for the continuous sputtering of tantalum-nitride film. This facility was put into operation by Western Electric at Allentown, Pennsylvania, in 1964,[70] and by 1980, tantalum-nitride was being used as the major resistive film in the technology.

1.3.7 Getter Sputtering

Theuerer and J. J. Hauser developed a novel sputtering technique that eliminated the need for ultrahigh vacuum in preparing thin films of materials sensitive to gaseous impurities.[71] This new technique, called "getter sputtering," differed from conventional sputtering in that it utilized the gettering action of sputtering material to purify the gaseous argon used in the discharge before it reached the specimen to be coated. This gettering action of part of the sputtered atoms produces an atmosphere within the anode cylinder surrounding the cathode, from which the sputtered atoms are ejected, which is very low in reactive gases such as oxygen, hydrogen, nitrogen, and carbon monoxide. A mass-spectrometer analysis performed within a few minutes of sputtering showed that the concentration of these gaseous impurities drops below detection, and in consequence, contamination by such interstitial impurities is prevented when deposition of the desired sputtered atoms on the specimen to be coated takes place.

Getter sputtering has been used successfully for the deposition of a wide variety of materials, such as superconductors, semiconductors, and magnetic alloys. Theuerer and Hauser demonstrated the power of getter sputtering by depositing superconducting tantalum films in a vacuum of 5×10^{-6} Torr—a vacuum of 10^{-10} Torr was required to obtain similar results by evaporation. Getter sputtering is also an extremely powerful technique when it is necessary to achieve a clean interface between various films, as for example, in the superconducting proximity effect.[72] (See section 1.4 in Chapter 9.)

1.4 Theoretical Contributions

Crystal growth involves processes which take place on at least three quite different length scales. On the smallest scale, it involves atomic or molecular rearrangement; on a microscopic scale, it involves segregation and diffusion of atoms or molecules rejected by the growing crystal; and on a macroscopic scale, heat flow and convection couple the growing crystal to its environment. The container, ambient gas, and furnace walls provide potential sources of contamination. Because of the complex interactions between these processes, crystal growth is still an art, and the high-quality crystals that are grown attest to the skill of the practitioners of this art. There has been, and there continues to be, considerable effort devoted to understanding these various processes, both individually, and how they interact during growth.

An important contribution was the analysis by J. A. Burton, R. C. Prim, and W. P. Slichter[73] of the role of thermally driven convective mass transport on the spatial distribution of impurities. (See section 5.3 of Chapter 11.) Earlier analyses had assumed that the liquid was well-mixed, and of uniform composition. The Burton-Prim-Slichter analysis showed that the impurities rejected by the growing crystal accumulate in a boundary layer near the growing crystal, and that the distribution of the impurities incorporated into the crystal depends on the strength of the convective mixing.

Impurities have a different equilibrium solubility in a crystal than in the matrix from which it is growing. The species rejected by a growing crystal accumulate in its vicinity and slow down the growth process by depressing the melting point of the interface. This results in a condition known as "constitutional supercooling"[74] since the liquid far from the crystal is supercooled more than the liquid in the vicinity of the crystal. This condition can result in an instability of the interface since a part of the crystal can grow faster if it penetrates the boundary layer surrounding the crystal. It is possible, therefore, to have a stable planar interface, cellular growth morphology, resulting from immoderate instability due to constitutional supercooling, and a dendritic growth due to a strong instability caused by several-percent impurity. These effects have been studied in considerable detail, both theoretically and experimentally, in order to delineate the growth patterns necessary to eliminate them. [Fig. 19-9]

Carruthers examined liquid flow patterns that arise from horizontal temperature gradients during horizontal crystal growth and deter-

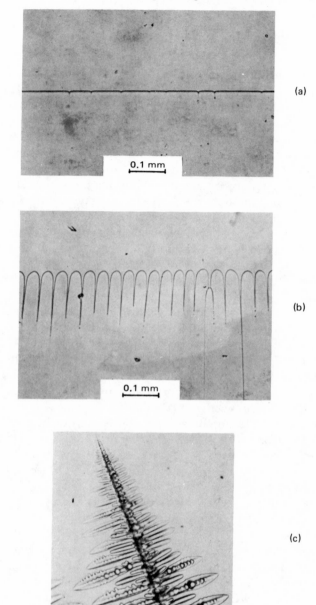

(a)

(b)

(c)

Fig. 19-9. Crystal growth patterns obtained by varying the concentrations of impurities: (a) a stable planar interface; (b) cellular growth resulting from moderate interface instability; (c) dendritic growth resulting from extreme interface instability.

mined the effect of these liquid flows on solute transport at the growing interface.[75] These flow patterns greatly influence the microscopic and macroscopic impurity segregation during crystal growth. For Czochralski growth, Carruthers and K. Nassau studied the convection patterns that arise from thermal gradients and from simultaneous crystal and crucible rotation.[76] For the latter case, a force field is produced by the rotation that controls the convection. Convective mixing and instabilities play important roles in crystal growth from melts of oxides, metals, and semiconductors, and extensive experimental and theoretical studies of these processes have grown from this early work. [Fig. 19-10]

Jackson developed a scheme by which materials can be grouped according to their growth morphologies, based on the concept of sur-

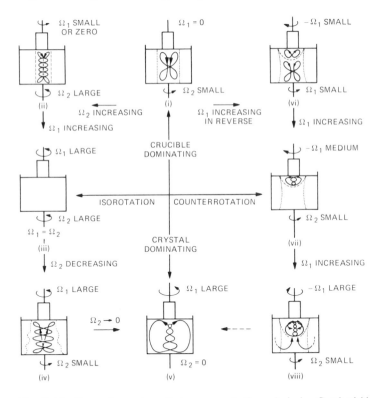

Fig. 19-10. Convection patterns that can occur in the melt during Czochralski crystal growth, according to Carruthers and Nassau. The crystal, suspended on a thin seed crystal, is shown in contact with the top surface of the melt, which is contained in a crucible. The convection patterns depend on the rotation rate of the crystal ($\Omega 1$) and of the crucible ($\Omega 2$). [Carruthers and Nassau, *J. Appl. Phys.* **39** (1968): 5210.]

face roughening.[77] The members of each group have a similar entropy change associated with crystallization. One group contains the metals and the rare gases growing from their melts. The entropy change is small and the interface is atomically rough. The members of this group exhibit a common set of growth features including planar growth, growth of rounded cells, and dendrite growth. In a second group, which includes melt growth of most organic materials and typical vapor growth, the entropy of crystallization is large and the interface is atomically smooth, resulting in strongly anisotropic growth rates and faceted crystals. A third distinct group of materials with very large entropy of crystallization, which include most polymers, grow spherulitically and are difficult, if not impossible, to grow as large single crystals. In the mid-1960s, Jackson and J. D. Hunt suggested that the morphology of eutectics could be classified according to the same scheme, taking into account the morphology of each of the two phases.[78] Extensive cataloging of eutectic morphologies have been made based on this scheme.

Using the classification scheme based on the entropy of crystallization, several organic materials known as plastic crystals were identified. These materials have solidification characteristics identical to the metals and are also transparent, so that their growth can readily be observed by transmission microscopy. Using these materials as analogs various solidification processes were studied, including the onset of interface instabilities, segregation during cellular and dendritic growth, the development of structure of castings, and dendritic growth morphology.[79] These studies led to the discovery of dendrite remelting, which is responsible for the grain structure observed in conventional castings. Jackson and Hunt made the first observations of the shape of a eutectic interface during lamellar growth, which occurs when two phases grow simultaneously from an alloy melt. They developed a theoretical model that was able to account in detail for observed interface shapes. They also studied the instabilities that permit changes in the lamellar spacing. The use of organic materials has been widely adopted by other laboratories to study solidification processes. The classification scheme for growth morphologies was based on a simple model of surface roughening and a qualitative understanding of the growth process. Its success suggested that crystal growth is a very complex cooperative process at the molecular level. The formation of new layers depends on the formation of clusters or islands on surfaces and this in turn depends implicitly on the adatom denoting, for example, how rough the surface is at the molecular level.

1.4.1 Impact of the Computer

The statistical mechanical problem involved cannot be solved analytically, but a combination of computer simulation and the analysis of various approximate models have resulted in a clear and detailed understanding of how growth proceeds. Using Monte Carlo simulation techniques, G. H. Gilmer has been able to extract the structure and the equilibrium properties of the surfaces as well as to make detailed predictions of growth rates: when the entropy of crystallization is small, the surface is rough on a molecular level and growth can occur very rapidly into an undercooled phase; when the entropy of crystallization is large, the surface is smooth on a molecular level and so new layers do not form readily.[80] The smoothness of a surface depends also on the crystallographic packing in the planes parallel to the surface. This effect produces a large multiplying factor: a small difference in packing can result in a large difference in growth rate, the resulting growth rate anisotropy is responsible for the familar crystalline shapes of crystals.

In the mid-1970s, analytical studies of surfaces in equilibrium led to the discovery by J. D. Weeks and coworkers of the surface roughening transition.[81,82] A surface does not go continuously from a smooth configuration to a rough configuration. The surface tension is continuous through this region, but the free energy of a step on a rough surface is zero, so that a rough surface is not locked onto the crystal planes. This accounts for the dramatic differences in morphology between, for example, the metals which "solidify" with rough surfaces, and minerals which "crystallize" with smooth surfaces.

Very far from equilibrium, spherulitic growth changes from "spikey" to massive.[83] In 1977, C. E. Miller demonstrated that this change in morphology could be explained by the prediction made by Gilmer, based on computer simulation, that the growth rate should become isotropic at large growth rates. In a computer simulation carried out in 1980, Gilmer also demonstrated the enhancement of surface nucleation rates caused by impurities, the interaction of impurities with surface steps, and the presence of surface segregation, both at equilibrium and during growth.[84] The computer has proved to be essential to elucidating the basic physical processes involved in crystal growth. [Fig. 19-11]

II. ZONE REFINING AND ZONE LEVELING

The recognition of the role that impurities play in determining the electrical properties of the semiconductors germanium and silicon in

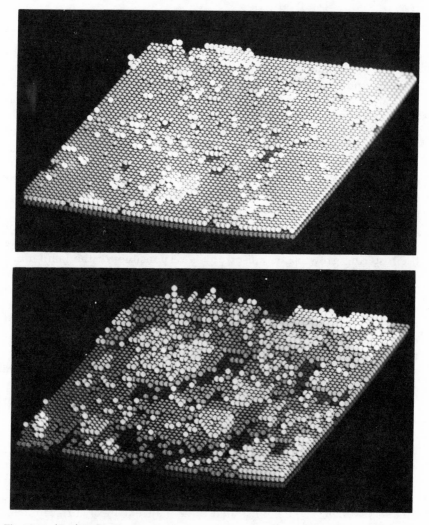

Fig. 19-11. (Top) Computer simulation of crystal surface below roughening transition (KT/ϕ-the ratio of the thermal energy, KT, to the bond energy, ϕ, is small.) Growth on this surface occurs by nucleation and spreading of islands. (Bottom) Computer simulation of crystal surface above roughening transition (KT/ϕ is large.) Growth on this rough surface is random and does *not* depend on the nucleation of new layers.

transistors pointed to the need for obtaining materials of unprecedented purity and for developing techniques to control added impurities of specific and very low concentration. These problems were solved in a significant and timely way by Pfann with the invention of zone refining and zone leveling in 1951.[85]

The zone-refining process depends on the fact that the solubilities of impurities are different in the liquid and in the crystal, and that the impurities tend to segregate in the phase in which they are most soluble. This segregation occurs in any freezing process, even in the normal freezing of a crucible of liquid. However, the amount of segregation or purification that can be obtained this way is limited by the solubility ratios. However, in the zone-refining process, as the short molten zone moves along the ingot, it moves the impurities to the end of the ingot boat. Repeated passes of the zones concentrate the impurities more and more, because the use of a narrow liquid zone does not allow the impurity segregated on earlier passes to remix throughout the ingot. [Fig. 19-12]

The concept of moving a small molten zone through a solid led to Pfann's invention of other zone-melting processes. Zone leveling is a

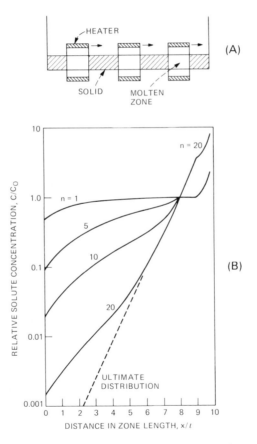

Fig. 19-12. (A) Schematic representation of zone refining. (B) Plots of relative impurity content along ingot for numbers, n, of zone passes for a distribution coefficient of 0.5 in an ingot ten zone-lengths long. [Pfann, in *Crystal Growth and Characterization* (1975): 54, 55.]

method for distributing a prescribed amount of impurity uniformly in a bulk solid. Temperature-gradient zone melting is a method for incorporating an impurity into a microscopic region of a solid by movement of a small molten zone through it to provide deep-lying p-n junctions, for example.

Pfann also made intensive analyses of the segregation effects during repeated zone passes and invented many configurations for the application of this method to a variety of materials.

The zone-refining process, first applied to metals by J. H. Wernick, produced metal crystals of unprecedented purity.[86] This made possible basic studies of the fundamental electric and magnetic properties of metals. The distribution of impurities between the solid and liquid phases in silicon and germanium were critically reviewed by F. A. Trumbore, C. D. Thurmond, and M. Kowalchik in work that was important to the controlled application of zone refining and zone leveling to these materials.[87,88]

Zone refining was the key to solving the purity problem in the early days of semiconductors. This development brought the purity of the materials under control to the point where device manufacture became a reality. It also found widespread use beyond the semiconductor area. In addition to having been used to purify many metals to the highest levels of purity, it has also been used extensively to purify a variety of organic materials. Pfann, Miller, and Hunt designed a zone refiner for these materials that is capable of sustaining several short zones stabilized by rotating the tube, so that the zone length is smaller than the diameter of the tube.[89] Zone refining also reduces the tendency of some organic materials to decompose during refining and has been used to produce many organic materials at the highest purity levels.

Zone refining is an important purification method applicable to a wide variety of materials. Its use continues as an important generic refining method. The principles developed by Pfann that underlie the zone-refining process have wide-ranging applicability in all crystal growth, casting, and segregation processes; they have added a new dimension to fundamental studies in materials science throughout the world.

III. CRYSTAL IMPERFECTIONS

The departure from the regular arrangement of atoms in crystals of various ideal structures (that is, cubic, hexagonal, and so on) is caused by a variety of imperfections that can be grouped into two broad categories: those arising from structural defects such as grain boundaries, vacancies, and dislocations, and those caused by impurities.

The high quality and purity of the crystals needed for semiconductor devices made these defects important, and at the same time provided a vehicle for studying them. Examples of structural defects discussed in this section include the first direct observation of dislocations using etching, theoretical and experimental work on dislocations in small angle grain boundaries, and studies of dislocation multiplication and motion. Impurities as intentional dopants are treated in the next section. In this section, work on oxygen as a major unintentional impurity is discussed. There have also been numerous studies aimed at identifying and eliminating other unwanted impurities and precipitates.

3.1 Defects and Dislocations

Defects in crystalline solids, including precipitates, that result from preparation and processing, may have pronounced effects on the electrical and optical properties of electronic materials. Since the mid-1930s, theoreticians had postulated that local regions of distortions or dislocations existed in crystals and that these could account for several crystal properties, particularly their relatively low values of mechanical strength. The local regions of distortion might selectively be attacked by special chemical etches.

The discovery by F. L. Vogel, Pfann, and coworkers that etch pits appearing on polished and etched crystal planes were the sites of emerging edge dislocations was made in 1953 during a study of the growth of germanium single crystals by zone leveling.[90] This was the first direct observation of dislocations, and it proved to be of enormous importance in further experimental and theoretical studies of dislocations and their behavior in crystals. A small-angle boundary separates two regions of a crystal or two crystals which are slightly misoriented with respect to each other. Geometrically, the boundary could consist of a parallel array of dislocations, with the angular misorientation between the crystals depending on the spacing between the dislocations. Pfann and his associates observed rows of etch pits, and measured the spacing between the pits. Then, using X-rays, they showed that there was an angular misorientation across a row of etch pitch. The angular misorientation which they measured agreed with the value calculated from the etch pit spacing. This demonstrated not only that the pits were at dislocations, but was the first direct evidence that small-angle grain boundaries are made up of dislocation arrays.

Prior to the experimental observation of dislocations, W. Shockley and W. T. Read analyzed theoretically the energetics of dislocation boundaries. A small-angle grain boundary which consists of an array of dislocations has a smaller energy than the same dislocations would have if they were randomly distributed. This is because the long-range stress fields from the dislocations cancel when they form an ordered array. This effect causes "polygonization" of the grain structure during post-deformation annealing.[91] Their predictions for the dependence of the grain boundary energy on misorientation were subsequently verified by several experimenters.

During deformation, the number of dislocations in a crystal increases dramatically. Typically, the dislocation density in an annealed sample will start at 10^7 to 10^8 dislocations per cm^2, and increase to 10^9-10^{11} disloc/cm^2 after heavy cold working. Dislocation interactions make it progressively harder for the dislocations to move, resulting in the well-known phenomenon called work hardening (the strength of a material increases during deformation). The mechanism responsible for dislocation multiplication was suggested by F. C. Frank and Read.[92] They demonstrated geometrically how a segment of a dislocation line could bow out and sweep around on the slip plane to produce a dislocation loop. Repetition of this process results in the generation of many dislocation loops, and a rapid increase in the dislocation density. This is known as a Frank-Read source.

The geometry, interactions, stress fields, and energetics of dislocations and dislocation arrays were the subject of the book by Read which had an important impact on the development of this field.[93]

Several other important Bell Laboratories contributions regarding dislocations in solids followed the excitement of the first direct observation of dislocations in germanium and silicon. Thermal fluctuations in the melt during crystal growth were shown by A. J. Goss, K. E. Benson, and Pfann to produce impurity banding that led to the formation of dislocations.[94] As discussed in section 1.3.5 of this chapter, Jackson and Wagner, using extinction contours, demonstrated that silicon whiskers did not contain axial-screw dislocations, thus overturning the prevalent belief of theorists.

J. R. Patel made extensive measurements of the velocity of dislocations in silicon and germanium and the dependence of the velocity on applied stress and doping levels.[95] An energy level associated with dislocation motion was identified in these studies. In the late 1970s, the energy level of the dislocation in silicon was identified by L. C. Kimerling and Patel using capacitance transient methods following careful deformation and annealing treatments.[96]

In the mid-1950s, Wernick and his associates investigated further the phenomenon of dislocations and etch pits in metals.[97] At that time, the consensus among materials scientists was that dislocations in metals must be marked with impurity atoms before etching reagents would be selective enough to reveal these defects. Wernick devised suitably sensitive etching reagents to expose fresh dislocations in several plastic metals and demonstrated that dislocations in metals do not have to be marked to be revealed as etch pits. The discovery that fresh dislocations in metal can be revealed by etching provided a major stimulus for basic plasticity studies of metals.

The motion of dislocations and other defects produces inelastic behavior in crystals. Displacement of these defects absorbs energy from an acoustic field and contributes to acoustic attenuation. This "internal friction" can be used to study the dynamic response of defects to an external stress. In addition to measuring the elastic constants of materials in single-crystal form, W. P. Mason and his associates developed many of the techniques for measuring internal friction in crystals, which provided impetus to the development of this field.[98-103] Studies based on these experimental methods have played a key role in the understanding of the dynamic response of defects, as well as in the origins of acoustic attenuation. Dislocation motion in metals and in quartz,[104-107] twinning in tin,[108] and magnetic domain-wall motion in $BaTiO_3$ and nickel[109] were investigated by Mason and coworkers using these techniques.

3.2 Oxygen as an Impurity in Silicon

Oxygen is present in silicon as an important impurity. In early work, J. R. Patel demonstrated that oxygen in silicon pinned the dislocations, much as carbon does in steel.[110] The necessity to stabilize the oxygen donor concentration in silicon with a low temperature anneal was explained by W. Kaiser, H. L. Frisch, and H. Reiss as a complexing reaction.[111] In dislocation-free silicon, the oxygen which is picked up from the SiO_2 crucible can precipitate out of solution during annealing. In the precipitate, SiO_2 occupies about the same volume as two silicon atoms, and so some silicon atoms are forced into interstitial positions (between the usual lattice sites) during precipitation. These interstitial silicon atoms collect in sheets, causing a local error in the packing sequence of the atoms known as a stacking fault. Further studies of this process by Patel, Jackson, and Reiss established controlled conditions so that the stacking faults did not form in the active regions of wafers where they could act as precipitate sites for heavy elements and thus destroy device performance, but rather the stacking faults could be made to grow only in inactive regions where they acted as gettering sites for unwanted heavy elements.[112] [Fig. 19-13]

IV. IMPURITY DOPING

Precise control of the concentration of acceptor or donor impurities in the semiconductor crystalline materials is of paramount importance for the fabrication of p-n junctions, transistors, and other semiconductor devices. The early p-n junctions were obtained by controlling the

Fig. 19-13. Stacking faults in silicon that result from oxygen
precipitation shown by X-ray topography.

concentration of the impurities during the pulling of the crystal from
the melt and depended on the relative liquid-solid distribution
coefficient of the impurities. This was followed by the alloy regrowth
method discussed in Chapter 11. C. S. Fuller's pioneering studies in
the 1950s of the diffusion of Group III and Group V elements in silicon and germanium led to the development of the thermal diffusion
process of impurity doping in the fabrication of semiconductor devices. For many years, this process played a dominant role in semiconductor technology. The ion-implantation process was developed a
decade later and involved the injection of high energy, charged atoms
as dopants. This technique made possible the attainment of more precise geometrical control of the depth of the injected impurities as well
as the cross-sectional geometry.

4.1 Doping by Diffusion

In the diffusion process for doping a semiconductor crystal with the
appropriate impurity, the crystal (for example, silicon or germanium)

is heated in an inert atmosphere, such as helium, in the presence of a gas (for example, BCl_3 or phosphorus vapor) containing the impurity atoms to be diffused into the crystal. The temperature is sufficiently high, but is below the melting point of the crystal, to produce appreciable vapor pressure of the impurity to be injected by diffusion. Control of the diffusion depth of the dopant is obtained by varying the temperature (by a range of about 1050°C to 1250°C for silicon) and the exposure time, which is usually on the order of a few hours. The penetration depth of the acceptor impurities in n-type semiconductors, or of donor impurities in p-type crystals, is determined by electrical measurements, such as locating the p-n barrier formed. An alternative method of diffusing the impurities is to place a film of the metal (for example, aluminum) on the semiconductor and heat treat the combination at the desired temperature and for an appropriate length of time.

Fuller and colleagues studied the diffusion properties of a large number of elements in germanium and silicon, particularly atoms of Group III (boron, aluminum, gallium, indium, and thallium) and Group V (phosphorus, arsenic, antimony, and bismuth) in silicon,[113] as well as lithium and copper in silicon and germanium.[114]

4.2 Ion Implantation

Ion implantation is the process of injecting charged atoms into a solid. The materials research scientist uses this process to alter the electrical, optical, chemical, magnetic, or mechanical properties of a solid.

In contrast with the thermal diffusion processes, ion implantation involves injecting ionized impurity atoms into the material. Because the impurities are in the form of an ion beam, great control of the quantity of the implanted dose and of the spatial extent of the implanted region is possible.

The implantation process found its first applications in the semiconductor field. In 1952, more than a decade before implantation was recognized as a technologically successful doping technique, R. S. Ohl reported perhaps the first ion bombardment experiment that improved device characteristics.[115] Patents on the ion implantation technique were awarded to Ohl and to Shockley in 1956 and 1957, respectively.[116,117] The modern era of ion implantation in science and technology began in the mid-1960s and was stimulated by interest and technical progress in a number of areas having to do with ion beams and solids. Of paramount importance in this development was the work of W. M. Gibson, as noted in Chapter 8 of this volume, who studied the phenomenon of ion channeling using the Rutgers University-Bell Labs tandem Van de Graaff accelerator.[118]

Stimulated by the development of the channeling technique, ion implantation as a doping technique began to be studied in detail. In 1968, Gibson reported on the modification of a number of semiconductors by ion implantation.[119] A. U. MacRae and T. E. Seidel made some of the first devices at Bell Labs by implantation.[120] Using channeling techniques, L. C. Feldman, W. L. Brown, and Gibson,[121] along with researchers in many laboratories around the world, made contributions to understanding the implantation process in silicon. These studies yielded very successful prescriptions for the use of ion implantation in the production of devices. Direct device fabrication by implantation moved forward at a rapid pace through the efforts of R. A. Moline and many others, as noted in a review article by MacRae.[122] By 1980, ion implantation techniques were adopted widely in the silicon integrated circuit technology for fabricating metal oxide semiconductor devices, high-power/high-frequency diodes, and bipolar integrated circuits.

Although semiconductors have dominated the development of ion implantation because of their technological importance, some research has also been carried out with insulators and metals. In insulators, the principal interest in the early 1970s was in the alteration of the index of refraction of transparent solids (amorphous SiO_2, in particular) by ion implantation in order to form optical waveguides of small dimensions in patterns that might be useful in optical circuits. R. D. Standley, Gibson, and J. W. Rodgers found that a wide variety of ions were effective, the major effect being caused by structural changes rather than by the presence of a specific impurity.[123] Studies with light ions by H. M. Presby and Brown showed that both electronic excitation in SiO_2 and elastic collisions of ions with nuclei of the solid caused changes in the refractive index.[124] In these early studies the optical loss in guides formed by implantation was relatively high.

In metals, J. M. Poate and his colleagues started a series of experiments in 1973 to investigate the metallurgy of the implantation process.[125] They studied copper binary alloys with implantation concentrations up to about 30 percent and observed the formation of equilibrium solid solutions, metastable solid solutions, and amorphous alloys. These studies demonstrated the strong similarities between implantation and the more conventional rapid quenching techniques. E. N. Kaufmann and collaborators chose beryllium as the host lattice for implantation studies because of the very low probability of dynamic replacement collisions and low defect densities.[126] The final impurity state within the solid should, therefore, represent the metallurgical or chemical propensities of the species involved. They implanted over 25 metallic elements into beryllium to form unique metastable substitutional and interstitial configurations, and in collaboration with the theorists J. R. Chelikowsky and J. C. Phillips, correlated these configurations using an extension of existing theory of metallic alloying.

These studies showed implantation to be a unique tool for producing alloyed surfaces, generating interest at Bell Laboratories and elsewhere in evaluating other properties of these surface alloys, such as corrosion resistance and hardness.[127]

Other new applications in the early 1970s included the work of R. Wolfe and J. C. North, who utilized ion implantation to control the properties of magnetic-bubble garnet films,[128] and the work of J. C. Dyment, North, and L. A. D'Asaro on modifications of GaAs.[129]

V. MASKING

The technique of masking in semiconductor devices dates back to the mid-1950s when the control of the geometry of impurity dopants in transistors and related semiconductor devices became important. Masking techniques were later applied more generally to the buildup of complex patterns of materials for the fabrication of integrated circuits.

5.1 SiO$_2$ Masks

The use of SiO$_2$ masks for controlling the geometry of impurity dopants in silicon was invented by C. J. Frosch [Fig. 19-14] and L. Derick in 1955 while they were conducting studies of the diffusion of impurities into silicon from a carrier gas at 1 atmosphere pressure.[130] They found that thin, uniform layers of SiO$_2$ would form on silicon when an oxidizing carrier gas was used, and that the SiO$_2$ layer acted as a barrier to the entrance of certain donor and acceptor impurities into silicon. They demonstrated further that impurities in a carrier gas could enter silicon through windows etched in the SiO$_2$ layer. The oxide mask permitted the precise control of the position of impurities in silicon, which led to the high density of circuit elements obtained by technology. Oxide masking evolved as a key step in the manufacture of silicon integrated circuits, and underlies the entire silicon integrated circuit industry.

5.2 Electron-Beam and X-Ray Resist Processed in Fine-Line Lithography

At the time of this writing, the manufacture of modern integrated circuits, involving the buildup of complex patterns of materials layer by layer, has been made possible by the use of masks to produce a desired circuit geometry. Radiation (usually ultraviolet) is projected through the "open" parts of the mask onto the circuit surface that has been previously coated with a "resist," that is, a material that is sensitive to the radiation. A positive resist is made more soluble by the

Fig. 19-14. C. J. Frosh, coinventor of the technique of using SiO_2 masking to control the geometry of impurity dopants in silicon.

action of the radiation, and the *exposed* areas of the circuit can be subjected to the next step in preparation (for example, etching, metallization, diffusion, and so on). Negative resists are less soluble following exposure to radiation, and the *unexposed* areas are laid bare by the developer. Resist materials are typically polymeric organic compounds that are tailored for sensitivity to the radiation, processing characteristics, and protection of the device circuit during the fabrication operation.

Ultraviolet radiation of wavelength 0.35 to 0.45 μm were employed in the manufacture of most microelectronic devices. As the technology progressed it became necessary to make patterns with ever smaller features, and diffraction effects become an important limitation. For dimensions in the range 1 to 2 μm, electron-beam, X-ray, and deep-ultraviolet techniques were being developed, and in each case, new resists were required.

5.2.1 Electron-Beam Resists

Electron-beam lithography is employed extensively to make high-quality masks for conventional ultraviolet patterning and to a lesser extent for direct production of semiconductor circuits. It utilizes a computer-driven beam of electrons that "draws" the required pattern. In 1970, R. D. Heidenreich developed a theoretical model of the electron-resist interaction and predicted the need for a high-sensitivity resist system.[131] In 1972, E. D. Feit, L. F. Thompson, and Heidenreich developed a negative-electron resist, COP, which is a copolymer of glycidyl methacrylate and ethyl acrylate.[132] This material was used extensively in the manufacture of master chromium masks with commercially available electron-beam exposure equipment. A second negative material developed by Thompson in 1978 proved to be particularly valuable because of its improved resolution and durability under plasma-etching conditions. This material is denoted GMC and is a copolymer of 3-chlorostyrene and glycidyl methacrylate.[133]

In 1973, Thompson and M. J. Bowden showed that poly(olefin sulfones) were useful for high-sensitivity, positive, electron-beam resists. Specifically, poly(butene-1-sulfone) (PBS) was developed and became used commercially in the manufacture of high-resolution chromium master masks.[134] In 1978, Bowden and Thompson discovered a novolac-based, positive, electron-beam resist that utilized poly(2-methylpentene-1-sulfone) as the irradiation-sensitive dissolution inhibitor. This material exhibited much improved plasma-etch resistance over PBS and proved to be capable of submicron pattern delineation.[135]

5.2.2 X-Ray Resists

X-ray lithography is a method used to obtain a 1:1 X-ray shadowgraph of a mask and to record the image in an underlying resist. Since X-rays have negligible scattering at wavelengths of only a few angstroms, this technique should, in principle, be able to reproduce submicron features. In 1977, G. N. Taylor developed a family of halogenated acrylate and methacrylate polymers designed as high-resolution, high-sensitivity X-ray resist materials.[136] The halogens, especially chlorine and bromine, were used as X-ray absorbers for palladium and rhodium X-ray radiation, respectively. Specifically, a resist based on poly(2,3 dichloropropylacrylate) was used to fabricate high-performance devices with 1-μm minimum features.

VI. PROCESSING OF MATERIALS WITH IONS, LASERS, AND PLASMAS

6.1 Ion-Beam Processing

In the late 1960s, ion-beam etching systems were in wide use for thinning samples for transmission electron microscopy. The ion sources in these systems were essentially the first stage of the proton accelerator designed by Rutherford in the 1930s for the transmutation of the elements. P. H. Schmidt and E. G. Spencer at Bell Laboratories demonstrated that a damage-free polished surface could be obtained by impinging ion beams at a grazing angle on a solid. For example, almost all the surface stresses were removed from the surface of a thin magnetic oxide (orthoferrite) platelet.[137] Schmidt and Spencer also demonstrated that ion-beam sputtering could be used to deposit thin films. Unlike conventional sputtering, ion beam deposition is carried out in a plasma-free vacuum environment and has been used for a wide range of materials.[138]

6.2 Annealing with Lasers

During the summer of 1977, scientists in the Soviet Union reported the use of intense laser irradiation to remove the lattice damage produced in silicon by ion implantation. Several scientists at Bell Labs conducted experiments to confirm the report and were able to determine the primary mechanism by which the annealing occurred. When the surface of a crystal is illuminated, the energy in the light beam is absorbed by electronic processes that rapidly transfer it to lattice vibrations, that is, to heat. This heating effect can also be obtained with electron or ion beams, and if sufficiently intense, can result in flash melting of the surface layer, which resolidifies when the pulse is extinguished.

6.2.1 Application to Epitaxial Growth and Control of Dopant Impurities

The mechanism of melting and resolidification observed with laser irradiation was studied in late 1977 by G. K. Celler, Poate, and Kimerling,[139] and by H. J. Leamy, G. A. Rozgonyi, and T. T. Sheng.[140] In their work, pulsed irradiation in the 10^{-7} to 10^{-8} second range was found to eliminate lattice damage from a surface layer with a thickness of a few thousand angstroms and, moreover, resulted in the placement of impurity atoms as dopants on regular sites in the silicon lattice by the epitaxial process. During liquification, impurities are redistributed by diffusion in the liquid, so that their final depth distribution is altered by pulsed-beam processing. This redistribution, along with the observation of imperfect regrowth where the melt did not penetrate through the damaged surface layer, provided the first clues to the mechanism of pulsed-beam processing.

The melting mechanism of pulsed-beam processing was verified by D. H. Auston and coworkers, who observed the characteristic reflectivity of a liquid-silicon surface layer during its brief lifetime, approximately 1 microsecond (μsec).[141] They measured the duration of the liquid layer and compared the results with thermal computations of the melting and freezing cycle.[142] The excellent agreement achieved served to further strengthen the melting picture. Subsequent work has verified and enriched the understanding of rapid solidification (approximately 1 m/sec at a quench rate of approximately 10^{10} K/sec!) and has also led to the discovery of several interesting and useful phenomena. For example, high-speed solidification can result in the trapping of impurities within the silicon in quantities that far exceed the equilibrium solubility. Epitaxial layers may be added to the crystal locally by processing vapor deposited polycrystalline layers of silicon. Alloy surface layers can be formed by processing metal thin films on silicon. These latter layers produce both Schottky and Ohmic contacts to the semiconductor and have been demonstrated for GaAs as well.

6.2.2 *Application to Removal of Damage Caused by Ion Implantation*

Laser irradiation for much longer periods, approximately 1 millisecond (msec), can also be effective in removing ion-implantation damage. A continuous-wave laser beam is scanned over the surface of a crystal that has been rendered amorphous by heavy ion damage. This amorphous layer is a thermodynamically distinct phase of greater free energy than crystalline silicon and can be epitaxially regrown onto a crystalline substrate if sufficient thermal energy is supplied to break the covalent Si-Si bond and provide some atomic mobility. The process can be accelerated enormously by short-time, high-temperature conditions that are achieved by scanned laser processing. At Bell Labs a group under the leadership of W. L. Brown studied the time and temperature dependence of the progressive growth of the crystal through the amorphous overlayer.[143] A second group used the reflectivity techniques mentioned previously to demonstrate the absence of melting during processing.[144] Two attributes distinguish beam processing from furnace heating in this case. First, only the rapid heating and quick quench (approximately 10^6 K/sec) achieved in beam processing permit high temperatures to be reached without the onset of bulk nucleation of crystallites within the amporphous layer. Second, the process is completed so rapidly that dopant atoms cannot diffuse more than approximately 10Å. Thus, the process is a favored candidate for device fabrication when precise control of shallow impurity layers is required.

The experience with silicon has also led to experimentation with the semiconductors GaAs, germanium, InP, and with heterostructure materials as well. In addition, this experience has led to a general realization that very rapid thermal processing can produce not only improved materials, but also can serve as a useful experimental tool.

6.3 Plasma Processing of Materials

The interaction of plasmas with semiconductor surfaces has proven to be of importance in preparation of certain materials. As early as the 1950s, rare-gas plasmas were used in ion sources to sputter-deposit and etch the surfaces of semiconductors. With the advent of radio-frequency sputtering in the 1960s, sputter deposition for the preparation of thin films began to be used on a large scale for the fabrication of electrical components. In 1964, J. R. Ligenza demonstrated that high-quality SiO_2 could be grown on silicon wafers by oxidation in an oxygen plasma excited by microwave radiation.[145]

In the 1970s, it was discovered that reactive plasmas could be efficient in etching the surface of silicon. Low-pressure discharges in NH_3-SiH_4 mixtures were used to deposit insulating layers of SiN on silicon. Plasma-deposited SiN is used as an encapsulating top layer in integrated circuits. At about the same time it was recognized that plasma etching could be used to add, literally, a new dimension to semiconductor processing. It was found that plasma etching is directional, so that, for example, the sharp features of a mask could be maintained on an atomic scale even when removing hundreds of atomic layers.[146-149] This discovery coincided with the drive for smaller-scale structures in integrated-circuit fabrication and has been used to great advantage in this application. The introduction of various chemical species into the plasma permits selective etching of different materials, and this is the basis of the "reactive ion etching" technique that is in widespread use in semiconductor processing.

In 1972, M. J. Vasile and G. Smolinsky developed methods of depositing polymeric films for lightguides using reactive plasmas.[150] They studied the reacting ion and neutral species and determined the underlying chemical processes in these and similar reactive plasmas which are useful for semiconductor processing.[151]

Research on radio frequency discharges confined by a magnetic field was carried out in the late 1970s by R. P. H. Chang.[152] By varying the exciting frequency, Chang found that he could couple the power resonantly into the plasma to heat the electrons as well as to modify the plasma density. More significantly, however, he discovered that copious amounts of negatively charged oxygen species can be generated on surfaces that are aligned in the plasma normal to the confining magnetic field. Using this fact, he demonstrated that at low temperatures thin oxide films can be grown on semiconductor surfaces (for example, SiO_2 on silicon).

Plasma processing found an important place in the "Very Large Scale Integration" technology that became the backbone of the electronics industry.

REFERENCES

1. R. A. Laudise, *The Growth of Single Crystals* (Englewood Cliffs, N.J.: Prentice-Hall, Inc., 1970).
2. A. C. Walker, "Piezoelectric Crystal Culture," *Bell Laboratories Record* 25 (October 1947), pp. 357-362.
3. G. E. Guellich, J. White, and C. B. Sawyer, "Report on Questioning of Profs. Pohl, Nacken, Spangenberg, Joos, Gunther, Dr. Chytrek, et al.," *U.S. Department of Commerce, Off. Pub. Bd., Report PB 006498* (1945).
4. A. C. Walker and E. Buehler, "Growing Large Quartz Crystals," *Ind. Eng. Chem.* 42 (July 1950), pp. 1369-1375.
5. G. T. Kohman, U.S. Patent No. 2,895,812; filed July 28, 1954; issued July 21, 1959.
6. J. P. Remeika, "A Method for Growing Barium Titanate Single Crystals," *J. Am. Chem. Soc.* 76 (February 5, 1954), pp. 940-941.
7. J. P. Remeika, "$GaFeO_3$: A Ferromagnetic-Piezoelectric Compound," *J. Appl. Phys.* 31 (May 1960), pp. 263S-264S.
8. J. P. Remeika, J. P. Espinosa, A. S. Copper, H. Barz, J. M. Rowell, D. B. McWhan, J. M. Vandenberg, and D. E. Moncton, "A New Family of Ternary Intermetallic Superconducting Magnetic Stannides," *Solid State Comm.* 34 (June 1980), pp. 923-926.
9. L. G. Van Uitert, W. H. Grodkiewicz, and E. F. Dearborn, "Growth of Large Optical-Quality Yttrium and Rare-Earth Aluminum Garnets," *J. Am. Ceram. Soc.* 48 (February 1965), pp. 105-108.
10. A. H. Bobeck, E. G. Spencer, L. G. Van Uitert, S. C. Abrahams, R. L. Barns, W. H. Grodkiewicz, R. C. Sherwood, P. H. Schmidt, D. H. Smith, and E. M. Walters, "Uniaxial Magnetic Garnets for Domain Wall 'Bubble' Devices," *Appl. Phys. Lett.* 17 (August 1, 1970), pp. 131-134; L. G. Van Uitert, W. A. Bonner, W. H. Grodkiewicz, L. Pictroski, and G. J. Zydzik, "Garnets for Bubble Domain Devices," *Mat. Res. Bull.* 5 (September 1970), pp. 825-835.
11. H. J. Levinstein, S. J. Licht, R. W. Landorf, and S. L. Blank, "Growth of High-Quality Garnet Thin Films from Supercooled Melts," *Appl. Phys. Lett.* 19 (December 1, 1972), pp. 486-488.
12. C. D. Brandle and A. J. Valentino, "Czochralski Growth of Rare Earth Gallium Garnets," *J. Cryst. Growth* 12 (January 1972), pp. 3-8.
13. W. A. Bonner, J. E. Geusic, D. H. Smith, L. G. Van Uitert, and G. P. Vella-Coleiro, "Growth and Characeristics of High Mobility Bubble Domain Garnets with Improved Temperature Stability," *Mat. Res. Bull.* 8 (October 1973), pp. 1223-1229; W. A. Bonner, J. E. Geusic, and L. G. Van Uitert, U.S. Patent No. 3,886,533; filed January 23, 1974, issued May 27, 1975.
14. S. L. Blank, R. Wolfe, L. C. Luther, R. C. LeCraw, T. J. Nelson, and W. A. Biolsi, "Design and Development of Single-Layer, Ion-Implantable Small Bubble Materials for Magnetic Bubble Devices," Proceedings of the 1978 Conference on Magnetism and Magnetic Materials, Cleveland, Ohio (1979), *J. Appl. Phys.* 50 (March 1979), pp. 2155-2156.
15. P. W. Bridgman, "Properties of the Alkali Metals," *Proc. Am. Acad. Sci.* 60 (October 1925), pp. 385-421.
16. J. Czochralski, "A New Method for the Measurement of the Velocity of Crystallization of the Metals," *Z. Physik. Chem.* 92 (1917), pp. 219-221.
17. A. Vernuil, *Ann. Chim. Phys.* 3 (1904), p. 20.
18. H. C. Theuerer, "Removal of Boron from Silicon by Hydrogen Water Vapor Treatment," *J. Metals* 8 (October 1956), pp. 1316-1319.
19. J. R. Carruthers and M. Grasso, "The Stabilities of Floating Liquid Zones in Simulated Zero Gravity," *J. Cryst. Growth* 13/14 (1972), pp. 611-614.

20. H. J. Guggenheim, "Growth of Single-Crystal Calcium Fluoride with Rare-Earth Impurities," *J. Appl. Phys.* **32** (July 1961), pp. 1337-1338; idem, "Growth of Highly Perfect Fluoride Single Crystals for Optical Masers," *J. Appl. Phys.* **34** (August 1963), pp. 2482-2485.

21. R. A. Cowley, G. Shirane, R. J. Birgeneau, and H. J. Guggenheim, "Spin Fluctuations in Random Magnetic-Nonmagnetic Two-Dimensional Antiferromagnets. I. Dynamics," *Phys. Rev.* **B15** (May 1977), pp. 4292-4302.

22. L. F. Johnson, H. J. Guggenheim, and R. A. Thomas, "Phonon-Terminated Optical Masers," *Phys. Rev.* **149** (September 1966), pp. 179-185; L. F. Johnson and H. J. Guggenheim, "Infrared-Pumped Visible Laser," *Appl. Phys. Lett.* **19** (July 15, 1971), pp. 44-47.

23. M. Eibschütz and H. J. Guggenheim, "Antiferromagnetic-Piezoelectric Crystals: $BaMF_4$ (M = Mn, Fe, Co, and Ni)," *Solid State Comm.* **6** (October 1968), pp. 737-739.

24. M. T. Hutchings, M. F. Thorpe, R. J. Birgeneau, P. A. Fleury, and H. J. Guggenheim, "Neutron and Optical Investigation of Magnons and Magnon-Magnon Interaction Effects in NiF_2," *Phys. Rev.* **B2** (September 1970), pp. 1362-1373.

25. H. C. Theuerer, "Purification of $SiCl_4$ by Absorption Techniques," *J. Electrochem. Soc.* **107** (January 1960), pp. 29-32.

26. H. C. Theuerer, "Epitaxial Silicon Films by the Hydrogen Reduction of SiCl," *J. Electrochem. Soc.* **108** (July 1961), pp. 649-653.

27. H. Nelson, "Epitaxial Growth from the Liquid State and Its Application to the Fabrication of Tunnel and Laser Diodes," *R.C.A. Review* **24** (December 1963), pp. 603-615.

28. M. B. Panish, H. J. Queisser, L. Derick, and S. Sumski, "Photoluminescence and Solution Growth of Gallium Arsenide," *Solid State Electronics* **9** (April 1966), pp. 311-314.

29. H. J. Queisser and M. B. Panish, "Luminescence of Zinc Doped Solution Grown Gallium Arsenide," *J. Phys. Chem. Solids* **28** (July 1967), pp. 1177-1184.

30. M. B. Panish and S. Sumski, "Ga-Al-As: Phase, Thermodynamic, and Optical Properties," *J. Phys. Chem. Solids* **30** (January 1969), pp. 129-137.

31. I. Hayashi, M. B. Panish, and P. W. Foy, "A Technique for the Preparation of Low-Threshold Room-Temperature GaAs Laser Diode Structures," *IEEE J. Quant. Electron.* **QE5** (April 1969), pp. 210-211.

32. M. B. Panish, S. Sumski, and I. Hayashi, "Preparation of Multilayer LPE Heterostructures with Crystalline Solid Solutions of $Al_xGa_{1-x}As$: Heterostructure Lasers," *Met. Trans.* **2** (March 1971), pp. 795-801.

33. J. R. Arthur, Jr., "Interaction of Ga and As_2 Molecular Beams with GaAs Surfaces," *J. Appl. Phys.* **39** (July 1968), pp. 4032-4034.

34. A. Y. Cho, "GaAs Epitaxy by a Molecular Beam Method: Observations of Surface Structure," *J. Appl. Phys.* **42** (April 1971), pp. 2074-2081; idem, "Film Deposition by Molecular-Beam Techniques," *J. Vac. Sci. Technol.* **8** (Sept./Oct. 1971), pp. S31-S38.

35. A. Y. Cho and I. Hayashi, "Epitaxy of Silicon Doped Gallium Arsenide by Molecular Beam Method," *Met. Trans.* **2** (March 1971), pp. 777-780.

36. A. Y. Cho and I. Hayashi, "p-n Junction Formation During Molecular-Beam Epitaxy of Ge-Doped GaAs," *J. Appl. Phys.* **42** (October 1971), pp. 4422-4425.

37. A. Y. Cho and J. R. Arthur, "Molecular Beam Epitaxy," *Progress in Solid State Chemistry* **10**, ed. J. O. McCaldin and G. Somorjai (Oxford: Pergamon Press, 1976), pp. 157-191.

38. A. Y. Cho and F. K. Reinhart, "Interface and Doping Profile Characteristics with Molecular-Beam Epitaxy of GaAs: GaAs Voltage Varactor," *J. Appl. Phys.* **45** (April 1974), pp. 1812-1817.

39. A. Y. Cho, C. N. Dunn, R. L. Kuvas, and W. E. Schroeder, "GaAs IMPATT Diodes Prepared by Molecular Beam Epitaxy," *Appl. Phys. Lett.* **25** (August 15, 1974), pp. 224-226.

40. W. C. Ballamy and A. Y. Cho, "Planar Isolated GaAs Devices Produced by Molecular Beam Epitaxy," *IEEE Trans. Electron Devices* **ED-23** (April 1976), pp. 481-484.

41. A. Y. Cho, J. V. DiLorenzo, B. S. Hewitt, W. C. Niehaus, W. O. Schlosser, and C. Radice, "Low-Noise and High-Power GaAs Microwave Field Effect Transistors Prepared by Molecular Beam Epitaxy," *J. Appl. Phys.* **48** (January 1977), pp. 346-349.

42. J. V. DiLorenzo, W. C. Niehaus, and A. Y. Cho, "Nonalloyed and *in situ* Ohmic Contacts to Highly Doped n-Type GaAs Layers Grown by Molecular Beam Epitaxy (MBE) for Field-Effect Transistors," *J. Appl. Phys.* **50** (February 1979), pp. 951-954.

43. R. A. Linke, M. V. Schneider, and A. Y. Cho, "Cryogenic Millimeter-Wave Receiver Using Molecular Beam Epitaxy Diodes," *IEEE Trans.* **MTT-26** (December 1978), pp. 935-938.

44. A. Y. Cho, "Growth of Periodic Structures by the Molecular-Beam Method," *Appl. Phys. Lett.* **19** (December 1, 1971), pp. 467-468.

45. W. T. Tsang and A. Y. Cho, "Growth of GaAs/Ga$_{1-x}$Al$_x$As over Preferentially Etched Channels by Molecular Beam Epitaxy: A Technique for Two-Dimensional Thin-Film Definition," *Appl. Phys. Lett.* **30** (March 15, 1977), pp. 293-296.

46. W. T. Tsang and M. Ilegems, "Selective Area Growth of GaAs/Al$_x$Ga$_{1-x}$As Multilayer Structures with Molecular Beam Epitaxy Using Si Shadow Masks," *Appl. Phys. Lett.* **31** (August 15, 1977), pp. 301-304.

47. R. S. Wagner and W. C. Ellis, "Vapor-Liquid-Solid Mechanism of Single Crystal Growth," *Appl. Phys. Lett.* **4** (March 1, 1964), pp. 89-90; idem, "The Vapor-Liquid-Solid Mechanism of Crystal Growth and Its Application to Silicon," *Trans. Met. Soc. AIME* **233** (June 1965), pp. 1053-1064.

48. S. M. Arnold, "The Growth and Properties of Metal Whiskers," *Bell Telephone System Monograph* **2635** (1956).

49. C. Herring and J. K. Galt, "Elastic and Plastic Properties of Very Small Metal Specimens," *Phys. Rev.* **85** (March 1952), pp. 1060-1061.

50. E. S. Greiner, J. A. Gutowski, and W. C. Ellis, "Preparation of Silicon Ribbons," *J. Appl. Phys.* **32** (November 1961), pp. 2489-2490.

51. K. A. Jackson and R. S. Wagner, "Extinction Contours in Whiskers," *J. Appl. Phys.* **36** (July 1965), pp. 2132-2137.

52. F. R. N. Nabarro and P. J. Jackson, "Growth of Crystal Whiskers," in *Growth and Perfection of Crystals*, ed. R. H. Doremus, B. W. Roberts, and David Turnball (New York: John Wiley & Sons, Inc., 1958), pp. 11-101.

53. P. Duwez, R. H. Willens, and W. Klement, Jr., "Continuous Series of Metastable Solid Solutions in Silver-Copper Alloys," *J. Appl. Phys.* **31** (June 1960), pp. 1136-1137; idem, "Metastable Electron Compound in Ag-Ge Alloys," *J. Appl. Phys.* **31** (June 1960), p. 1137.

54. R. H. Willens and E. Buehler, "Rapid Quenching of Reactive and Refractory Alloys from the Liquid State," *TMS-AIME* **236** (February 1966), pp. 171-174.

55. H. S. Chen and C. E. Miller, "Centrifugal Spinning of Metallic Glass Filaments," *Mat. Res. Bull.* **11** (January 1976), pp. 49-54.

56. B. T. Matthias, T. H. Geballe, R. H. Willens, E. Corenzwit, and G. W. Hull, Jr., "Superconductivity of Nb$_3$Ge," *Phys. Rev.* **139A** (August 1965), pp. 1501-1503; R. H. Willens, E. Buehler, and B. T. Matthias, "Superconductivity of the Transition-Metal Carbides," *Phys. Rev.* **159** (July 1967), pp. 327-330; R. H. Willens and E. Buehler, "The Superconductivity of the Monocarbides of Tungsten and Molybdenum," *Appl. Phys. Lett.* **7** (July 1, 1965), pp. 25-26.

57. E. A. Nesbitt, R. H. Willens, H. J. Williams, and R. C. Sherwood, "Magnetic Properties of Splat-Cooled Fe-Co-V Alloys," *J. Appl. Phys.* **38** (March 1, 1967), pp. 1003-1004.

58. R. H. Willens, E. Buehler, and E. A. Nesbitt, "Inductance Thermometer," *Rev. Sci. Instr.* **39** (February 1968), pp. 194-196.

59. R. H. Willens, "Melt Extracted MnAl and MnAlC," *IEEE Trans. on Magnetics* **16** (September 1980), pp. 1059-1061.

60. H. F. Fruth, "Cathode Sputtering, A Commercial Application," *Physics* **2** (April 1932), pp. 280-288.

61. "Metal Sputtering: A Promising New Technique for Printed Circuitry," *Bell Laboratories Record* **36** (November 1958), p. 426.

62. D. A. McLean, "Microminiaturization with Refractory Metals," *IRE WESCON Conv. Rec.*, Part **6**, (August 18-21, 1959), pp. 87-91.

63. R. W. Berry and D. J. Sloan, "Tantalum Printed Capacitors," *Proc. IRE* **47** (June 1959), pp. 1070-1075.

64. R. W. Berry, U.S. Patent No. 2,993,266; filed June 16, 1958; issued July 25, 1961.

65. H. Basseches, "The Oxidation of Sputtered Tantalum Films and Its Relationship to the Stability of the Electrical Resistance of These Films," *IRE Trans. Comp. Parts* **CP-8** (June 1961), pp. 51-56.

66. H. Basseches, "The Oxidation of Sputtered Tantalum Films," *J. Electrochem. Soc.* **109** (June 1962), pp. 475-479.

67. H. Basseches, P. L. McGeough, and D. A. McLean, U.S. Patent No. 3,148,129; filed October 12, 1959, issued September 8, 1964.

68. D. Gerstenberg and C. J. Calbick, "Effects of Nitrogen, Methane, and Oxygen on Structure and Electrical Properties of Thin Tantalum Films," *J. Appl. Phys.* **35** (February 1964), pp. 402-407.

69. D. Gerstenberg and E. H. Mayer, "Properties of Tantalum Sputtered Films," in *Proc. Elec. Components Conf.* (Washington, D.C., 1962), pp. 57-61.

70. A. M. Hanfmann, "Simplified Operations Analysis in Continuous Sputtering of Thin Films," *Western Elec. Engr.* **10** (October 1966), pp. 11-17.

71. H. C. Theuerer and J. J. Hauser, "Getter Sputtering for the Preparation of Thin Films of Superconducting Elements and Compounds," *J. Appl. Phys.* **35** (March 1964), pp. 554-555.

72. J. J. Hauser, H. C. Theuerer, and N. R. Werthamer, "Superconductivity in Cu and Pt by Means of Superimposed Films with Lead," *Phys. Rev.* **136A** (November 1964), pp. 637-641.

73. J. A. Burton, R. C. Prim, and W. P. Slichter, "The Distribution of Solute in Crystals Grown from the Melt. Part I. Theoretical," *J. Chem. Phys.* **21** (November 1953), pp. 1987-1991.

74. W. A. Tiller, K. A. Jackson, J. W. Rutter, and B. Chalmers, "The Redistribution of Solute Atoms During the Solidification of Metals," *Acta Met.* **1** (1953), pp. 428-437.

75. J. R. Carruthers, "Thermal Convection in Horizontal Crystal Growth," *J. Crystal Growth* **2** (February 1968), pp. 1-8.

76. J. R. Carruthers and K. Nassau, "Nonmixing Cells due to Crucible Rotation During Czochralski Crystal Growth," *J. Appl. Phys.* **39** (October 1968), pp. 5205-5214.

77. K. A. Jackson, "Nature of Solid-Liquid Interfaces," in *Growth and Perfection of Crystals*, ed. R. H. Doremus, B. W. Roberts, and D. Turnball (New York: John Wiley & Sons, Inc., 1958), pp. 319-324.

78. J. D. Hunt and K. A. Jackson, "Binary Eutectic Solidification," *TMS-AIME* **236** (June 1966), pp. 843-852.

79. K. A. Jackson and J. D. Hunt, "Transparent Compounds That Freeze Like Metals," *Acta Met.* **13** (1965), pp. 1212-1215; K. A. Jackson, J. D. Hunt, D. R. Uhlmann, and T. P. Seward, III, "On the Origin of the Equiaxed Zone in Castings," *TMS-AIME*

236 (February 1966), pp. 149-157; K. A. Jackson and J. D. Hunt, "Lamellar and Rod Eutectic Growth," *TMS-AIME* **236** (August 1966), pp. 1129-1142.

80. G. H. Gilmer, "Computer Simulation of Crystal Growth," *J. Crystal Growth* **42** (December 1977), pp. 3-10; H. J. Leamy, G. H. Gilmer, and K. A. Jackson, "Statistical Thermodynamics of Clean Surfaces," *Surface Physics of Materials I*, ed. J. M. Blakeley (New York: Academic Press, 1975), pp. 121-188.

81. J. D. Weeks, G. H. Gilmer, and H. J. Leamy, *Phys. Lett.* **31** (1973), p. 549; S. T. Chui and J. D. Weeks, "Phase Transition in the Two-Dimensional Coulomb Gas, and the Interfacial Roughening Transition," *Phys. Rev.* **B14** (December 1976), pp. 4978-4982.

82. J. D. Weeks and G. H. Gilmer, "Dynamics of Crystal Growth," in *Advances in Chemical Physics* **40**, ed. I. Prigogine and S. A. Rice (New York: John Wiley & Sons, 1979), pp. 157-228; G. H. Gilmer and K. A. Jackson, "Computer Simulation of Crystal Growth," *Current Topics in Materials Science, Volume 2, Crystal Growth and Materials*, ed. E. Kaldis and H. J. Scheel (Amsterdam: North Holland Publishing Co., 1976), p. 79; K. A. Jackson, "The Present State of the Theory of Crystal Growth from the Melt," *J. Crystal Growth* **24** (October 1974), pp. 130-136.

83. C. E. Miller, "Faceting Transition in Melt-Grown Crystals," *J. Crystal Growth* **42** (December 1977), pp. 357-363.

84. G. H. Gilmer, "Computer Models of Crystal Growth," *Science* **208** (April 25, 1980), pp. 355-363.

85. W. G. Pfann, "Principles of Zone Melting," *J. Metals* **4** (July 1952), pp. 747-753; W. G. Pfann, *Zone Melting*, Second Ed. (New York: John Wiley & Sons, 1966).

86. J. H. Wernick, K. E. Benson, and D. Dorsi, "Zone Refining of Bismuth," *J. Metals* **9** (July 1957), p. 996; J. H. Wernick, J. N. Holstetter, L. C. Lovell, and D. Dorsi, "Dislocation Etch Pits in Antimony," *J. Appl. Phys.* **29** (July 1958), pp. 1013-1018; J. E. Kunzler and J. H. Wernick, "Low Temperature Resistance Measurements as a Means of Studying Impurity Distributions in Zone-Refined Ingots of Metals," *Trans. Met. Soc. AIME* **212** (December 1950), pp. 856-860.

87. F. A. Trumbore, "Solid Solubilities of Impurity Elements in Germanium and Silicon," *Bell System Tech. J.* **39** (January 1960), pp. 205-233.

88. C. D. Thurmond and M. Kowalchik, "Germanium and Silicon Liquidus Curves," *Bell System Tech. J.* **39** (January 1960), pp. 169-204.

89. W. G. Pfann, C. E. Miller, and J. D. Hunt, "New Zone Refining Techniques for Chemical Compounds," *Rev. Sci. Instr.* **37** (May 1966), pp. 649-652.

90. F. L. Vogel, W. G. Pfann, H. E. Corey, and E. E. Thomas, "Observations of Dislocations in Lineage Boundaries in Germanium," *Phys. Rev.* **90** (May 1953), pp. 489-490.

91. W. Shockley and W. T. Read, Jr., "Quantitative Predictions from Dislocation Models of Crystal Grain Boundaries," *Phys. Rev.* **75** (February 1949), p. 692; idem, "Dislocation Models of Crystal Grain Boundaries," *Phys. Rev.* **78** (May 1950), pp. 275-289.

92. F. C. Frank and W. T. Read, Jr., "Multiplication Processes for Slow-Moving Dislocations," *Phys. Rev.* **79** (August 1950), pp. 722-723.

93. W. T. Read, Jr., *Dislocations in Crystals* (New York: McGraw-Hill Book Company, 1953).

94. A. J. Goss, K. E. Benson, and W. G. Pfann, "Dislocations at Compositional Fluctuations in Germanium-Silicon Alloys," *Acta Met.* **4** (1956), pp. 332-333.

95. J. R. Patel and A. R. Chaudhuri, "Charged Impurity Effects on the Deformation of Dislocation-Free Germanium," *Phys. Rev.* **143** (March 1966), pp. 601-608.

96. L. C. Kimerling and J. R. Patel, "Defect States Associated with Dislocation in Silicon," *Appl. Phys. Lett.* **34** (January 1, 1979), pp. 73-75.

97. J. H. Wernick, J. N. Holstetter, L. C. Lovell, and D. Dorsi, "Dislocation Etch Pits in Antimony," *J. Appl. Phys.* **29** (July 1958), pp. 1013-1018; L. C. Lovell, J. H. Wer-

nick, and K. E. Benson, "Dislocation Etch Pits in Tellurium," *Acta Met.* **6** (1968), pp. 716-720; L. C. Lovell and J. H. Wernick, "Dislocation Etch Pits in Bismuth," *J. Appl. Phys.* **30** (February 1959), pp. 234-235; idem, "Dislocation Etch Pits and Polygonization in High Purity Copper," *J. Appl. Phys.* **30** (April 1959), pp. 590-592; J. H. Wernick and E. E. Thomas, "Dislocation Etch Pits in High-Purity Cadmium," *TMS-AIME* **218** (August 1960), pp. 763-764.

98. R. M. Bozorth, W. P. Mason, H. J. McSkimin, and J. G. Walker, "Elastic Constants and Internal Loss of Single Nickel Crystals," *Phys. Rev.* **75** (June 1949), pp. 1954-1955.

99. W. L. Bond, W. P. Mason, and H. J. McSkimin, "Elastic and Electromechanical Coupling Coefficients of Single-Crystal Barium Titanate," *Phys. Rev.* **82** (May 1951), pp. 442-443.

100. R. M. Bozorth, W. P. Mason, and H. J. McSkimin, "Frequency Dependence of Elastic Constants and Losses in Nickel," *Bell System Tech. J.* **30** (October 1951), pp. 970-989.

101. W. P. Mason, "Rotational Relaxation in Nickel at High Frequencies," *Rev. Mod. Phys.* **25** (January 1953), pp. 136-139.

102. W. P. Mason, "Dislocation Relaxations at Low Temperatures and the Determination of the Limiting Shearing Stress of a Metal," *Phys. Rev.* **98** (May 1955), pp. 1136-1138.

103. W. P. Mason, "Relaxations in the Attenuation of Single Crystal Lead at Low Temperatures and Their Relation to Dislocation Theory," *J. Acous. Soc. Am.* **27** (July 1955), pp. 643-653.

104. See reference 103. Also, see W. P. Mason, "Effect of Dislocations on Ultrasonic Wave Attenuation in Metals," *Bell System Tech. J.* **34** (September 1955), pp. 903-942.

105. H. E. Bömmel, W. P. Mason, and A. W. Warner, Jr., "Experimental Evidence for Dislocations in Crystalline Quartz," *Phys. Rev.* **99** (September 1955), pp. 1894-1896.

106. H. E. Bömmel, W. P. Mason, and A. W. Warner, Jr., "Dislocations, Relaxations, and Anelasticity of Crystal Quartz," *Phys. Rev.* **102** (April 1956), pp. 64-71.

107. W. P. Mason, "Dislocation Relaxations in Metals and Single Crystal Quartz," *Deformation and Flow of Solids Colloquium*, Madrid, September 1955 (Berlin: Springer-Verlag, 1956), pp. 314-322.

108. W. P. Mason, H. J. McSkimin, and W. Shockley, "Ultrasonic Observation of Twinning in Tin," *Phys. Rev.* **73** (May 1948), pp. 1213-1214.

109. See reference 100.

110. J. R. Patel, "Impurity Clustering Effects on Dislocation Generation in Silicon," *Discussions of the Faraday Society* **38** (1964), pp. 201-210.

111. W. Kaiser, H. L. Frisch, and H. Reiss, "Mechanism of the Formation of Donor States in Heat-Treated Silicon," *Phys. Rev.* **112** (December 1958), pp. 1546-1554.

112. J. R. Patel, K. A. Jackson, and H. Reiss, "Oxygen Precipitation and Stacking-Fault Formation in Dislocation-Free Silicon," *J. Appl. Phys.* **48** (December 1977), pp. 5279-5288.

113. C. S. Fuller and J. A. Ditzenberger, "Diffusion of Donor and Acceptor Elements in Silicon," *J. Appl. Phys.* **27** (May 1956), pp. 544-553.

114. C. S. Fuller and J. A. Ditzenberger, "Diffusion of Lithium into Germanium and Silicon," *Phys. Rev.* **91** (July 1953), p. 193; C. S. Fuller and J. C. Severiens, "Mobility of Impurity Ions in Germanium and Silicon," *Phys. Rev.* **96** (October 1954), pp. 21-24; C. S. Fuller and J. D. Struthers, "Copper as an Acceptor Element in Germanium," *Phys. Rev.* **87** (August 1952), pp. 526-527.

115. R. S. Ohl, "Properties of Ionic Bombarded Silicon," *Bell System Tech. J.* **31** (January 1952), pp. 104-121.

116. R. S. Ohl, U.S. Patent No. 2,750,541; filed January 31, 1950, issued June 12, 1956.

117. W. Shockley, U.S. Patent No. 2,787,564; filed October 28, 1954, issued April 2, 1957.

118. C. Erginsoy, H. E. Wegner, and W. M. Gibson, "Anisotropic Energy Loss of Light Particles of MeV Energies in Thin Silicon Single Crystals," *Phys. Rev. Lett.* **13** (October 26, 1964), pp. 530-534; W. M. Gibson, C. Erginsoy, H. E. Wegner, and B. R. Appleton, "Direction and Energy Distribution of Charged Particles Transmitted Through Single Crystals," *Phys. Rev. Lett.* **15** (August 23, 1965), pp. 357-360.

119. W. M. Gibson, F. W. Martin, R. Stensgaard, F. Palmgren Jensen, N. I. Meyer, G. Galster, A. Johansen, and J. S. Olsen, "Electrical and Physical Measurements on Silicon Implanted with Channeled and Nonchanneled Dopant Ions," *Can. J. Phys.* **46** (1968), pp. 675-688; E. Laegsgaard, F. W. Martin, and W. M. Gibson, "Positive Sensitive Detectors Made by Ion Implantation in Silicon," *Nuclear Instru. Methods* **60** (March 1968), pp. 24-26.

120. T. E. Seidel and A. U. MacRae, "Some Properties of Ion Implanted Boron in Silicon," *TMS-AIME* **245** (March 1969), pp. 491-498; idem, "The Isothermal Annealing of Boron Implanted Silicon," in *Ion Implantation,* ed. F. H. Eisen and L. T. Chadderton (London: Gordon and Breach, 1971), pp. 149-154; J. L. Merz and L. C. Feldman, "Photoluminescence of Oxygen in ZnTe Introduced by Ion Implantation," *Appl. Phys. Lett.* **15** (September 1, 1969), pp. 129-131.

121. L. C. Feldman and J. W. Rodgers, "Depth Profiles of the Lattice Disorder Resulting from Ion Bombardment of Silicon Single Crystals," *J. Appl. Phys.* **41** (August 1970), pp. 3776-3782; S. T. Picraux, W. L. Brown, and W. M. Gibson, "Lattice Location by Channeling Angular Distributions: Bi Implanted in Si," *Phys. Rev.* **B6** (August 1972), pp. 1382-1394; J. K. Hirvonen, W. L. Brown, and P. M. Glotin, "Structural Differences in Light and Heavy Ion Disorder in Si Studied by Single and Double Alignment Channeling Techniques," in *Ion Implantation in Semiconductors,* ed. I. Ruge and J. Graul (Berlin: Springer-Verlag, 1971), pp. 8-16.

122. A. U. MacRae, "Recent Advances in Ion Implanted Junction-Device Technology," in *Ion Implantation in Semiconductors,* ed. I. Ruge and J. Graul (Berlin: Springer-Verlag, 1971), pp. 329-334.

123. R. D. Standley, W. M. Gibson, and J. W. Rodgers, "Properties of Ion-Bombarded Fused Quartz for Integrated Optics," *Appl. Optics* **11** (June 1972), pp. 1313-1316.

124. H. M. Presby and W. L. Brown, "Refractive Index Variations in Proton-Bombarded Fused Silica," *Appl. Phys. Lett.* **24** (May 15, 1974), pp. 511-513.

125. J. M. Poate, W. J. DeBonte, W. M. Augustyniak, and J. A. Borders, "Formation of Substitutional Alloys by Ion Implantation in Metals," *Appl. Phys. Lett.* **25** (December 15, 1974), pp. 698-701; A. G. Cullis, J. M. Poate, and J. A. Borders, "The Physical State of Implanted Tungsten in Copper," *Appl. Phys. Lett.* **28** (March 15, 1976), pp. 314-316; J. M. Poate, J. A. Borders, A. G. Cullis, and J. K. Hirvonen, "Ion Implantation as an Ultrafast Quenching Technique for Metastable Alloy Production: The Ag-Cu System," *Appl. Phys. Lett.* **30** (April 15, 1977), pp. 365-368.

126. E. N. Kaufmann, R. Vianden, J. R. Chelikowsky, and J. C. Phillips, "Extension of Equilibrium Formation Criteria to Metastable Microalloys," *Phys. Rev. Lett.* **39** (December 26, 1977), pp. 1671-1675; R. Vianden, E. N. Kaufmann, and J. W. Rodgers, "Impurity Lattice Location in Ion-Implanted Beryllium: Measurements and Systematics," *Phys. Rev.* **B22** (July 1980), pp. 63-79.

127. *Ion Implantation Metallurgy,* ed. C. M. Preece and J. K. Hirvonen (New York: Metallurgical Society of AIME, 1980).

128. R. Wolfe, J. C. North, R. L. Barns, M. Robinson, and H. J. Levinstein, "Modification of Magnetic Anisotropy in Garnets by Ion Implantation," *Appl. Phys. Lett.* **19** (October 15, 1971), pp. 298-300; R. Wolfe and J. C. North, "Suppression of Hard Bubbles in Magnetic Garnet Films by Ion Implantation," *Bell System Tech. J.* **51** (July/August 1972), pp. 1436-1444.

129. J. C. Dyment, J. C. North, and L. A. D'Asaro, "Optical and Electrical Properties of Proton-Bombarded *P*-Type GaAs," *J. Appl. Phys.* **44** (January 1973), pp. 207-213.

130. C. J. Frosch and L. Derick, "Surface Protection and Selective Masking During Diffusion in Silicon," *J. Electrochem. Soc.* **104** (September 1957), pp. 547-552; L. Derick and C. J. Frosch, U.S. Patent No. 2,802,760; filed December 2, 1955, issued August 13, 1957.

131. R. D. Heidenreich, L. F. Thompson, E. D. Feit, and C. M. Melliar-Smith, "Fundamental Aspects of Electron Beam Lithography. I. Depth-Dose Response of Polymeric Electron Beam Resists," *J. Appl. Phys.* **44** (September 1973), pp. 4039-4047.

132. L. F. Thompson, E. D. Feit, and R. D. Heidenreich, "Lithography and Radiation Chemistry of Epoxy Containing Negative Electron Resists," *Polymer Eng. Sci.* **14** (July 1974), pp. 529-533.

133. L. F. Thompson and E. M. Doerries, "Negative Electron Resists for Direct Device Lithography," *J. Electrochem. Soc.* **126** (October 1979), pp. 1699-1702.

134. L. F. Thompson and M. J. Bowden, "A New Family of Positive Electron Beam Resists—Poly(Olefin Sulfones)," *J. Electrochem. Soc.* **120** (December 1973), pp. 1722-1726; M. J. Bowden and L. F. Thompson, "Electron Irradiation of Poly(Olefin Sulfones). Application to Electron Beam Resists," *J. Appl. Polymer Sci.* **17** (October 1973), pp. 3211-3221.

135. M. J. Bowden, L. F. Thompson, S. R. Fahrenholtz, and E. M. Doerries, "A Sensitive Novolac-Based Positive Electron Resist," *J. Electrochem. Soc.* **128** (June 1981), pp. 1304-1313.

136. G. N. Taylor, G. A. Coquin, and S. Somekh, "Sensitive Chlorine-Containing Resists for X-Ray Lithography," *Polymer Eng. Sci.* **17** (June 1977), pp. 420-429.

137. P. H. Schmidt, E. G. Spencer, and E. M. Walters, "Ion Milling of Magnetic Oxide Platelets for the Removal of Surface and Near-Surface Imperfections and Defects," *J. Appl. Phys.* **41** (October 1970), pp. 4740-4742.

138. P. H. Schmidt, "Superconductivity of Transition Metal Thin Films Deposited by Noble Gas Ion Beam Sputtering," *J. Vac. Sci. Technol.* **10** (Sept./Oct. 1973), pp. 611-615; P. H. Schmidt, R. N. Castellano, H. Barz, B. T. Matthias, J. G. Huber, and W. A. Fertig, "Superconducting Ion Beam Sputtered Chromium Metal Thin Films," *Phys. Lett.* **41A** (October 9, 1972), pp. 367-368.

139. G. K. Celler, J. M. Poate, and L. C. Kimerling, "Spatially Controlled Crystal Regrowth of Ion-Implanted Silicon by Laser Irradiation," *Appl. Phys. Lett.* **32** (April 15, 1978), pp. 464-466.

140. H. J. Leamy, G. A. Rozgonyi, T. T. Sheng, and G. K. Celler, "Periodic Regrowth Phenomena Produced by Laser Annealing of Ion-Implanted Silicon," *Appl. Phys. Lett.* **32** (May 1, 1978), pp. 535-537.

141. D. H. Auston, C. M. Surko, T. N. C. Venkatesan, R. E. Slusher, and J. A. Golovchenko, "Time-Resolved Reflectivity of Ion-Implanted Silicon During Laser Annealing," *Appl. Phys. Lett.* **33** (September 1, 1978), pp. 437-440.

142. C. M. Surko, A. L. Simons, D. H. Auston, J. A. Golovchenko, R. E. Slusher, and T. N. C. Venkatesan, "Calculation of the Dynamics of Surface Melting During Laser Annealing," *Appl. Phys. Lett.* **34** (May 15, 1979), pp. 635-637.

143. J. S. Williams, W. L. Brown, H. J. Leamy, J. M. Poate, J. W. Rodgers, D. Rousseau, G. A. Rozgonyi, J. A. Shelnutt, and T. T. Sheng, "Solid-Phase Epitaxy of Implanted Silicon by cw Ar Ion Laser Irradiation," *Appl. Phys. Lett.* **33** (September 15, 1978), pp. 542-544.

144. D. H. Auston, J. A. Golovchenko, P. R. Smith, C. M. Surko, and T. N. C. Venkatesan, "cw Argon Laser Annealing of Ion-Implanted Silicon," *Appl. Phys. Lett.* **33** (September 15, 1978), pp. 539-541.

145. J. R. Ligenza, "Silicon Oxidation in an Oxygen Plasma Excited by Microwaves," *J. Appl. Phys.* **16** (September 1965), pp. 2703-2707.

146. E. O. Degenkolb, C. J. Mogab, M. R. Goldrick, and J. E. Griffiths, "Spectroscopic Study of Radio-Frequency Oxygen Plasma Stripping of Negative Photoresists. I. Ultraviolet Spectrum," *Appl. Spectroscopy* **30** (Sept./Oct. 1976), pp. 520-527.

147. C. J. Mogab, "The Loading Effect in Plasma Etching," *J. Electrochem. Soc.* **124** (August 1977), pp. 1262-1268.

148. C. J. Mogab and T. A. Shankoff, "Plasma Etching of Titanium for Application to the Patterning of Ti-Pd-Au Metallization," *J. Electrochem. Soc.* **124** (November 1977), pp. 1766-1771.

149. M. J. Vasile and G. Smolinsky, "Organosilicon Films Formed by an RF Plasma Polymerization Process," *J. Electrochem. Soc.* **119** (April 1972), pp. 451-455.

150. See reference 149.

151. G. Smolinsky and M. J. Vasile, "Mass-Spectrometric Ion Sampling from Reactive Plasmas. II. Mixtures of Vinyltrimethylsilane and Argon," *Intern. J. Mass Spectrometry and Ion Physics* **12** (September 1973), pp. 147-158; idem, "Mass-Spectrometric Ion Sampling from Reactive Plasmas. III. Mixtures of Vinyltrimethylsilane and Argon or Helium," ibid. **13** (April 1974), pp. 381-393; idem, "Ionic and Neutral Products of an RF Discharge in Methane," ibid. **16** (January 1975), pp. 137-149; idem, "Mass-Spectrometric Sampling of the Ionic and Neutral Species Present in Different Regions of an RF Discharge in Methane," ibid. **18** (October 1975), pp. 179-192; idem, "The Chemistry of the Radio-Frequency Ethane Discharge," ibid. **21** (October 1976), pp. 263-277; idem, "The Chemistry of the Ethylene Radio-Frequency Discharge," ibid. **22** (November 1976), pp. 171-183; idem, "The Chemistry of Radio-Frequency Discharges: Acetylene and Mixtures of Acetylene with Helium, Argon, and Xenon," ibid. **24** (May 1977), pp. 11-23; idem, "The Radio-Frequency Discharge Chemistry of Benzene and Mixtures with Helium, Argon, or Xenon," ibid. **24** (July 1977), pp. 311-322.

152. R. P. H. Chang, "Some Properties of Plasma-Grown GaAs Oxides," *Thin Solid Films* **56** (January 1979), pp. 89-106.

Chapter 20

Characterization Techniques

The behavior of materials in communications technology depends commonly on their composition and structure. Sometimes, the requirement is to achieve the highest possible purity, as in the reagents for lightguide fibers; or the greatest structural perfection, as in the silicon for large-scale integrated circuits. Sometimes, the purpose is to establish and control the level of an additive or dopant, as in the technology of electronic devices. These requirements have stimulated Bell Laboratories scientists to develop new, powerful instrumental methods for characterization. This chapter reviews some of these advances. Electrical detection methods, which started soon after the discovery of the transistor, included the measurement of resistivity, Hall effect, mobility, and junction capacity. The techniques of mass spectroscopy were adapted to cover a wide variety of trace impurities. The very powerful techniques of electron microscopy and X-ray fluorescence spectroscopy were largely developed at Bell Laboratories, and the highly sensitive analytical techniques made possible with neutron activation and the use of lasers have contributed greatly to the measurement of materials.

I. ELECTRICAL DETECTION METHODS — CAPACITANCE SPECTROSCOPY

The electrical properties of semiconductors have been of vital concern because they determine most of the useful applications of this class of materials and sensitively reflect the state of purity and perfection of the material. The evolution of electrical characterization techniques has foreshadowed not only an explosion in practical, technological advances, but also a new frontier in the understanding of the fundamental properties of condensed matter.

The technologically relevant transport properties of a semiconductor material are the concentration of conducting (free) charge carriers, the mobility of the carriers, and the lifetime of nonequilibrium (minority) carriers that are introduced to modulate the conductivity. The early

---

Principal authors: D. C. Joy, L. C. Kimerling, R. A. Laudise, and D. W. Mitchell

characterization of free charge-carrier concentrations in silicon and germanium with Hall effect and resistivity measurements by F. J. Morin and J. P. Maita remain a definitive method for establishing the fundamental electronic properties of these materials.[1] Studies of mobility and nonequilibrium carrier kinetics were initially performed at Bell Laboratories by J. R. Haynes and W. Shockley in a classic series of experiments that bear their names.[2] R. N. Hall of General Electric,[3] Shockley, and W. T. Read[4] soon developed the theory for understanding the behavior of crystalline defects as recombination centers for minority carriers. C. Herring contributed to the theoretical formulation of charged carrier scattering and the functional dependence of mobility on lattice perfection and temperature.[5] From the research of T. H. Geballe, Herring, G. W. Hull, J. E. Kunzler, Morin, and G. L. Pearson, a fundamental understanding of magnetoresistance,[6] piezoresistance,[7] thermoelectric power,[8] and thermomagnetic phenomena[9] was developed.

With the advent of planar device technology, measurement of free carrier concentration "on-line" by sheet resistivity, as developed by A. Uhlir and F. M. Smits, became a primary characterization tool.[10] Modern industry standards relating carrier concentration, mobility, and resistivity in silicon, germanium, and GaAs were established by J. C. Irvin and S. M. Sze.[11]

C. S. Fuller and J. A. Dietzenberger applied sheet-resistivity measurements in an important series of studies that derived diffusion coefficients for the technologically significant doping impurities in silicon and germanium.[12] At the same time, H. Reiss, Fuller, and Morin used bulk-resistivity measurements to demonstrate and define the chemical influence of free carriers in determining impurity solubilities and defect equilibria in crystalline semiconductors.[13] These fundamental principles have critically influenced later developments in the understanding of diffusion and defect phenomena in semiconductors.[14,15]

1.1 Junction Capacitance Measurements

The semiconductor electrical junction (p-n, Schottky, and MOS) is the primary building block of modern solid state circuits. As sheet-resistivity measurements characterized isolated layers, junction capacitance and conductance measurements were developed to study junction structures. These measurements represent the single most powerful probe of the electrical properties of semiconductor materials. The basic methods for characterization of electronic states at the insulator-semiconductor interface were developed by E. H. Nicollian and A. Goetzberger.[16] Depth profiles of free charge-carrier concentration beneath the semiconductor surface can be determined from observations of the variation of junction capacitance with applied voltage.

The application of this technique became widespread following the development of two ingenious schemes for direct data analysis by J. A. Copeland and G. L. Miller.[17,18] Junction-capacitance transient analyses by C. T. Sah have provided a unique tool for characterization of imperfections and impurities that influence junction performance as recombination centers.[19] The application of the measurement was popularized by a flurry of activity at Bell Labs, during which bias pulsing and transient correlation techniques were introduced.[20,21] Most notably, application of these techniques has provided a sensitive measure of material purity and perfection, characterization of the local electrical properties of recombination centers, and the discovery of the new phenomena of multiphonon relaxation processes and electronically stimulated solid state reactions.[22] During the 1970s, Bell Labs scientists and engineers developed a complete science of semiconductor junction spectroscopy, which employs capacitance transient spectroscopy, scanning electron microscope, charge collection microscopy, and electroluminescence to characterize fully the properties of imperfections in semiconductors.[23]

II. MASS SPECTROSCOPY

In the 1950s, the surge of activity in solid state physics at Bell Laboratories was accompanied by major advances in chemical analysis. Among these was mass spectrometry of solids, which was developed to measure trace quantities of impurities in semiconductors. Mass spectrometry had been in use for several decades with gases and volatile liquids. In this technique, the atoms or molecules to be studied are ionized by bombardment with an electron beam within an evacuated chamber, emerge through a slit system into a region of high vacuum, and then are passed through electric and magnetic fields that separate the particles according to mass and charge.

For accurate spectrometric analysis of solids, it is necessary to avoid the preferential volatilization of some elements in the sample compared with others. N. B. Hannay used a mass spectrometer having a radio-frequency spark source that imposed pulses of energy upon the sample.[24] The eroded material formed positively charged ions that were then analyzed in the spectrometer. The spark source had special merit in that it ionized all elements with about the same efficiency, displaying no bias toward the selection of certain elements. Since the ions exhibited a large spread of initial energies, it was necessary to allow focusing in both direction and velocity. This was achieved by the geometry of the electrostatic and magnetic analyzers and the slit system. The trajectories of the ions were brought to focus at a plane beyond the exit of the analyzers. Therefore, the simultaneous detection of ions over a wide range of masses could be achieved with a flat photographic plate that was positioned in this plane. [Fig. 20-1] Commercial instruments basically similar to the Bell Laboratories mass spectrometer have since come on the market.

Hannay [Fig. 20-2] and A. J. Ahearn found that the most important factors limiting the sensitivity of this type of instrument originate from traces of organic contamination in the source chamber and from diffuse scattering between the ion beam and the residual gas.[25] Further modifications of the apparatus made it possible to determine trace elements in the range of a part-per-billion atomic fraction of the major component in favorable cases.[26,27] The effectiveness of spark-source mass spectroscopy in measuring trace impurities in semiconductors was demonstrated by Hannay and Ahearn in studies of antimony, germanium, boron, and silicon.[28] [Fig. 20-3] The results were found to be in good qualitative agreement with those of measurements of electrical conductivity in the same materials. The technique has been applied successfully to a host of analyses by Ahearn and C. D. Thurmond on the impurities in gallium phosphide,[29] and by D. L. Malm to the compositions of surface films.[30]

III. ELECTRON MICROSCOPY

Microscopy is one of the most powerful characterization tools available to the materials scientist. The transmission electron microscope further expands this power because of the improved spatial resolution made possible by the much shorter wavelength of the electrons. The first electron microscopes were developed in Germany in the 1930s. Early in World War II, scientists at RCA built electron microscopes based on an instrument constructed in Toronto, Canada, in 1938 by

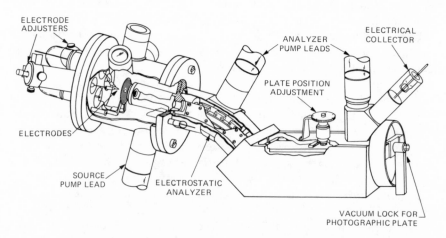

Fig. 20-1. Radio-frequency spark source mass spectrometer.

Fig. 20-2. N. B. Hannay has made fundamental
contributions to the techniques of mass spectroscopy,
particularly for the detection of trace impurities in
semiconductors. He was vice president of research at
Bell Laboratories from 1973 to 1982.

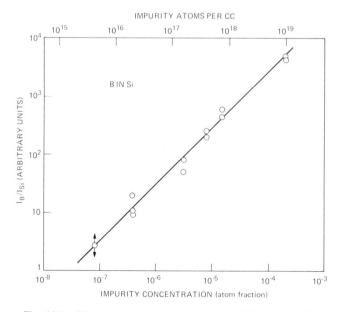

Fig. 20-3. Mass spectrometric determination of boron in silicon.
Note the high sensitivity of the signal and its linearity over a large
dynamic range.

Hillier and Prebus. These instruments were of relatively low accelerating voltage of 30 to 50 keV, and as a consequence, they could only penetrate very thin sections of material and were used for surface studies. The technique used was to make a replica of the surface to be examined, for example, by evaporating carbon onto the surface and then depositing a thin layer of collodion over it to form a film that could be peeled off for study. In 1943, R. D. Heidenreich and V. G. Peck devised the silicon-oxide replica technique, which rapidly became the standard method of high resolution surface study.[31] It offered replicas with a resolution of about 200 angstroms (Å), which was essentially the limit of the microscope. Using this technique, Heidenreich and Shockley were able to study for the first time the details of slip lines on plastically deformed metals.[32,33] Heidenreich and coworkers also made notable contributions to the study of the advanced magnetic alloys being developed (for example, Alnico-V), by combining the replica technique (for microstructural studies) with reflection electron diffraction (for crystallographic data).

3.1 Transmission Electron Microscope

The goal of being able to look at the metal itself, rather than a replica of its surface, was finally achieved in 1949 when Heidenreich [Fig. 20-4] devised the electrochemical thinning technique, which made it possible to produce metal foils that are transparent to electrons.[33] The resulting transmission-electron image contained vastly more information because the contrast was produced by Bragg diffraction of the electrons by the lattice of the specimen. This revolutionary approach made possible the observation of previously postulated phenomena such as twins, subcell grain structures, growth steps, and so on. The dynamical theory of electron diffraction was introduced by Heidenreich and L. Sturkey, among others, to explain the contrast effects observed.[34] By very detailed studies of the parameters limiting the performance of his instrument, Heidenreich was able, with suitable modifications, to improve the resolution of the images steadily up to about 10Å. The culmination of this activity was the observation, first at Cambridge University and almost simultaneously by Heidenreich, of dislocations in crystals.[35] At the time of this writing, the modern commercial transmission electron microscope is essentially the instrument that he created.

3.2 Scanning Electron Microscope

The rapid evolution of the transmission electron microscope was paralleled by the development of the scanning electron microscope (SEM), in which a finely focused beam of electrons is scanned in a ras-

Fig. 20-4. R. D. Heidenreich made outstanding contributions to improving the resolving power of the electron microscope for surface studies and transmission microscopy.

ter over a solid specimen. A signal returned by the specimen (for example, the backscattered electrons) is used to modulate the brightness of a cathode-ray tube scanned in synchronism with the beam. In this way, a magnified map of the sample is built up. When the incident beam impinges on a semiconductor, it produces a high density of electron hole pairs that, by the application of a bias field, can be separated and made to produce a current flow in an external circuit. In the region of electrically active defects, however, many of these electron hole pairs will recombine and the current in the external circuit will decrease. Therefore, a beam scan can be made to map out the presence of electrically active defects (dislocations, stacking faults, and so on) in the specimen. This technique, electron beam induced conductivity (EBIC), became of major significance as a tool for studying semiconductor devices. Its applications were first described by J. J. Lander and coworkers,[36] and by W. Czaja and J. R. Patel,[37] and later, in work by H. J. Leamy and L. C. Kimerling.[38]

3.3 Electron Energy Loss Spectroscopy

Chemical microanalysis by means of electron-optical instruments is possible because of the ionizations produced by the incident beam. These can be detected and characterized either by a measurement of the wavelength (or energy) of the X-ray photons produced in the subsequent decay—a technique applicable to both bulk and electron transparent specimens—or by measurements of the energy loss suffered by the transmitted electrons as a result of these ionizations. This second technique is of special value because it is very sensitive to the lighter elements (carbon, nitrogen, oxygen, and so on) which produce X-rays that are too "soft" to be readily detectable. Work by D. C. Joy and D. M. Maher in developing this technique of electron energy loss spectroscopy as an adjunct to the electron microscope has produced a microanalytical method that combines very high sensitivity—typically 10^{-18} gram (gm) of material—with good spatial resolution (on the order of 100Å).[39] [Fig. 20-5] The technique is of great value in the study of the chemistry of boundaries, interfaces, and so on in semiconductors. In addition, significant electronic and structural information can be deduced from fine structures in the energy loss spectrum.

IV. X-RAY FLUORESCENCE SPECTROSCOPY

The use of X-rays to measure the elemental composition of materials began only a few years after W. C. Roentgen's discovery of X-rays in 1895. It was recognized quite early that the impingement of high-energy X-rays upon matter produces secondary, or fluorescent, X-rays that have wavelengths characteristic of the elements being irradiated. G. J. Moseley's classic research (from 1910 to 1913) showed that a definite relationship exists between the wavelengths of X-rays and the atomic number of the element emitting the radiation. These facts, coupled with the rapid development of X-ray tubes and spectrometers, made X-ray spectrography an analytical tool of great potential. Major advances in X-ray techniques occurred during World War II, in large part through the extensive work on the chemistry of radioactive elements for which new instrumentation had to be developed.

The earliest uses of X-rays for chemical analysis required that the sample under investigation be made the target within the X-ray tube and that the spectra be recorded photographically. These procedures were too tedious for routine analyses, although they were highly effective for certain problems that could not be handled by conventional means. The fluorescence method removes the burden of installing the sample as the target inside the X-ray tube. Instead, the sample is bombarded with a beam from a sealed X-ray tube and emits

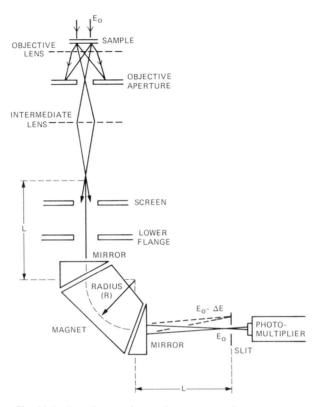

Fig. 20-5. Ray diagram for an electron energy loss spectrometer fitted to a transmission electron microscope. For the system described here, $R = 15$ cm and $L = 30$ cm. [Joy and Maher, *J. Microscopy* **114** (1978): 90].

secondary X-rays. These fluorescent X-rays are analyzed according to wavelength by impingement on a high-quality crystal that spreads out the spectrum of wavelengths, which are then detected by a device that converts them into electrical pulses that are amplified and recorded. With these technical developments, X-ray fluorescence spectroscopy became an important method of chemical analysis. Through the work of T. C. Loomis and K. H. Storks, [Fig. 20-6] Bell Laboratories made major advances in the techniques of X-ray fluorescence spectroscopy in microanalysis.[40] [Fig. 20-7] An apparatus called a milliprobe was designed for analytical studies of very small samples, inclusions, or surface contaminations. The instrument was designed to examine regions with dimensions of only about 0.01 centimeter (cm). This high spatial resolution was achieved in the spectrometer by a mechanism that uses a system of highly accurate bar links rather than precision gears to position the analyzing crystal that scans the

Fig. 20-6. K. H. Storks developed the technique of X-ray
fluorescence spectroscopy in chemical analysis.

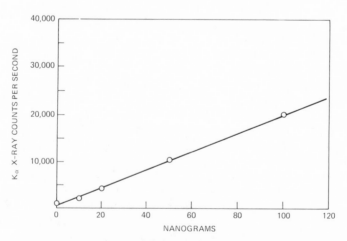

Fig. 20-7. Calibration plot for the quantitative determination of cobalt
at the parts-per-billion (ppb) level by the coprecipitation microdot
milliprobe (COPREX) technique. The sensitivity and linearity shown
are representative of the quantitative determination of elements such
as iron, nickel, chromium, manganese, zinc, and molybdenum, as well
as many elements in other parts of the Periodic Table.

spectrum of wavelengths. The sensitivity to fluorescent X-rays was further increased by housing the spectrometer in a vacuum chamber, thereby preventing the scattering of X-rays by the air. The milliprobe made it possible to study with unprecedented detail and sensitivity such objects as inhomogeneous materials, diffusion layers, wear tracks on contact surfaces, and the uniformity of thickness of plated, evaporated, or sputtered films.

The chief advantage of the milliprobe in analyzing samples was its ability to look only at a small area of interest and ignore the rest of the sample. However, it found equally important use in the analysis of "trace" components of materials. The procedure involves dissolving the entire sample in a suitable solvent (for example, an acid), selectively precipitating out the trace ingredient, and measuring its amount by X-ray fluorescence spectroscopy. It has long been recognized by chemists, however, that trace elements tend not to come out of solution quantitatively and reproducibly. In the 1960s, C. L. Luke developed analytical procedures based on the phenomenon of coprecipitation, whereby a trace element can be induced to precipitate if another suitable element is added in small quantity.[41] The larger mass of the solute is left in solution. For example, trace quantities of lead, zinc, cadmium, and manganese precipitate from dilute carbamate solution with the addition of copper (II) as a coprecipitant. The precipitate is collected on a fine-pore filter and is examined by the X-ray spectrometer. An important part of Luke's work was the choice of coprecipitants that would not "interfere" with the X-ray fluorescence spectra of the trace elements to be analyzed. Thus, in addition to having the right chemistry to come out of solution with the trace elements, the coprecipitants must have spectra that do not obscure the X-ray lines belonging to the elements under study. This technique of coprecipitation X-ray ("coprex") analysis was shown by Luke to enable measuring many elements in microgram quantities. He developed coprecipitation procedures for most of the elements of the Periodic Table. Further refinements by J. E. Kessler and coworkers made it possible to concentrate the precipitate on a very small area of the filter and to analyze this spot with the X-ray milliprobe spectrometer.[42] This development extended the sensitivity of detection to the range of 10^{-8} to 10^{-9} gram. Such sensitivity proved valuable for examining impurities in semiconductors and in glasses for optical fibers.

V. ULTRATRACE AND MICROANALYSIS OF CONTAMINANTS

5.1 Computerized Emission Spectrograph

In 1975, an important step in the improvement of instruments for multielement trace analyses at Bell Laboratories was taken by D. L.

Wood, A. B. Dargis, and D. L. Nash, who set up a fully computerized, emission-spectrographic analyses facility.[43] Their system used a prism-echelle spectrograph having an exit image that matched in size with an image converter capable of transforming ultraviolet to visible wavelengths. The light output from the converter was then measured by a digital television camera controlled by a dedicated minicomputer. The intensities of 400 analytical lines could be measured every second during the excitation of a sample. This multielement system, with the capability of displaying intensity versus time, is well suited for the profiling of impurities in electroplating deposits.

5.2 Neutron Activation and Radioisotope

In the early 1970s, raw materials for production of optical waveguide fibers having impurities of such elements as copper, nickel, manganese, cobalt, chromium, iron, and vanadium of only a few parts per billion were sought. Extraordinarily sensitive and reliable ultratrace methods were required for identifying contaminants responsible for unacceptable loss in waveguide fibers, screening available raw materials, pinpointing deficiencies of raw-material purification processes, and detecting sources of contamination during preform manufacture and fiber drawing. At Bell Laboratories, significant contributions were made in improving the accuracy and applicability of ultratrace characterizations of waveguide materials using neutron activation and radioisotope techniques.[44] New interference-free radiochemical separation techniques and methods for production of homogeneously doped, trace-element standards for waveguide materials analysis were introduced by J. W. Mitchell [Fig. 20-8] and coworkers.[45,46]

Because of the extraordinarily high sensitivity (10^{-6} to 10^{-12} gm), extremely broad applicability (approximately 60 elements), specificity, and relative freedom from contamination problems, neutron activation has been applied to answer a number of other important questions and to solve several significant analytical problems. For example, microanalyses of a few milligrams of polywater showed the presence of appreciable amounts of sodium. Additional analyses by spark-source mass spectrometry, electron microprobe, and X-ray fluorescence showed potassium, chlorine, SO_4^{-2}, carbon, and oxygen in major amounts (1 to 35 percent) and calcium, boron, silicon, nitrogen, and sulfur in small amounts. These results aided in characterizing polywater as little more than poly-contamination.[47] Nuclear separation schemes have been exploited to develop the most sensitive and specific method available for determining ultratraces of gold in effluent wastes from Bell System recovery processes.[48] The Bell System's manufacture of high-density (64 K) memory devices depends

Fig. 20-8. J. W. Mitchell made fundamental contributions to neutron activation and ultratrace analysis.

critically on reducing the occurrences of soft errors caused by ionizing radiations emitted by ultratrace impurities in ceramic components of chip housing. A nuclear method based on fission track counting was perfected to determine quantitatively parts-per-trillion levels of uranium, the most prominent alpha-particle emitting impurity present in components of microprocessor chip mounting units that are commercially available.[49]

5.3 Chemical Analysis

Historically, chemical procedures have been essential in ultratrace analyses to improve detection limits and eliminate interferences. By the mid-1970s, chemists at Bell Laboratories, using appropriate combinations of chemical techniques and high-sensitivity analytical instrumentation, had made significant strides toward lowering the limits at which reliable quantitative elemental analyses could be performed.[50,51] Contamination-free procedures were introduced for chemical processing of samples, and new methods were developed for ultrapurifying analytical and MCVD reagents.[52,53] A low-temperature sublimation process of broad applicability for the highly efficient purification of compounds, which are liquids under ambient conditions, was applied to the preparation of analytical reagents of the highest possible purity.

5.4 Laser-Based Instruments for Analysis

Bell Laboratories chemists have also been developing laser-based instrumentation for ultratrace and microanalyses. A unique intracavity dye-laser spectrometer was designed and constructed to meet a stringent amplitude stability specification, an essential feature for use in quantitative analyses.[54] [Fig. 20-9] This system exploits a novel and convenient approach for null-type measurements of intracavity absorption using an electro-optic cell. Using ultrapurified analytical reagents and controlling contamination during chemical processing of samples, T. D. Harris and Mitchell applied laser intracavity spectrophotometry to detect sub-part-per-billion iron impurities in MCVD reagent chemicals.[55] Another laser-based analytical system has been applied to solve a microanalysis problem plaguing the semiconductor industry for several decades, that is, the accurate determination of moisture within very small void spaces (approximately 40 microlamberts) of hermetically sealed packages containing microprocessor

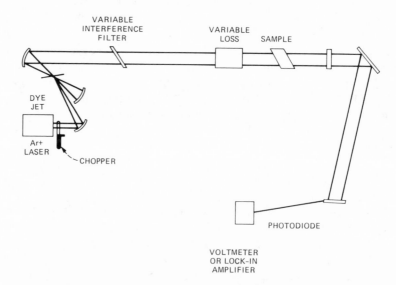

Fig. 20-9. Analytical laser intercavity absorption spectrometer. The argon laser is the pump for the dye laser. The chopper reduces the power absorption in the sample to prevent the formation of the thermal lens effect in the aqueous sample. The standard, highly reproducible intracavity loss, to which the sample is compared, is provided by the electro-optic (Pockel) cell.

chips. J. A. Mucha and P. R. Bossard developed a derivative infrared diode laser absorption technique that eliminated all inadequacies of techniques previously applied to this measurement problem.[56] A modulated laser tuned to the most intense absorption line of water provides a derivative signal for the water vapor content of a package within a millisecond of its rupture and exposure to the evacuated test cell. [Fig. 20-10] With this technique, it is possible to determine a contamination of 100 parts per million water in a 40-μL volume to $\pm$10 percent.

Additional advances in ultratrace and microanalyses were expected to result from exploiting the tunability, spectral brightness, and spatial resolution capabilities of laser-based instrumentation as this work moved into the 1980s.

This is an excellent example of the benefits of proper instrumentation. At the same time, the instruments are made possible by the superb quality of the research. It illustrates more generally the role of the materials effort described in the last ten chapters. The research was greatly facilitated by the advances in our understanding of the physics of the solid state and by the technology it generated and, in turn, made possible more precise experimentation and definitive theoretical interpretation of experimental results.

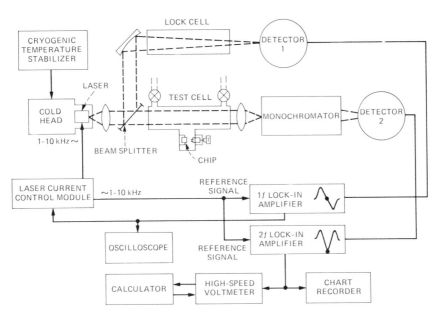

Fig. 20-10. An infrared frequency-stabilized laser, operating at an absorption frequency of water, is modulated to obtain a derivative signal. The specimen chip is crushed mechanically after the test cell is evacuated. Standard lock-in electronic techniques are used for sensitive signal detection.

REFERENCES

1. F. J. Morin and J. P. Maita, "Electrical Properties of Silicon Containing Arsenic and Boron," *Phys. Rev.* **96** (October 1954), pp. 28-35.
2. J. R. Haynes and W. Shockley, "Investigation of Hole Injection in Transistor Action," *Phys. Rev.* **75** (February 1949), p. 691.
3. R. N. Hall, "Germanium Rectifier Characteristics," *Phys. Rev.* **83** (July 1951), p. 228.
4. W. Shockley and W. T. Read, Jr., "Statistics of the Recombinations of Holes and Electrons," *Phys. Rev.* **87** (September 1952), pp. 835-842.
5. C. Herring, "Transport Properties of a Many-Valley Semiconductor," *Bell System Tech. J.* **34** (March 1955), pp. 237-290.
6. G. L. Pearson and C. Herring, "Magneto-Resistance Effect and the Band Structure of Single Crystal Silicon," *Physica* **20** (1954), pp. 975-978.
7. F. J. Morin, T. H. Geballe, and C. Herring, "Temperature Dependence of the Piezoresistance of High-Purity Silicon and Germanium," *Phys. Rev.* **105** (January 1957), pp. 525-539.
8. T. H. Geballe and G. W. Hull, "Seebeck Effect in Silicon," *Phys. Rev.* **98** (May 1955), pp. 940-947.
9. C. Herring, T. H. Geballe, and J. E. Kunzler, "Phonon-Drag Thermomagnetic Effects in n-Type Germanium. I. General Survey," *Phys. Rev.* **111** (July 1958), pp. 36-57.
10. A. Uhlir, Jr., "The Potentials of Infinite Systems of Sources and Numerical Solutions of Problems in Semiconductor Engineering," *Bell System Tech. J.* **34** (January 1955), pp. 105-128; F. M. Smits, "Measurement of Sheet Resistivities with Four-Point Probe," *Bell System Tech. J.* **37** (May 1958), pp. 711-718.
11. J. C. Irvin, "Resistivity of Bulk Silicon and of Diffused Layers in Silicon," *Bell System Tech. J.* **41** (March 1962), pp. 387-410; S. M. Sze and J. C. Irvin, "Resistivity, Mobility and Impurity Levels in GaAs, Ge, and Si at 300K," *Sol. St. Electron.* **11** (June 1968), pp. 599-602.
12. C. S. Fuller and J. A. Dietzenberger, "Diffusion of Donor and Acceptor Elements in Silicon," *J. Appl. Phys.* **27** (May 1956), pp. 544-553.
13. H. Reiss, C. S. Fuller, and F. J. Morin, "Chemical Interactions Among Defects in Germanium and Silicon," *Bell System Tech. J.* **35** (May 1956), pp. 535-636.
14. R. B. Fair and J. C. C. Tsai, "A Quantitative Model for the Diffusion of Phosphorous in Silicon and the Emitter Dip Effect," *J. Electrochem. Soc.* **124** (July 1977), pp. 1107-1118.
15. L. C. Kimerling, "Electronic Stimulation of Defect Processes in Semiconductors," *Conf. Ser. Inst. Phys.* **46** (1979), pp. 56-73.
16. E. H. Nicollian and A. Goetzberger, "The Si-SiO$_2$ Interface-Electrical Properties as Determined by the Metal-Insulator-Silicon Conductance Technique," *Bell System Tech. J.* **46** (July-August 1967), pp. 1055-1133.
17. J. A. Copeland, "A Technique for Directly Plotting the Inverse Doping Profile of Semiconductor Wafers," *IEEE Trans. Electron Dev.* **ED-16** (May 1969), pp. 445-449.
18. G. L. Miller, "A Feedback Method for Investigating Carrier Distributions in Semiconductors," *IEEE Trans. Electron Dev.* **ED-19** (October 1972), pp. 1103-1108.
19. C. T. Sah, L. Forbes, L. L. Rosier, and A. F. Tasch, Jr., "Thermal and Optical Emission and Capture Rates and Cross Sections of Electrons and Holes at Imperfection Centers in Semiconductors from Photo and Dark Junction Current and Capacitance Experiments," *Sol. St. Electron.* **13** (June 1970), pp. 759-788.
20. H. Kukimoto, C. H. Henry, and F. R. Merritt, "Photocapacitance Studies of the Oxygen Donor in GaP. I. Optical Cross Sections, Energy Levels, and Concentration," *Phys. Rev.* **B7** (March 1973), pp. 2486-2499.

21. D. V. Lang, "Deep-Level Transient Spectroscopy: A New Method to Characterize Traps in Semiconductors," *J. Appl. Phys.* **45** (July 1974), pp. 3023-3032; G. L. Miller, J. V. Ramirez, and D. A. H. Robinson, "A Correlation Method for Semiconductor Transient Signal Measurements," *J. Appl. Phys.* **46** (June 1975), pp. 2638-2644; L. C. Kimerling, "New Developments in Defect Studies in Semiconductors," *IEEE Trans. Nucl. Sci.* **NS-23** (December 1976), pp. 1497-1505.

22. G. L. Miller, D. V. Lang, and L. C. Kimerling, "Capacitance Transient Spectroscopy," *Ann. Rev. Mat. Sci.* **7**, ed. R. A. Huggins (Palo Alto, CA: Annual Reviews, Inc., 1977), pp. 377-448.

23. L. C. Kimerling, "Defect Characterization by Junction Spectroscopy," *Defects in Semiconductors*, Proc. Mat. Res. Soc. Annual Meeting, ed. J. Narayan and T. Y. Tan (Boston: Elsevier North Holland, Inc., 1981), pp. 85-95.

24. N. B. Hannay, "A Mass Spectrograph for the Analysis of Solids," *Rev. Scientific Instru.* **25** (July 1954), pp. 644-648.

25. N. B. Hannay and A. J. Ahearn, "Mass Spectrographic Analysis of Solids," *Analytical Chem.* **26** (June 1954), pp. 1056-1058.

26. A. J. Ahearn and D. L. Malm, "Background Reduction in Photographs of Mass Spectra," *Appl. Spectroscopy* **20** (Nov./Dec. 1966), pp. 411-414.

27. N. B. Hannay, "Mass Spectrographic Analysis of Solids," *Science* **134** (October 20, 1961), pp. 1220-1225.

28. See reference 25.

29. A. J. Ahearn and C. D. Thurmond, "Mass Spectrographic Detection of Molecular Species in Group III-V Compounds," *J. Phys. Chem.* **66** (March 1962), pp. 575-576.

30. D. L. Malm, "RF Spark, Source Mass Spectrometry for the Analysis of Surface Films," in *Physical Measurement and Analysis of Thin Films*, ed. E. M. Murt and W. G. Gulder (New York: Plenum Press, 1969), pp. 148-167.

31. R. D. Heidenreich and V. G. Peck, "Fine Structure of Metallic Surfaces with the Electron Microscope," *J. Appl. Phys.* **14** (January 1943), pp. 23-29.

32. R. D. Heidenreich and W. Shockley, "Electron Microscope and Electron-Diffraction Study of Slip in Metal Crystals," *J. Appl. Phys.* **18** (November 1947), pp. 1029-1031.

33. R. D. Heidenreich, "Electron Microscope and Diffraction Study of Metal Crystal Textures by Means of Thin Sections," *J. Appl. Phys.* **20** (October 1949), pp. 993-1010.

34. R. D. Heidenreich and L. Sturkey, "Crystal Interference Phenomena in Electron Microscope Images," *J. Appl. Phys.* **16** (February 1945), pp. 97-105.

35. R. D. Heidenreich, "Electron Diffraction and Microscopy of Metals," *Modern Research Techniques in Physical Metallurgy* (Cleveland: American Society for Metals, 1953), pp. 51-71.

36. J. J. Lander, M. Schreiber, Jr., T. M. Buck, and J. R. Matthews, "Microscopy of Internal Crystal Imperfections in Si *p-n* Junction Diodes by Use of Electron Beams," *Appl. Phys. Lett.* **3** (December 1, 1963), pp. 206-207.

37. W. Czaja and J. R. Patel, "Observations of Individual Dislocations and Oxygen Precipitates in Silicon with a Scanning Electron Beam Method," *J. Appl. Phys.* **36** (April 1965), pp. 1476-1482.

38. H. J. Leamy, L. C. Kimerling, and S. D. Ferris, "Silicon Single Crystal Characterization by SEM," in *Scanning Electron Microscopy 1976 I.*, ed. O. Johari (Chicago: IIT Research Inst., 1976), pp. 529-538.

39. D. C. Joy and D. M. Maher, "A Practical Electron Spectrometer for Chemical Analysis," *J. Microscopy* **114** (November 1978), pp. 117-129.

40. T. C. Loomis, "X-Ray Spectroscopy as an Analytical Tool," *Annals of the New York Academy of Sciences* **137**, ed. E. M. Weyer (New York: The New York Academy of Sciences, 1966), pp. 284-296; T. C. Loomis and K. H. Storks, "X-Ray Microanalysis

in Chemistry," *Bell Laboratories Record* **45** (January 1967), pp. 2-7.

41. C. L. Luke, "Determination of Trace Elements in Inorganic and Organic Materials by X-Ray Fluorescence Spectroscopy," *Anal. Chim. Acta* **41** (May 1968), pp. 237-250.

42. J. E. Kessler, S. M. Vincent, and J. E. Riley, Jr., "A Micro Co-Precipitation Technique for Use in X-Ray Fluorescence Analysis" *Talanta* **26** (January 1979), pp. 21-24.

43. D. L. Wood, A. B. Dargis, and D. L. Nash, "A Computerized Television Spectrometer for Emission Analysis," *Appl. Spectroscopy* **29** (July/August 1975), pp. 310-315.

44. J. W. Mitchell and J. E. Riley, Jr., "Practical Applications of Neutron Activation and Radioisotope Techniques in Optical Waveguide Research and Development," *J. Radioanal. Chem.* **38** (1977), pp. 79-96.

45. J. W. Mitchell, "An Interference-Free Substoichiometric Extraction Procedure for General Applications in Neutron Activation Analysis," *Radiochem. Radioanal. Lett.* **24** (January 30, 1976), pp. 123-136.

46. J. W. Mitchell, L. D. Blitzer, T. Y. Kometani, T. Gills, and L. Clark, Jr., "Homogeneously Doped Silica Matrices for Trace Element Standards in Neutron Activation Analysis," *J. Radioanal. Chem.* **39** (1977), pp. 335-342.

47. D. L. Rousseau and S. P. S. Porto, "Polywater: Polymer or Artifact?," *Science* **167** (March 27, 1970), pp. 1715-1719.

48. J. W. Mitchell, J. E. Riley, Jr., and V. Payne, "Substoichiometric Neutron Activation Determination of Gold," *J. Radioanal. Chem.* **43** (1978), pp. 371-380.

49. J. E. Riley, "The Analysis of Ceramic Semiconductor Packages for Traces of Uranium via Fission Track Counting," *Anal. Chem.* **53** (March 1981), pp. 407-411.

50. J. E. Kessler and J. W. Mitchell, "Quantitative Ultratrace Elemental Analysis by X-Ray Fluorescence Spectrometry," *Anal. Chem.* **50** (October 1978), pp. 1644-1647.

51. T. Y. Kometani, "Flameless Atomic Absorption Spectrometric Determination of Ultratrace Elements in Silicon Tetrachloride," *Anal. Chem.* **49** (December 1977), pp. 2289-2291.

52. M. Zief and J. W. Mitchell, *Contamination Control in Trace Element Analysis* (New York: John Wiley & Sons, Inc., 1976).

53. J. W. Mitchell, U.S. Patent No. 3,992,159; filed June 23, 1975, issued November 16, 1976; idem, "Purification of Analytical Reagents and Other Liquids by Low Temperature Vacuum Sublimation," *Anal. Chem.* **50** (February 1978), pp. 194-196.

54. J. S. Shirk, T. D. Harris, and J. W. Mitchell, "Laser Intracavity Spectrophotometer," *Anal. Chem.* **52** (September 1980), pp. 1701-1705.

55. T. D. Harris and J. W. Mitchell, "Sub-Part-per-Billion Iron Determination by Laser Intracavity Absorption Spectrometry," *Anal. Chem.* **52** (September 1980), pp. 1706-1708.

56. J. A. Mucha and P. R. Bossard, "Water Vapor Measurements in Integrated Circuit Packages Using An Infrared Diode Laser," *Proc. Conf. on Moisture Measurements and Control for Semiconductor Devices* (1980).

Credits

Figure 1-2 from H. J. Williams and W. Shockley, *Phys. Rev.* Vol. 74 (1949). Copyright 1949 by the American Institute of Physics. Reprinted with permission.

Figure 1-3 from C. Kittel and J. K. Galt, *Solid State Physics* Vol. 3 (1956). Copyright 1956 by Academic Press, Inc. Reprinted with permission.

Figure 1-4 from E. A. Nesbitt, *Encyclopedia of Chemical Technology* Vol. 12 (1967). Copyright 1967 by Interscience Publishers, Inc. Reprinted with permission.

Figure 1-6 from J. F. Dillon and H. E. Earl, *Am. J. Phys.* Vol. 27 (1959). Copyright 1959 by the American Institute of Physics. Reprinted with permission.

Figure 1-8 from A. M. Clogston and V. Jaccarino, *Phys. Rev.* Vol. 121 (1961). Copyright 1961 by the American Institute of Physics. Reprinted with permission.

Figure 1-9 from R. C. Fletcher et al., *Phys. Rev.* Vol. 95 (1954). Copyright 1954 by the American Institute of Physics. Reprinted with permission.

Figures 1-10 and 1-11 from G. Feher., *Phys. Rev.* Vol. 114 (1959). Copyright 1959 by the American Institute of Physics. Reprinted with permission.

Figure 1-12 from G. F. Imbusch and S. Geschwind, *Phys. Lett.* Vol. 18 (1965). Copyright 1965 by the North-Holland Publishing Co. Reprinted with permission.

Figure 1-14 from R. L. Cohen, *Science* Vol. 178 (1972). Copyright 1972 by the American Association for the Advancement of Science. Reprinted with permission.

Figure 1-15 from I. Nowik and S. Ofer, *Phys. Rev.* Vol. 153 (1967). Copyright 1967 by the American Institute of Physics. Reprinted with permission.

Figure 6-3 from Jost et al., *Chem. Phys. Lett.* Vol. 37 (1976). Copyright 1976 by North Holland Publishing Co., Amsterdam. Reprinted with permission.

Figure 6-5 from R. L. Fork, B. I. Greene, and C. V. Shank, *Appl. Phys. Lett.* Vol. 38 (1981). Copyright 1981 by the American Institute of Physics. Reprinted with permission.

Figure 6-6 (A) from C. K. N. Patel, *Optical and Quantum Electronics* Vol. 8 (1976). Copyright 1976 by Chapman and Hall, Ltd., London. Reprinted with permission.

Figure 6-6 (B) from C. K. N. Patel et al., *Science* Vol. 185 (1974). Copyright 1974 by the American Association for the Advancement of Science. Reprinted with permission.

Figure 6-8 from L. H. Germer and W. S. Boyle, *J. Appl. Phys.* Vol. 27 (1956). Copyright 1956 by the American Institute of Physics. Reprinted with permission.

Figure 6-11 from A. Libchaber and C. C. Grimes, *Phys. Rev.* Vol. 178 (1969). Copyright 1969 by the American Institute of Physics. Reprinted with permission.

Figure 6-16 from R. G. Shulman et al., *Science* Vol. 205 (1979). Copyright 1979 by the American Association for the Advancement of Science. Reprinted with permission.

Figure 8-5 (A) and (B) from W. L. Brown, *Radiation Effects in Semiconductors* (1968). Copyright 1968 by Plenum Publishing Corp., New York. Reprinted with permission.

Figure 8-9 from A. K. Sinha and J. M. Poate, *Appl. Phys. Lett.* Vol. 23 (1973). Copyright 1973 by the American Institute of Physics. Reprinted with permission.

Figure 8-12 from J. Als-Nielsen et al., *Phys. Rev.* Vol. B12 (1975). Copyright 1975 by the American Institute of Physics. Reprinted with permission.

Figure 8-12 from J. Als-Nielsen et al., *Sol. State Phys.* Vol. 9 (1976). Copyright 1976 by Academic Press. Inc. Reprinted with permission.

Figure 9-3 from W. J. Merz, *Phys. Rev.* Vol. 91 (1953). Copyright 1953 by the American Institute of Physics. Reprinted with permission.

Figure 9-5 from D. Maydan, *Proceedings of the IEEE* Vol. 61 (1973). Copyright 1973 by the Institute of Electrical and Electronics Engineers. Reprinted with permission.

Figure 9-6 from R. C. Dynes, *Phys. Rev. Lett.* Vol. 30 (1967). Copyright 1967 by the American Physical Society. Reprinted with permission.

Figure 18-2 from R. R. Hart, B. C. Wonsiewicz, and G. Y. Chin, *Metall. Trans.* Vol. 1 (1970). Copyright 1970 by the Metallurgical Soc. of AIMMPE. Reprinted with permission.

Figure 19-8 from Finch, *J. Molecular Biology*, Vol. 8 (1964). Copyright 1964 by Academic Press, Inc. Reprinted with permission.

Figure 19-10 from J. R. Carruthers and K. Nassau, *J. Appl. Phys.* Vol. 39 (1968). Copyright 1968 by the American Institute of Physics. Reprinted with permission.

Index